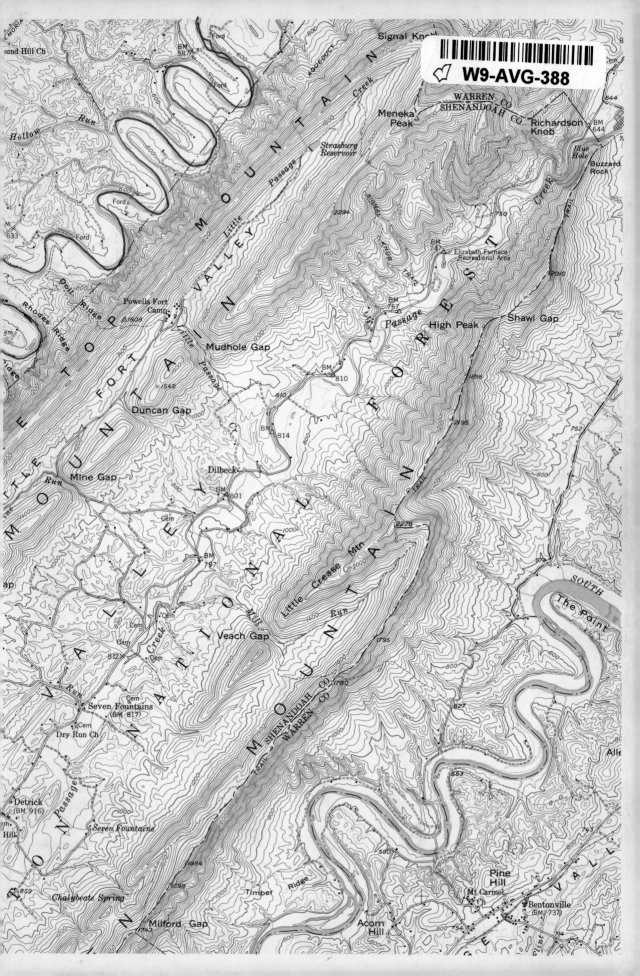

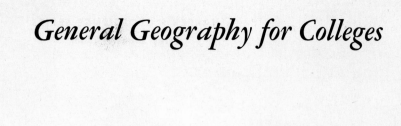

General Geography for Colleges

HARPER'S GEOSCIENCE SERIES
Carey Croneis, Editor

Can papyrus grow where there is no marsh?
Can reeds flourish where there is no water?

Job 8:11

Lower Manhattan, Heart of the World's Largest City. The wealth of the city is evidence of the enormous commerce which is the basis of its existence. The harbor consists of the estuary of the Hudson River. (Courtesy, Port of New York Authority.)

General Geography

FOR COLLEGES

BY

O. D. VON ENGELN, Ph.D.
Cornell University

AND

BRUCE CARLTON NETSCHERT, Ph.D.
Resources for the Future, Inc.

CLARE M. O'GORMAN, Cartographer

HARPER & BROTHERS, PUBLISHERS, NEW YORK

GENERAL GEOGRAPHY FOR COLLEGES

Copyright © 1957, by Harper & Brothers

Printed in the United States of America

All rights in this book are reserved.
No part of the book may be used or reproduced in
any manner whatsoever without written permission
except in the case of brief quotations embodied in
critical articles and reviews. For information address
Harper & Brothers, 49 East 33rd Street,
New York 16, N. Y.

Library of Congress catalog card number: 57-6261

Contents

The hope of the authors of this textbook is to promote geographic literacy. To acquire such literacy it is, first of all, essential that the student should become acquainted with the names, location, nature, and significance of the places that comprise the basic reference points of world geography. Just as a child must acquire a vocabulary before he can become acquainted with literature, so also must a geographic vocabulary be acquired before a rewarding study of geography becomes possible.

Accordingly, the book begins with a survey of the Landmarks of the World. Through it the student is encouraged at the outset to acquire an overall concept of the earth's chief physical features. There follows a chapter on towns and cities, their origins and growth, to provide understanding of the phenomenon whose appearance in the history of mankind is an early mark of civilization. This is followed by an exposition of the cartographic methods which provide visual representation of geographic locations and distribution. In order to cover the fundamental physical factor of environment, the review of backgrounds concludes with a brief analysis of the principles of meteorology.

Surveys have shown repeatedly that college-trained Americans of recent decades are rather generally unable to locate and envisage the places which regularly recur in the datelines of the world news, and that commonly they lack awareness of the differing physical environments of the diverse regions of the earth's surface. This is a deplorable gap in the basic education of those who are

considered to be the intelligent and informed citizens of the country. In view of our ever-increasing involvement in the affairs of the whole world a comprehensive knowledge of places and peoples would seem an inescapable requirement for understanding the problems that collectively and successively are posed by our international position.[1]

The educational deficiency revealed by such surveys probably can be ascribed to insufficient training in geography extending all the way from the grade schools through the colleges. Doubtless it derived from the tendency to treat the subject at all levels as a social science, and the teaching effort continues to integrate geography, anthropology, history, sociology, civics, economics, and technology as a conglomeration of disciplines which substitutes for geography. Thus the fundamentals necessary for an understanding of the social aspects of geography may never be acquired.

In part such dilution of geography is the outcome of a flight from two earlier misconceptions regarding the content and teaching of the subject. A century ago the study of geography was largely a sterile memorization of names and locations, capes and counties, mountains and rivers, and political boundaries. More recently, at the upper levels, it

[1] As noted editorially in the *Washington Post and Times Herald* of December 7, 1954: "It is estimated that 65 percent of high school students go out into a cold war world with little idea of the locations or backgrounds of places on the strategic battlefront, and without any historical or geographical orientation for making the decisions on foreign policy that ultimately come back to the voters."

was marked by adherence to the concept of rigid geographic determinism. According to this doctrine the economic, cultural, and political status of peoples and nations is established and fixed by their physical environment and technological advancement. Now the pendulum is at the other end of a swing. At present the utilization of any and every environment is held to depend fundamentally on the native genius of the inhabitants, with a slight concession to the factor of differing degrees of competence or of progress in the utilization of natural resources. (It may be noted that British geographers have not been impressed by this interpretation, and manifest their astonishment at the phenomenon in their reviews of publications by American geographers.)

Between these two extremes there is a realistic middle ground. It is fitting in geography to become acquainted with the personal attributes and modes of living of the peoples of different countries, and their several patterns of land use in order to appreciate the variations in culture they exhibit. But when such surveys are concerned rather exclusively with historical backgrounds, they are not a substitute, by themselves, for acquaintance with the rudiments of physical geography. The scrub-clean housewifery of the Dutch was an impossibility for the Boer immigrants of arid South Africa, no matter how ingrained it was as a cultural trait.

The second part of the book, two thirds of the whole, is devoted to a serial review of the climatic regions of the world, based on the Köppen classification. In this review each climatic type is defined, its economic utilization indicated, and its world distribution set forth. There follows a survey of each region of each type. For many countries this involves their partition among climatic regions of different kinds, which highlights the frequent disparity between political divisions and physical units. At some point in the presentation, however, each country is discussed as such and the geographic significance of its existence as a national entity is noted.

The treatment in the regional surveys is

deliberately and frankly rather encyclopedic. Although the objective of the present volume is to inculcate the fundamentals of general geography, this does not necessitate merely a dry-as-dust recital of facts. The descriptions of lands and their utilization are sufficiently comprehensive to provide color and flavor in the presentation. The maps are made directly relevant to the text by excluding from them all items not referred to in the descriptions and exposition. Insets provide direct comparison of dimension and area of foreign regions with states and regions in the United States. Words rather than symbols are used to indicate product location and distribution. (The type size is not directly proportional to relative output and importance, but is roughly indicative of relative significance.) The illustrations are included to supplement the text and the maps, especially for environmental circumstances not readily conveyed by word or diagram.

Pedagogical considerations have not been neglected. A logical sequence of topics is maintained throughout; assignments can be made progressively throughout the course. Thus the instructor is free to develop such phases of the subject as he finds especially interesting, and free to make his own contributions to supplement the content, with assurance that the overall view is adequately covered by the text. Organization of the text is not, on the other hand, so tightly interlocked as to prevent departures from the sequence, as presented, by any teacher who may have strong convictions about the order of treatment of topics and regions. By careful selection and omission the book can be used successfully for a one-term course; but it is the conviction of the writers that the average college student should be familiar with the whole content as a minimal background to geographic literacy.

Use of the index to assemble readily all matter pertaining to a particular country or topic is recommended when an overall view of that subject is sought. Illustrations pertinent to each subject are also assembled under the appropriate index headings.

Questions, inserted at suitable intervals,

are suggestive rather than comprehensive. They indicate the kind of knowledge one should acquire from conning the text. This will permit a step-by-step check on how well the content of the book is being assimilated. Boldface type calls attention to key words. The derivation of technical terms and names is, in some instances, given where this will aid understanding.

Statistical information is conveyed in round numbers; areal data are typically presented by comparison with the sizes of American states. Production of commodities is given relatively—that is, by rank in world output—reflecting the writers' view that production statistics are too ephemeral to have enduring significance. Statistics in tables are, more often than not, ignored by the student; if they are learned under compulsion, they involve the most sterile type of rote memorization.

A word should be added about the fuller treatment and greater emphasis given to regions remote from and unfamiliar to most American readers. Through newspapers, automobile travel, and by conversational contacts most Americans acquire, rather unsystematically to be sure, an adequate comprehension of the local environment. This does not mean that the discussions of the various climatic regions of the United States are less fully presented than those of other countries. The American scene does not, however, receive the consideration that its relative geographic significance for American students would warrant in comparison with the space devoted to such lands as Paraguay and Mongolia. It is these distant horizons that this book seeks to lift into view and make part of the student's geographic competence.

The writers wish to acknowledge their debt to a very broad section of recent geographic literature as source material for this book. The absence of specific references in the text is not intended to connote originality of content, but is consistent with the purpose of the book to present a new pedagogical approach using available facts and concepts. General references for the use of both teacher and student are listed for each chapter in an appendix. The choice has been limited to readily available, recent books such as are likely to be found in a small library.

A special debt is owed to Clare M. O'Gorman, cartographer for the book. Her skill and judgment have greatly enhanced its potential usefulness for both teacher and student. Jack D. Anglin and Russell H. Armentrout, Jr., ably assisted in the preparation of the maps. Thanks are due also to Kathleen and Frank Spagnolo, who gave much time and patience to the preparation of the line drawings and diagrams.

In conclusion, the authors wish to admit the probability of errors. It is hoped that whatever mistakes may have been made will not significantly affect the value of the book. They will be humbly grateful, however, for notice of any slips that may be discovered.

O. D. VON ENGELN
BRUCE CARLTON NETSCHERT

Ithaca, N.Y.
Washington, D.C.
January, 1957

Landmarks of the World

CHAPTER 1

Landmarks of the World—Oceanic

■ INTRODUCTION

It is essential to a competent understanding of the world that one know the major features of the earth's surface by name—what and where they are. Accordingly, this book on general geography begins with an account of the "Landmarks of the World," those geographical features that are the background of human existence, past and present. Although the geographic environment of a people does not finally determine its history and attainments, geographical factors do exercise influences that may be recognized in all periods of development. Western civilization is no exception to this generalization. Unless, accordingly, there is acquired at the outset of geographic study knowledge of the distribution of the chief landmarks of the world, and some measure of appreciation of the significance of each of these, further progress in geographic learning will be impeded to a discouraging degree.

The serious student should therefore familiarize himself with all the place names presented in the paragraphs that follow, acquiring at the same time a knowledge of their locations (a school atlas should always be at hand) and a concept of the nature of their importance. Some of these place names derive significance directly from their geographical expression, that is, from what they are; others from their historical, economic, or literary associations. The selection made by the authors may not altogether meet the approval of informed persons. Some omissions will be due to inadvertence; others will reflect the inevitable limitations that a textbook presentation imposes.

It may be assumed that at least the names and locations of the earth's major units—the continents and the oceans—are known to all students who enter upon this study. Also, that they will know that the Antarctic Continent and the subcontinent Greenland are completely or almost completely buried under glacial ice. These great basic items, the oceans and continents, are comprised of seas, gulfs, bays, straits, isthmuses, islands, plains, plateaus, mountains, lakes, and rivers, to which man has added his cities. For the most part it is these subdivisions that constitute landmarks. Each subdivision may be considered collectively as a type, but reference to the specific occurrences is required to develop the landmark significance. Further, the student should endeavor to become informed about each item as it is related to human activity in the broadest sense of the phrase.

■ THE SEAS

GEOGRAPHIC SIGNIFICANCE

The term "sea" is here used comprehensively to include gulfs and bays in addition to those water expanses commonly called seas. All three names refer to water areas that are considerably smaller than any ocean and that are more or less surrounded by land, or "landlocked." The degree of the enclosure

3

varies between wide extremes, but there is no consistency about the use of the terms with reference either to the completeness or incompleteness of landlocking or to order of size. Some seas are wholly enclosed; others are only vaguely outlined by the adjacent shores. Some bays are far larger than many seas.

Collectively considered, seas are geographically significant on several counts. First, they provide access by water transportation for a greater or lesser distance to inland points. Water transport is regularly much cheaper than any kind of overland movement of goods (except, perhaps, pipelines for fluids and gas). Therefore, many points of interior Europe, in terms of freight costs, are nearer the Atlantic seaboard of the United States than are places in the interior of North America, so deeply penetrated is Europe by seas.

Physically, the presence of seas is an important factor in modifying the climate of lands adjacent to their shores. All water bodies exercise a moderating effect on the temperature of the lands they adjoin, and may also affect the rainfall. The measure of these influences is directly dependent on the size of the water area and on the direction and force of the winds of the region. The windward coast (i.e., the shore against which the prevailing winds blow) benefits more than the lee coast.

In view of what has been stated in regard to the irregular application of the terms "sea," "gulf," and "bay," all three are considered as one class of geographic landmarks and treated in accordance with their association with the different continents (Fig. 1.1).

EUROPEAN SEAS, GULFS, AND BAYS

The **Mediterranean Sea,** with an area of almost one million square miles, is probably the outstanding geographic item of all the world for peoples with European cultural backgrounds because of its significance in the history and development of Western civilization. The peoples and nations from which European civilization arose were all located on or near Mediterranean shores. In-

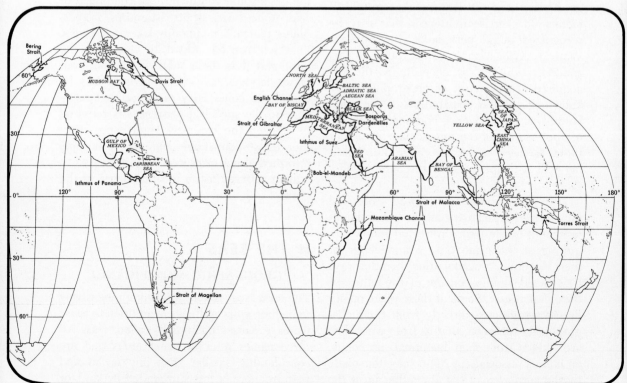

Fig. 1.1—Landmarks of the World: Seas, Gulfs, Bays, Straits, and Isthmuses.

cluded are the Egyptians, Jews, Cretans, Greeks, Romans, Phoenicians, and, more remotely, the Mesopotamians. The comparatively calm waters, the low tides, the short distances between landfalls, and the numerous sheltered harbors of the Mediterranean were geographic circumstances that prompted men to learn the art of marine navigation. Moreover, when a new coast was reached along Mediterranean shores the adventurers were not repelled or disheartened by strange climatic circumstances, for all the region is within the same climate. The relatively easy crossings of the Mediterranean led to the early development of commerce and permitted the interchange of culture and ideas.

The **Black Sea,** 160,000 square miles in extent, is connected with the Mediterranean by narrow straits. It was known and utilized by the ancients but its stormier waters and the hostile, barbarous peoples of its shores discouraged occupation and exploitation of those lands in early times. The Mediterranean folk resorted to its north coast for supplies of grain but were not much interested in going farther. In modern times the Black Sea has provided the Russians with a base for shipbuilding and the training of a navy. But the Russians always recognized that they were prevented from free participation in world commerce because their emergence from the Black Sea could be blocked at will by whoever held the straits leading to the Mediterranean and from the Mediterranean into the open ocean. A major aim of Russian foreign policy has been to secure guarantees of the availability of these routes to Russian ships.

The **Aegean Sea,** in the northeastern part of the Mediterranean, is famous because of its association with the mythology and history of the ancient Greeks.

Near the middle of the north side of the Mediterranean is the long, narrow bay between Italy and the Balkans called the **Adriatic Sea.** Although small and only a branch of the Mediterranean, the Adriatic had an early importance because the Venetians, located at its head, carried on great trade activities during medieval times. Goods from Asia were ferried across the Mediterranean and up the Adriatic for disposal in continental Europe. The Venetians also served as a travel agency for the Crusaders at a very considerable profit to themselves.

Beyond the Mediterranean along the west coast of continental Europe is the **Bay of Biscay,** chiefly notorious because of its stormy crossings on voyages from the north of Europe to the Mediterranean.

If the Mediterranean was the sea around which all enterprise was centered in ancient times, then at a later date the **North Sea** and the **Baltic Sea,** in the north of Europe, acquired a similar focal significance. These are both large seas, and the relation between them is somewhat like that between the Mediterranean and the Adriatic. The North Sea is less landlocked than the Mediterranean and is lashed by terrific storms. To offset this, however, its shores are indented by many large, well-sheltered harbors and by quiet waters behind island "fences" parallel to the coast. Accordingly, these were the training grounds of the Vikings, the "Sons of Calm Water," who became the hardiest, boldest sailors of their day. The Vikings were first prompted to sail into the open waters, despite their peril, by the large catches of fish that could be made in the North Sea. Fish from the North Sea remain a great resource in modern times.

Navigation of the Baltic is adversely affected by an ice cover in winter and it is not the rich fishing ground that the North Sea is. Nevertheless it was the scene of remarkable commercial activity in the early history of northwestern Europe. Hides, tallow, wool, lumber, and other products from along its shores were shipped to the south and west and exchanged for industrial goods and the products of sunnier, warmer lands. Although the North Sea and Baltic commerce has declined from its former rank relative to total world commerce, it is larger today than it ever was before. These seas are now also the focus of a highly developed network of river and canal waterways in their surrounding lands.

WESTERN HEMISPHERE SEAS, GULFS, AND BAYS

The Western Hemisphere has few seas of world landmark importance. In North America the immense **Hudson Bay**, 500,000 square miles in area, is famous because of its association with the Hudson's Bay Company fur enterprise but is otherwise mostly lacking in geographical significance. Its desolate shores, nearly devoid of resources, and its shallow, stormy waters have not attracted much human activity. Curiously, it has no large fish population; hence no fishing fleets sail its waters. At the southern end of the continent the **Gulf of Mexico** is, by contrast, bordered by shores rich in a variety of resources, agricultural, forest, and mineral, and supports large fisheries.

The island-enclosed **Caribbean Sea** is the only sea associated with the coast of South America. The Caribbean, however, is a well-known geographic landmark because of its intimate connection with the history of the Western Hemisphere from the time of Columbus' voyages of discovery through the period of the conquistadors. The Caribbean, accordingly, is a name to conjure with when reference is made to tropical seas, pirates, gold, and conquest.

ASIATIC SEAS, GULFS, AND BAYS

Neither Africa (except its Mediterranean shore) nor Australia has seas or other interruptions of the coastline of sufficient consequence to have acquired landmark fame. But the waters about the borders of Asia are rather generally subdivided into well-known units.

Cut off from the Mediterranean by a low, sandy land barrier is the long, narrow **Red Sea** between Africa and Asia. When the barrier was cut by a ship canal, the Red Sea became part of the overseas route between Europe and the Orient. The Red Sea is completely surrounded by desert shores, unproductive except for some petroleum, so that it has little economic significance locally. It is, however, geographically significant in that it was the site of the crossing of the Israelites from Egypt into Palestine, and its eastern shores are the center of Moslem culture and religious interest.

The **Persian Gulf** penetrates deeply inland, but is, like the Red Sea, surrounded by desert or semidesert country and is cut off from interior Asia by a wide belt of rugged territory difficult to traverse. Further, although the shore regions at the head of the Gulf comprise one of the world's largest oil fields the chief market for this oil is not to the south. The demand is from western Europe, so that pipe lines westward to the Mediterranean shores tend to compete strongly with shipment by tankers through the Gulf and the Red Sea.

Because of the great importance of India to Great Britain in the past the waters surrounding India are well known. In a passage to India the **Arabian Sea** is crossed after the Red Sea has been traversed. The Arabian Sea, between Arabia and India, is so little landlocked that it is rather a misnomer to call it a sea, especially as the more enclosed waters between India and Burma are named the **Bay of Bengal.**

On the east coast of Asia the **Yellow Sea** is more definitely outlined and exhibits strongly the characteristic for which it is named. Its waters over vast areas are colored by the yellow sediment washed into it from China. Northwest of it the **Sea of Japan** between Japan and the mainland is even more enclosed than the Yellow Sea but has acquired only slight geographic fame because it is little frequented by overseas shipping. In contrast, the **East China Sea** to the south is the main approach route to the major ports of the Chinese coast.

■ STRAITS AND ISTHMUSES

GEOGRAPHIC SIGNIFICANCE

A strait is a narrow water connection between two larger bodies of water; an isthmus is a narrow land connection between two larger expanses of land. Straits constrict the movement of shipping, isthmuses block such transportation. On the other hand, straits are barriers to overland carriage, whereas isthmuses are routes for such traffic. Thus whoever controls the site of a strait or isthmus dominates the trade routes it affects and in time of war can permit or refuse passage, overseas or overland, and hence govern much military activity.

MEDITERRANEAN STRAITS AND ISTHMUSES

No other strait rivals in geographic importance the **Strait of Gibraltar,** connecting the Mediterranean Sea with the Atlantic Ocean. Through it the early Mediterranean peoples first emerged to voyage upon the high seas. Under British control its rock-bordered entrance has for many years symbolized fortress strength.

At the other end of the Mediterranean the **Dardanelles** and **Bosporus** straits serve to connect the larger sea with its smaller neighbor, the Black Sea. Even more completely than at Gibraltar, control of these passages can prevent the passage of ships between the two water bodies, as the straits are very narrow and long.

Where an isthmus is situated athwart sea routes effort has been made to eliminate the obstruction by digging a canal as early as engineering competence indicates the feasibility of such a project and the volume of commerce warrants the undertaking. This is true of the **Isthmus of Suez,** where the **Suez Canal** was completed in 1869. Until that time the expense of transshipment across the isthmus was so great that the long route to the Far East around the southern tip of Africa was cheaper. By way of Suez the distance between London and Bombay is reduced by 4500 miles. Although all liners between Europe and Asia, as well as tankers from the Arabian Gulf, use the canal, toll rates are so high that low-value cargoes are still sent by the longer route.

The importance of the canal for the British Empire would be difficult to overstate, despite the dwindling of the Eastern portion of that empire. As one writer pointed out (before India, Burma, and Ceylon became independent): "The Suez Canal is one of the knots in the web of empire where the routes which bind its parts are caught together at a point of exceptional and critical strategic character. . . . Nearly 65 percent of the land and more than 75 percent of the population controlled by Great Britain face the Indian Ocean or lie just beyond its margins."[1]

The canal was built by the French despite British opposition to the project. But within six years after its completion the British had secured control of the company and in nine more years domination over all the lands adjacent to the canal and its approaches.

At the south end of the Red Sea is another, lesser known and relatively narrow strait, **Bab-el-Mandeb,** held by the British.

THE ENGLISH CHANNEL

Although Gibraltar is probably the most famous strait in the world, its fame is based chiefly on its historical background. In modern times the **English Channel** may be said to surpass it as a route for shipping and in strategic significance. Since 1066 its existence has preserved the British Isles from invasion by continental enemies, and in the World Wars permitted Britain to be used as a springboard for launching the Allied attacks on Germany.

PANAMA

The other world-famous isthmus and canal is that of **Panama,** at the narrowest point of the land barrier that the continents of the New World interpose between the Atlantic and Pacific Oceans. After North and South America were discovered many exploratory voyages had as their chief objective the search for a water route across the lands between the two oceans. Since no such channel exists, the possibility of breaching the Panama isthmus was early considered but was not finally accomplished until 1914. The Panama Canal has much the same political significance for the United States that the Suez Canal had for Great Britain. The com-

[1] Derwent Whittlesey, *The Earth and the State,* Henry Holt and Co., 1944, p. 120.

mercial importance of the Panama Canal is even greater. On a voyage between New York and San Francisco it saves 7900 miles. Moreover, the long, dangerous voyage around the south end of South America is far more costly than are canal tolls for any ship. The Panama Canal has also made commercial exchange between New York and the west coast of South America both feasible and profitable.

STRAIT OF MALACCA

The **Strait of Malacca,** the remaining strait of first importance as a geographical landmark, is located at the southeast tip of Asia. The strait is not well known by its correct name, as it is usually identified with the city of Singapore that is located on its shore. The Strait of Malacca is the only practical water route between the Indian and Pacific oceans. Although other water passages exist in this area they are little used, partly because they are less direct, partly because they are dangerous to navigate owing to coral reefs and other obstructions.

STRAITS OF LESSER IMPORTANCE

Five additional straits are listed on world maps and are significant in separating important land areas. **Torres Strait** separates the northeast tip of Australia from the great island of New Guinea, but it is off the main trade routes.

The **Mozambique Channel** is a wide passage between the Portuguese colony of Mozambique in East Africa and the French island of Madagascar, both of which are only slightly developed regions.

The **Strait of Magellan** is at the southern tip of South America. It is remote and little used but is of first importance historically. It was the sea route into the Pacific from the east during the period of world exploration and the sailing-ship era. During this time it became notorious for the difficulties of its passage. The Panama Canal made it practically obsolete as an ocean highway.

Bering Strait, at the northwest tip of North America between Alaska and Siberia, and **Davis Strait,** at the northeast tip of the continent between North America and Greenland, have never been as significant as the Strait of Magellan despite their geographic prominence. They do figure in the early exploration annals, for when Spain controlled the narrow overland passage at Panama and denied access to the western coasts of the Americas to other nationals northeast and northwest passages through the Arctic Ocean around Asia and North America were feverishly sought by the other colonial powers. After discovery, both passages proved to be quite impractical for commercial shipping.

QUESTIONS. What is a geographical landmark?[2] What varieties of landmarks are there? How is the word "sea" used in geography? How does the existence of the seas affect commerce? Climate? What sea is named as the world's outstanding geographic landmark of that type? Why? What uses have been made, past and present, of the Black Sea? Why is the Aegean Sea famous? When was the Adriatic Sea important? Compare the North and Baltic seas with the Mediterranean and Adriatic seas. What is the great resource of the North Sea?

What are the characteristics of Hudson Bay? Why is it so well known? What is the distinctive geographic background of the Caribbean Sea? Why is the Persian Gulf an exception to a generalization made in regard to seas and commerce? In what respect does the Arabian Sea fail to qualify as a "sea"? How does the Yellow Sea get its name? Why is the Sea of Japan relatively obscure? What is the significance of the East China Sea?

Define a strait; an isthmus. What is the effect of each on land and water transportation? What is their military significance? Why are the Dardanelles and Bosporus straits especially significant? State in brief the history of the Suez Canal. Why have the British attached so much importance to its possession? Why would possession of the Bosporus, the Dardanelles, and the Suez Canal not

[2] For class use it is suggested that each student be assigned a "landmark" to look up in an encyclopedia and to report on to the class. Many of the questions supply leads in regard to the kind of information to be sought. By this means the geographic significance of the different places can be greatly enhanced for the student.

solve Russia's ambition of unhindered access to the oceans? Why is the English Channel so significant? What is the political and commerical importance of the Panama Canal for the United States? Why is the Strait of Malacca so much used? Name and locate five straits geographically conspicuous but of little practical importance.

■ ISLANDS

GEOGRAPHIC SIGNIFICANCE

Islands are distinctive geographic items in that they are entirely surrounded by water. They serve as "landmarks" because they constitute, so to speak, "signposts in the ocean wastes." Islands exert a geographic influence in that they have tended to produce populations with distinctive, "insular" characteristics, each peculiar to its particular island or island group. The degree of such insularity is governed by the measure of the remoteness of the island in place and time, with reference to other islands and the nearest continental land mass.

Some islands have special geographic sig-

nificance because of historical associations, others because they function as way stations to transoceanic traffic, still others because of distinctive positions of different kinds.

Among the larger oceanic islands, or those over 25,000 square miles in area, the ones that occur as members of a group commonly attain particular prominence. This eminence among islands appears to result from the characteristic occurrence of such island groups at only short distances from the shores of continents (Fig. 1.2).

THE BRITISH ISLES

The island group of outstanding importance is the **British Isles**. Its premier importance derives from its size, which allows the accommodation of a population numbering tens of millions. Second, the lands of the British Isles are agriculturally productive, a prime factor in promoting the initial growth of a large population. Third, they originally possessed one of the world's large stores of the basic mineral resources, coal and iron, a circumstance of fundamental importance for the development of a modern great nation. Last, as an island group, the separation of

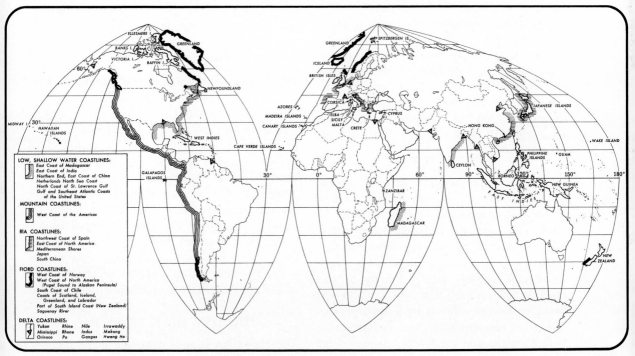

Fig. 1.2—Landmarks of the World: Islands and Coastlines.

the British Isles from the continent of Europe by a natural moat (the English Channel) of sufficient width to deter invaders but not so broad as to handicap commerce is a geographic factor that perhaps outweighs any of the others in its significance for British history. Jointly these several geographic circumstances have contributed greatly to the long-continued importance of Great Britain in world affairs.

JAPAN

The size and position of the **Japanese Islands** in their relation to Asia strikingly duplicate those of the British Isles in their relation to Europe. Unlike the British, the Japanese for centuries exploited the insular aspect of their position to a perverse extreme. Once they were forced to renounce their isolation, however, the Japanese were quick to appreciate the analogy between the geographic position of their country and that of Britain and to seek a realization of the destiny to which this parallel seemed to point. That they attempted to achieve their ends by force and at the expense of the neighboring continental nations instead of through the development of a sound, self-sustaining industrial and commercial national structure indicates a failure to capitalize correctly upon the geographical possibilities inherent in the island nature and position of the Japanese homeland. It should be added, however, that the Japanese Islands are not so richly endowed with natural resources as the British Isles originally were.

NEW ZEALAND

Lack of the basic mineral resources essential to attainment of greatness among modern nations also handicaps the **New Zealand** islands. These, like Britain, are rich agriculturally and have a climate very similar to that country's. It is an interesting historical circumstance, perhaps owing largely to this climatic resemblance, that New Zealand was occupied and developed by British people. The great remoteness of New Zealand from both Australia and the North Atlantic center of Western civilization has fostered an inde-

pendent and progressive national development in New Zealand with British traits and ideals as its background. New Zealand has a high standard of living and the highest national health level of the world.

EAST INDIES AND WEST INDIES

The **East** and **West Indies** are similar in name, in nature, and in their position in relation to Asia and North America, respectively. They differ from the island groups previously considered in that they are situated in regions of tropical climate. Because of this geographic circumstance their exploitation in modern times has been chiefly by plantation agriculture, the devotion of vast estates to single crops, such as sugar cane. During the discoveries period they were eagerly resorted to for spices. In the colonial period that followed, sugar from the first was the major production. The island environment permitted the white invaders to gain secure domination over the native populations and to compel them, or imported labor, to do the work of cultivation. At the same time the island geography provided a tempering, by ocean breezes, of the extremes of tropical heat and humidity for the resident white supervisors and officialdom.

THE PHILIPPINES

The history of the **Philippine Islands** runs parallel with that of the two Indies groups. They too are situated in the belt of tropical climate. Like the West Indies they were subjugated and exploited by the Spanish and became a source of sugar and other tropical produce. The Philippines remained geographically obscure, however, until after the Spanish-American War of 1898–99. Under American auspices the Filipinos were encouraged to become self-governing and to develop the resources of the islands for the general benefit of the native population. In 1946 the islands were granted independence.

THE HAWAIIAN ISLANDS

The **Hawaiian Islands,** situated in the middle of the Pacific, escaped the colonial domination imposed on most other tropical and subtropical islands during the discoveries period and remained under native rule until they became a United States possession in 1898. Because of their position in the Pacific ocean waste of waters the Hawaiian Islands early became the resort of seafarers, whalers, and traders from many European nations and proved to be a fertile field for American missionaries. The native Hawaiians, never very numerous, were soon converted to Christianity and commonly intermarried with the peoples from other lands, which later included many Chinese and Japanese. Although sugar cane and pineapples were profitable crops for export, the climate of the islands is mild and delightful rather than tropical and oppressive. As a consequence there has developed a population of extraordinarily diverse antecedents, a comely people, in happy possession of their homeland. With the development of air transportation the importance of the geographic mid-Pacific position of the Hawaiian Islands is greatly enhanced.

LESSER ISLAND GROUPS

Certain groups of small islands have acquired geographic prominence through historical associations. Thus the **Azores, Madeira, Canary,** and **Cape Verde Islands** off the west coast of Europe and Africa between Portugal and the center of the western bulge of Africa are landmarks in the history of the early voyages of the south Europeans into the open waters of the Atlantic beyond Gibraltar. At each successive landfall—Madeira, Canary, Cape Verde—reached going south, the Portuguese navigators were encouraged to push on until eventually they achieved the rounding of the southern tip of Africa and could sail east to their desired goal, India. In like manner the Azores were a stepping stone in the voyages westward leading to the discovery of the New World. Pushing out into the unknown expanses of the Atlantic waters was a fearful undertaking, and new islands on the way were hailed with delight, as their presence gave assurance that catastrophe, in the form of drop-

ping off the edge of the flat earth, would not immediately befall.

A somewhat similar interest attaches to the **Galapagos Islands,** 600 miles west of the coast of South America in the equatorial region. These remote islands have geographical fame because of the enormous turtles found there and because Charles Darwin visited them and found the nature of their fauna and flora of extraordinary interest in connection with his theories of the development of life. In World War II their position off the western entrance to the Panama Canal made the Galapagos a significant station in the defensive strategy of the area, and the United States established bases there.

The **Virgin Islands,** on the outer arc of the West Indies, have a somewhat parallel strategic significance for the eastern end of the canal and on this account were purchased in 1917 by the United States from Denmark.

Midway, Wake, and **Guam,** islands in the mid-Pacific beyond Hawaii, are not properly an island group but acquired recognition just prior to World War II as they came into use as way stations on transpacific commercial air routes. During the war their importance was enormously enhanced through their utilization as air and naval bases in the Pacific campaigns.

SINGLE LARGE ISLANDS

The large islands of the arctic, north of North America, can be treated as an island group, for they are close spaced and are situated immediately offshore from the mainland, as are many of the typical island groups previously considered. Nevertheless they have no great collective significance. **Greenland** (almost a continent in size) is buried under a blanket of ice. **Baffin, Ellesmere, Victoria,** and **Banks** islands are large, but are mostly barren, lowland arctic wastes. Their past geographic significance has been in supplying an environmental background for the tales of arctic explorers. Establishment of weather and air stations for air travel over the polar regions, and development of mineral resources, should considerably enhance their future economic importance.

Iceland and **Spitzbergen,** in the Arctic Ocean to the east of Greenland, have a larger significance. Since their shores are bathed by warmer waters from the south their climate is considerably ameliorated from polar extremes. Iceland, in consequence, has been for hundreds of years inhabited by an enlightened people with a long cultural history. This, in view of its high latitude location, is enough to give Iceland geographic distinction. Spitzbergen, still farther north, is correspondingly less endurable but has important mineral resources that are exploited.

Although situated much farther to the south, **Newfoundland,** at the southeastern corner of Canada, partakes of the bleakness of the arctic islands. In the past it has had serious economic difficulties, but new industries and the establishment of a great air base for transatlantic travel have brought new activities and greatly strengthened its economy.

New Guinea, in the East Indies, is the largest island in the world after Greenland. **Borneo,** another East Indian island, is the third; **Madagascar,** an island east of South Africa, is fourth. The latter belongs to France and is slightly larger than the home country.

Ceylon, off the southeast coast of India, in contrast to Madagascar is densely populated and intensively cultivated. This is partly because Ceylon is so close to the mainland, partly because of different historical circumstances. Under British rule Ceylon became a great plantation producer of tropical products.

SMALL ISLANDS

There are certain small islands that have only minor economic significance but that are well known as geographical names because of historical or other associations. This is especially true of the small islands of the Mediterranean. **Crete** and **Cyprus** are sites of some of the earliest developments of civilization. **Sicily,** at the toe of Italy, had great importance as a source of grain in the days of the Roman Empire. **Malta,** between Sicily and Africa, has been a strategic fortress on the main east-west Mediterranean trade

route since earliest times, and a major base on the British Empire life line since the early nineteenth century. **Corsica** and **Elba** were the birthplace and place of exile, respectively, of Napoleon. (Later, Napoleon was finally exiled to the tiny, remote island of **St. Helena** in the South Atlantic.)

In another class is **Zanzibar,**[3] off the east coast of central Africa. Zanzibar is representative of a number of small islands that have served as springboards for the conquest of adjoining mainlands. Their separation from the continent permitted them to be occupied as secure military bases and trading posts and in tropical latitudes afforded an environment that mitigated the debilitating climatic conditions of the adjacent continental areas. Zanzibar more than any of the others of its kind acquired the greatest fame in the days of African colonization.

Hong Kong, like Zanzibar, is an island outpost from which the adjacent continental portion of Asia could be exploited. Hong Kong is separated from the Chinese mainland by only a narrow strait. The island is British owned and has been used solely as a commercial base. The fine harbor afforded by the adjacent waters contributed greatly to the success of the offshore enterprise.

■ COASTLINES

GEOGRAPHIC SIGNIFICANCE

Coastlines could be more appropriately referred to as geographic environments than as landmarks. They are nevertheless distinctive because they can be considered separately from both the land at their back and the sea in front, and they are geographically important apart from the landmarks that are characteristic of these larger domains. Coastlines are the meeting place of land and water. They comprise a type of province which is usually restricted to a belt at most only a few miles wide.

[3] From the Persian *zanz* and Indian *bar,* together meaning "Country of the Black Man."

In primitive times man tended to cling to this coastline environment because the interior lands were covered by dense primeval forests or were otherwise difficult to penetrate, subdue, and inhabit. The coastline, on the other hand, afforded a foothold in the open, permitted along-shore travel on land, while the sea provided sustenance and even clothing and shelter in the form of furs and hides that could be fashioned into garments and tents. Where interior peoples emerged on coastlines their existence was usually greatly affected by the new fields of activity open to them. Fishing and seafaring were pursuits that brought to the fore qualities of daring and enterprise previously unrealized.

In modern times, the coastline is where overland transportation connects with marine transportation. Thus the nature of the coastline is significant in that it determines the character of the harbor facilities that are available. If these are excellent and the hinterland is productive and routes into it are easy, commercial activity thrives. At the other extreme, a lack of all these items may cause a coastal province to remain unoccupied and desolate.

The strategic importance of possession of the coastline province for control of the interior was early realized by invaders from overseas. The last remaining easy possibility of such seizure is the coastline of the Antarctic Continent. Immediately after World War II there was a flurry of activity by a number of nations to establish coastline claims in that uninhabited land.

TYPES OF COASTLINES

Coastlines may be divided into two general classes: smooth coastlines, where land and sea meet along a continuous, more or less straight line; and irregular coastlines, where land and sea are interfingered. This purely descriptive classification must be supplemented by reference to the effects of the relations between land and sea levels. Many coastlines have recently experienced depression or are still sinking. ("Recently" is here used in the geological sense, which may mean thousands of years. The rate of land movement is so slow that ordinarily its progress within historical time is determined with some difficulty. But the fact of its occurrence in the past may be readily inferred in many places from historical as well as geological evidence.) In these reaches land formerly above sea level is now covered with water. Such "submerged" coastlines are characteristically irregular, with bays and long, narrow inlets extending up what were formerly river valleys. Contrariwise, where the land has been uplifted the "emergent" coastline is usually straight. A portion of the sea bottom, which is likely to be smooth, has become dry land. As a result the new contact between water and land tends to approximate a straight line across a smooth, gently sloping surface.

Where mountain ranges rise directly from the sea and extend parallel to the coast, the coastline is likely to be rather straight regardless of whether submergence or emergence has occurred. But even in this case the submerged coast is less regular than the emerged coast.

Low, Shallow-Water Coastlines

The land of a low, smooth coastline tends to be a low-lying plain. The water offshore is shallow, with its depth increasing only very gradually seaward. In extreme instances, such as that of the **east coast of Madagascar,** the transition from land to water is so insensible that it is difficult to determine where the line between land and water should be drawn. There is a complete gradation from one to the other through swamp conditions. Other, less extreme examples of such coastlines occur on the **east coast of India,** the **northern end of the east coast of China,** the **Netherlands North Sea coast,** the **north coast of the St. Lawrence Gulf,** the **Gulf** and **southeast Atlantic coasts of the United States.** These last two have, however, experienced slight sinking since the time of a major uplift, so that they are now irregular in low relief, as witness **Chesapeake Bay.**

The shallow water offshore on such low coasts causes the waves to break some distance out from land and to build up a bar or beach there, which may be continuous for long distances. In such instances it is commonly possible to dredge out a channel in the sheltered water behind the bar or through the beach to provide à protected, inland waterway along the coast (Fig. 1.3). This has been done on the southeastern coast of the United States and, at intervals, still farther north. The waterway can be used, however, only by small craft and barges.

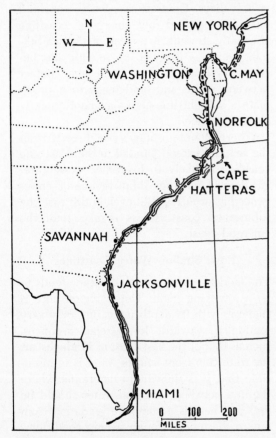

Fig. 1.3—The Intracoastal Waterway. This provides a protected coastal route for pleasure craft and small commercial shipping behind the sheltering chain of islands and bars along the southeast coast of the United States.

Mountain Coastlines

Mountain coastlines are not necessarily those small, highly localized areas where the waves break directly on cliffs or mountains that "march to the sea." The general condition is that mountains parallel the coast, separated from the sea by only a narrow

beach. In a few instances the beach may be absent. The one example of this type is more or less continuous along the western coast of the Americas, between Oregon and southern Chile. For some 6000 miles the coast is paralleled by the mountains, the longest almost unbroken stretch of relatively smooth coastline in the world. As the mountains have recently been elevated it is an emergent coast, but the water deepens rapidly offshore.

Fig. 1.4—The Northwest Coast of Spain, a Ria Coastline.

Ria Coastlines

"Ria" is the Spanish word for an embayment of the sea that occurs where marine waters extend up the lower portion of a former stream valley. Ria coastlines are necessarily submergent. The type example is the **northwestern coast of Spain** (Fig. 1.4), where the term originated. On ria coasts there is not only interfingering, where drowned valleys alternate with projecting ridges, but usually in addition countless smaller embayments (Fig. 1.5) notching in to the sides of the higher ground, so that the actual shoreline between two points may be many times longer than the straight-line distance between them. The **eastern coast of North America** from New York to Newfoundland illustrates this condition. **Casco Bay**, at Portland, Maine, has in addition many small

Fig. 1.5—Ria Embayment on the Northwest Coast of the Iberian Peninsula, at Cabo Carvoeiro, Portugal. (Courtesy, Portuguese Embassy.)

Fig. 1.6—Fiord, Milford Sound, New Zealand. The straight, precipitous mountain walls and deep water far inland are characteristic of fiords. (Courtesy, New Zealand Embassy.)

islands offshore, the projecting tops of drowned ridges. Other ria coastlines occur along the **Mediterranean shores**, in **Japan**, and in **South China**.

When the valley of a large river is drowned at its mouth a very wide embayment is formed extending deep inland. Such an embayment is known as an "estuary." Estuaries are most common along the shores of **western and northern France**, in **Germany**, and in the **British Isles**. Among the most important estuaries are those of the **Thames, Seine, Elbe,** and **Weser** rivers. The **Hudson River** is another famous example (Frontispiece).

Fiord Coastlines

"Fiords" were formed in mountainous coastal regions during the ice age by glaciers that moved down to the sea through main valleys, scouring out the bottoms of the valleys to depths of hundreds of feet and making their sides nearly vertical (i.e., producing a U-shaped cross section). In many instances the scour was so deep that with the melting of the ice the sea came up the valley for many miles and in great depth. It is thought by some that there was also sinking of the land, in which case fiord coasts would be submergent. Fiords are extraordinary in that they enable the sea to reach far inland through twisting, narrow valleys, yet with no shallowing. This was strikingly illustrated during World War II, when the Germans hid their greatest battleships in the Norwegian fiords miles from the sea.

By their origin fiords are restricted to non-tropical regions. The type locality is the **west coast of Norway**, where they received their name. Other fiord coastlines are: the **west coast of North America from Puget Sound to the Alaskan Peninsula;** the **southern coast of Chile;** the **coasts of Scotland, Iceland, Greenland,** and **Labrador;** and portions of the **South Island** (New Zealand) **coast** (Fig. 1.6). The **Saguenay River** is a well-known example in eastern Canada.

Delta Coasts

A delta is formed at the mouth of a stream by the accumulation of sediment which the stream drops when it reaches the sea and its

Fig. 1.7—Delta, Small Scale, in Lake at the Terminus of Collier Glacier, Cascade Mountains, Oregon. (Courtesy, Ruth S. Hopson.)

current ceases (Fig. 1.7). During floods streams spread over the older parts of their deltas and drop sediment, so that the deltas tend to be built up above sea level. As the goal of the water in the stream is the sea, the delta also tends to be built out from land as the stream flows over the previously accumulated sediment.

Obviously, the rate of growth of the delta is directly related to the amount of sediment which the stream is carrying and the depth of the water. Some streams are so loaded with sediment that their deposition rapidly builds a bar or shoal across their mouths; in extreme cases this may cause the mouth of the stream to be shifted from time to time to new outlets. As the function of streams as highways into the interior is a geographic factor of great significance, the delta-building characteristics of a particular stream are evidently a matter of considerable importance in its utilization as a river route.

It should be noted that not all streams have deltas, for if the stream carries little or no sediment it cannot form one. This is true, for example, of the St. Lawrence River. Nor can a delta be formed where there is a strong ocean current across the mouth of the stream, as the current will carry away the sediment as fast as it is dropped by the stream. For this reason, therefore, and because of the fineness of its sediment the Amazon has no delta.

One of the great delta-building rivers of the world is the **Mississippi**. Navigational channels across its delta are kept open only by constant dredging and the construction of jetties. Some streams, such as the **Po** of Italy, extend their deltas so rapidly that former port cities find themselves miles inland in the course of a few centuries. Still other streams combine rapid delta building with frequent shiftings of their channels, so that it is not possible to develop a port at their mouths. The great French port of Marseille is 30 miles to one side of the **Rhone** mouth; the port of Karachi in India is 15 miles from the mouth of the **Indus**. Other great delta developments occur at the mouths of the **Nile, Rhine, Orinoco,** and **Yukon**.

QUESTIONS. What effect has island environment on island populations? Why are island groups that include large islands especially significant geographically? What is the most important large island group? What were its geographic advantages? What island group most closely matches the premier group in characteristics? What geographical reasons are there for the success of the British settlement of New Zealand? How do both the East and West Indies differ in nature and utilization from the groups previously considered? How does the history of Philippine development differ from that of Hawaii? Name some small island groups that are historically important; strategically important.

What has been the geographical past of the large islands of the arctic north of North America? What are their names? What are their possible future uses? What circumstances gave Iceland geographic distinction? Why is Spitzbergen inhabited by Europeans? Name and locate the four largest islands of the world. Compare the utilization of Madagascar with that of Ceylon. Name six small islands that are well known because of the historical events with which they are connected. Zanzibar is a representative example of the use of small islands for what particular purpose? Name another such island.

Characterize coastlines as a geographic phenomenon. Why did primitive peoples resort to them? What gives significance to coastlines in modern times? What are the two great classes of coastlines? Name examples of each. What is the nature of a submerged coastline? Account for smooth, low coastlines. Describe the east coast of Madagascar. Account for the characteristics of the shoreline of Chesapeake Bay. Under what conditions are protected inland marine waterways possible? Where is the longest almost unbroken, smooth coastline in the world? What is its nature? What is a ria coast? Give examples. Name four important estuaries. What is the nature of a fiord coast? Where are fiord coasts prominently developed? How are deltas formed? Name four great delta developments.

CHAPTER 2

Landmarks of the World—Continental

■ PLAINS

INTRODUCTION

The word "plain" in common usage usually denotes a tract of land that is flat, level, and low lying (Fig. 2.1). As used in geography with reference to extensive areas, on the other hand, the term has a much broader meaning. Various formal definitions agree that a plain as a geographic unit need not have a plane surface, is not necessarily horizontal, and is not necessarily near sea level. The term is, however, generally restricted to areas within which there is not more than 500 feet difference in elevation. In other words, the valleys of plains are shallow.

The great example of an inclined plain that also attains high altitude is the **Great Plains** region of North America (Fig. 2.2). This rises to an elevation of 5000 feet, higher than many plateaus, but because the rise is gradual and continuous the term "plain" is, by common consent, used to designate this province.

Fig. 2.2—Plains: Great Plains South of McDonald, New Mexico. (Courtesy, John C. Frye.)

The significance of plains in human history and present-day activities cannot be over-emphasized. *Although less than one-half of the land surface of the earth can be classified as plains, some 90 percent of the world's population is located on plains.* Only in tropical America, where the heat of the lower altitudes compels the inhabitants to seek relief in the uplands, are considerable populations not resident on plains. All of the great cities of the world are on plains; it is relatively rare to find one of greater than 100,000 population not so situated. Moreover, it has

Fig. 2.1—Plain, Lower St. Lawrence Valley. In the distance one of the Monteregian Hills rises above the level of the plain. (Courtesy, Service Cine-Photographic, Province of Quebec, Canada.)

been found that most ancient civilizations regularly developed on plains. Evidently plains are and have been of major importance in man's development and current activities. Why?

It should first be recognized that not any and every plain possesses superior advantages for human habitation. Factors of climate (chiefly temperature and precipitation) also determine environmental suitability. The arctic wastes of polar North America and the western portion of the Sahara of Africa, for example, although plains, provide slight attraction, if any, for human settlement.

ENVIRONMENTAL ADVANTAGES OF PLAINS

The environmental advantages of plains to a great extent apply conjointly and are thus difficult to list in any order of rank. The following list of advantages should be considered, therefore, as a whole rather than as a series of separate factors of progressively declining importance.

1. The suitability of plains for agriculture is indisputably one of their more important advantages. Water runs slowly over their more or less level surfaces, so that wearing away of the land by its flow is slight and agriculture is "permanent." Valley plains are commonly areas of deposition, so that soil fertility is often maintained naturally. Levelness lightens the labor of cultivation, both by encouraging extensive, large-scale agriculture (as opposed to the terrace agriculture of hillsides) and by facilitating the use of machines to increase the effectiveness of human labor (Fig. 26.12). In the "corn states" of North America, for example, as much as 70 to 80 percent of the total land area is suitable for farm use.

It has been said that agriculture is the foundation of permanent progress in civilization. It is no coincidence that nearly all the major agricultural nations are situated on plains, or that the great cereal-producing areas of the world are all plains land.

2. Nearly equal in importance with suitability for agriculture is the relative ease of overland transportation common to plains. This was a significant factor in the early development of nations. Ready mobility invites travel and the interchange of goods and ideas so necessary to progress and political unification of large areas. In modern times ease of transportation has been of ever increasing importance. Before the advent of railroads the natural navigable waterways common to plains were augmented by extensive networks of canals, a transportation facility that can be provided on a large scale only on plains. In the United States canal construction began too late (just before the development of the railroads) to attain lasting significance. In Europe, on the other hand, canals were early constructed so generally that they have never lost significance in the transportation systems of many of the countries. France has 3000 miles of canals, Germany 1400 miles. The Low Countries and Russia (and in Asia, China) have dense networks of canals covering the plains regions of their territories.

The suitability of plains for the construction of railroads is evident. There are few if any steep grades to overcome; it is possible to establish routes in all directions and to follow straight lines between points. As a consequence the roads can be built and maintained cheaply. But railroads are not constructed merely because of topographic suitability. Population must be sufficiently dense to permit profitable operation, and dense networks result only where there is also noteworthy economic activity.

This is well illustrated in the case of Buenos Aires, Argentina. In its early years this city could not compete successfully for trade and prestige with contemporary rival cities of the region. Then the agricultural and especially cattle-raising potentialities of the plain on which Buenos Aires is situated were discovered. Once these potentialities were exploited, the population expanded and Buenos Aires flourished, becoming a center of economic activity that fostered the parallel growth of railroads. The widespread pampas plains, which initially handicapped development of the city because of their own undeveloped status, now served to permit the easy construction of the magnificent railroad network centered on the Argentine capital.

In another instance there was no such initial disadvantage. The city of Chicago was early surrounded by developed agricultural lands. It grew rapidly as a trade and manufacturing center, and its location on a plain, among other reasons, greatly facilitated its eventual establishment as the railroad capital of the nation. Similarly Paris, London, Berlin, and Moscow, although all centers of large populations because of political, economic, and agricultural factors, have been able to become the hubs of railroad networks because of their plains sites.

3. The uniformity of plains conditions and the fact that many plains extend over vast areas tend to bring about political and cultural uniformity in countries whose territory consists largely of plains. Thus the wide plains regions of the United States facilitated its expansion, and the uniform environment they provided fostered the maintenance of political coherence. Such uniformity serves also to offset the tendency to disintegration to which large territories are subject after their initial assimilation into a single political organization. The opposite result is demonstrated by the Balkan countries of Europe and by certain regions of South America. In such areas topographic irregularity has so far prevented large-scale political combinations and has favored the retention of the existing political and cultural differences evident in each of those small nations.

4. Plains may contain vast timber resources to which access is relatively easy. The timber resources on the plains of North America were of first importance in its early modern development (Fig. 2.3). It has been estimated that at the beginning of colonization approximately one-half the total continental area was forest covered. With growth in population density, however, crops take precedence over timber, which is then allowed to remain only on rough terrain unsuited for agriculture, and to which access is relatively difficult.

Timber is still important on the remote

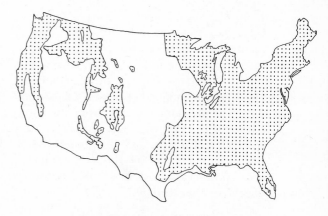

Fig. 2.3—Original Timber Regions of the United States. (Compare with plains areas of the United States shown in Fig. 2.4.) (After U.S. Department of Agriculture.)

plains of Canada, Finland, and especially Siberia, where immense areas of coniferous forest represent the major remaining timber resources of the world.

5. The coal, petroleum, salt, and potash deposits of the world for the most part underlie plains. On the other hand, the earth's crust is comparatively poor in metallic minerals under the plains areas. The great low-grade coal reserves of the United States are in the Great Plains province; vast petroleum- and natural-gas-producing areas also underlie plains areas of this country and Canada. Similarly, the coal and oil of Europe, Asia, and South America are mainly produced from plains regions.

This is not to say that the existence of the mineral resources is due to the occurrence of the plains area, or vice versa. The presence of mineral resources depends upon geologic conditions and circumstances; the existence of a plain in a mineral region may or may not be related.

6. In consequence of the advantages listed above most of the great industrial centers of modern society are situated on plains. Level arable land permits the maintenance of a large population. This, in turn, insures both a labor supply and a market. Where plains and bodies of water are associated both land and water transportation facilitates the assemblage of raw materials and marketing of finished goods. Finally, the common occur-

rence of coal, oil, and gas for power within plains areas has made possible the development of the gigantic industrial centers of modern civilization. Chicago and Detroit in the United States; London, Birmingham, and Liverpool in England; Brussels, Ghent, and Liège in Belgium; the multiple industrial centers of the Ruhr region of Germany; Moscow, Kiev, Kharkov, and Dnepropetrovsk in Russia—all depend on the availability of great power resources from the plains on which they are situated.

PLAINS LANDMARKS OF THE WORLD

Most of the world's plains are centered around the Atlantic Ocean or are tributary to it either physically or economically (Fig. 2.4). The most important of them in recent world history has been the **"North" European Plain.** This is a composite of the plains areas of England, France, Belgium, the Netherlands, Germany, Denmark, southern Sweden, Russia, Poland, Hungary, Finland, and, by extension, the Po plain of northern Italy.

The western portion of this composite plain was the site of the great development of modern European civilization. The Ukraine and the Danubian plain of Rumania were for a long time the "breadbasket" of Europe through their large wheat production. Now the steppe plains of the Volga region are also being utilized in vast collective farms for wheat production.

In North America the plains comprise the major portion of the continent east of the Rocky Mountains and their foothills. The **Great Plains** between 1880 and 1940 became the "breadbasket" of this continent and, during the two World Wars, of a large portion of the world. The wheat fields of the western Great Plains merge eastward into the corn and hog belt, another food region with an enormous volume of production. The **Gulf Coastal Plain** in the south, and the **Atlantic Coastal Plain** and **Piedmont** of the southeastern United States are somewhat less significant for food production but as regions of the cash crops cotton and tobacco are of first importance in the country's agriculture.

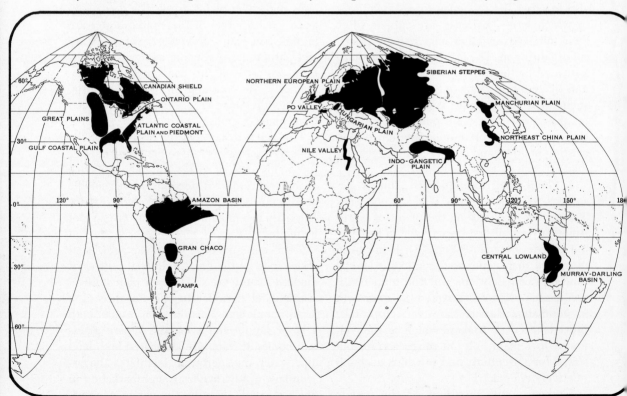

Fig. 2.4—Landmarks of the World: Plains.

Except for the northern extension of the wheat-producing Great Plains and the **Ontario Plain,** Canada's plains are better known for their minerals than for their agricultural yield. The world's prime sources of nickel and the newly important uranium ores are both in this region.[1] The territory thus exploited is, however, only a small portion of the total plains region of Canada. The northeastern **Canadian Shield** of ancient crystalline rocks has been largely stripped bare of soil by ice age glaciers. The arctic climate of the Northwest Territories effectively precludes their use for agriculture.

In South America the largest plain is that of the **Amazon Basin.** Climate (equatorial heat), floods, and tropical forest together have prevented utilization of this area in any degree comparable to that of Canada, the United States, Europe, and Russia. The **Pampa** of Argentina and the **Gran Chaco** of Argentina, Paraguay, and Bolivia are the other major plains regions of the continent. The former is the most populous area of South America; the latter is a remote area climatically and otherwise as difficult for development as the Amazon Basin.

As in North America, the shores of the Arctic Ocean in Europe and Asia are bordered by a wide plain that is a treeless marsh in summer, a bleak waste of frozen ground in winter—the tundra. Southward the tundra merges into a forest belt, the taiga, like that of Canada similarly situated. Yet farther south the plains areas become grasslands, prairie-like in the west but deteriorating to sparse, arid lands eastward: the **Siberian steppes.** This vast tract has somewhat the same potentialities as those already realized in the Canadian section of the Great Plains region. The Soviet Union is working feverishly to realize these potentialities in the steppe country.

The western borderlands of the Persian Gulf and much of the country of Iraq com-prise another plains region. In India the **Indo-Gangetic Plain** south of the Himalayas has been for ages the center of Indian development. In the Far East the plains of **northeast China** and **Manchuria** are in part densely populated and are centers of much of the industrial progress that has been made in China.

In Australia there are two large plains areas: the great **Central Lowland** that runs north-south as a belt through the continent east of its central line; and a smaller area, the **Murray-Darling Basin,** the wide floors of two river basins after which it is named, in the southeast.

The African continent has less plains area than any of the others. The valley and delta of the Nile are nevertheless an outstanding plain of first significance historically and modernly, despite its limited extent. In view of the demonstrated importance of large plains in facilitating material progress it is not surprising that Africa has remained for so long the least developed continent. Since the Egyptian (or perhaps the Carthaginian) civilization there has been no indigenous commercial and industrial development in Africa comparable to that on the other continents. The narrow lowlands that border the African coasts are so restricted in area or so inhospitable climatically as to be of little significance as plains regions.

QUESTIONS. Although plains are generally the most advantageous environment for man, some plains are almost totally unutilized; give examples and explain the reasons for each case. Explain the significance of the large plains areas in the growth and development of the United States. Compare the disadvantages and advantages of one of the large plains mentioned in the text. What is unusual about the products of the Canadian plains?

■ PLATEAUS

INTRODUCTION

The terms "plain" and "plateau" are unfortunately not applied consistently. Usage determines which word designates the specific

---

[1] This is an exception to the statement that plains are not usually the source localities of the world's metallic minerals; it is due to the fact that these areas are underlain by types of rock unlike those that typically underlie plains.

Fig. 2.5—Plateaus: Colorado plateaus, Painted Desert, Arizona. (Spence Air Photos.)

occurrence. Particular examples vary widely, but a plateau typically is a table-like upland whose summit level surface has a difference in elevation of less than 500 feet. This relatively level upland surface characteristically occurs at an altitude of 2000 feet or more above sea level and terminates abruptly in a steep declivity on at least one side (Fig. 2.5). Although their surfaces are rather level, plateaus are commonly dissected or transected by notably deep, steep-sided valleys. Plains, on the other hand, are almost always terminated on at least one side by a sea or the ocean. Plateaus are commonly inland regions; if they extend to the sea they regularly terminate in cliffs or there is a narrow strip of plain or low hills between the upland edge of the plateau and the shoreline.

Like plains, plateaus present certain advantages and disadvantages to human utilization. In plateaus, however, the disadvantages usually outweigh the favorable circumstances.

PLATEAU HANDICAPS

1. The greatest single characteristic of the plateau environment is quite the reverse of that of the plains, namely, the difficulty rather than facility of transportation. To begin with, the plateau upland is in most instances relatively inaccessible; it cannot be easily attained from adjacent regions. Internal movement is blocked, moreover, by the deep transecting and notching valleys, which thus constitute barriers rather than thoroughfares (Fig. 2.6). Their steep sides, the narrowness of their bottoms, and the fact that their floors are often clogged with boul-

ders make transportation by road or rail along them difficult if not impossible. Yet transportation on the summit level across such valleys is a formidable undertaking. Under primitive conditions a descent and ascent of the precipitous sides is necessary; if bridging is attempted the engineering problems are difficult to solve and costly to overcome. Moreover, not one but many bridges must usually be built if free movement is to be achieved.

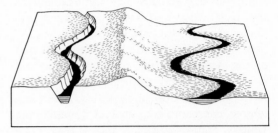

Fig. 2.6—Plain Versus Plateau Topography. Stream valleys on a plain (right) and plateau (left) are shown here diagrammatically. The plain valley is wide and low; access to the stream is easy, and commerce is aided. The plateau valley is deep and steep-sided. Although narrow in comparison with the plain valley, it is not easily bridged and is thus a barrier to commerce. Commerce along the stream, even if the stream is large enough and the bed smooth enough to permit navigation, involves getting in and out of the canyon, usually an insuperable handicap.

As a result the cheap, bulky commodities of first importance for all commerce and industry cannot be marketed profitably as export products, and if imported become luxury items in plateau areas. The cost of "civilized" living is unduly high. Accordingly, only special circumstances that offset the transportation difficulties permit the exploitation of plateau regions in accord with their provision of natural resources.

2. Plateaus are generally less suited for agriculture than are plains. Most plateaus tend to be arid; there is commonly insufficient rainfall for production of crops by standard agricultural practices. The major streams flow so far below the plateau level as to make difficult their utilization for irrigation (Fig. 2.6). Melt-water from nearby snow-capped mountains may be available, however. High altitudes mean an average

annual temperature lower than that of sea level at the same distance north or south of the equator. In the so-called "temperate" and subpolar regions the temperatures on plateaus may be so much reduced as to not only limit agriculture but also make human existence unpleasant.

Nevertheless plateaus are not without significance for agricultural utilization. One tropical plateau is the site of the world's largest coffee source. Wheat does well in many plateau regions. Plateaus, in fact, contribute materially to the world's food supply. The semiarid environment which favors wheat growing is also conducive to successful stock raising. Indeed, the most typical activity of plateau environments is the pasturing of cattle, sheep, or goats.

3. The plateau environment generally tends to hamper social progress. The difficulties of transportation operate to isolate plateau populations. Interchange of culture, ideas, and products is greatly restricted, and inbreeding is sometimes a conspicuous feature. The reverse of all these trends is manifest in plains regions.

PLATEAU ADVANTAGES

1. In all tropical regions the effect of altitude offsets in large measure the numerous handicaps of the plateau environment. Plateaus serve to demonstrate the fundamental unlikeness of the tropical and nontropical regions of the earth, for between the two regions the advantages and disadvantages of plains and plateaus are reversed. The low altitudes and broad valleys that generally facilitate human activity on plains retard and handicap it in tropical regions. Contrariwise, the lower temperatures of plateaus that render them inhospitable in the colder regions are their prime attraction in the tropics. The debilitating heat and moisture of the lowland tropics are well known. The drier, cooler plateau climate mitigates these extremes to such a degree that in many cases conditions may be more congenial than summer in Europe and North America. The heavy rainfall of the tropics tends to inundate low-lying, slowly drained flatlands,

whereas even heavy downpours run off rapidly in plateau country.

Insect-transmitted diseases are a great problem in the tropics. The billions of mosquitoes that breed in the swamps and marshes of the lowlands carry diseases so effectively as to have decimated even indigenous populations. It is thus small wonder that the capitals and important cities of tropical areas are commonly located in the highlands, and that populations regularly are concentrated in the higher altitudes.

DDT and other new insecticides have, of course, wrought dramatic changes in lowland areas of the tropics through special projects of international and philanthropic organizations, but the expense of the constant maintenance of health measures remains a serious local economic burden.

2. The other major advantage of plateaus for human utilization, less important now than formerly, is their easy defensibility. Historically, this has given some plateaus great political importance. Those that were centrally situated have also tended to become the sites of govermental cities.

PLATEAU LANDMARKS OF THE WORLD

Africa, the continent most deficient in plains, consists essentially of one great plateau which has, however, several distinctive subdivisions (Fig. 2.7). Thus a vast region in the south has an average altitude of some 3000 feet. Much of the **Sahara** is between 1000 and 3000 feet. The **Congo Basin** is about 1000 feet above sea level. The highest section, the **Ethiopian Highlands,** is a northeastern outlier of the main plateau.

Because of the universality of plateau topography in Africa the handicapping features of such environment are conspicuous. Although African rivers are among the world's largest they are, with the exception of the Nile, ill suited and little utilized for navigation. Their basic defect is the abrupt plunge they make, by cataracts and waterfalls, from the high plateau to the narrow belt of costal lowlands. The Nile is an exception because it makes the descent by stages

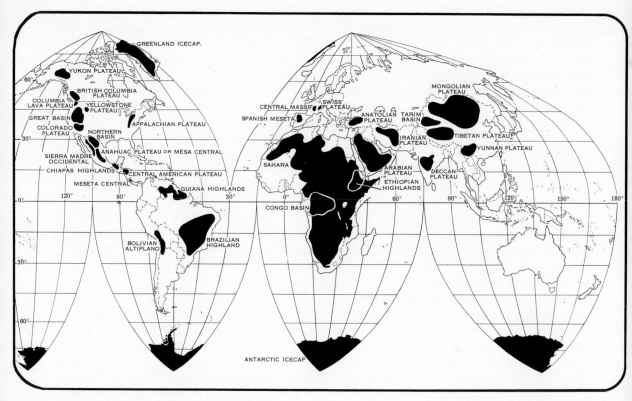

Fig. 2.7—Landmarks of the World: Plateaus.

far inland. Accordingly, it has provided an ideal water highway, in its long north-south traverse, utilized from prehistoric times until the present. On the other hand, the tremendous hydroelectric power potentialities of African rivers have future economic significance that will largely offset their unsuitability for navigational use.

Asia is also in large part a continent of plateaus, both interior and coastal. The **Anatolian Plateau** of Turkey exemplifies the function of a plateau environment as a political nucleus and a preserver of "racial purity." The **Arabian Plateau** comprises almost the entire Arabian peninsula and is an example of extreme plateau aridity. The **Iranian Plateau,** the **Mongolian Plateau** and the **Tarim Basin** of central Asia are typical semiarid interior plateau areas. The **Deccan Plateau** of India includes much of the southern portion of that subcontinent. The northwestern part of the Deccan was built up by successive outpourings of lava in thick flows;

its area is largely devoted to cotton production. The **Tibetan Plateau** is the heart of central Asia and the highest of all plateaus. Its average altitude of more than 12,000 feet has given it the name "Roof of the World." It is the supreme example of plateau isolation, which here has functioned to foster an extreme religious nationalism. Finally, the much dissected **Yunnan Plateau** of southwestern China is a remote, little-known region rich in undeveloped mineral resources.

Europe possesses only one plateau of appreciable size, the **Spanish Meseta,** between 1500 and 3500 feet in elevation. Like the Anatolian Plateau of Turkey it is the political and cultural focus of Spain. Topographically it dominates the Iberian Peninsula as completely as the continental plateau of Africa dominates that continent. The **Central Massif** of France resembles the Spanish Meseta in position and nature but is much smaller; compared to the Meseta it is wholly without significance for French culture and politics. On the other hand, the **Swiss Plateau** north of the Alps is essentially Switzerland. As this plateau is on routes through the Alps from northern and western Europe to Italy it has escaped the blight of isolation common to most plateaus and is instead the seat of an enlightened people and an enterprising nation. Even so, three languages are officially spoken in Switzerland, an indication of the enduring separative influence of the plateau environment.

South America contains four major plateaus: the **Brazilian Highland** in the southeast of that country; the **"Altiplano,"** which constitutes much of Bolivia and parts of Peru and Chile, and is second to the Tibetan Plateau in altitude; the **Patagonian Plateau** of southern Argentina; and the **Guiana Highlands** of the northeastern coast. The first two are good examples of the two main types of plateaus—those which stand higher than the surrounding lands (the "tableland" type in Brazil) and those which are surrounded by higher mountains (the "intermontane" type in Bolivia).

Development of the resources of the Brazilian Highland has lagged because of the engineering difficulties and costs of road and rail building from the coast; the Bolivian Altiplano is even more difficult to attain. The Guiana Highlands are actually quite inaccessible except by air, so sheer and high are their terminal cliffs, and the Patagonian Plateau is remote and barren.

Besides these there are in South America the small intermontane **Venezuelan, Colombian, and Ecuadorian plateaus** on which the capitals of these tropical countries exist.

The diversity of nations and failure of intercommunication between them which is characteristic of South America may in considerable degree be attributed to the plateau topography of so much of the continent. To be sure, the plateau lands of North America are hardly less extensive, but these uplands are rather easily accessible, and tropical heat and humidity do not adversely affect the major plains regions from which they are approached.

Central America greatly resembles South America in its relief and utilization aspects. Here again tropical heat and plateau topography underlie national diversity and disunity because of intensive occupation of the plateau uplands without significant intercommunication between them. From south to north appear the **Meseta Central** of Costa Rica, the **Central American Plateau** of Nicaragua and Honduras, and the **Chiapas Highlands,** partly Guatemalan, partly Mexican. Beyond that the much larger **Anahuac Plateau,** or **Mesa Central,** of Mexico extends northward, bounded on the west by the higher **Sierra Madre Occidental.** (The latter is a lava plateau so dissected and rough it is thought of as a mountain range.) In characteristic fashion the capitals and national activities in most of these countries are on plateau summits. The Mesa Central of Mexico declines gradually in altitude northward through the **Northern Basin** to the American boundary, so that the overland approach from the United States to the Mexican capital is not topographically difficult.

On its western side the Northern Basin of Mexico merges with the great **Colorado Plateau** of Arizona. It is in this plateau that the Colorado River has cut the stupendous Grand Canyon, the supreme expression of the plateau "gorge-valley."

North and west of the Colorado Plateau the vast **Great Basin** country of Utah and Nevada is encountered. Its eastern border in Utah furnishes another instance of the potentialities of the plateau environment in fostering the development of individualistic human communities. It was here that the Latter-Day Saints (Mormons), after being compelled by persecution to abandon several successive plains settlements, were finally able to practice their religious beliefs in relative freedom.

Still farther north, in Idaho, Oregon, and Washington, lies an intermontane plateau 200,000 square miles in extent. This is the **Columbia Lava Plateau,** a duplication in many respects of the Deccan Plateau of India. The **Yellowstone Plateau** of northwestern Wyoming with its geysers and hot springs is also an intermontane region of lava flows, as is the **British Columbia Plateau** in Canada. The farthest north of these intermontane developments is the **Yukon Plateau** of the Yukon Territory and Alaska.

In eastern North America the only plateau of any consequence is the **Appalachian Plateau**. It is small in comparison with the western developments of the plateau topography and a departure from the rule of low economic activity in regions of winter cold. This difference results from the fact that much of it is blanketed with thick glacial soils and is there traversed by wide, flat-floored valleys that afford throughways for road and rail routes and considerable acreage for productive agriculture. Outside the glacial belt, however, there is evident the isolation of plateaus induced by narrow valleys.

The icecaps of **Greenland** and **Antarctica** are not strictly plateaus, but in a broad classification of landmarks they fit best there since they exhibit nearly all the criteria of plateaus—level, high summit tracts, with steep borders, inaccessibility, inutility. They are, however, practically undissected expanses of snow and ice, except as deep ice cracks (crevasses) are considered the equivalent of the gorge-valleys of their land counterparts.

> **QUESTIONS.** Distinguish between plains and plateaus. List the advantages and disadvantages of tropical plateaus and plains; of nontropical plateaus and plains. Explain the significance of the lists. Suppose Europe were composed mainly of plateau lands rather than plains; how would this possibly have affected European history? Would a coastline bordering a plain be as likely to have a large population and great economic activity as a coastline bordering a plateau? Why? Why are the disadvantages of nontropical plateaus as environments less important now than formerly? What continent is virtually a single plateau? What effect has this had on the utilization of that continent? Where are the Asiatic plateaus located? Which is the world's highest? Which is a lava plateau? Which plateaus have a dry climate?
>
> Why is the Spanish Meseta the most significant of the European plateaus? Where are the South American plateaus located? Explain the difference between "tableland" and "intermontane" plateaus. What effect have these plateaus had on the political geography of South America? What does the Grand Canyon typify as a plateau phenomenon? What is the name of the only important plateau in the eastern United States? In what respects is it unusual as a plateau? Why are the icecaps of Greenland and Antarctica listed as plateaus?

■ MOUNTAINS

INTRODUCTION

Mountains are often defined as "regions where local differences in altitude are 2000 feet or more." But "mountains" may be of much less height and may occur in such a wide variety of forms as to defeat any attempt at a specific definition. It may be noted, however, that "hill-lands," intermediate in altitude between plains and mountains, are also intermediate in other characteristics. The emphasis here given to mountains is less on size and aspect than on the effect they have on man's activities, hence on their significance as landmarks.

MOUNTAIN DISADVANTAGES

1. Mountains are the least hospitable of the major landforms for human habitation. It is possible for man to acclimate himself to the diminished supply of oxygen available in high mountain altitudes, but it is not so easy to overcome the handicap imposed on his activities by the lowering of the temperature at great heights, especially where this lowering occurs in elevations above the "snow line," i.e., the altitude above which the temperatures are so low that snow persists throughout the year.

2. The general unsuitability of mountain lands for agricultural utilization is obvious. Even where slopes are sufficiently gentle to permit cultivation they are likely to possess only a thin cover of soil. The floors of mountain valleys are, in general, too narrow to possess substantial areas of arable land. Such acreage as does exist there is commonly subject to devastation by floods.

It is thus surprising to find even one major

power—Japan—whose area is predominantly mountainous. Only 30 percent of the total area of the Japanese Islands is naturally suited to agricultural development. This is mostly the lands of narrow alluvial and coastal plains at the base of the mountains.

3. It is even more difficult to link up different districts within mountains by adequate transportation facilities than it is to connect regions within plateaus. The substantial highways and well-engineered railroads that are built are through routes, utilized to overcome the mountain barrier between lower lands on either side. Internal roads may be built to serve mining communities and to connect these with the through routes. With such exceptions communication and commerce within mountains tend to be limited to trails and tracks suitable at best for clumsy carts or only for pack animals and human porterage. Only high-value and low-bulk products repay the transportation costs to markets remote from the mountain sources. Other than minerals few mountain products can qualify for such commerce.

4. In mountains the isolation of the inhabitants extends to the family level. A homestead may be miles removed from the nearest neighbor and such separation may be by difficult terrain as well as by distance. Instead of promoting friendliness mountain isolation apparently engenders feuds and lawlessness and may result in inbreeding and decadence.

MOUNTAIN RESOURCES

1. In the United States a chief source of lumber is the mountain forest region of Washington, Oregon, and California. This is not uncommonly the case also in other parts of the world. In many mountain areas there are considerable expanses of slope that support a lush growth of grass and other verdure; these tracts afford pasturage to cattle, sheep, and goats and make animal husbandry the chief dependence of relatively dense mountain populations. Such areas are usually available for pasture only during the warm season, so that it is the practice in

many countries to drive the herds to the upland regions for summer pasture and keep them during the winter either on lower pastures (which gives the grass in each pasture site a chance to grow again) or on stored fodder. This seasonal migration (called "transhumance") is often an important factor in the pattern of human activity in a mountain region.

2. The great mineralized areas of the world, the sources of most of the metals essential to modern industrial development, occur, with a few notable exceptions, in mountain territories. This is the result of a definite geological relationship between the formation of ore deposits and the processes associated with mountain building in the earth's crust. However, the conclusion that all mountainous regions are important sources of metallic ores is not warranted. In many places ore deposits that may once have been present have been eroded away in earlier geological periods; in other mountains, ores may be so deeply buried as to be undiscoverable or unattainable; and some mountain masses seem never to have had any ore deposits.

The distribution and concentration of the ores of the various metals is remarkably sporadic. It is possible for one or two countries to control almost the entire world's supply of a given metal. Thus for many years the United States was the sole source of molybdenum and China of antimony. Where rich ores exist in quantity the great cost and effort necessary to overcome the physical obstacles to their recovery and transportation from mountain regions may prove to be economically justified.

3. Abundant hydroelectric power in mountains is a resource that has been exploited only recently on a large scale. By contrast with the power sites in other regions, those in mountains combine small volume with great height rather than large volume and small descent. As it is much cheaper to install long tubes to carry the water to the power station than to construct huge dams and provide massive machinery, such mountain power developments furnish

large outputs of power at low cost. The availability of cheap power immediately makes industry possible and permits a higher standard of living and larger populations in such fortunate mountain regions.

4. At present mountain regions are being increasingly utilized as both summer and winter recreational areas. The scenic prospects, the clear, clean air, and the sports possibilities together suffice to attract multitudes of work-weary visitors from lowland regions near and far. The accommodation of these vacationers then becomes a main business for the mountain inhabitants.

5. As with plateaus, the high altitudes of mountains moderate tropical heat and hence provide agreeable living conditions at intermediate elevations. Moreover, where the tropical mountains rise directly from low plains to lofty heights temperatures ranging from equatorial heat to polar cold appear in belts as the slopes are ascended. Accordingly the products of all climatic zones are immediately available at the middle altitudes at the expense of only short travel up or down. Vertical transport is arduous, but as the distances are relatively short the up-and-down haul is not a great deterrent to commerce, especially since such trade is ideally complementary. Bananas from the tropical lowland realm may be exchanged for corn and potatoes from above. Until the advent of refrigeration, ice from snow-capped summits was regularly brought down to cool lemonade made from lemons grown in the tropical climate at the mountain base.

CLIMATIC INFLUENCE OF MOUNTAINS

Far outweighing in importance the various disadvantages and advantages of mountains as sites for human habitation and utilization are their dominating effects on the world's climates. The degree of this influence depends on the elevation, the continuity, and the location of the mountain ranges. Mountains make complex what would otherwise be a relatively simple climatic pattern.

The chief effect is on the distribution of humidity. Thus, mountain systems force winds blowing across them to precipitate their moisture content as rain or snow on the windward slopes. Areas on the lee side of a mountain range tend to be arid. They are said to lie in the "rain shadow" of the mountains. In extreme cases such shadowing results in deserts.

MOUNTAINS AS BARRIERS

As barriers, mountains affect plant and animal life even more than they do man and his activities. Marked differences in flora and fauna occur on opposite sides of a mountain range. Along with the climate these biological differences significantly modify the nature of human activity on the two sides. Mountains also act as "divides" between systems of watercourses. The "Continental Divide" of North America, chiefly along the crest of the Rocky Mountain ranges, is the line from which water flows to the Pacific Ocean on the one side, the Atlantic (or Gulf of Mexico) on the other.

DISTRIBUTION OF MOUNTAINS

Broadly speaking, the Pacific Ocean is ringed around by a system of mountains. Another system of great extent runs through southern Asia, Europe, and North Africa. Lesser systems tend to be isolated in occurrence. Only those considered as "world landmarks" are shown in Fig. 2.8.

North American Mountain Landmarks

The major mountains of North America are concentrated in the western third of the continent. The **Rocky Mountains** extend from northern Canada to the Mexican border, marking the western limits of the flatlands, hence of extensive agriculture. Farther west animal husbandry is the chief rural activity. The **Basin Ranges** are short mountain chains west of the Rockies that string across and interrupt the surface of the Great Basin plateau. Both the Rockies and Basin Ranges are rich in minerals, so that mining is a notably developed industry. Moreover, the mountain scenery is increasingly exploited through the national parks (Yellowstone,

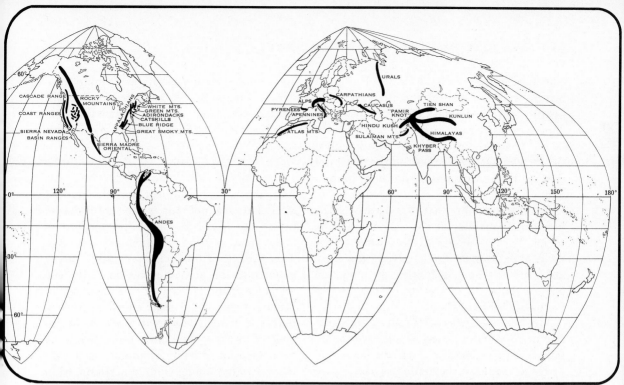

Fig. 2.8—Landmarks of the World: Mountains.

Glacier, etc.) and by private enterprise (such as at Sun Valley, Idaho) for recreational use.

Bordering the Pacific coast there is a mountain belt almost as continuous as the Rockies which it parallels. In between these two systems lie the intermontane plateaus previously listed. The chains along the shore from Alaska to Mexico are the **Coast Ranges.** In Washington, Oregon, and northern California the Coast Ranges are backed up inland by the **Cascade Range,** and to the south in California by the massive block of the **Sierra Nevada.**

In eastern North America only the southern portion of the **Appalachians**—the **Great Smoky** and **Blue Ridge mountains**—are truly mountainous. The northern Appalachians are much less rugged, with ridges commonly less than 3000 feet above sea level. However, four other mountain masses in eastern North America deserve mention because of their significance in American history and literature—the **Adirondacks** and **Catskills** in New York, the **Green Mountains** of Vermont, and the **White Mountains** of New Hampshire.

Much of the eastern coast of Mexico is paralleled by the **Sierra Madre Oriental,** the eastern counterpart of the "mountains" of the Sierra Madre Occidental. (See above, p. 25.)

South American Mountain Landmarks

The continent of South America is dominated by the **Andes,** which extend without a break along its full north-south length on or near the Pacific coast. The Andes constitute a topographic barrier to overland travel and transport that is matched in few places elsewhere in the world in completeness and difficulty. The Andes can be surmounted in only a few spots throughout their length and then not without the utmost effort. They have the further distinction of being the site of the highest permanent human settlement, which is at an elevation of 17,100 feet, just below the snow line, in Peru. The Indian inhabitants are not there from choice but because they were forced off better lands at lower altitudes by the invading Spaniards and their descendants.

European Mountain Landmarks

The **Alps** are the most famous mountains of Europe. They are situated mostly in Switzerland, the one country lying wholly within a plateau and mountain area that has attained modern industrial and commercial success.

The significance of the Alps for European history from the time of Hannibal has been notable. Before the days of the Romans the Alps were part of the mountain barrier north of the Mediterranean that served to protect the developing civilizations on the shores of that sea from incursions by northern barbarians.

It is noteworthy that the hydroelectric power potentialities of the entire mountain region have been intensively exploited by Switzerland, France, and Italy. In the Alps, also, the tourist possibilities of mountain country have been developed to a degree unapproached elsewhere.

The **Pyrenees,** between France and Spain, also exemplify the barrier function of mountains. On their opposite sides two languages (from a common beginning, Latin), two cultures, and two nations (France and Spain) have evolved. On the other hand, although the **Carpathians** of Hungary, Poland, Czechoslovakia, and Rumania have been an important factor in determining the outcome of wars and the shifting of boundaries, languages and cultures have not been contained by the barrier they interpose. Instead the conflicting elements have spilled across it from either side, so that unending friction has resulted. In early times the Carpathians functioned like the Alps to protect the developing Mediterranean civilizations, but exploitation of the mountains themselves in later days provided the basis of the troubles.

The **Urals** are of great significance for Soviet Russia as an important mineral source. They also formerly afforded geographers an arbitrary boundary line between Europe and Asia. Until the establishment of the Soviet regime Russia was traditionally the territory to the west of the Urals, Siberia, its undeveloped possession, to the east. In contemporary Soviet Russia this distinction is of much less consequence.

The **Apennines,** which form the rough backbone of the Italian peninsula, are less-well-known European mountains. However, they constitute much of Italy's area and effectively split it down the middle by interposing a difficult barrier to transportation

and communication across it. Despite meager resources the Apennines are in part densely populated, a circumstance that contributes largely to Italy's perennial economic troubles.

Asiatic Mountain Landmarks

Asia, the largest continent, has the greatest mountain area, not only because of its larger extent but also because of the proportionately great area of mountains it contains. The famous **Himalayas** are first among mountains, the highest peaks on earth. The influence of the Himalayas on the climate of India is dominating; their effectiveness as a barrier is scarcely less great. Since the beginning of history they have protected India from invasion directly from the north. On the west they merge into the **Hindu Kush** mountains, another imposing chain. North of the Himalayas, beyond the Tibetan Plateau, are the **Kunlun Mountains,** one of the many little-known ranges of central Asia. Still farther north, across the Tarim Basin, are the **Tien Shan** mountains. The Hindu Kush, Kunlun, and Tien Shan constitute part of a pattern of mountains, basins, and intermontane plateaus similar to that of western North America, but on a far grander scale and oriented east-west instead of north-south. All these Asiatic ranges converge on the west in what geographers call the "**Pamir Knot**" (Fig. 2.9), the place where India, Sinkiang, and Siberia meet. The **Sulaiman Mountains** extend southward from this node, and as they are not so lofty as the other systems some measure of overland transportation is possible between Pakistan and

Fig. 2.9—View in the Pamirs. Zerin-Zamin peak. (W. Rickmer Rickmers.)

Fig. 2.10—Khyber Pass, Pakistan. (Courtesy, Embassy of Pakistan.)

Afghanistan via the **Khyber Pass** (Fig. 2.10).

The remaining significant Asiatic mountain range is the **Caucasus,** which extends northwest to southeast across the Caucasian peninsula and together with highlands south of the Caspian Sea cuts Russia off from Iran. What is perhaps the extreme case of the insulating and isolating effect of the mountain environment occurs in the Caucasus. There 31 distinctive national groups of from 1000 to 5000 people have developed in the isolated valleys, each with its own language and culture. Many of these people had never seen a wheeled vehicle until their isolation was brought to an end under the present Soviet regime.

Mountain Landmarks on Other Continents

Only the **Atlas Mountains** along the northwest Mediterranean coast of Africa merit reference as landmarks on that continent. In Australia there are no mountains of sufficient prominence to deserve mention except for the **Great Dividing Range** along the eastern side of the continent. It is possible that the Antarctic Continent has magnificent mountains, but if so they are so completely engulfed in glacial ice as to be relatively inconspicuous, and have remained undiscovered. Only small ranges and isolated peaks are known.

QUESTIONS. Why are electrified railroads found in so many mountainous regions of the more industrialized countries? What unusual type of agriculture is often found in mountainous regions? Why? Why do mountains in tropical regions have climatic belts on their slopes? What is meant by the term "rain shadow"? What is a "divide"? Where are the great mountain belts of the world? What economic activity is common to both the Rocky Mountains and the Basin Ranges? Where are the only true mountains of eastern North America? What circumstances of the Andes give them special significance as a world landmark? Contrast the present significance of the Alps in Europe with their former significance. Contrast the effect of the Pyrenees with that of the Carpathians on the general history of their neighboring regions. Why are the Urals less significant than they formerly were? How do the Apennines constitute a major disadvantage to Italy? Discuss the position and relative historical importance of the mountain ranges that converge in the Pamir Knot.

■ LARGE LAKES

INTRODUCTION

With relatively few exceptions the lakes of the world merit listing as world landmarks only because of large size. Small lakes are usually unimportant as commercial highways except locally, because of the costs of two transshipments (involving labor and breakage), one at each end of a short voyage. It is uneconomical to load goods on a carrier unless they can be transported cheaply by it over a long enough distance to warrant the expense of handling at both ends. This is true of lake navigation in only a few instances.

However, large lakes usually present fewer navigational hazards than do other inland waterways. The channel depth is regularly sufficient, and there are no tides or currents to complicate navigation. On the other hand, ships on some lakes are subject to the dangers of violent storms with little room in which to maneuver.

Yet large lakes, because of their size, have considerable geographic significance aside from their possible utilization as trade routes. Such lakes commonly exert a climatic influence directly proportional to their extent. All bodies of water modify the temperature extremes of surrounding lands, especially those to the leeward. In some instances this influence is great enough to be a determinant for climate—e.g., to prevent early frosts and damage from warm spells too early in the spring—but commonly it is noticed only in the form of cooling breezes from over the water which temper summer heat. Lakes are obviously important in addition as a source of drinking water for cities. Finally, lakes function significantly as reservoirs and insure a regular flow to their outlet rivers. These streams are consequently enhanced in usefulness for power production and irrigation diversion. These are the obvious purposes of the man-made lakes behind great dams; natural lakes serve the same ends on a larger scale.

Lakes as World Landmarks

The North American continent is uniquely endowed with lakes; it possesses 12 of the 22 largest lakes of the world (Fig. 2.11). Five of these, connected by natural waterways, are the **Great Lakes of North America—Superior, Michigan, Huron, Erie,** and **Ontario.** They are, indeed, "Great" Lakes; no other lakes anywhere in the world rival them in importance or as landmarks.

This unique status of the Great Lakes derives from the following circumstances: (1) They are large and deep enough to eliminate the hazards ordinarily encountered in lake navigation; (2) together with the St. Lawrence River they form a continuous waterway from the ocean for 1700 miles into the interior of the continent (of this distance 1000 miles is on the lakes themselves); (3) the water route they provide extends east-west, coinciding with the direction of major movement of bulk products; (4) their hinterlands supply such goods, chiefly grain and iron ore, in enormous volume; (5) they are relatively free from the hazards of great storms; (6) their overflow waters illustrate the function of lakes as natural reservoirs and provide one of the world's great hydroelectric sites at **Niagara Falls.**

The significance of the fourth point is made evident by statistics. The **Soo Canals** between Lakes Superior and Huron handle an annual tonnage three times as great as either the Panama or the Suez Canal. The western Lakes region is the world's greatest source of iron ore (over 80 million tons are shipped annually) and one of the leading producers of wheat (as well as other grains) and pulpwood. The region to the east and south of the Lakes is the world's greatest source of coal and one of the leading manufacturing and steel-making regions.

The Great Lakes as a water route unfortunately are not free of impediments. Their natural water connections were originally interrupted at various points by rapids and falls. These barriers are now, however, circumvented by canals. Their shores afford only few good natural harbors, but this defect also has been largely remedied by dredging and the construction of breakwaters. The insurmountable handicap to their use for navigation is winter freezing, which stops the great bulk transport of ore, coal, and wheat entirely and restricts other traffic to a fraction of summer operations. The cost of laying up the lake boats over the winter is enormous, but the expense of such capital tie-up is largely compensated for by extremely efficient operation during the open seasons. Ore boats are now refueled in passage in order to make greater space available for cargo.

The remaining large lakes of North America are all in Canada, west of Hudson Bay. Arranged in a rough sequence from north to south they are: **Great Bear Lake, Great Slave Lake, Lake Athabaska,** and **Lake Winnipeg.** Except as winter sledge routes and as landing places for amphibian and skiplanes they are of little economic importance at present.

The list of Western Hemisphere lakes includes **Lake Nicaragua,** in the country of the same name. The lake lies in the Central American isthmus, is connected to the Caribbean by a small stream, and is separated from the Pacific by only about 20 miles of relatively low land. It has often been mentioned as a link in the route of a proposed second canal to supplement the Panama Canal.

South America's single large lake is **Lake**

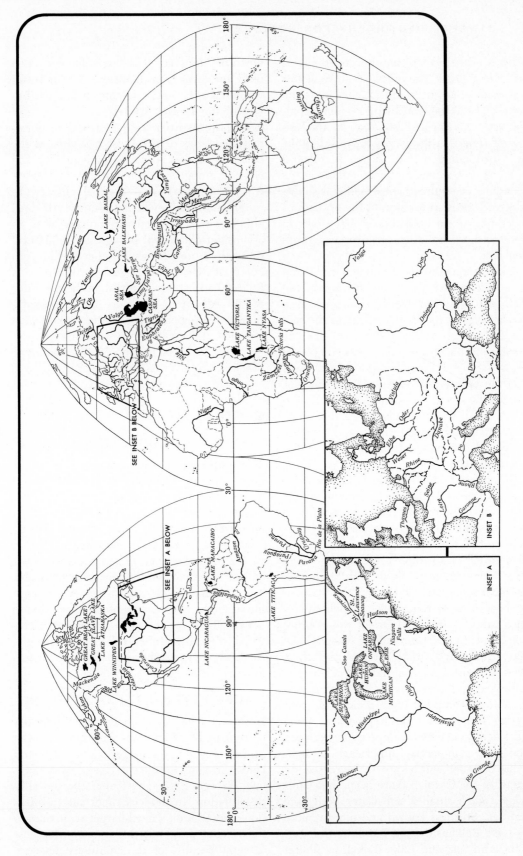

Fig. 2.11—Landmarks of the World: Lakes and Streams.

Titicaca, situated on the border between Peru and Bolivia. The unique feature of this lake is its great altitude—12,500 feet—"the highest lake in the world with regular steamboat service." Surprisingly enough, the volume of traffic on its waters is considerable. The surrounding region is rich in mineral resources but exceedingly mountainous. As a consequence railroad construction is so difficult and costly as to warrant the expense of transshipment on both shores of the lake in preference to building an overland route around it.

Lake Maracaibo, in northwestern Venezuela, is in reality a very shallow arm of the Caribbean Sea; however, it functions as a lake because of its slight depth and the fact that a bar across its sea inlet restricted entry to ships until a 21-mile canal was completed across the bar. Its major importance derives from the occurrence on its eastern shore of one of the great petroleum fields of the world. Small steamers ply in all directions across its 8000 square miles and provide cheap and convenient transportation to the export points.

The greatest lake of Asia is the **Caspian Sea,** a completely landlocked body of salt water approximately 170,000 square miles in area. Its shores are large producers of petroleum, so that fleets of oil tankers are in operation on it. An all-water route up the Volga River connects the oil fields with Stalingrad and other large cities of Russia. The Caspian has been a trade route since ancient times, when caravans from the Orient would bring their goods to its eastern shore, whence they were transported up the Volga and by a series of portages eventually reached the Baltic Sea and Scandinavia. If the Russians are able to complete their project for connecting the Black and Caspian seas by a canal across a lowland depression between them, the commercial importance of both bodies of water will be greatly increased.

East of the Caspian there is another landlocked, much smaller, salt-water body, the **Aral Sea.** Still less known and more remote are **Lake Balkhash,** some 700 miles due east of the Aral Sea, and **Lake Baikal,** in Siberia north of Mongolia. The last named is much used for local transportation; it is a freshwater lake, its outlet feeding a main tributary of the Yenisei River.

In eastern Africa a great structural deformation of the earth's crust has created the basins of **Lakes Victoria, Tanganyika,** and **Nyassa,** along with numerous smaller lakes. All are situated in a tropical climate, in rough and little-developed country. All three are, however, utilized for transportation to a considerable extent because of the natural route they provide where other facilities do not exist. The other large lake of Africa is **Lake Chad,** situated on the southern border of the Sahara in a remote but potentially productive region. It is a shallow lake which expands and contracts to a remarkable degree with seasonal changes in the amount of precipitation over its drainage area.

■ STREAMS

INTRODUCTION

The outlines of the drainage basins of large streams delineate a type of natural geographic region. Within any such basin tributaries descend systematically with steep headwater gradients and gently sloping lower courses to the trunk stream. Within such a drainage basin stream courses are the easiest overland routes because the water grade ordinarily provides a smooth, though increasingly steep, ascent to the divide height. This is especially significant in regions of considerable relief. Accordingly, roads, and especially railroads, tend to follow the valley lines.

AGRICULTURAL USE OF STREAMS

In the early history of civilization the particular virtue of streams was that they were the source of water for irrigation of cultivated lands. Streams in ancient Egypt, Mesopotamia, Greece, India, and China all exemplify this relation. In modern times such utilization continues on a much larger scale than in the remote past, but this is somewhat lost to sight because of the enormous development of commerce and industrial activities since. In primitive times agriculture often so greatly surpassed all other gainful pursuits as to be almost the sole concern of a people.

In another respect, however, the relation between streams and agricultural production is still popularly recognized. Lands adjoining stream courses are regularly regarded as most favorable for crops, for during the high-water periods when streams overtop their banks fine soil is deposited over wide tracts of adjacent lowlands—the floodplain areas. Such soils are not only naturally fertile but are also perennially renewed. As a consequence it is customary to refer to the agricultural yield of the Mississippi, the Po, the Indus, or any river basin, even though such phrasing includes considerably more than the flood-plain lands. It indicates how river basins and agriculture go together.

On the other hand, inordinate flooding is the great defect of many streams. Whereas the gentle annual overflow of the Nile is inconvenient, its constructive effects more than offset this. But catastrophic floods may occur on even the smallest of streams in many localities.

By different methods, which range from building control dams and providing vast basins to catch silt in the headwaters to channel straightening and dredging near the mouth, the danger and destruction from major floods can be averted except in unusually extreme cases. But the significance of such floods lies in the fact that if they occur where there is no protection the damage they do is of disastrous proportions; if the floods are prevented by engineering works the cost of these is a heavy charge on the economic activities of the people occupying the areas that would otherwise suffer.

NAVIGATIONAL USE OF STREAMS

The relation between overland routes and water grades was set forth above. Native travel and early exploration mostly followed waterways. Even small streams will float a canoe, and such streams, especially in primevally forested country, afford the easiest entrance to interior areas. Indeed, until the advent of the airplane much of northern Canada was unknown except along the waterways. Again, in the colonization of North America, though rapids in every stream along the southeastern Atlantic seaboard blocked farther penetration inland to ocean craft, nevertheless the upstream continuation of the rivers afforded the easiest routes with smaller vessels for advance westward. Because it was so difficult to surmount the much more formidable rapids and falls of Africa it remained for long the "Dark Continent," that is, the unknown continent.

In after years the development of overland transportation facilities has greatly curtailed river navigation. In competition with roads and railroads the defects and limitations of streams as transportation routes are found to be so detrimental to their use as to leave only a few to function significantly as water highways.

A river may be unsuited for modern navigational use because: (1) It is not big enough and deep enough to float boats of sufficient size to make its use worth while; (2) the navigational reach is too short to warrant the cost of transshipments; (3) its windings result in too great an increase in the distance between terminal points; (4) it is interrupted by rapids and falls that have to be overcome by constructing canals around them; (5) its course is contrary to the direction of the main flow of trade; (6) it fluctuates too severely in volume; (7) its current is too strong for upstream movement; (8) it may be closed by ice in winter; (9) diversion of water for irrigation may impair navigational use. Nevertheless, where interconnection between different rivers by canals is feasible, as in Europe, a large use is made of rivers that under different circumstances would not be utilized for transport.

Rivers as Barriers and Boundaries

Until comparatively recent times large rivers functioned significantly as barriers to transportation and communication, and as defense lines in war. Crossings were feasible only where a ford or ferry was available, or where a bridge could be and had been built.

Since the beginning of the twentieth century these limitations have become practically nonexistent. Engineering science and materials make possible a bridge anywhere that traffic demands it. In war a bridge can be improvised so quickly that established crossings have lost much of their former strategic value. Earlier established bridgeheads, however, at the sites of the easiest crossings, continue to be focal points of transportation routes and population centers.

Despite the fact that their courses shift to a considerable degree, a circumstance that leads to local and international boundary disputes, streams are favorite boundary lines. If the minor shifts are disregarded rivers constitute natural, clearly marked lines easily referred to and in the larger sense fixed. Even though crossings are now easily managed, communities on opposite sides of a large river are definitely separated and tend to have independent organizations.

On a larger scale the function of rivers as trade routes tends to outweigh their significance as barriers, so that rivers generally unite rather than divide cultures.

STREAMS AS WORLD LANDMARKS

Without question the greatest river of the world is the **Amazon.** In length (3900 miles) it is exceeded by two other streams, but in all other comparisons it is a class by itself. The Amazon owes its enormous volume to two circumstances—the tremendous tropical rainfall and general flatness and low elevation of its basin, and the consequent low gradient of its course. It is 200 miles wide at its mouth; its discharge makes the ocean fresh for 100 miles from shore; ocean-going ships can proceed to Manaos, 1000 miles from its mouth (and only 125 feet above sea level), where the minimum low-water depth is 40 feet; large river steamers can proceed to Iquitos, 1000 miles farther upstream; at the Peruvian border, a short distance below Iquitos, the river is already two miles wide; 11 of its 28 major tributaries are themselves navigable for 1000 miles, so that motor launches can reach 3600 miles from the river's mouth during high-water periods. Most

of "Amazonia," the basin of the Amazon, would be inaccessible except by air were it not for the river and its tributaries. On the other hand, floods regularly spread over tens of thousands of square miles and make most of the lower reaches of the river basin permanently uninhabitable.

There are other South American streams which are large but suffer by comparison with the Amazon, queen of all rivers. Thus the **Magdalena** of Colombia is a major transportation route, though its navigation is hampered by low-water periods and a shifting channel containing snags and sand bars. The **Orinoco** of Venezuela, with fewer natural defects, is important chiefly as the route for exporting the output from the large iron mines in its lower basin.

In the southeast the **Uruguay** and **Paraguay-Parana** rivers converge to form a large, shallow estuary known as the **Rio de la Plata.** At tremendous expense Argentina keeps a channel open into Buenos Aires through the sand bars that build up at the head of the bay. Upstream from the Rio de la Plata the separate rivers each permit vessels of nine-foot draft to go 2000 miles into the interior at high-water stages. The commercial importance of the system is considerably greater than that of the far larger Amazon system.

The great river system of the North American continent is that of the **Mississippi-Missouri.** Its length of 3988 miles from source to mouth makes it the second longest system of the world. Although the Mississippi has at least a nine-foot channel up to St. Louis, 1300 miles from its mouth, it carries only a small percentage of the total United States internal commerce. In view of the ideal central location of the Mississippi, the fact that its hinterland includes the major agricultural regions of the country and many of its largest industrial areas, and its possible use as an all-water route to the sea for cheap, bulk transportation with little if any transshipping, the reasons for so slight a utilization of its possibilities are not immediately self-evident.

But the Mississippi has a winding, shifting

channel, and the Missouri dries up almost completely in times of drought. Neither of these defects, however, is so detrimental as the direction of its course. The north-south flow of the Mississippi is at right angles to the major east-west flow of commerce in the United States. This conclusion is neatly confirmed by the statistics of traffic on the **Ohio River,** the second large tributary of the Mississippi. Over the east-west course of the Ohio 35 percent of all river traffic in the nation is moved, a volume greatly exceeding that of the mother stream. Yet even the Ohio trade is mostly local, as carriage beyond its upstream and downstream limits involves transshipping. The pressure of east-west traffic in the United States is further evidenced by the bridging of the lower Mississippi despite the great cost entailed.

North America has several other major rivers. The **Colorado** is a source of power, irrigation, and city water for large areas of Arizona, Nevada, and California. Los Angeles gets a large part of its city water supply from the Colorado through a 392-mile aqueduct. The Colorado is probably most famous for its mile-deep **Grand Canyon.** The

Fig. 2.12—Grand Coulee Dam, Columbia River, 1951. Lake forming in the upper Grand Coulee equalizing reservoir. The size of the dam may be gauged from the cars on its top. Note also the height the water must be lifted to the equalizing reservoir. This is a disadvantage due to the plateau circumstance. (Courtesy, U.S. Bureau of Reclamation.)

Columbia River of the northwestern Pacific states is well known for its salmon fisheries and the Grand Coulee (Fig. 2.12) and Bonneville dams, both gigantic power and irrigation projects. The atomic plant at Hanford, Washington, uses the waters of the Columbia for cooling purposes.

The **Rio Grande** on the southern United States boundary with Mexico is an outstanding example of a poor boundary stream. The river practically disappears during the dry season, and when it does flow in full volume is constantly changing its course. Each change brings up the question whether the original boundary remains regardless of the river or whether the boundary follows the river's changes. At El Paso, Texas, a part of the city itself has been involved in such a change, and because of the uncertainty of national jurisdiction and ownership much valuable land remains unused and undeveloped. Fortunately, the amicable relations of the two governments concerned precludes the possibility of conflict over these boundary disputes, but much money and effort is still being expended in efforts to decide the various problems raised by the shifts in the river's course.

In Alaska the large river is the **Yukon,** utilization of which is limited by winter ice. The **Mackenzie** of northwestern Canada is practically devoid of traffic, as it flows north into the frozen Arctic Ocean.

The greatest river on the eastern side of the continent is the **St. Lawrence,** the outlet of the Great Lakes. Despite its rapids and the fact that it is frozen for four months of the year it is a much utilized stream. The **St. Lawrence Seaway** around the rapids above Montreal provides a direct sea connection for all ports of the Great Lakes and makes the St. Lawrence an important transportation artery.

The **Hudson River** of New York is itself of relatively small value but provides a wide and deep water connection with the New York State Barge Canal and through the canal the Great Lakes. Ocean ships can come up the Hudson estuary to Albany, at the eastern terminus of the canal.

In Europe the network of canals by which its rivers are interconnected and the volume of freight requiring transport have given many of them an importance out of all proportion to their size. The **Danube,** however, is a major river by any standard. A stream 1750 miles long, it is the most international of all rivers. Germany, Austria, Hungary, Yugoslavia, Bulgaria, and Rumania all border the Danube on at least one bank along some part of its course. Unfortunately the Danube, like the Mississippi, flows in the wrong direction; its mouth in the Black Sea is at a near dead end for trade. This does not preclude its utilization for short-haul movements along its course, but even these possibilities are not fully utilized because of international frictions and jealousies.

The **Rhine,** like the Danube, is international, with a course through and between four countries (Switzerland, France, Germany, and the Netherlands). As the boundary between France and Germany it has in the past demonstrated the virtues of a river marker. It is probably the world's most completely improved stream for water transport. The volume of traffic on it is immense because its course is through the most highly industrialized region of continental Europe.

The other rivers of northwestern Europe —the **Thames, Seine, Weser,** and **Elbe**—all drain into the rather restricted confines of the North Sea and form a net of natural trade routes radiating from it as a hub. These rivers were intensively developed as waterways at an early date and still carry large tonnages. The Rhine is the master stream of this whole network and its interconnecting canals.

The prominent streams of the Baltic region are the **Oder** and **Vistula,** both of less importance than those previously mentioned.

In addition to the Seine, France is drained by the **Garonne, Loire,** and **Rhone,** which between them provide water routes from the interior of the country to all of its bordering seas. With canal interconnections they provide a highly flexible system of internal water transportation.

The chief river of Italy is the **Po,** note-worthy more because of the amount of sediment it annually pours into the head of Adriatic Sea than for its use as an artery of trade. All the rock waste brought down by streams from the south slopes of the Alps is carried to the sea by the Po. City after city has failed to maintain itself as an Adriatic port on the coast of its rapidly expanding delta. Only Venice, off to one side, has persisted until now despite the inexorable seaward advance of the land due to the Po deposits.

In European Russia the **Dvina** flows to the Baltic Sea, the **Dnieper** and **Don** to the Black Sea, and the **Volga** to the Caspian Sea. They are all navigable far up their courses because their slow, deep flow across plains conserves volume in relation to rainfall. They are all much utilized, but annual freezing greatly curtails the volume of traffic. The Volga is the largest Russian river and the most important commercially, but because its course is not in line with the major flow of trade its traffic is far less than might be expected in view of its size. The affectionate phrase "Mother Volga" is indicative of the river's place in the history of Russia. Because their radial flow favors canal interconnections the Russian rivers will continue to be further utilized in the future.

In Siberia there are three rivers of great volume and length, the **Ob, Yenisei,** and **Lena,** all of which flow northward into the Arctic Ocean. Like the Mackenzie of North America they would be vastly more useful if their flow were in the opposite direction. Because of their northward flow they are all subject to tremendous floods in spring, when melting occurs in their upper courses before the river ice breaks up in their lower stretches. Despite these handicaps and the long icebound season, the Russians have been using these streams, especially the Yenisei, for a steadily increasing volume of traffic. They provide north-south feeders and distributaries for the Trans-Siberian Railroad and thus make all the interior of Siberia more accessible.

The **Amur,** which rises in Manchuria and empties into the Sea of Okhotsk, is still another large stream of growing commercial importance as Siberia and its resources are developed. It is a good example of a boundary stream, as is also the **Yalu** along the northern border of Korea.

In central Asia there are two little-known rivers, the **Syr Darya** and **Amu Darya,** of considerable size. The former is fed by meltwaters from the snows of the Tien Shan mountains, the latter by those of the Pamir-Altai ranges. Both discharge into the Aral Sea. Both also flow through an arid region so that their importance for transportation and irrigation is large; they make possible a sizable population is what would otherwise be an uninhabited wasteland.

India and Pakistan have three great streams, the **Indus, Ganges,** and **Brahmaputra.** The first named, in northwestern India and Pakistan, is probably the most intensively developed stream in the world for irrigation purposes. It is like the Nile, outstanding as a stream which has made possible, from very early times, a dense population in an arid region. The Ganges is the best known of the Indian rivers and largest in size. Its name comes from the Sanskrit word meaning "the stream," an indication of the regard in which it is held. Indeed, it is the holy stream of the Hindus. The alluvial plain in northeast India on which it and the Brahmaputra have their courses supports one of the largest populations of the world.

To the east of India are the **Irrawaddy, Menam,** and **Mekong,** the trunk streams of Burma, Thailand, and Indochina respectively. Each of these streams is the great trade artery of its country; its valley is the center of population.

In China the greatest stream is in the north, the **Hwang Ho,** or **Yellow River,** 2700 miles in length. It is notorious as the most destructive of all rivers in flood. Its lower reaches extend across a broad plain, but, as many have pointed out, it flows *on* its plain, not in it. Although the Chinese have built great dikes and levees to hold the river in its course they have been unable to prevent the continual silting up of the channel. As a consequence the level of the river bed through the years has been raised higher and

higher above the surrounding plain. The river also is thus too shallow for any but small boats.

During flood times the overstrained levees almost invariably break; water pours through the gap and inundates thousands of square miles of land so level there is no place the inhabitants can find refuge. Some Hwang Ho inundations have been of such volume that it has required two to three years for the water to recede. Scores of thousands have suffered famine and death in consequence. Another result of such flooding is the paradox that this, one of the earth's most densely populated and most fertile regions, is without a single large city.

In contrast to the Hwang Ho, the **Yangtze Kiang**[2] of southern China, 3200 miles long, is an almost ideal river. Ocean ships can proceed to Hankow, 630 miles upstream, and river traffic to a point 1630 miles inland. The river flows, moreover, in the natural trade direction; its hinterland is rich and contains a population greater than that of the entire Western Hemisphere. It has a minor defect in that the swift current of its upper reaches makes the upstream progress of river boats slow and difficult. The Chinese have connected the Yangtze with the Hwang Ho and smaller streams by an elaborate canal network, but this system has never attained the importance it might have had because of the Chinese failure to discover or achieve the engineering principle of the lock. It was therefore impossible for a boat to pass from one canal or stream to another of even slightly different level; and the necessary transshipment meant higher costs and an impediment to traffic.

Thus it is that China's railroads, inadequate as they are, have already superseded the canal and river system in importance. The canals have in modern times fallen into such disuse that their chief importance now is as a source of silt to the farmer with which to fertilize his land.

The remaining streams of Asia to be mentioned are the **Tigris** and **Euphrates,** the twin

[2] *Ho* in North China, *Kiang* in South China, mean "river."

river system of Iraq. It was their water that irrigated the ancient civilizations of Ur, Nineveh, Babylon, and Ctesiphon. The downfall of these civilizations came with the destruction of the irrigation works by Arab nomads. Not until the twentieth century has any attempt been made to restore them and make the land once more productive.

In Africa the greatest river is the **Nile.** Its course of 4000 miles makes it the world's longest stream. Like the Tigris and Euphrates it was the site of one of the earliest developments of human civilization—the Egyptian culture. For more than 5000 years its lower valley has seen continuous human habitation. It does not have the defect of rapids and waterfalls in its lower course common to all other rivers in Africa.

The **Congo** in west central Africa perfectly exemplifies this difficulty. Although the volume of the Congo approaches that of the Amazon, the Congo is navigable from the sea for only 90 miles upstream from its mouth. Navigation of the upper reaches is also discontinuous because of the presence of additional rapids.

In the western "bulge" of Africa the main stream is the **Niger.** Its middle course is an important source of water for irrigation use in an arid country.

There are three large streams in South Africa: the **Zambezi** and **Limpopo** drain to the southeast coast; the **Orange** flows west to the Atlantic. They are at present of little economic significance, but the Zambezi is well known because of the scenic wonder of its **Victoria Falls** (Fig. 2.13).

In Australia the single river system of any importance is the **Murray-Darling,** in the southeast corner of the continent. The Murray is a major source of irrigation water in a continent markedly deficient in rainfall.

Fig. 2.13—Victoria Falls, Zambezi River. (Courtesy, Union of South Africa, Government Information Office.)

QUESTIONS. Why must a lake be of considerable size if it is to have any economic importance? Describe the resources and economic activity in the Great Lakes hinterland which provide the basis for their enormous commerce. What one great advantage would the Great Lakes acquire if they were situated in a tropical climate? Would the Great Lakes be of only minor importance if they had no connection with the St. Lawrence? Explain. Compare the situations of the Great Lakes and the lakes of eastern Africa with respect to trade routes. In what respect is the commerce on Lake Maracaibo similar to that on the Caspian Sea?

Discuss the agricultural utilization of streams. List at least five factors that may make a river unsuitable as a major transportation route. Under what circumstances are streams poor boundary markers? Why does the Amazon deserve the term "queen of rivers"? Compare the Magdalena, the Orinoco, and the streams of the Rio de la Plata system as transportation routes and the degree to which they are utilized. Why are the possibilities of the Mississippi-Missouri river system as a transport route so little realized? In what respects does the general use of rivers of the western United States differ from that in the East? Why does the St. Lawrence have a special economic significance despite the handicap of winter freezing?

In what respects are the Danube and Rhine similar? Dissimilar? Why are the rivers of northwestern Europe more important in commerce than those of eastern Europe? What is the unusual characteristic of the Po River? What characteristic of the rivers of European Russia makes them good as trade routes? What is the greatest single handicap to large-scale utilization of the northern Siberian rivers? What characteristics do the Syr Darya and Amu Darya have in common? What is the most significant feature of the Indus River? The Ganges? Why are the floods of the Hwang Ho so unusually destructive? Compare the usefulness of the Yangtze Kiang with that of the Hwang Ho. What was the fundamental defect of the Chinese canal system? What is the common feature of the Tigris, Euphrates, and Nile rivers? In what respect is the Nile unusual for an African river?

CHAPTER 3

Landmarks of the World—Cities

■ ORIGINS OF CITIES

INTRODUCTION

The preceding chapters have discussed the natural, or physical, landmarks of the world. The discussion now turns to cities, man-made landmarks that exist only because of human activities and that have identity and history, in contrast to the anonymity and nonhistorical existence of the landscape itself.

Cities are ordinarily thought of only as places where large numbers of people are crowded together within a small area. In comparing cities the number of inhabitants usually serves as the sole measure for assessing their relative importance. Certainly such assemblages of large numbers of people together with the structures they erect, clustered on limited tracts of land, are the visible expression of the city phenomenon. But this superficial approach completely disregards the essential significance of cities, namely, the answer to the question: Why have people congregated thus at certain places? When cities are examined with this question primarily in mind they are found to have interesting geographic backgrounds that provide a valuable means of measuring their true importance. Moreover, an analysis of

Fig. 3.1—Type Cities of the World Mentioned in the Text.

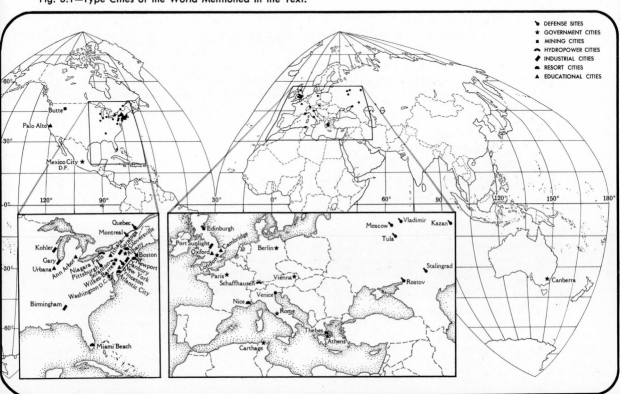

the geographical basis of cities provides a clearer understanding of the particular flavor and kind of importance possessed by geographic regions than is possible through descriptions of their physical aspects only.

SPECIFIC SITES OF CITIES

It is obvious that each city must have had a beginning or founding, the time when the first settlement was made at that site. Such first settlement consisted in placing a structure, a human habitation or some other building, at a particular point. For besides the presence of people, the other direct expression of a city's existence is, as noted, the assemblage of dwellings and those buildings utilized for economic and other activities. The question, then, with regard to the *specific site* of any city is: Why was the city founded at just that spot?

Defense Sites

An examination of the origins of the majority of the world's large cities (Fig. 3.1), especially the beginnings of almost all the older ones of both the Old World and the New, discloses that the specific site in nearly every instance was a vantage point for defense against enemy attack. The place most commonly chosen was the *summit of a hill* (Fig. 3.2). Man in earlier times had to overcome opponents by hand-to-hand conflict. The occupants of a hill summit could resist attack most effectively, for they were aided by the force of gravity in all types of encounter.

Accordingly, one finds that the first inhabitants of **London** clustered at the top of a low hill above the Thames. The "Seven Hills of **Rome**" is a familiar reference in literature. On their summits were perched the villages of the primitive Romans, who met for trade on the low ground between the hills, an area that later became the famous Roman Forum. The tourist visitor to Rome who is well informed on the geography of cities cannot fail to be impressed by this relationship of defensible sites and market place. **Athens** first occupied the Acropolis, the steep rock hill central to the agricultural Athenian plain. **Edinburgh,** Scotland, originated on the rocky crag that is still a focal point of the city, along the strand of the Firth of Forth. The picturesque hill towns of the Mediterranean coasts are relics of ancient sites relying on hill positions for safety. On the Russian plains such cities as **Moscow, Tula, Rostov, Vladimir,** and **Kazan** developed around elevated fortified positions.

Fig. 3.3—Paris, Early Panoramic View Showing, Upper Right, the Île de la Cité, the Island in the Seine Where the City Began.

Where no hill was at hand an *island in a stream* was commonly the choice of location as an exact site. Hostile forces were thus confronted with the problem of crossing a belt of water before they could come to grips with the island inhabitants, who meanwhile could make preparations to repel the assault. The most famous example of such a primary specific site is **Paris** (Fig. 3.3), which began on the island in the Seine on which the Cathedral of Notre Dame stands today.

Fig. 3.2—Hill City, With Wall Fortification, Near Nice, France. (O. D. von Engeln.)

The islands of **Venice,** Italy, were similarly utilized. **Montreal,** Canada, has both the hill and island features. The site of original settlement in **Boston** was on a tongue of land so isolated from the mainland that it was in effect an island (Fig. 3.4).

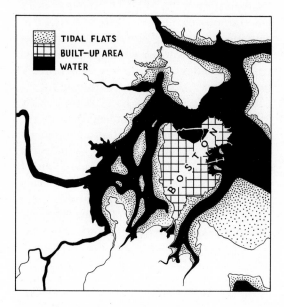

TIDAL FLATS
BUILT–UP AREA
WATER

Fig. 3.4—Early Site of Boston, Massachusetts. Much of the area shown here as water is now filled in. (After L. P. Powell (ed.), Historic Towns of New England.)

Second to a summit or island location is a *peninsula,* commonly the tongue of land at the junction of two streams. **Pittsburgh** (originally Fort Duquesne) at the confluence of the Allegheny and Monongahela rivers perfectly exemplifies such a site. The heart of the city still remains there and is now referred to as "the Golden Triangle" because of the wealth it represents. Such a specific site, when it is not also a high place, must be supplemented as a defensive position on the base of the triangle by a man-made fortification, a stockade or fort. **New York City** (Fig. 3.20) was founded on the southern tip of Manhattan Island. But the island was too large for defense by the early small population and so was utilized as a peninsular site. Wall Street remains as a place name to indicate the site of the island defense line. **Quebec** is another example of a peninsular site.

In a few instances *dry land within a swamp* has been utilized. Invaders were handicapped because the morass made infantry advance impossible, and shallow water precluded the easy use of boats and barges. Early **Berlin** was thus located, a remnant of the early environment being preserved as the *Spree Wald.* **Mexico City** could also be considered an example of this type, as could **London.**

Finally, if no natural defenses exist they must be provided by human construction; recourse is had to *walls and moats.* **Vienna** is an outstanding example of such development (Fig. 3.5). The walls of Vienna have long since been leveled and its moat filled in. The ground they once occupied has become the magnificent *Ringstrasse,* or "Circle Street." (The former ramparts of "hill" cities are also the basis of circular boulevards, as in Moscow.)

In modern warfare such defense factors have, of course, lost all significance. Instead, it is the streets and structures of the city itself that serve the population in defense against final assault and occupation by hostile forces. The defense of **Stalingrad** in World War II provides the perfect example of such utilization. Accordingly, in the founding of modern cities other factors (which needed to be given consideration also when defense was a primary objective) acquire first importance. These are factors essential to *living and growth* as contrasted with those that served in early days to permit survival.

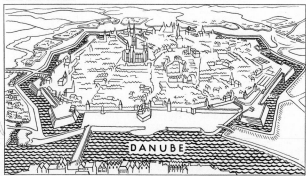

DANUBE

Fig. 3.5—Vienna Around 1630, Showing the Walls and Moat. (Compare with Fig. 24.5.) (After H. S. Churchill, The City Is the People.)

Growth Factors for Specific Sites

First of the factors essential for satisfactory living conditions is an adequate supply of *drinking water*. If water for domestic use is not easily accessible in sufficient volume, a large population center is impossible. The second requisite is *dry ground,* and the third is *level ground* of considerable area. Where all three of these conditions are properly satisfied a settlement of considerable numbers can be conveniently accommodated. With growth in population it may become necessary (and at the same time financially possible) to tap nonlocal water supplies, to fill in wet lands, and to occupy adjacent hilly areas. But when the beginning is made the immediate site must provide these advantages or early progress is impeded and perhaps completely checked.

GENERAL SITES OF CITIES

Theoretically any original settlement, once successfully established, might in time grow to be a city. Actually very few do. If the settlement is made by a tribal or other group, or starts as a military camp, a small village may come immediately into existence. In some few places, however, large cities are eventually built up. Beyond the propitious circumstance or circumstances that prompted the erection of the original structure or structures, other factors pertaining to the *general site* must be favorable if a significant concentration of population is to develop around a specific site. Its location must permit and support the functioning of a city as an agglomeration of people through their profitable engagement in economic activities. This point directs attention immediately to the occupations of the people who live in cities, which in turn requires a classification of cities by "purpose," or the general source of income of the city's inhabitants.

■ TYPES OF CITIES

1. *The Governmental City.* Most of the great cities of early times were at the start governmental centers, or became such early in their history. **Thebes, Athens, Carthage, Rome, Paris, London, Berlin, Vienna** are recalled at once as having such backgrounds. The survivors among this list still function as governmental centers. At present **Washington,** D.C., **Albany,** N.Y., **Mexico City,** D.F., and **Canberra,** Australia (Fig. 3.6) stand as clearcut examples of the same class. It is true that activities other than government or support of government workers develop in these governmental cities. Nevertheless their primary function is as a center of government.

2. *The Mining City.* Even more readily identified than the governmental city is the mining city. A large concentration of mineral resources in a limited area, yet of sufficient size to permit the profitable operation of many mines within the district for many years, in itself insures the concentration of a considerable population of mine workers. This mining group requires a variety of services for its maintenance and a central meeting point for the housing of its collective business activities, together with personnel to do the work. As a consequence a mining city grows and flourishes in accord with the prosperity of the mines in the area. **Butte,** Montana (Fig. 3.7), **Scranton** and **Wilkes-Barre,** Pennsylvania, are outstanding examples of mining cities in the United States.

3. *The Hydropower City.* If the availability of a large hydroelectric potential is substituted for the presence of mineral resources, a basis is afforded for a city in some respects similar to the mining city. The latter, however, exists chiefly to serve the needs of the mining community, whereas the population of a city based on hydropower is composed primarily of workers in industries concentrated there because of the energy source. Further, unlike the mineral resources, which will in time be exhausted, the hydropower remains permanently available.

Such cities are not numerous. The outstanding example is **Niagara Falls,** New York; another example is **Schaffhausen,** Switzerland. More such cities may grow up in the future if large hydroelectric sites at remote localities in South America, Africa, and Asia are fully developed.

Fig. 3.6—Canberra, Australia, a Governmental City. Note the absence of conspicuous business and industrial districts. (Courtesy, Australian News and Information Bureau.)

Fig. 3.7—Butte, Montana, a Mining City (Mines in the Background). The general absence of vegetation is due to the blighting effect of smelter fumes in former times. This has been corrected and trees are now becoming established (see lower right-hand corner of picture). (Courtesy, Butte Chamber of Commerce.)

Fig. 3.8—Kohler, Wisconsin, an Industrial City. Air view of residences and factory. (Courtesy, Kohler Company.)

4. *The Industrial City.* Industrial cities are a mixed lot. In some instances a single giant corporation has created a city by fixing on a particular location for its plant. The United States Steel Corporation plant at **Gary**, Indiana, illustrates this development. **Kohler**, Wisconsin (Fig. 3.8) (bathtubs), and **Port Sunlight**, England (soap), are other cities in which single corporations have been responsible for city communities. More commonly numerous enterprises under different ownership have been concentrated in one center, as at **Gloversville**, New York (gloves), and **Danbury**, Connecticut (hats). These are industrial cities pure and simple.

Birmingham, Alabama, has a more complex background. It is partly a mining city, for iron ore, coal, and limestone are present there in close association. But these are the basic materials for the steel industry, which has developed to such an extent that Birmingham is chiefly an industrial city. In many cities industry is an adjunct to the chief function of the city, which places it under any one of the other classes.

Fig. 3.9—Miami Beach, Florida, a Resort City. Note the numerous large hotels along the beach. The city of Miami is in the background, across Biscayne Bay. (Courtesy, Miami Beach News Bureau.)

5. *The Resort City.* Many population centers exist solely because of the resort facilities their sites provide. **Miami Beach**, Florida (Fig. 3.9), is first on such a list in the United States, but there are many others—e.g., **Atlantic City**, New Jersey—of lesser magnitude in this country. Niagara Falls was formerly in this class before the resort aspect was almost completely subordinated to the industrial development. In Europe **Nice**, France, has somewhat the same superior status as a resort city that Miami Beach has in the United States, and again there are numerous lesser centers as exclusively resort based as is Nice.

6. *The Educational City.* Great educational establishments, if located outside of cities that have other major backgrounds, serve to maintain considerable urban populations in their own right. **Oxford** (Fig. 3.10) and **Cambridge** in England are the classic examples. In the United States **Princeton**, New Jersey, **Ithaca**, New York, **Urbana**, Illinois, **Ann Arbor**, Michigan, **Palo Alto**, California, all qualify as educational cities.

The governmental and educational cities have in common a factor of considerable importance to their relatively opulent development: they are largely supported by money derived from economic activities elsewhere, through taxes, endowments, and tuition payments; and the pursuits of the majority of the inhabitants, academic and bureaucratic, are practically unrelated to the functioning of the cities themselves.

Fig. 3.10—Oxford, England, an Educational City. Oxford University buildings are in the center of the picture. (Courtesy, British Information Services.)

Survey of Preceding City Types. When the preceding types of cities are collectively considered they are found to possess certain important characteristics in common. First, they depend on particular circumstances of their sites, wholly unrelated to city functioning; second, if these peculiar circumstances are terminated or made inoperative, the city center declines and indeed may disappear. The reference here is not to cities of earlier civilizations that perished with the culture under which they flourished, but to cities belonging to the present world order. The perfect examples are the mining cities of the American West known now as "ghost towns." When the ore deposits on which they were based were worked out the cities' inhabitants moved away. From these complete abandonments there are various gradations extending to a "dead town" persistence, population aggregates which exist but have no vitality, relics of earlier activity. A resort city does not disappear completely because fashions and facilities for vacationing change, but it loses its vigor (e.g., **Saratoga**, New York, **Newport**, Rhode Island); there is no growth in numbers of either people or structures; the old people die, the old structures decay.

It becomes evident, then, that the types of cities thus far listed are not representative in the geographical sense. Of course, they all come into being and attain importance because of geographic circumstances; they are, however, only incidental to such circumstances. In other words, they are not cities in their own right; they do not exist and expand because they are functioning as cities. Except as a city exists and persists by virtue of its own functioning (that is, by providing services only it can offer) it is not a true, representative city. In this sense only the *commercial city* is the true, or representative, city.

THE COMMERCIAL CITY

As here used, the term "commercial city" is applied to any concentration of population and structures, great or small, that exists because it facilitates commerce. Hence in this connotation very small communities may be dignified by the term "city."

The commerce that such cities facilitate is the exchange of goods, or simply the change in ownership of goods. To effect this change of ownership the merchandise concerned must ordinarily be moved from one place to another, nearby or remote. Thus the business of transportation and distribution is the basic activity of commerce. Another activity almost invariably associated with this is "break of bulk." The seller in a business transaction regularly has a stock or shipment of goods of the same kind. This inventory he sells piecemeal, parceling it out. In such partitioning another extremely important factor is involved—the accumulation of large stocks or the arrival of large lots at points where it is necessary to change from one mode of transportation to another, always in decreasing order of magnitude with reference to the bulk of the material that is handled. A full progression might include from ship to shore, then by inland navigation, by train, by truck, by cart, by pack animal, and finally by human porterage. The airplane has become, with respect to some commodities and particular shipments, a disturbing or irregular transportation facility that interrupts the progression in certain instances. It is, however, of minor significance relative to the bulk of commerce and hence in the functioning of commercial cities.

QUESTIONS. What makes a city? How is a city started? Distinguish between the specific and general sites of a city. What kind of specific site was the originating point of most cities? Give classes of such cities and a specific example of each class. What other factors are essential for the growth of a city at a given specific site? How do the conditions of the general site affect the increase in size of a city?

Name the different types of cities. Which was the first in existence? How do mining cities and hydropower cities differ in permanence? Give examples of each type of cities. Why are all of these "vulnerable" as city units? State why a commercial city may be regarded as the representative city.

■ COMMERCIAL CITIES

The order of importance of commercial cities is in general as follows: (1) seaport cities, (2) lake port cities, (3) river port cities, (4) overland route cities. Within these classes there are subclasses of varying degrees of importance. The general order of importance as given above derives from the following analysis.

Seaport cities are first in importance because the oceans are a free, interconnected highway over which ships may proceed between all quarters of the globe. Accordingly, the goods available at any seaport can be conveyed to any other seaport by the cheapest type of transportation, the ocean ship. The cost of ocean shipment per ton-mile[1] is so low (for quantity shipments) that goods of low unit value may profitably be conveyed to market over thousands of miles of ocean distance.

Lake transportation, as was noted in Chapter 2, is highly significant in only one part of the world—the Great Lakes. The Russian utilization of the salt Caspian Sea is, however, of some importance. To the extent that suitable goods are available for transfer, lake shipping shares in the low-cost advantages of ocean shipping.

River and canal navigation is subordinate to railroad traffic in developed regions for a variety of reasons, chief among which is slowness. Inland waterways in these regions, despite great expenditure for improvements, may not carry the traffic they are potentially able to handle.

Overland route cities have in common the characteristic that they were established and have grown where two or more such routes intersect. Their potentialities are determined by the importance of the intersecting routes, the extent and productivity of the territories the routes serve, and what may be described as the unique advantage of the principal intersection that is their basis.

In retrospect it is also clear that among

[1] The ton-mile is obtained by multiplying weight by distance. Thus a shipment of 1000 tons for 400 miles involves 400,000 ton-miles.

ancient cities, originally founded on defense sites, only those located at places where commerce could also function exceptionally well attained great size and persisted through the centuries. Possible exceptions to this rule are those like Rome and Athens, which have lived on as governmental cities. It is also true that by coincidence a city founded because of the presence of mineral resources or resort facilities may prove to be at a location where trade can also thrive. In that instance the original basis for city development may come to be completely subordinated to the later commercial activities of the inhabitants.

SEAPORTS

The status of seaport cities as the most important of man's communities is dramatically underlined by the fact that approximately one-half of the world's cities with over one million population are seaports (some can be reached by ocean-going ships although they may not be actually on the coast). **New York, Philadelphia, Los Angeles, Montreal,** and **San Francisco** in North America; **Antwerp, Barcelona, Glasgow, Hamburg, Leningrad,** and **London** in Europe; **Bombay, Calcutta, Hong Kong, Karachi, Kobe, Manila, Osaka, Shanghai, Tientsin,** and **Yokohama** in Asia; **Melbourne** and **Sydney** in Australia; **Rio de Janeiro** and **Buenos Aires** in South America—all these cities are among the most important on their respective continents, and all are seaports (Fig. 3.11).

It is obvious that seaports do not develop at any random location along the seacoast. If such were the case the number of seaports would be far greater than it is. To become a seaport of significance for world trade a location must satisfy certain specifications in regard to the specific site and the general site.

The first qualification of the specific site is that it be a good harbor, which ideally requires fulfillment of the following conditions:

1. There should be protection from the open sea and its storms. Wherever there is

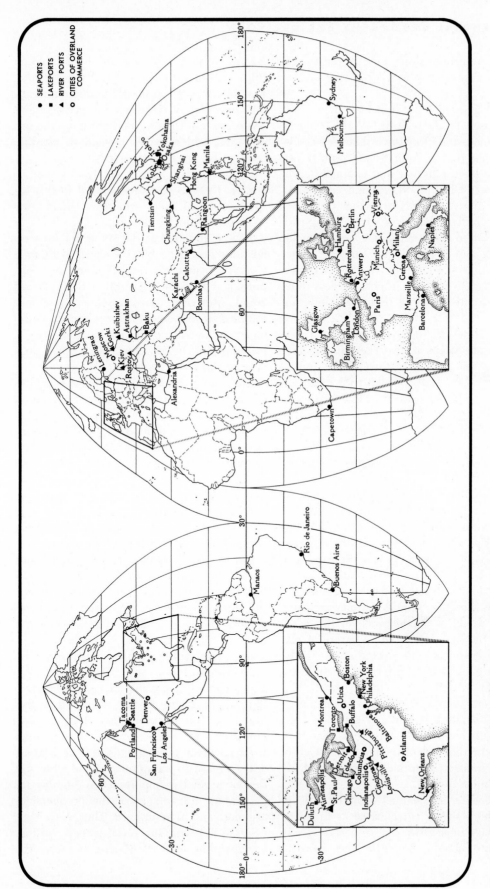

Fig. 3.11—Commercial Cities of the World Mentioned in the Text.

no such protection, ships must go out to sea during storms or run the risk of being driven ashore.

2. There should be sufficient depth for large vessels of deep draft. World trade is tending more and more toward larger vessels and deeper drafts. A first-class port is required to have a harbor and channel depth of 40 feet. On the other hand, excessive depth requires too long an anchor chain.

3. The harbor should be large enough to hold anchored ships and allow easy maneuvering. A ship in port is not carrying cargo and therefore not earning. Hence the easier it is to maneuver while in port the less time is wasted and the more profit the ship can earn.

4. The tides should be moderate. Tides are generally smallest near the equator and larger as one proceeds toward the poles. They are also small in relatively enclosed bodies of water such as the Mediterranean, the Baltic, and the Caribbean seas, and the Gulf of Mexico. Estuaries increase the range of the tides. The extreme is reached in the Bay of Fundy, Nova Scotia, where the difference between high and low tide averages 50 feet. In addition to affecting the depth of water in a harbor, tides scour and fill the harbor bottom and its approaches, posing construction and maintenance problems. The great ports of the west coast of England are hampered by excessive tides and must use tidal basins constructed at great expense.

5. The shoreline should permit extensive dockage facilities. Some ports on the west coast of the Americas have no harbor at all. Ships must anchor unprotected at sea while their cargoes are transferred to lighters (small barges with cargo-handling facilities). Not all cargo can be handled in this manner, and the operation can in any event be carried on only in relatively calm seas. Shanghai also suffers from lack of such facilities. Cargo must be transferred to and from an anchorage five miles away.

6. The entering channel should be deep and without strong currents, so as to minimize navigational risks.

7. There should be little fog hazard. Again, time and money are wasted when ships are forced to lie to until the fog lifts. Few nontropical ports escape this disadvantage completely. However, it is becoming less important than formerly through the use of radar, which makes navigation possible through fog even in crowded harbors.

8. The harbor should not freeze over in winter. Russian ports suffer most in this respect. Few of them are not icebound for some period during the year.

Few, if any, harbors satisfy all these specifications perfectly, but the more of them a given port can claim the larger and more important it is likely to be, other things being equal. Moreover, once a seaport is firmly established many adverse conditions can be offset or overcome by engineering works, provision of breakwaters, and other construction and dredging.

The second qualification of the specific site is that it afford the essentials for living noted previously: an ample supply of drinking water and dry, level ground for buildings. Here again, although the provision was adequate at the founding of the seaport, if later these facilities prove to be too limited for the expansion of the city, commonly they can be enlarged by engineering works. Thus it was profitable to the city of **Seattle** to remove completely a large hill within its limits.

But no matter how safe and commodious the harbor, and how ideal the living conditions, no great seaport will develop without the third qualification—geographic circumstances of the general site that warrant the city's existence. In brief, it should lie on a major trade route or routes, there should be easy transportation access to the interior, and it should, if possible, have a productive hinterland. Then, in the degree that this hinterland is richly productive and extensive, and access to it is easier and simpler than from adjacent competing sites, the seaport will increase in importance. Rival sites will decline in relative importance as the superior geographic advantages of the premier site are more and more utilized. Thus, New York (Fig. 3.12) has far outdistanced Boston, Philadelphia, and Baltimore because the

Fig. 3.12—New York City, the World's Premier Seaport and Commercial City. In foreground are piers where ocean liners dock. (Courtesy, NYSPIX-Commerce.)

route to the interior of the continent from New York is much easier than from the rival cities and leads directly to the richest productive areas.

New York was initially vastly superior to the other ports in this respect in that a variety of facilities were available. The river-canal route to the Great Lakes was paralleled first by roads, then by railroads. The rival cities tried desperately to match these natural facilities by elaborate canal engineering but failed to achieve any notable degree of success.

The ideal port site is the *estuary,* or drowned river. Europe and its ports have profited greatly from a fortunate situation in this respect. No point in western Europe is more than 400 miles from salt water. The great world ports of New York, Montreal, London, Liverpool, Philadelphia, Buenos Aires, Antwerp, Hamburg, and Sydney are all on estuaries.

Seaports at the mouths of large rivers or inland some distance from them possess many of the advantages of the estuary type of harbor. The valley of the river, even if the stream itself is unnavigable, provides a route to the interior down which the produce of all the river's drainage area naturally flows and up which goods brought from overseas are transported. **New Orleans, Portland** (Oregon), **Buenos Aires, Rotterdam, Marseille, Alexandria, Calcutta, Rangoon,** and **Shanghai** exemplify the river-mouth sites. **Manaos,** 1000 miles up the Amazon, is the extreme case of an inland position reached by seagoing vessels of large size.

Where no large river valley affords entrance the head of a broad bay may be the best site for a seaport along a considerable reach of coast. Even though not protected by sheltering heights near at hand the waters of such bays do not experience the violence of waves in the adjacent open sea. The manner of wave progression insures that the waves will lose their force when they have moved some distance into the bay area. Moreover, the head of the bay has the inland position that permits the easy collection and distribution of goods from the enclosing land arms of the bay. In North America **Boston, Baltimore, Seattle,** and **Tacoma** have such sites. **Leningrad, Genoa,** and **Naples,** in Europe, **Capetown** in Africa, **Tokyo** and **Osaka** in Japan, **Manila** in the Philippines, and **Melbourne** in Australia are other important examples.

LAKE PORTS

Unless the Baltic, Mediterranean, and Black Sea ports are placed in the lake port class, only **Astrakhan** (actually located inland on the Volga delta), **Baku** on the Caspian, and the cities of the North American Great Lakes can qualify as large lake ports. Many of the latter have positions like head-of-bay sites on the seacoast in that they are at the ends of the lakes. Outstanding is **Chicago** at the southern end of Lake Michigan, a great "bay" extending far into the rich prairie lands of the interior United States. **Duluth** is at the western end of Lake Superior, **Toledo** and **Buffalo** at the two ends of Lake Erie, **Toronto** near the end of Lake Ontario. (With the St. Lawrence Seaway these Great Lakes ports become technically seaports as well.) **Cleveland** has an along-shore position, but, like those of the others, its site is at the mouth of a drowned river valley. The land of northeastern North America is slowly being tilted up, so that areas to the north are rising. The effect of this has been to spill the water of the south sides of the lakes into the valley notches that streams had previously cut in their rims. Thus Chicago is at the mouth of the Chicago River, Toledo at the mouth of the Maumee River, Cleveland at the mouth of the Cuyahoga River. Aside from the relative lack of productivity of the lands on the Canadian side of the Great Lakes, these protected harbor conditions have been a favorable factor of large importance in the growth of the American Great Lakes ports.

RIVER PORTS

No more than seaports and lake ports are river ports located at random. The specific site is regularly one where deep water and a high bank afford a good landing place. This combination in effect constitutes a good harbor. Drinking water is assured by the stream. Ample expanse of level ground is the requisite of next importance.

Specific site requirements for river ports are commonly available at many points. It is, therefore, the circumstances of the general sites that are most significant in the development of river cities. Approximately in order of importance, the following types of location foster the settlement and growth of river ports.

The junction of a navigable tributary is exemplified by **Pittsburgh** (Fig. 3.13). The tributaries insure the collection at such points of the products of their basins. Break of bulk and transshipment at the junction point are appropriate consequences of the meeting of routes.

The head of navigation is of necessity a port of ultimate destination for a river cargo, and the transfer point for distribution overland. **Minneapolis** and **St. Paul** have this position on the Mississippi, as does **Chungking,** on the Yangtze in China. If a falls or rapids necessitates the use of a canal or portage around the obstruction the slowing or halting of the voyage prompts loading and unloading, with consequent changes in ownership—that is, commerce. **Louisville,** Kentucky, owes its origin and early development to the rapids in the Ohio River at its site.

Fig. 3.13—Site of Pittsburgh, Pennsylvania. A stream junction.

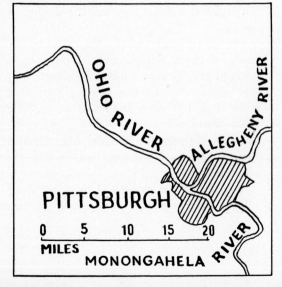

Fig. 3.14—Site of Detroit, Michigan. A stream barrier across a land route.

Where the water barrier opposed by a stream is considerable, land routes tend to converge on narrow places crossed by ferry, bridge, or tunnel. **Detroit** (Fig. 3.14) is especially representative of such a location. Although the barriers here are Lakes Huron and Erie, the site on the short, narrow Detroit River which connects the lakes automatically focuses land traffic between the east and west and facilitates the interception of the parade of lake ships past its water

Fig. 3.15—Site of Cincinnati, Ohio. A large stream bend.

front. In Russia such towns as **Rostov, Kuibyshev, Gorkiy,** and **Kiev** are situated where east-west overland routes cross north-south rivers.

Where the course of a river over a long reach is unmarked by any special feature a principal port commonly develops *at the head of a large bend.* At such points goods may be collected and distributed radially over the shortest distances overland on both the outer and inner sides of the bend. This is the position of **Cincinnati,** Ohio (Fig. 3.15). Such a site corresponds to that of a seaport or lake port at the head of a bay.

OVERLAND ROUTE CITIES

Although many inland cities of America that were originally settlements in forest country are now quite exclusively served by overland routes, they were first located with reference to their positions on stream routes of very minor importance. Such small streams served to float a barge or canoe, and thus bulky goods could be both brought in and shipped out much more cheaply than by pack horse or wagon when roads were poor or nonexistent. Presumably this was also true of the settlement of many European cities, though historical records of such first occupation do not exist. In much of China minor watercourses are still generally utilized in such fashion. Further, as noted above, where topographic relief is considerable the river gradient is later quite invariably followed by roads and railroads.

Aside from this primary association with watercourses, certain inland sites are geographically indicated for city development. They are all associated with and conditioned by the intersection of land routes. The relative importance of the sites is governed by the importance of the routes which intersect, and somewhat by their nature.

A distinctive type of site is the intersection of a route across mountains, the outlet of a mountain pass, with the main highway of the plain parallel to the base of the mountain chain. **Denver,** Colorado, **Atlanta,** Georgia, **Munich,** Germany (Fig. 3.16), and **Milan,** Italy, are conspicuous examples of this type.

Fig. 3.16—Site of Munich, Germany. Intersection of route parallel to mountains with route across mountains. (Principal railroads indicated.)

In contrast is the site centrally located on wide plains. With travel in such case equally feasible in any direction, the center of a circle is the most convenient place for all peripheral traffic to meet. It is the point of shortest haul from outlying areas in any direction. **Indianapolis**, Indiana (Fig. 3.17), and **Columbus**, Ohio, aside from their governmental function, have a large significance in wholesale distribution by reason of their central location. **Paris** is the outstanding example of this type of location. Traffic of all France focuses on and radiates from the city. **Moscow** is another example of first importance, as are **Berlin** and **Vienna**—all center-of-plains cities.

Fig. 3.17—Site of Indianapolis, Indiana. Center of plains area. (Principal railroads indicated within state boundaries.)

In the same manner that the meeting of a route across mountains with one along plains is definitely marked as a trade center and hence for city growth, intersections of major axial routes (i.e., those that meet at approximately right angles) are the appropriate points for commercial activity. The importance these centers achieve depends on the significance of the routes. In this class all gradations may be observed. Thus **Utica**, New York, is situated where the route along the Mohawk Valley is joined by a major route into the hill country to the south. At the other end of the scale is the country crossroads town (Fig. 3.18) and finally the intersection that commands nothing more than a filling station. Even so, the filling station at an obscure crossroads is better located for business than one located merely by the side of the road.

Fig. 3.18—Melbourne, Iowa, a Country Crossroads Town, Population 510. Such places serve as local rural trading centers much as shopping plazas serve the suburban areas of large cities. (Courtesy, Iowa Development Commission.)

QUESTIONS. Name the classes of commercial cities in the order of their importance. Name two regions where lake port cities are important. Why has river and canal transport declined? By what circumstances is the importance of overland route cities governed? Why are seaport cities preëminent? What is the first essential for the specific site of a seaport city? What are the characteristics of a good harbor? What geographic circumstances of a general site finally determine the growth of a seaport? Illustrate by comparing New York and rival cities. List and characterize various kinds of harbor sites. What type of general location do most Great Lakes ports have? Specific location? What are the specific and general site requirements of a river port? What geographic circumstance governed the original specific sites of overland route cities in the forested regions of North America? What geographic circumstances governed their later growth? Describe three types of overland route intersections.

■ MAKE-UP OF CITY POPULATIONS

1. *The Principals.* It should be clear from the preceding discussion that unless a city is situated geographically to facilitate trade it does not qualify in its own right as a permanent population center; it does not function as a true city unless it is a commercial city. Accordingly, the principal persons of representative cities are the merchants. This status is reflected in the organization of chambers of commerce for all such centers, great or small. The voice of the chamber of commerce is regularly very persuasive in the political conduct of city affairs. Measures inimical to the interests of the traders are frowned upon. The chamber provides slogans—"Trade in Bellyria," "Boost Crocania," and the like.

In the major centers the traders comprise a much more varied group than merely the retail merchants. In fact, the latter are in certain respects actually parasitic, although their standing is of course entirely respectable. At the top in the great commercial centers are the importers and exporters, the brokers and bankers (money and credit can be considered as much merchandise as fish and steel rails), the commission merchants, warehousemen, jobbers, and wholesalers. As individuals and as corporation officers such principals constitute a considerable group of people. Add to their number all the employees who handle the goods, make the purchases and sales, do the clerical and advertising work, and there is a rather large population assembled solely to carry on trade activities.

2. *The Industrialists.* The casual conclusion of most persons in regard to the population of most cities would be that the heads of manufacturing enterprises and their employees constitute an essential element and the preponderant group in a city population. Their number is admittedly great, yet the principals of the industrial enterprises have comparatively little interest in and do not assume leading roles in the chambers of commerce. They may offer approving nods and even provide funds for the chamber's activities, but they are seldom its chief promoters.

On the other hand, the industrial establishments are concentrated in and about the commercial cities precisely because these are great trading centers. It is the manufacturer's business to bring together a variety of raw materials, to process and assemble them into a finished product, and then, ordinarily, to place them by trade channels in the hands of the ultimate consumer. Often he also supplies other industries with components or accessories. The making of containers for packaging goods is an example of this second type of manufacturing business.

It is clear that the place where the largest stocks of raw materials, of the widest variety, will be immediately available is the prime commercial city, the seaport. From seaports, grading down the scale of importance of commercial city types, the volume of goods on hand and their variety will decline proportionately, except that local products may be accessible in large supply according to the location of the center. For this reason some specialized industries are more advantageously established near the source of their peculiar supplies than at the general centers.

Further, precisely the same transport facilities that make possible the concentration of raw materials required and sought by the processor and assembler are available for the distribution of their finished products. Here the manufacturer located at the great general center is at an advantage.

Finally, the industrialists and their operatives provide a large increment to the city population. These persons, together with those associated with the merchants and the rest of the city population, also afford a large immediate market for many varieties of consumers' goods.

3. *The Auxiliary Forces.* Warehouses, stores, offices, factories, hotels, homes, schools, churches, and other publicly used buildings must be erected and maintained to house businesses and people. Thus large numbers of persons in every big city are engaged in the building trades. A somewhat equivalent number is employed in transport —trucks, subways, buses, and taxicabs— hauling goods and people. Communications —mail, telephone, and telegraph—must also be serviced. A large volume of printing is necessary. Professional people—doctors, dentists, nurses, lawyers, and clergymen— add their quota. Public servants—teachers, policemen, firemen, and sanitation workers —are another large contingent. In housing, servants and hotel workers are also part of the city population.

An illustration of the different types of activity and their relative importance in the representative city is offered by an analysis of employment in the greatest of them all— New York City. A study made of employment in 1950 by the New York State Department of Labor and the New York City Department of City Planning showed the following composition of total employment:

Major Categories of Employment	Percent of Total
Manufacturing	29.8
Services	14.9
Retail trade	13.1
Government	10.7
Wholesale trade	10.1
Finance, insurance, and real estate	9.3
Transportation, communication, and public utilities	8.4
Contract construction	3.7

From these enumerations it is clear that the commercial activities of a representative city may bring together a large number of city inhabitants resident within its confines and suburbs, although only a fraction of the population participates directly in commerce. The commercial city as such, moreover, provides nothing basically new—no

product of farm, forest, mine, or sea. Except for the industrial enterprises it may have attracted, it simply distributes, modifies, and brings together the yield of workers elsewhere.

In this connection it is significant that, as a percentage of the total population, the rural population of the United States declined between 1900 and 1950 from 60 percent to 36 percent. Meanwhile, the total population of the country increased from 76 million to more than 160 million.

■ THE ANATOMY OF CITIES[2]

Progressive Placing of City Structures. Aside from the people who live there, the visible expression of a city is its buildings. Since these were not all erected at one time, there must have been some order in the progressive occupation of the city site. With reference to ancient cities, especially those whose origins were defensive sites, not much is known of this order in many instances. But in the case of many American cities the history is known from the start. In the representative, functioning, commercial type the order of development and other factors relating to the anatomy of such centers have considerable practical significance for owners of real estate. It is found that geographic factors govern and determine the effects achieved. It also appears that ignorance of the principles involved has led to some costly mistakes in city planning.

Commercial cities exist through their efficacy in facilitating the exchange of goods; hence the trader who first appeared on the scene located his store or warehouse (the specific site) where it was immediately in contact with the transportation means by which the merchandise was brought to or shipped from the place. By sea, lake, or river, this was the most convenient landing point. Along highways it was situated as related

[2] R. M. Hurd's *Principles of City Land Values* is the basis for much of the content presented under this topic.

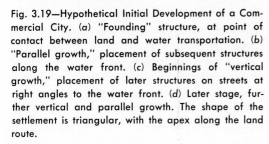

Fig. 3.19—Hypothetical Initial Development of a Commercial City. (a) "Founding" structure, at point of contact between land and water transportation. (b) "Parallel growth," placement of subsequent structures along the water front. (c) Beginnings of "vertical growth," placement of later structures on streets at right angles to the water front. (d) Later stage, further vertical and parallel growth. The shape of the settlement is triangular, with the apex along the land route.

above, i.e., where two land routes intersected.

The first competitor of the "founding" settler would choose a site to the right or left of the original structure for his establishment or at another corner of the intersection. As such placing proceeded with the advent of still other merchants a row of edifices parallel to the shore or main highway would be established and progressively lengthened (Fig. 3.19).

At some point in this process a newcomer would conclude that a position at either end of the row would be so remote from the contact point, say the landing place, that he would fare better by utilizing a site in the rear of the original structure. As still later newcomers followed suit there would gradually be built up a row behind the first row and eventually the settlement would, in plan view, be composed of a triangular block of structures with the apex of the triangle at right angles from the line of the row along the shore.

The first order or type of growth is called *parallel growth,* the second, *vertical* or *perpendicular growth,* respectively parallel or perpendicular to the trade route. It should

be borne in mind that this is an idealized account of the *initial* development of a commercial settlement. Once internal circulation becomes facilitated by good roads, a new merchant in a growing community will give first attention to the convenience of his prospective customers in selecting his site. Such convenience is dependent on ease of access to what becomes the retail business district. But this accessibility is determined by the street pattern, which in turn inherits its main axes from the traffic routes that were the basic geographic factors in fixing the site of the original settlement.

Open Sites Versus Restricted Sites. At some city sites suitable ground for the indefinitely long extension of parallel growth is available. These are referred to as *open sites.* In others some obstruction—a hill, a swamp, a stream—limits extension; these are *restricted sites.* In the restricted sites vertical growth was compelled or forced unduly, and this affected the later development of the city.

With the exception of the truly metropolitan centers the immediate and direct contact with the transport facilities providing connection with the outside world loses some of its significance as the city grows. Then the original site is gradually abandoned by retail business. The early general store in time is replaced by a department store. One reason for the displacement is that the original structures become inadequate and antiquated; they are, however, still serviceable for other uses and hence are not torn down. Another is that as growth takes place with expansions of commercial and industrial activity the city population attains great size, and considerable residential districts develop. Then it proves most profitable for the chief retail establishments of the city to keep in most convenient touch with the better residential districts.

It has been found that as a consequence of these circumstances the center of the business district of American water-front cities (as expressed by real-estate values) moves away from the water front at the rate of one block every 20 to 40 years if the principal street is parallel to the water front. If the principal street is at right angles to the water front the rate may be as high as one block in 8 to 12 years.

The rule of displacement cannot be applied too broadly, however. As roads replace rivers and railroads replace roads, the significance of original sites is greatly altered. In seaports and lake ports warehousing becomes important along the water front as the commercial activities expand. In time, different types of land within the city are allocated to specific uses.

In those population centers that have grown up in the railroad age or been modified in their development during that period, there is a marked difference between cities of moderate size and metropolitan centers. Assuming that initially they were all alike—that is, settlements around railroad stations where contact was made with the outside—then those that never grew, that had no geographic features to promote commercial development, have remained much as they were when founded, a cluster of structures around the railroad station. Those that grew moderately have followed the rule with regard to migration of the main retail business center away from the station that was the point of origin. Such cities have attained an independence of functioning that makes the immediate contact with the distribution facility a matter of less importance than it was at the beginning. Probably most persons can easily call to mind at least one city of moderate size in which the railroad station is well away from the present center of the city.

In the process of growth, facilities for internal movement of the goods that arrive or are shipped out are elaborated, so that minor increases in hauling distance are of little significance. The merchants of such cities, further, have little or no interest in the majority of the people who come from the outside. These are chiefly commercial travelers, salesmen who seek orders from the merchant and industrial groups. Their convenience is unrelated to the profitable functioning of the center. Others who arrive are visiting relatives, or tourists passing through whose only purchases are meals and hotel accommodations.

As a city becomes a metropolitan center the migration away from the railroad terminals is reversed. In such cities the persons who arrive acquire supreme importance. The commercial people are chiefly buyers instead of sellers. They come to purchase stocks from wholesalers for retail distribution in outlying centers. It distinctly behooves the metropolitan commercial center to cater to these persons. Further, the noncommercial visitors come for more or less protracted stays, to purchase personal wardrobes, to go to theaters, or to patronize other attractions available only in a metropolitan city. Both groups are well supplied with money. In response to this lure the center of the retail district of the city tends to move back toward the rail terminals. This tendency is remarkably illustrated by developments in New York City.

But few cities can attain metropolitan eminence. There commonly develops in those of lesser importance, but still of considerable size, a sort of no man's land in the abandoned belt between the point of origin and the existing retail business district. This is a territory occupied by shabby, outmoded structures, old stores converted to other uses, or to inferior sales purposes, second-hand goods, and the like; small factories, cheap hotels, and rooming houses. It is a section with no apparent future.

Although it is not always possible to foretell what geographical factor or factors will be of first importance in the growth of a city, one principle of planning seems to have general application: the streets that traverse the long axis of the city should be the closest spaced and the widest thoroughfares. These will ordinarily correspond to the axis of parallel growth. Great mistakes have been made on this score. When New York City's streets and avenues north of Houston, 9th and 13th streets were laid out in 1907 it was thought the main traffic of the city would be east-west, between the shipping in the Hudson and East rivers. Crosstown streets, accordingly, were laid out 200 feet apart, whereas the north-south avenues were spaced 600 to 900 feet apart (Fig. 3.20). The traffic congestion that has ensued de-

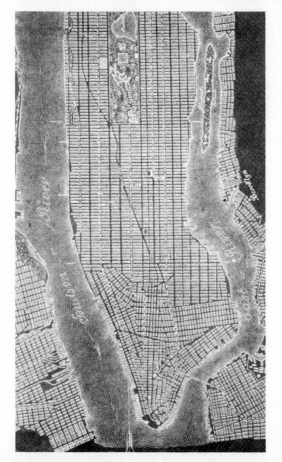

Fig. 3.20—Plat of Lower Manhattan Island. The street plan north of the early city site provides many streets for east-west traffic, few for north-south traffic, but except for a few major routes across the city, most traffic is up- and down-town.

rives in no small part from this error. Modernly the east ends of many crosstown streets in New York City are as devoid of traffic as are suburban residential streets; some, indeed, are blocked off to provide neighborhood playgrounds.

Central Growth Versus Axial Growth. A distinction may also be made between *central* and *axial* growth. Axial growth operates through the force of attraction; it is dynamic and accretionary. Central growth derives from internal pressure; it is static and involves filling in (Fig. 3.21).

As a city expands, newcomers seek ground for their buildings. Their arrival is prompted by a desire to participate in the city's functioning; hence it is entirely appropriate that they should attach themselves at the end of the line of previously erected buildings along the chief thoroughfares leading into the city. This is an extension of the concept of parallel and vertical growth. Along these main routes the most direct access to the center of the city is had; there transportation facilities are available. Neighborhood stores as well as residences find locations on such routes most desirable. The development of shopping centers either at peripheral locations on main roads or at interior sites, in both instances locations where ample cheap land is available for sprawling, one-story retail establishments and for customer parking, is a phenomenon of the automobile age that also fits into this analysis.

When growth along the main routes becomes overextended, new arrivals find it more advantageous to fill in the segments between the main roads. The preference then is for an interior location because of the shorter distance from the city center. This is a special expression of the principle of parallel and vertical growth and also illustrates central growth.

The demand for space within the focal center eventually brings about the filling in of all vacant lands, to the extent that "hole-in-the-wall" stores appear as a phenomenon occupying narrow spaces originally left between adjoining buildings. When all open

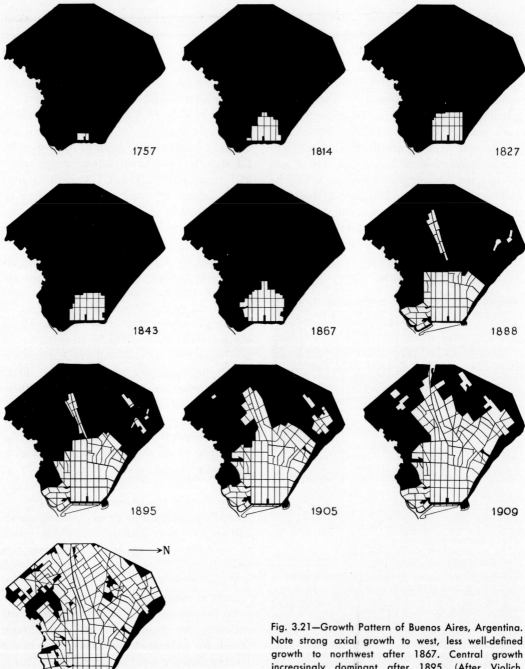

1757

1814

1827

1843

1867

1888

1895

1905

1909

→N

1932

Fig. 3.21—Growth Pattern of Buenos Aires, Argentina. Note strong axial growth to west, less well-defined growth to northwest after 1867. Central growth increasingly dominant after 1895. (After Violich, Cities of Latin America.)

ground is utilized, further space within the district may be had only by going up or down. The result is a cluster of tall buildings on the best locations. It is economical to make room for their construction through wrecking older, lower structures. Sometimes it even pays to excavate stories underground.

It may be added here that the vitality of a city can be judged to a considerable extent by the measure of current building activity. Cities in and around which practically no new construction is in evidence during prosperous times have reached or passed their climax as population centers under the conditions in existence. A new development such as the provision of additional transportation facilities may, however, induce a rejuvenation after a period of decadence.

In consequence of combined axial and central growth the pattern of a city situated at the center of a level plain where growth is not restricted in any direction and where equally productive territory exists along all

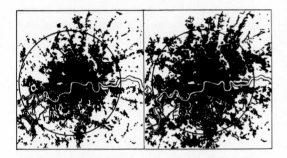

Fig. 3.22—Growth Pattern of London, England, Illustrating "Star" Result on Generally Open Site. Upper, 1914; lower, 1929. Built-up areas black. Circles, of same diameter, are to aid comparison. Note areas of axial and central growth. (After Saarinen, The City: Its Growth, Its Decay, Its Future.)

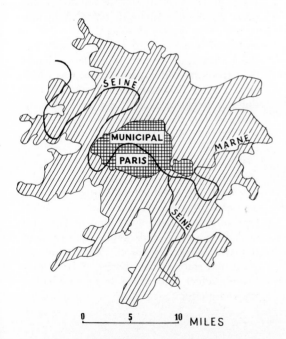

Fig. 3.23—Built-Up Areas of Metropolitan Paris, France, Showing Modified "Star" Plan. (Compare with Fig. 3.22.) (After Chapman, "Paris," in Great Cities of the World.)

radii from the focal point will be that of a star with long points and a raised center (Fig. 3.22). If the site is restricted by barriers of one kind or another, axial growth is asymmetrical, with some extremely long points, others short and stubby (Fig. 3.23).

Allocation of City Lands. As a city matures, the utilization of its lands is progressively differentiated. Where differences in altitude exist within the city area this geographic factor has great importance. The lowest lands are occupied by factories of the type whose products are of large size or low cost. These are surrounded by the homes of the lowest-paid workmen. Along railroads and water fronts the ground is used for yards and warehouses. Lighter manufactures, wholesale and jobbing houses occupy the intermediate belt of higher and commonly drier ground, together with the shabby residential structures previously referred to. The level focal area is the site of the best retail business district, together with office buildings. The activities such stores and structures house command the highest ground rents.

Within the business district there is a further segregation that becomes more and more marked with the passage of time. Department stores, specialty and jewelry shops, 5- and 10-cent stores and drug stores acquire the best locations, those where the traffic focuses. These establishments pioneer the migratory movement toward the expanding high-class residential sections. Ringed around this nucleus appear theaters, hotels, furniture stores, automobile salesrooms, and similar enterprises that require large floor space. These are excluded from the central section because of rental costs. Purchase of furniture or a car is a special occasion, so that customers find it no hardship to go outside the focal district to "shop" for their selections. Formerly firms in the same line of business thought it desirable to locate some distance away from a competitor. It has been found, however, that this is an erroneous concept. When all businesses of a kind are concentrated in one area each enterprise gets a larger volume of trade than it would if it were isolated. Customers who fail to find what they seek in one place are able conveniently to try next door and will commonly make a purchase, whereas otherwise they might give up the idea altogether.

In Oriental cities, where shrewd trading is best understood, all types of business are thus segregated, although this derives in part from trade and family associations designed to keep newcomers from establishing an enterprise of the particular kind located in a given district.

Any interruption to the continuity of business structures within the retail center is a handicap. Accordingly, parks and public buildings are out of place there. They must be by-passed with some effort by the shopper. (On the other hand, the use of open spaces for parking lots is a different matter. These afford a convenience for those using the downtown business, shopping, and recreation facilities.) When banks were utilized almost exclusively by businessmen they were in the same category with courthouses and the like. But modernly, when large numbers of people have checking accounts, banks may appropriately be made directly accessible (without detriment to other businesses) by locating them on main thoroughfares. If parks are present in the business section, positions opposite them are best suited for hotels because light and air are assured the occupants.

Because west winds prevail and are strongest in America and Europe the "West Side" is regularly the preferred residential section. The wind carries the dust and smoke of the city over to the east side. The London "West End" is a familiar example. Where the prevailing wind is from another direction it is always the windward side that is preferred. Residences are also much influenced by altitudes. The finest residences occupy the highest sites. Surveys have disclosed that even along single streets in a given section the housing is invariably poorer where depressions in the general topography occur.

QUESTIONS. Who are the most important persons in a representative city? Why do industries locate in representative cities? (Give specific reasons.) Make a list of the classes of people, by occupations, that constitute the population of a representative city. From personal knowledge of a city you are familiar with make an estimate of the percentage of the whole which each class comprises. What services do city populations provide in return for their support? How did the relative number of urban and rural residents change between 1900 and 1950?

Where is the first building of a commercial city erected? Where will the two succeeding buildings be placed? When will a different type of site first be chosen? How may these different placings be designated? How does an open site differ from a restricted site? How does growth (with reference to retail business) proceed after a city has attained considerable size? What rule in regard to this point applies to American cities? Why are metropolitan centers an exception to the general rule? What part of an average city has the lowest land values? Why? How should city streets be laid out with respect to width and spacing between parallel streets? Distinguish between central and axial growth. Account for the existence of "hole-in-the-wall" stores. How may the vitality of a city be judged?

What kind of patterns do the outlines of city developments make? State how and why city lands are eventually allocated to particular uses. If a flood occurs in a city, what type of activity and what kind of land are most seriously affected? Which side of town is preferred for residences? Why? How do parks and statues affect business? How does altitude affect land values in the residential areas of a city?

Location and the Representation of Position

CHAPTER 4

Determining Location and Position

■ INTRODUCTION

It is intended that the preceding chapters should make the reader aware of the existence and distribution of the chief natural landmarks of the world and the nature of the major man-made geographical foci, the cities. The textual presentation would have lost most of its value, however, had it not been supplemented by maps showing the locations of the items listed and characterized. In other words, geographic study of unfamiliar areas is almost completely meaningless unless a map is available to make clear the location, distribution, and positional relations of the geographic features under discussion.

Many simple maps are no more than sketches; the information they are intended to convey is evident on inspection. For a correct and full interpretation of accurately drawn maps, on the other hand, it is essential to know the principles of their construction. By what means are the positions of the different items on the map determined and designated? In what respects are the representations accurate? Such knowledge is important not only for the practical use of maps but also for the understanding of world concepts it will provide; it is an essential to geographic literacy.

Accordingly, the following two chapters are devoted to world concepts as they are derived and given representation by means of maps.

The first problem to be considered is that of the determination of *location* and *posi-*tion. It is important to understand the distinction between these two concepts. "Location" is a reference to a certain absolutely determined point, while "position" is always stated in relation to the location of other points. For example, a particular monument is "located" at a certain spot, *X;* its "position" is 90 feet in a certain direction from a given highway intersection.

■ DIRECTION

Everyone in the course of his life does some traveling to unfamiliar cities, states, or countries. On such travels the problem of finding one's way back home may never arise, or if it does, it usually involves nothing more than following the correct highway markings as indicated on a road map. But for purposes of geography this pragmatic means of finding one's way about is not enough. The geographic problem is to determine one's location, and the position of other places with reference to that location, in a standardized, objective manner that will enable anyone else to come to the same conclusion through repetition of the same procedure. Further, it is the problem of representing one's position on the earth with reference to these places. Then the question becomes one of maps and mapping.

When a person is in new or unfamiliar surroundings it is commonly said that he must orient himself. The word "orient" is from the Latin *oriens,* meaning "to rise," and suggests the East, or direction in which the sun rises. Here is the first clue to the solution of the problem of location: the need for a means by which *direction* may be determined and stated.

In the old game of blindman's buff the player is blindfolded, turned around several times, then put on his own to hunt for the others of the company. The player may be in his own home, certainly the most familiar of all surroundings, yet he feels totally lost. He is unable to tell where he is or where the other players are even if they have not moved. The blindfolded person gropes uncertainly, for he has temporarily lost all sense of direction. It is the same in the geographic problem of location. Without a means for determining direction it is impossible to know either location or the relative position of things.

In approaching the problem of making a precise and accurate determination of direction it is necessary first to consider the position of the earth in the solar system and universe. This is also an important consideration in developing an understanding of climate, winds, and ocean currents.

The earth is a free sphere in space with a diameter of roughly 8000 miles and a circumference of 25,000 miles.[1] It is one of a number of similar bodies, the planets, all of which move around the sun in their respective elliptical paths, or orbits. In relation to the earth and the other planets the position of the sun is fixed.

In following its orbit the earth is said to *revolve* around the sun (Fig. 4.1); the time taken to make one complete revolution is the solar year.

While revolving in its orbit the earth also spins, or *rotates*. The two points on the earth's surface located on the theoretical axis of rotation are known as the poles. The earth's axis is not at right angles to the plane

[1] The earth's actual shape, due to centrifugal and other stresses, is that of an oblate spheroid, or sphere flattened at the poles and bulging at the equator. Many calculations have been made to determine the amount of oblateness. Hayford in 1910 calculated a polar diameter of 7899.98 miles and an equatorial diameter of 7926.68 miles, a difference of less than one-half of one percent of the average diameter.

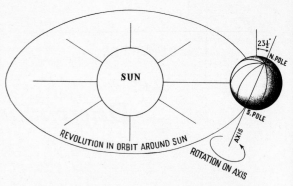

Fig. 4.1—The Revolution and Rotation of the Earth. The "vertical" line through the earth is perpendicular to the plane of the orbit. The axis is inclined 23½° from such an imaginary line. The direction of rotation is from west to east, causing the sun to appear to rise in the east and set in the west. The diagram is schematic, without scale of size or distance.

of its orbit (which would simplify many matters) but is inclined from the vertical at an angle of 23.5 degrees.

This distinction between revolution and rotation should be clearly understood, for only confusion can result if the two terms are used interchangeably. The earth revolves about the sun and rotates on its axis.

DETERMINATION OF DIRECTION

Method No. 1. The direction of rotation is constant, so that the daily rising of the sun in one portion of the sky and setting in another led to the early recognition of east and west in man's history. The point to be noted here, however, is that in order to cause the sun to rise in the east the direction of the earth's rotation must be from *west to east*, for the sun itself does not move in relation to the planets.

During the sun's apparent daily progression across the sky it must at some time reach the high point on the arc which its path describes. This point may be readily determined. Up to the instant when it is reached the sun's height is increasing; immediately thereafter it is decreasing. Although the size of the arc varies with the seasons it is always bisected at this high point; that is, the point is halfway between east and west. Accordingly, the sun's daily high point will always lie along the same line from the position of any given observer, throughout the year. It is a line of constant direction—the north-south line.

This line can be crudely determined by setting a stake in the ground and, as the sun approaches its high point, marking the length of the shadow it casts at short intervals of time (Fig. 4.2). One shadow will be the shortest. Its direction will be the same day after day, at right angles to an east-west line and therefore by definition a north-south line.

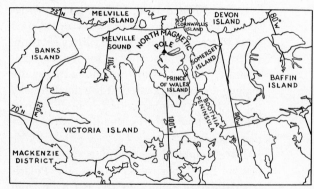

Fig. 4.3—Location of the North Magnetic Pole in 1954.

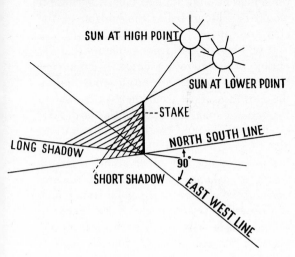

Fig. 4.2—Method of Obtaining True Direction from the Sun's High Point. At the highest point in its daily path across the sky the sun produces the shortest shadow, in a north-south line. At any other time of day the shadow of an object is longer, and in a different direction. With north and south determined, east and west are easily found by a line at right angles to the north-south line.

Method No. 2. When confronted with the problem of determining direction the reader will probably think first of the magnetic compass. A compass can be successfully employed, however, only after true direction has been determined by other means. The earth is a giant magnet, with magnetic north and south poles; but these are not located at the true, or geographical, poles on the axis of rotation (Fig. 4.3). Moreover, the magnetic poles are not fixed but for reasons still not fully understood vary appreciably in location from year to year. To use a compass accurately one must know the "declination,"[2]

[2] Also known as "deviation" in navigation.

or angle between true, absolute north and magnetic north. Hence the problem of finding actual north-south direction is not properly solved with the magnetic compass; the answer is only a working approximation.

Method No. 3. Another method more recently developed for determining direction, especially on shipboard, is the gyrocompass. In this instrument a heavy wheel is rotated at high speed and so mounted that the force of gravity, working through a mercury counterbalance system, causes its axis to assume a due north-south alignment. The mercury system also operates on the gyroscope to counteract any force that would tend to make it deviate from the true north-south line its axis is indicating. This is, then, a method that determines true direction, but one which requires the use of a complicated, expensive instrument.

Method No. 4. The standard method for precise and accurate determination of direction (in the Northern Hemisphere) without the aid of direction-finding equipment is by observation of the North Star, *Polaris*, which is almost on the same line as the axis of the earth.[3] It is actually about one degree two minutes from the projection of the axis, but this small, constant deviation can easily be corrected for by computation. Thus a line from the observer through a marker aligned with the North Star is essentially a north-south line. By virtue of its position, so nearly

[3] Although Polaris has been used for centuries as a navigational aid, recent developments in navigational science have made dependence on it much less than is popularly believed.

"over" the North Pole, Polaris does not describe the large circle in the sky other stars seem to trace because of the earth's rotation. (This apparent motion can be simply demonstrated on a clear, moonless night by leaving a camera pointed at the northern sky exposed for a suitable period. The developed film will show as arcs the light streaks of many stars.)

The thoughtful reader may raise an objection here that observations on Polaris from different points on the earth or from different positions on the earth's orbit would not be alike but would yield varying errors from true north. This is not the case, however, for Polaris is so extremely remote from the earth and the entire solar system that the distances on the earth's surface or even over the diameter of its orbit are too trivial to alter Polaris' apparent position. Whenever and wherever observations are made in the Northern Hemisphere, Polaris is found to appear almost exactly in line with the earth's axis.[4]

In summary, the four methods that may be used to determine direction are:

1. Observation of the sun at its culmination (high point in its path). This gives a true north-south line.

2. Magnetic compass with correction for declination. True north must previously be known to apply the correction. The magnetic poles are not fixed points.

3. Gyrocompass. True north obtained directly, but this expensive and complicated instrument is not commonly available and in any event must be calibrated for true north found by some other means.

4. Polaris observation. True north obtained by lining up Polaris and a natural or artificial object on the earth's surface. Can be done anywhere in the Northern Hemisphere. There is substantially no variation in the position of the star.

[4] In the Southern Hemisphere the constellation of the Southern Cross serves similarly, though not as well, with respect to the South Pole, as it is farther off the line of the earth's axis.

■ LOCATION

North-South Position. The next problem is the determination of *location.* Again Polaris is initially used. Because it is approximately in line with the earth's axis Polaris will appear to be directly overhead, or 90° from the horizontal, to an observer at the North Pole. An observer on the equator looking north, on the other hand, would, theoretically, be able to see Polaris directly on the horizon, or at 0° elevation. (An observer just south of the equator could not find Polaris because it would be hidden below the horizon by the curvature of the earth.)

It will be recalled from geometry that the outline of a sphere is a circle. A circle contains 360°;[5] therefore a north-south line on the earth's surface from the North Pole to the equator spans a quarter of the earth's circumference, or 90°. The Polaris observations also range from 0° at the equator to 90° at the poles; hence any observation on Polaris will give at once the number of degrees north of the equator of the point from which the observation was made. A 35° angle of observation means an observation from 35° north of the equator, and similarly for any other reading.

A measurement in angular degrees is unfortunately not directly useful for determining distance on the earth's surface. The degrees must be converted into an accepted unit of measurement. The standard land mile of 5280 feet, known as the "statute mile,"[6] has no simple mathematical relationship with degrees of the earth's circumference. But the *geographic,* or *nautical, mile* used by the United States Coast and Geodetic Survey is 6076.1 feet and equals one minute of one degree of the arc from the equator to either pole.[7] Thus one degree

[5] A degree is further divided into 60 minutes, and each minute in turn equals 60 seconds. These "minutes" and "seconds" measure distance, not time.
[6] The statute mile is derived from a Roman distance measurement, the *milia passuum* (1000 paces) of a marching legion. The pace here equals two steps.
[7] The nautical mile is supposed to be 1/21600 of a great circle, but because the earth is not a perfect sphere there are different values for the approximation. Thus the British nautical mile is 6080.0 feet. A value of 6080.2 feet was used in the United States until 1955.

equals 60 geographic or nautical miles, and a Polaris observation can be converted immediately into a standard distance measurement on north-south lines.

This ratio between degrees of the circle and nautical miles holds true, however, only on great circles, which may be defined as circles in planes passing through any two points on the surface of the earth and through the center of the earth. (Three points determine a plane. Using a point on the equator and a pole for two points insures that the plane of the arc will pass through the center of the earth.) A great circle may also be defined as any circle that describes a circumference of the earth.

The only east-west great circle is the equator, which marks that circumference of the earth midway between the poles. The equator is the starting point of north-south measurement; if each degree north of the equator is marked off by a separate line at its appropriate distance from the equator the result is a series of circles all parallel to the equator which progressively diminish in diameter from equator to pole. (If parts of degrees as well as full degrees are thus marked, the number of circles is correspondingly larger and their spacing correspondingly narrower.) These imaginary circles are the measurement of north-south direction in degrees. They are analogous to the marks on a ruler, which are at right angles to what they measure. In like manner, the circles run east-west but actually measure north-south distance.

The distance north or south of the equator is known as *latitude*,[8] and a point 40° 16′ 38″ (read "40 degrees, 16 minutes, 38 seconds") north of the equator would be 40° 16′ 38″ "north latitude." The parallel circles described above which measure latitude are known as *parallels*, or *parallels of latitude* (Fig. 4.4).

[8] From the Latin *latitudo,* breadth. The world known to the ancients was roughly the area surrounding the Mediterranean Sea, with the unexplored ocean extending indefinitely to the west and the lands of the Orient reaching far to the east. The world so conceived was roughly rectangular in shape, and the north-south direction measured its "width," the east-west direction its "length."

Fig. 4.4—The Parallels. The globe has here been sliced perpendicular to the poles and the slices lifted apart. The edge of the slice, along the surface of the globe, is a parallel. The largest parallel, the equator, is a great circle, since it measures a circumference of the globe.

East-West Position. The problem of location is partially solved by the determination of position on a north-south line. If, further, the determination of position on an east-west line can be made, the solution will be complete, for from geometry it is known that the intersection of two lines determines a point, in this case a point on the surface of the earth.

In determining the north-south position it was found that two "natural," or directly available references—the North Star and the equator—provided a basis for reckoning. Unfortunately there are no such natural references for east-west position. The difficulty this interposes in determining east-west position is solved by observing carefully the sun's apparent daily path across the heavens.

The culmination point of the sun marks noon, or midday, for the place on the earth's surface where the observation is made. Moreover, at a given instant of time the sun is highest not only at the place of observation but at every point on the north-south line through that place. Such a line will run from pole to pole, and it will be exactly noon at the same time everywhere on that line. These north-south lines may, therefore, be used to measure east-west direction, or

Fig. 4.5—The Meridians. The globe has been sliced through the poles into sections, like an orange. One of the sections on the left has been lifted out. The edges of the globe along the gap are meridians. Each meridian is half of a great circle; two meridians comprising the same great circle are 180° apart.

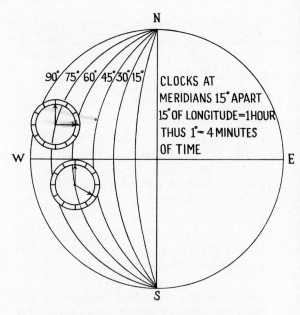

CLOCKS AT MERIDIANS 15° APART 15° OF LONGITUDE=1HOUR THUS 1°= 4 MINUTES OF TIME

Fig. 4.6—Determination of East-West Position by Means of Time Difference. Two accurate clocks are 15° of longitude apart. Each has been set at local noon for its location by noting the high point on the sun's daily path there. A check by radio between the two places reveals that there is a one-hour difference in the time they show. The clock to the west is found to be one hour behind the one on the east, because the earth rotates from west to east and takes 24 hours for a complete turn; hence 15° equals one hour (360° ÷ 24).

degrees of *longitude*,[9] and are known as *meridians*,[10] or *meridians of longitude* (Fig. 4.5).

Because of the earth's rotation the sun is at the culmination point for only an instant. At the next instant it is noon on a line immediately adjacent to the west. Thus noon sweeps around the face of the earth in 24 hours, the time for one complete rotation of the earth on its axis. With 360° in a circle, dividing that figure by 24 (the number of hours required for a complete rotation) gives the number of degrees the noon line moves in an hour—15°. Thus, if two points, A and B, are 15° apart on an east-west line on the earth's surface, when it is noon at A, B will be one hour from noon, either before or after.

This difference in culmination time between places at different east-west locations permits determination of position in that direction. A very accurate clock known as a "chronometer" is set at precise noon at a particular location. When a chronometer is carried to a spot east or west of the first place, a difference in time is noted between

the reading on the chronometer and the actual noon time at the new place. This time-distance can then be converted into degrees by the relationship one hour equals 15° (Fig. 4.6). Whether the direction is east or west of the place where the chronometer was originally set can be determined by whether the chronometer time is ahead of (say, one o'clock) or behind (say, eleven o'clock) the time at the second place. The culmination point, or noon, moves with the apparent movement of the sun from east to west; it follows that if noon by the chronometer comes before noon at the new observation point, the new place is west of the place where the chronometer was set. Or, more simply, if the chronometer shows noon before it is noon at the new place observation, then this place must be west of where the chronometer was set; if exactly one hour, then exactly 15° of longitude.

[9] From the Latin *longus*, length. (See footnote 8.)
[10] From the Latin *meridiones*, noon. Hence also the expressions "A.M." (ante meridian) and "P.M." (post meridian), or before noon and after noon, respectively. Twelve o'clock noon is written 12 M., or 12 o'clock meridian (time).

■ THE PRIME MERIDIAN AND THE INTERNATIONAL DATE LINE

In order to standardize this method of determining longitude it is necessary to fix upon one point for the 0°, or basic meridian. At first several nations used their own capitals as the determining place for this prime meridian. Eventually a practical consideration led to the universal acceptance of the Observatory of Greenwich, near London, England, as the best place.

This practical consideration is the location of the critical 180° meridian, halfway around the world from the prime meridian. With Greenwich noon as the prime meridian, the 180° line runs through the open spaces of the Pacific Ocean throughout its length, a fact that obviates many difficulties that would arise if the line marked points in densely populated regions.

At 180°, or 12 hours away from Greenwich noon, it is midnight, the beginning of the day and also of the *date*. So it is at the 180th meridian that each date begins on earth. Along this line it is first, say, 12:01 A.M. on the twenty-fourth of August. But if the twenty-fourth is just beginning at the 180th meridian, it must still be the twenty-third on any meridian to the west and back all the way around the earth, getting progressively farther "behind" in time until 24 hours' difference is attained and the full circumference of the earth has been traversed.

But this is back at the 180th meridian again. It will be seen at once that if one crosses this meridian it is necessary to make some sort of adjustment because of the fact that, theoretically, a dual date (or time 24 hours apart) exists on it. In crossing the 180th meridian going westward, a date is omitted from the calendar. Thus one goes from 8:00 A.M. of the tenth to 8:00 A.M. of the eleventh, or if at midnight, from the tenth to the twelfth, omitting 24 hours at the very point at which the dates change, and so losing a *date*.[11]

[11] As a matter of convenience it is the common practice on shipboard to change date at midnight re-

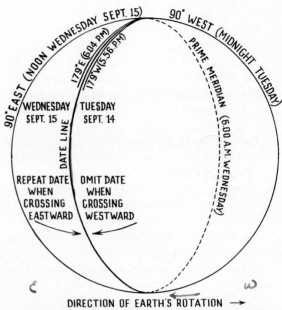

DIRECTION OF EARTH'S ROTATION →

Fig. 4.7—The International Date Line and Time Differences Around the World. The diagram shows the date line, the prime meridian (on the opposite side of the earth), the meridians of 90° east and 90° west, and the hour of the day on the three meridians at the same instant of time. When it is 6:00 A.M. on the prime meridian it is midnight, or six hours later, on the meridian 90° west. At 90° east it is noon, or six hours ahead of the prime meridian. Since the international date line is the dividing line between dates, there is theoretically no date on it. The date and time are shown for one degree on each side of it: at 179° east it is just past 6:00 P.M., or slightly more than six hours ahead of the time at 90° east. At 179° west it is almost 6:00 P.M., or slightly less than six hours behind 90° west—but this is the previous date, since there is a total of 24 hours' (less 8 minutes) time difference between the two 179° meridians.

The diagram is schematic in two respects: (a) The international date line does not coincide with the 180° meridian throughout its length, but zigzags to give portions of the same political territories the same date; and (b) the time shown on the 179° meridians is "sun time," based on the true noon at each meridian. Actually, time around the earth is kept in "zones" averaging 15° wide, with an even hour or half-hour time difference between adjacent zones.

This omission or "loss" of 24 hours in westward travel across the 180th meridian results because travel has been in the same direction as the progression of time around the earth. That is, there has been actual passage

gardless of what hour of the day the 180th meridian is actually crossed.

of time while the traveler has been moving through places of different time. In westward travel this time of passage is in effect added to the local times, and so must be compensated for at the point where dates are considered to begin. In still other words, the westward traveler has been consistently lengthening his sunlight days (getting more than he would if he stayed at one point) so that when he arrives at the 180th meridian he has already enjoyed the equivalent of a whole day, hence must be content to skip a date. In eastward travel the opposite is true, and so time must be added in crossing the 180th meridian, which is accomplished by repeating the date, or 24 hours. Such a traveler would thus live through, say, two October 15's.

Because the date begins at the 180th meridian and because of the adjustment of hours and dates in travel across it, that meridian is known as the *international date line* (Fig. 4.7). Actually, the date line does not coincide with the 180th meridian throughout its north-south course. In some places, such as the Aleutian Islands, it has been arbitrarily moved out into the open sea so as to keep the date uniform within the same land region.

In the foregoing discussion of east-west position, conversion of longitude degrees

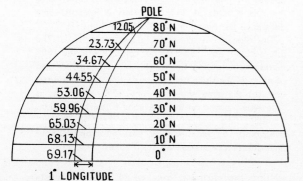

POLE

12.05	80° N
23.73	70° N
34.67	60° N
44.55	50° N
53.06	40° N
59.96	30° N
65.03	20° N
68.13	10° N
69.17	0°

1° LONGITUDE

Fig. 4.8—Effect of Convergence of the Meridians. Because of the convergence of the meridians the distance measured by a degree of longitude varies with latitude. The diagram shows the number of statute miles in a degree at each ten degrees of latitude. A theoretical degree of longitude at the pole has no distance at all.

into distance was not considered. As the equator is the only east-west line that is a great circle it is only along it that one degree of longitude is equal to 60 nautical miles. Why this ratio does not hold on the parallels is obvious from the convergence of the meridians to points at the poles. The higher the latitude—that is, the farther away from the equator—the less distance in miles between any two meridians which, in degrees, are the same distance apart (Fig. 4.8). Accordingly, conversion tables have been computed to show the length in miles of a longitude degree at each degree or partial degree of latitude. This information is commonly supplied on globes along the international date line for the parallels of every 10, 15, or 20 degrees.

■ CELESTIAL NAVIGATION

In actual practice observation of the sun, called "shooting the sun," is not the only method employed for longitude determination. Tables printed in the *Nautical Almanac* permit the use of any one of a number of stars, planets, and even the moon to compute a location in terms of longitude and latitude. In all cases the basic knowledge required is that of the culmination, or transit across the meridian, of the star in relation to the Greenwich time of its transit across the prime meridian.

These methods for determining latitude and longitude are not very rapid. They are suited for position fixing from a land station or a slow-moving ship. A change in location of two or three miles while the computations are being made is not of much significance. It is a different matter, however, with an airplane flying several hundred miles an hour. Then the time required in determining location is an important factor.

For long-distance air navigation, especially over oceanic areas, location is determined by "celestial navigation." The advantage of this procedure is that it does not involve separate determinations of latitude and longitude but produces the navigator's location directly for him in the form of a point on a map.

The procedure involves sighting on two different stars simultaneously or in rapid succession. This yields—for reasons beyond the scope of this discussion—two lines on the navigator's map. His position is somewhere on each of the lines, which means, of course, that it can be only where the lines intersect.

QUESTIONS. Distinguish between location and position. Distinguish between the revolution and rotation of the earth. Summarize and compare the four methods for determining direction. Define "declination." Explain why the angle of Polaris above the horizon equals the number of degrees from the equator of the point of observation. What is the difference between the statute mile and the nautical mile? What special significance does the nautical mile have? In what direction do the parallels run? What directions do they measure? A chronometer set at site X is 3½ hours slow when taken to site Y. How far apart are X and Y? What direction is Y from X? Philadelphia, Pennsylvania, is approximately on the 75th meridian west; Moscow, U.S.S.R., is approximately on the 45th meridian east. How far apart in longitude degrees are the two cities? When it is 4:00 P.M. in Philadelphia what time is it in Moscow? Why is the 180th meridian called the international date line? Explain why a date is dropped when going west across the international date line and added when going east across it. Why does distance measured in degrees along a parallel vary with north-south distance? What is the great advantage of celestial navigation over other methods of determining location?

CHAPTER 5

Maps—Their Construction and Use

Maps are essential to the study of geography. The following discussion of cartography, or the construction of maps, will enable the reader better to understand and interpret the maps that appear in later chapters. More important, it will provide a general appreciation of the utilization of maps. The following pages are unavoidably more technical and difficult than those preceding, but the reader should bear in mind, in his wrestling with geometrical concepts, that a knowledge of the rudiments of cartography is one of the elements of geographic literacy.

Map construction poses problems beyond that of determining the location of a point on the earth's surface from which observations are made. It is necessary to devise means for representing in a form convenient for practical use not only the positions of many places and their relation to each other but also outlines of lands and states, the courses of rivers, the trends of mountain ranges—in fact all distributional features of geography.

■ INITIAL PROCEDURES

The first step in making a map of a land surface is to determine precisely the location of the particular point where the map is begun. Next, a level line is measured very accurately in an exactly known direction from that point. This is the *base line*. It should be as long as is conveniently possible—say, three miles. Extreme precautions are taken to have the measurements accurate, as any errors made in laying out the line will be greatly magnified on parts of the map remote from the base line.

Next, a "plane table" (a drawing board mounted on a tripod, with provisions for setting and clamping it in any desired position), is set up directly over one end of the base line, with the board horizontal. On the paper mounted on this board a line is then drawn "over" the base line in precisely the proper direction (using the necessary sighting instruments). A scale[1] has previously been decided upon which will make, for example, one mile on the ground equal to five inches in length of line on the board. If the base line is three miles long, then the line on the board is drawn fifteen inches long.

With the board fixed rigidly in its position a series of sights is then taken on different permanent, readily identifiable, prominent objects, and lines are drawn toward those objects on the paper without, however, marking off any distance (Fig. 5.1). Then the plane table is taken to the other end of the base line where it is again set up so that the point at the other end of the base line on the paper is exactly over that point on the ground, and the line is in line with the

---

[1] The scale of a map is the relationship between a distance on the earth and the distance which represents it on a map. The meaning of "large scale" and "small scale" should be thoroughly understood. "Scale" has nothing to do with the size of a map. The larger the scale the smaller the distance a unit on the map represents. A map of a city, for example, is likely to be on a scale of one inch to one-half mile—a large scale. The map itself may be the size of a desk top. A world map may be on a scale of one inch to 50 miles. This is a small scale, but the map may occupy an entire wall.

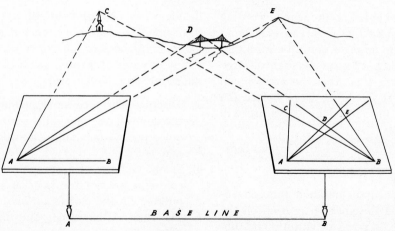

BASE LINE

Fig. 5.1—Mapping Procedure with a Plane Table. In this schematic diagram the base line is not shown in true proportion. Sightings are taken on several points from one end of the base line. Sightings on the same points from the other end of the base line (with the plane table correctly oriented) intersect the lines drawn along the first sightings. The points of intersection show the relative positions, to scale, of the objects sighted.

actual base line. The same series of objects is sighted upon from this new location. The objects are on the line of sight from both ends of the base line; hence their location on the paper will be where the two lines of sight for each object intersect. The distances will be in the proper relationships because the triangles sighted and those drawn are similar triangles and hence have proportional sides.[2]

THE PROBLEM OF THE EARTH'S CURVATURE

Maps and charts[3] are flat pieces of paper, whereas the earth's surface is curved to conform to a sphere. Because the earth is so large this does not make much difference in maps of small areas, but when a large area is to be mapped attempts at accurate representation of the earth's curved surface on the flat paper are beset with complications.

[2] The use of the plane table described here should not be thought of as the only map-making procedure. It is presented as a representative method of using a precisely determined point as the basis for the construction of a map.

[3] Maps portray land areas, charts sea areas.

In the example of mapping given above it will be remembered that the base line was assumed to be perfectly horizontal. Owing to the earth's curvature, however, at the end of one mile along this line the earth's surface would be eight inches below the horizontal; at the end of two miles, two feet eight inches; at the end of three miles, six feet; and so on (Fig. 5.2).

1 MILE   2 MILES   3 MILES

8"   2' 8"   6'

Fig. 5.2—Effect of the Earth's Curvature. Because of the earth's curvature a "horizontal" line is not the same thing as a "level" line. The line of sight of a telescope directed at the horizon over a large lake would coincide with a length of cord or wire held perfectly horizontal over the lake surface. A horizontal line would not, however, be at right angles to a plumb bob at different points along its length. At the end of one mile the horizontal line would be eight inches higher on the mast of a ship on the "level" surface of the lake; at the end of two miles, two feet eight inches; and so on. In other words, the "level" surface of the lake is the surface of the curved earth.

Assume that an area two miles square (i.e., two miles along each side) is to be mapped. If a map scale of six inches equal one mile is adopted, the map will be 12 inches on a side. For the distance of two miles the deviation from the horizontal would be two feet eight inches[4] (about $\frac{1}{2000}$ of a mile), which

[4] The formula for determining the amount of curvature of the earth's surface away from the horizontal is: $\frac{2}{3}$ the distance in miles, squared, equals the departure from the horizontal in feet.

would be represented on the map, according to the selected scale, by less than $\frac{1}{300}$ of an inch. So minute an error could be safely ignored even with the use of such a large scale. It follows, then, that the area shown on a map must be rather large before the complications introduced by curvature will be appreciable.

■ PROJECTIONS

The previous chapter outlined the conventional means of designating location on the earth's surface, in terms of latitude and longitude measured by the parallels and meridians. Together, these imaginary circles form a network or *grid,* and by means of their intersections the location of a point on the earth's surface can be accurately designated. Accordingly, the basic problem of map and chart making is to devise schemes for transferring the latitude-longitude grid in accordance with a definite plan from the spherical surface of the earth to the flat surface of a map. Any such system is called a *projection;* it is properly based on a mathematical solution of the problem.

The problem of projection will be appreciated by cutting a tennis ball in half and attempting to press one half out flat. (This illustrates what is involved in mapping an entire hemisphere on flat paper.) The half ball can be flattened only by distortion, by tearing or stretching some areas and compressing others.

The problem is solved in the construction of globe maps (miniatures of the earth's sphere) by printing the map on narrow segments, or "gores." Thus it is possible to stretch and move each gore the slight amount necessary to bring about an even fit between contiguous gores all around. The narrower each gore is, and the greater the number of gores, the less stretching is necessary. One test, then, of the accuracy of a globe map is to note how many gores were used in its construction.

The procedure followed by the globe maker in fitting flat pieces of paper to a sphere is a mechanical adaptation. The endeavors of cartographers are directed toward the same end, but they must make much more comprehensive adjustments.

The types of distortion that may be introduced into a projection are:

A. Distance. Distance is unequal in different directions (i.e., one mile north-south is not equal to one mile east-west on the map).
B. Shape. Outlines of geographical or political areas are not the same as their true outlines on the earth's surface.
C. Direction. A line of constant direction is not a straight line, as in nature, but a curve.
D. Area. The areas of geographical or political units are not shown in their true proportions.

According to which type of distortion they attempt to correct, projections can be classified as:

1. Equidistant. Distances are equally measured in all directions on the map.
2. Conformal. Areas show the same shape they have on a globe.
3. Azimuthal. All lines through a certain point on the map show true and constant direction.
4. Equal-area. The area of different regions on the map is shown to correct proportion.

It should be noted that the distortion in B and D above cannot be overcome together through any single projection. The correction of one distortion is possible only by an increase in the other.

REPRESENTATIVE TYPES OF PROJECTIONS

1. The Mercator Projection

The best-known and most commonly used projection for world maps or maps of large areas is the *Mercator chart,* first constructed in 1569 by the man whose name it bears in Latinized form.

Since the coming of the air age it has been the fashion to discredit the Mercator projection because of its failure to show true relationships in the circumpolar areas. Greenland, for example, appears in such a projection to be larger than South America, whereas it is actually only one-eighth as large. It is true that the Mercator projection has this defect, but for certain uses it is indispensable. It was not until the development of the airplane and the ability to travel with facility over the polar regions that anyone was greatly concerned over this exaggeration. In other words, the Mercator projection exhibits the various distortions in a minimal degree in the middle latitudes and is quite free of them in the equatorial regions. These are the regions occupied and utilized by civilized man, and the seas that are commonly sailed by his ships.

The Mercator is a modification of a general type of projection known as the *cylindrical projection*. In the mathematical construction of this projection it is assumed, theoretically, that a sheet of paper is wrapped around the globe so as to form a cylinder touching the earth at the equator and open at both ends (Fig. 5.3). It is assumed further that for the purpose of projecting the latitude-longitude grid from the globe to the paper (whence the term "projection") the eye of the observer is at the center of a transparent earth looking out in all directions toward the paper.

The equator can then be traced as a circle on the paper; the parallels can be "projected" from the surface of the earth along the line of sight and traced as circles where they meet the paper. The meridians are similarly "projected," or conceived as being bent back from their convergence at the poles until they are straight lines on the paper.

When the cylinder is then cut along the line of one of the meridians and unrolled, a pattern of meridians and parallels at right angles to each other (as on the globe) is revealed. The parallels appear as straight horizontal lines parallel to the equator, the meridians as straight vertical lines.

The particular merit of this scheme is that the cardinal, or four primary, directions are straight lines north-south and east-west and are at right angles, as in nature. Mercator's

Fig. 5.3—Theoretical Construction of a Cylindrical Projection. Here the cylinder is tangent at the equator. Note the extreme distortion toward the poles. The meridians do not converge and the parallels are all equal in size to the equator.

improvement of the general cylindrical projection was to devise mathematically an adaptation so that *all* directions, not merely the cardinal ones, would be correctly shown by straight lines. Thus any direction line intersects the elements of the grid at a constant angle. Such a straight line of constant direction is known as a **rhumb line.**

This was a quality of first importance to navigators, for by connecting any two points between which they desired to sail with a straight line on the Mercator chart they would be assured that this line would show exactly, by its latitude and longitude intersections, the direction of the course to be followed. The Mercator projection was further suited to mariners' needs because ship navigation is mostly confined to the middle and low latitudes. In the equatorial and low latitudes the Mercator is the best possible projection for all-round accuracy. In fact, the extension of this statement may be presented as a principle with regard to the accuracy of all tangent projections (there are many types in which the paper is not conceived as touching the globe) as follows: *A tangent projection is most accurate at the place of tangency of the "map" with the globe of the earth.*

From this it follows that if there could be more than one point or line of tangency, the accuracy of a projection would be greatly increased. A cartographer named Gall achieved this for the low latitudes by further modifying the Mercator projection. Instead of a single tangency at the equator he conceived two tangencies, one at 45° north latitude, the other at 45° south latitude. In theory he utilized a cylinder slightly smaller in diameter than the earth, one that would cut into the earth at the 45° parallels and pass beneath the circumference of the equator (Fig. 5.4). The virtue of this modification is that it distributes the distortion errors throughout the map. In the equatorial regions the scale is smaller than normal; toward the poles, beyond the 45° parallels, the scale is exaggerated, but not so much as in the standard Mercator projection.

An important variety of the Mercator is

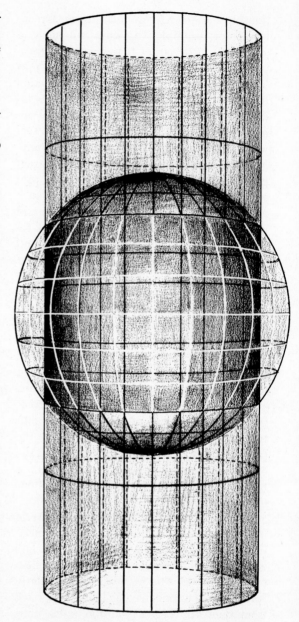

Fig. 5.4—Theoretical Construction, Gall Modification of Mercator Projection. The cylinder intersects the globe at the 45° parallels. (Compare with Figs. 5.3 and 5.9.)

the *transverse Mercator.* In this projection (actually the Gall modification is used) the base is a meridian rather than the equator. All the advantages and disadvantages of the Mercator are present in this transverse use of the projection, but with the additional special advantage of extension without limit in the north-south direction with no change in scale error. The greatest single disadvantage of the Mercator—the increase of scale error away from base (in this instance the meridian of tangency, referred to as the central meridian)—is dealt with by limiting the use of the projection to a zone 6° wide. A series of 60 such zones thus encompasses the globe, with a new principal meridian and new projection for each one.

The transverse Mercator has been adopted as the world standard for military use in artillery fire control. As angles of azimuth (direction) on the projection are equivalent to their true values on the surface of the earth, and as at any point corrections for distance measurements are the same in all directions, the transverse Mercator is ideal for plotting artillery fire.

The Mercator is indispensable for long-distance navigation because it shows all directions as straight lines, in correct relation to the latitude-longitude grid. It alone, however, will not serve navigational needs. Most ocean travel is along east-west lines, but if a due east-west course is followed, say, across the North Atlantic from New York to Oporto, Portugal, it is some 200 miles longer than a great-circle route between the two points.

The importance of great circles in mapmaking and navigation derives from the fact that the shortest line connecting two points on the surface of a sphere is a portion of the *circumference* of the sphere as drawn through those points. A great circle measures the earth's circumference; thus the shortest distance between any two points on the earth's surface is along a great-circle route between them.

Just why this should be so will perhaps become clearer if it is remembered that the shortest distance between any two points is a straight line. The farther any line connecting the points departs from a straight line the greater will be its length. The line on the surface of a sphere that most closely approaches a straight line is that arc having the greatest diameter. But on a given sphere no arc can have a diameter exceeding that of the sphere itself. Therefore, arcs of the circumference (great-circle routes) are the shortest distance between points on the earth's surface. Thus the necessity arises of having a projection that will show great circles as straight lines.

2. The Great-Circle, or Gnomonic,[5] Projection

In the *gnomonic projection* the eye is again conceived to be at the center of the earth. The map paper, however, may be placed tangent to any selected *point* on the surface of the globe.[6]

The latitude-longitude grid on a gnomonic projection varies according to the location of the point of tangency. If the point is at the North or South Pole, as in the **polar gnomonic projection,** the grid consists of a series of concentric circles, the parallels (the smallest being closest to the point of tangency, the others being progressively larger with increasing distance from that point), and a series of radiating lines, the meridians, with the pole as their hub (Fig. 5.5). In the equatorial gnomonic projection the point of tangency is on the equator, and if it is on neither the equator nor the poles the result is an oblique gnomonic projection. In these two types the grid becomes quite complicated.

Any gnomonic projection represents a great circle as a straight line because such a circle on the globe defines a plane through two points on the surface and the center of the globe. Since the projection of the plane, so defined, is made onto another plane (that of the map), the intersection of the great-circle plane with that of the projection is, by geometry, a straight line—i.e., the intersection of two planes. Conversely, any straight line on a gnomonic projection defines a plane connecting two points on the surface and passing through the earth's center; hence it is the trace of a great circle.

[5] *Gnomon*, the Greek word for the needle of a sundial, is the root of this word. The mathematics employed in the construction of a sundial is similar to that used in constructing a gnomonic projection.
[6] Tangency is not strictly necessary, as the use of any plane parallel to a tangent plane merely increases the scale of the projection in proportion to the theoretical distance of the plane from the center of the earth.

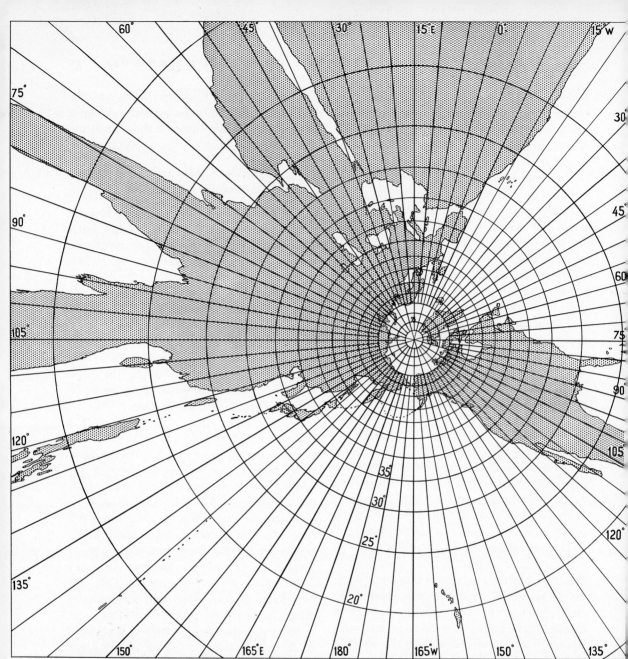

Fig. 5.5—A Polar Gnomonic Projection. A straight line between any two points on this projection is a great-circle route. Note the great distortion with distance from the pole. Such a map is used only for its "great-circle feature."

For this reason gnomonic projections are often referred to as "great-circle charts."

The procedure followed when the great-circle and Mercator charts are used in long-distance navigation is, in general terms, as follows: First, a straight line is drawn on the great-circle chart between the starting point and the destination (or between two desired points of a given course). The points of intersection of this line with the lines of the latitude-longitude grid are then noted. These are plotted, or marked on a Mercator chart and then connected. The result is a curved line representing the great-circle route between the origin and destination.[7] But to travel precisely along such a curved line would be a difficult task involving a continual change of direction. This difficulty is obviated by changing the direction of sailing only a comparatively few times, with the result that the path of sailing is actually a

[7] It is also possible, knowing the two end points, to construct mathematically a great-circle course directly on a Mercator chart.

series of rhumb lines which together approximate a circle (Fig. 5.6).

There are, however, shortcomings in the use of a great-circle projection. It is a characteristic of the projection that the spacing between the successive parallels is not constant, so that as one proceeds in any direction from the point of tangency a degree of latitude does not represent a constant number of miles. In short, distance cannot be measured accurately on the projection.

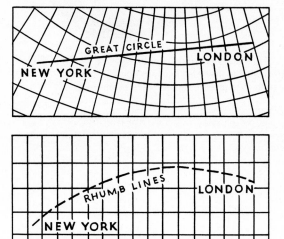

Fig. 5.6—Navigational Procedure Using Gnomonic and Mercator Charts. On a trip between New York and London a straight line is drawn between the two points on a gnomonic chart. The intersections of the line with the latitude-longitude grid are then marked on a Mercator chart. The resulting curve is approximated by a series of rhumb lines. On the trip, the heading is changed slightly at intervals; the result is a close approximation to a great-circle course.

3. The Azimuthal-Equidistant Projection

The quality of true distance is obtained in the *azimuthal-equidistant projection,* a modification of the gnomonic projection. The gnomonic is merely changed so that the parallels *are* spaced equally, and the true distance of any point from the point of tangency is accurately shown. Certain new distortions are added, however. The only straight lines on the map that are great circles are those which pass through the point of tangency (in the polar projection these are the meridians), and the alteration of the position of the par-

allels seriously distorts shapes in proportion to the distance from the point of tangency. Offsetting these new limitations is the added advantage of the ability to represent the other hemisphere of the earth (which must be omitted in the true gnomonic projection) by adding the parallels of that hemisphere in regular order beyond those of the first hemisphere.

In the development of world-wide air travel it was not long before the azimuthal-equidistant projection was recognized as ideal for representing global relationships hitherto hidden by the commonly used projections. By constructing an azimuthal-equidistant map with any given city as the point of tangency (Fig. 5.7) it is possible to show simultaneously: (1) the great-circle (airline) route from that city to any other point on the map as a straight line, (2) the true direction from the city to any other point, and (3) the true distance from the city to any other point. Such a map is unique in the possession of all three of these qualities for a single point.

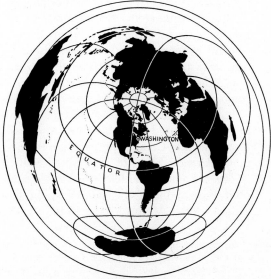

Fig. 5.7—Azimuthal-equidistant Projection Centered on Washington, D.C. Note the complex latitude-longitude grid and the extreme distortion toward the periphery of the map. Nevertheless, a straight line from Washington to any other point on the map shows the great-circle route, true direction, and true distance. This type of projection is popular with the air forces of the various nations of the world.

4. The Conic Projection

The theory of construction of the *conic projection* is that the eye at the center of the earth projects the latitude-longitude grid upon the inner surface of a cone the apex of which is usually over one of the poles and which is tangent to the earth along a parallel (Fig. 5.8). The cone is slit along any desired meridian and laid out flat to provide the map surface. The resultant grid consists of meridians radiating from a polar hub and evenly spaced along concentric arcs which are the parallels.

In accordance with the principle of accuracy at the locus of tangency the simple conic projection represents a true scale along the parallel of tangency, known as the *standard parallel*. North and south from the standard parallel distortion increases greatly with distance, while the projection as a whole is neither equal-area nor conformal. Nevertheless, the conic projection, in general, is by its very construction well suited for the middle latitudes, for any parallel can be chosen as the standard parallel for a construction.[8]

Although numerous modifications of the simple conic projection have been devised so as to eliminate or reduce its inherent errors, only two are pertinent to this discussion. The first is the *Lambert conformal conic* projection, with two standard parallels (Fig. 5.9). The several advantages of this projection caused it to be adopted by the Department of Commerce for use in the Sectional Airways Maps of the United States.[9] In effect, Lambert modified the simple conic projection in much the same fashion that Gall modified Mercator's projection.[10] The

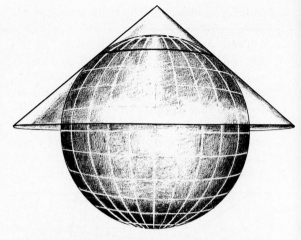

Fig. 5.8—Theoretical Construction of a Conic Projection. The theoretical cone is tangent to the globe along the "standard parallel," here emphasized.

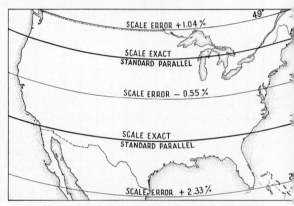

Fig. 5.9—Scale Errors on a Lambert Conformal Conic Projection of the United States Using 33° and 45° North as the standard parallels. The diagram shows the maximum positive and negative scale errors present on a representation of the United States with such a projection. With standard parallels of 29° and 45° north the maximum scale error would be only 1.2 percent.

introduction of two standard parallels reduces distortion in general so that any quadrangle of the grid possesses the same proportions that it does on the globe. The scale is progressively larger than normal north and south of the standard parallels and is progressively smaller than normal toward the parallel midway between them. In the United States these standard parallels are

[8] The theoretical limits of tangency are the equator and the poles. At the former the tangent cone becomes a cylinder, and the projection is a general cylindrical projection; the latter reduces the cone to a plane—the polar azimuthal-equidistant projection.

[9] The rectangular shape of the United States, with its longer east-west direction and the middle latitude of the country, permits maximum accuracy of scale and direction through use of this projection.

[10] There is a technical difference, however, in that the Lambert modification involves computing from two parallels of a simple conic projection so that they become in effect standard parallels. This is not

the same as introducing two standard parallels by conceiving a "secant cone" similar to Gall's "secant cylinder."

either 33° and 45° north or 29° and 45° north, depending on the latitude of the region being mapped.

The second modification of the simple conic projection is the *polyconic projection*.[11] This is probably the most popular of all projections for representation of the United States and areas within its borders, chiefly because it has been adopted by the United States Geological Survey and numerous other goverment agencies. In this projection the earth's surface is divided into a number of narrow latitude belts. For each belt a separate cone of projection is used; the nearer the belt to the pole, the flatter its respective cone (Fig. 5.10). As used, however, this principle is slightly modified.

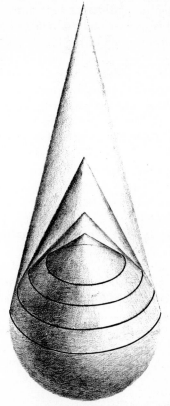

Fig. 5.10—Theoretical Construction of a Polyconic Projection. The heavy lines on the globe are the respective standard parallels for the cones. Although a series of cones is shown here for a hemisphere, in actual practice the projection is used for relatively restricted latitudinal areas, and the standard parallels are much closer together.

[11] Polyconic—"many cones."

The latitude-longitude grid of this projection consists of a straight, vertical *central meridian* with parallels that are non-concentric arcs equally spaced along it. In other words, a degree of latitude is constant along the central meridian (i.e., the scale is true), and the arcs of the parallels are flattened differentially toward the east and west. From this it follows that the polyconic projection is neither conformal nor equal-area. Scale distortion is proportional to the distance from the central meridian, but within 560 miles of the central meridian it is less than one percent.

The main advantage of this projection, aside from its suitability for the middle latitudes, is the ease with which small areas may be mapped independently but on a master plan. Thus, in the United States Geological Survey's topographic maps of the United States the majority of individual maps cover only 15 minutes of one degree and have an exceedingly small error, so that a considerable number of them covering a large region *in toto* may be fitted together to portray a large area with the same small error.

5. The Mollweide Projection

A projection that has the quality of equal area is essential for a map on which to show the world-wide geographical distribution of anything. In presenting the overall distribution of people, a product, or a phenomenon, an equal-area projection assures the viewer that he is getting a true idea of how the item is spread over the face of the earth.

The *Mollweide projection* (Fig. 5.11) achieves this purpose by presenting the earth as an ellipse whose major axis (the equator) is twice the length of its minor axis—the pole-to-pole distance (i.e., a meridian). Since the equator is a great circle and a meridian one-half a great circle this is the correct proportion. As on the globe, the parallels are parallel to the equator, but their spacing for the projection must be computed through complicated mathematics to insure that areas everywhere are proportional. Meridians other than the minor axis,

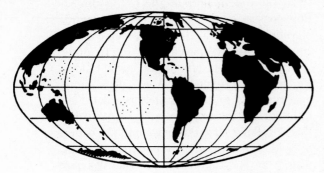

Fig. 5.11—The World. Mollweide projection.

or central meridian, are parts of ellipses. This projection shows the pole as a point, so that shapes in high latitudes and in areas remote from the center are badly distorted.

6. Interrupted Projections

Equal-area projections, such as the Mollweide, have the least distortion along the central meridian when used for world maps. Yet, if it is desired to take advantage of this by putting the central meridian through the center of North America, Asia is cut in half, and if the central meridian is placed in Europe, the shape of North America is distorted. Interrupted projections avoid these faults, at the same time that they retain much of the virtue of the Mollweide, by providing each of three or more segments with a central meridian each, so that there is continuity where the segments join in the equatorial latitudes, and gaps between the segments in the higher latitudes. There is also the possibility in interrupted projections of using portions of different projections (on the same scale) for the equatorial and higher latitudes. By this means equal area is preserved while better conformal qualities (true representation of geographical shape) are retained. (The world distribution maps in this book use a Boggs interrupted projection.)[12]

[12] The list of representative projections considered herein is summarized as follows:

    I. Cylindrical projections
        Mercator modification
        a. Gall modification
        b. Transverse Mercator projection

■ TOPOGRAPHIC MAPS

Projections, as noted previously, are simply methods for transferring the latitude-longitude grid from the globe to a plane surface. All of them result in the construction of a *planimetric*[13] map, the main function of which is to show locations and areal relationships. But for many purposes this is not sufficient. The irregularity of the earth's surface is commonly an important factor. Accordingly, a means must be sought for adding to the planimetric map a representation of high and low places. When this is done the map becomes a "relief" or "topographic"[14] map. There are several commonly used types of such relief maps.

But before considering topographic maps specifically a clear understanding of the difference in meaning of the terms "elevation," "altitude," "height," and "relief" is essential. Elevation and altitude are synonymous; both refer to vertical distance above a given plane of reference, which for all ordinary purposes is sea level. Height, on the other hand, is defined as difference in elevation or altitude. The height of a building measures its distance above the surrounding area, not above sea level. Relief is the range of height within a given area (Fig. 5.12).

For example, the top of Pike's Peak in Colorado has an *elevation* or *altitude* of 14,108 feet, the vertical distance from sea level to its summit. The *elevation* of Denver, Colorado, is 5280 feet. Thus the *height* of Pike's Peak above Denver is 8829 feet. The lowest point in Death Valley is 280 feet below sea level; the summit of Mount Whitney is 14,501 feet above. Since these are the lowest and highest points in the continental

    II. Gnomonic projections
        Azimuthal-equidistant projection
    III. Conic projections
        a. Lambert conformal
        b. Polyconic
    IV. Mollweide projection
    V. Interrupted projections
[13] From the Latin *planus*, "plane"; *metrum*, "measure."
[14] From the Greek *topos*, "place"; *graphein*, "to write."

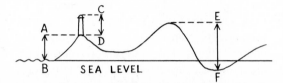

Fig. 5.12—Elevation, Altitude, Height, and Relief. The diagram illustrates the definition of these terms. Elevation and altitude refer to the distance above sea level (*AB*). Height is the distance of one thing above another (*CD*). Relief is the difference between maximum and minimum elevation or altitude, including distance below sea level, if any (*EF*).

United States, the maximum *relief* of the country as a whole is 14,781 feet.

HYPSOMETRIC COLORING[15]

Hypsometric coloring is best adapted to small-scale maps of large areas, on which there is not sufficient room to show individual mountains, valleys, and other minor topographic features. Instead, the relief is indicated on a regional scale by using green for all areas between sea level and a given altitude (500 feet or 1000 feet), yellow for the next equal division of elevation, brown of progressively darker shades for higher divisions, and red, purple, or white for regions of great altitude.

The advantages of this method are several: The general relief of a region can be seen at a glance. The color green is symbolic of the cultivated and fertile lowlands; the color brown suggests the more or less bare rocks of higher altitudes; and the white brings to mind the snow-covered highest altitudes.

The great disadvantage is the tendency to overinterpret the symbolism of the colors. For example, the green may represent a low-altitude desert as well as a fertile lowland.

An improvement on the hypsometric color method is the *stereographic* method devised by a Viennese professor of cartography. This uses intergraded tints rather than sharply delineated shades and combines the tints with an oblique violet shading and the use of a symbol for cliffs. The result is almost like a

plastic model in the completeness of representation, with the added advantage of clear detail visible on closer inspection. The stereographic method is particularly suited for mountainous country and for this reason has become a popular method in Switzerland and Scandinavia.

During the latter part of World War II the United States Geological Survey began using similar colors on some of its contour maps. Oblique shading with color tints related to elevation is applied to maps of certain areas of unusual topographic interest. The result is termed a shaded contour map (see end papers). The three-dimensional effect thus achieved is valuable for teaching purposes.

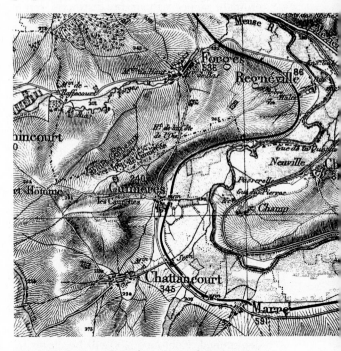

Fig. 5.13—Portion of Hachure Map of Region Near Verdun, France. Note the subtle proportion between length and thickness of an individual hachure mark relative to the steepness of the slope.

HACHURING[16]

The principle of hachuring is the use of closely spaced short lines to indicate gradients or hill slopes. The lines are drawn in

[15] From the Greek *hypsos*, "pertaining to height."

[16] From the French *hacher*, "to hack."

the direction water would run down the slope, with the thickness of each line proportional to the gradient, or angle of slope at that point. Thus the steeper the slope, the darker the appearance of the hachures (Fig. 5.13).

In constructing a hachure map a complete contour map (see below) is first made, the angle of slope is everywhere measured, and the hachures are then drawn in by a highly trained artist. The costly steps involved, the comparatively few artists able to do the work, and, above all, the introduction of color printing in 1870 have tended to make hachuring obsolete. Moreover, hachuring is unsatisfactory for small-scale maps of large areas, as individual mountains and their subordinate slopes cannot be distinctly represented. Finally, hachures show only the relative height, not the elevation of points on a map.

CONTOURING[17]

Contouring is used at present by almost all the countries of the world for governmental maps on which relief is shown. The great value of the contour map is that it enables the user to read by inspection the elevation of any point on the map. Its basic element is the *contour line*, which can be simply defined as a line connecting all points of equal elevation.

An excellent explanation of the contour line has been given by Raisz: ". . . Consider the zero contour line to be sea level. If the sea were to rise 10 feet, the new shore line would be the 10-foot contour line. Similarly the 2-, 3-, 4-, etc. foot contour lines could be determined. Contour lines will be closer together where the slope is steep, and mountainous areas will appear dark on the map. It is obvious that a contour will always be horizontal and perpendicular to the direction of running water at that surface."[18] Since it is not practical to draw contours for every foot of elevation, even for regions of moderate relief, one of the first decisions in planning a contour map is to decide how many feet of elevation should separate successive contour lines. The decision results in the choice of a *contour interval*. If it is decided that a five-foot difference in elevation should be between the contour lines, then the contour interval is five feet; the first contour line is the 5-foot line, the second the 10-foot line, the third the 15-foot line, etc., up to the highest elevation in the area represented by the map.

The contour interval is usually fixed after determining the difference in elevation between the highest and lowest points on the map. Maps of low-lying, level plains and flat river valley bottoms may have contour intervals of as little as two feet. The contours may even then be spaced widely apart. The other extreme is in the great mountain regions of the world, where, with relief up to 10,000 feet, the contour interval may be set at 50, 100, or several hundred feet. For average conditions the interval is commonly 20 feet, which results in a good balance between the precise altitude determination possible for any spot and the legibility of the map.

The reader should keep clearly in mind the distinction between the contour interval and the spacing of the contours. The contour interval is fixed upon beforehand as one of the elements of the map; the spacing of the contours results from the relief being depicted.

Another aid to the understanding of contour lines and their interpretation is to conceive a contour as representing a "layer" of the earth's surface, all of which is at the same elevation above or below sea level. A "layer" represented by the 10-foot contour line on Australia, for example, would have an outline almost like that of the continent and would be of large extent. So large, in fact, that on any map save one of the entire continent only a portion of that layer could be shown, and the 10-foot contour line would pass on and off the map's edges. But if higher contour lines and their "layers" are selected in succession, it is not long before a "layer" is

---

17 From the French *contourner*, "to compass about."
18 By permission from *General Cartography*, by E. J. Raisz. Copyright, 1938. McGraw-Hill Book Company, Inc., p. 129.

found that is not a continuous sheet. This means that many places on the continent are not so high as the elevation represented by the contour. Wherever an area is separated from another of the same elevation by places of lower elevation there would be separate pieces of the same "layer," and as one progressed to the higher "layers" these pieces would become small enough to fit completely on a map of a small area. A glance at a topographic map (see end papers) will show how this makes the lower contours discontinuous, in that they repeatedly go off the edge of the map and reappear somewhere else, and makes the higher contours separate pieces of their respective "layers," or, as the geographer says, "closed contours" (i.e., the contour line encloses an area).

As an aid in using contour lines the map maker usually makes the 50-foot, 100-foot, or 1000-foot contours (depending on the contour interval) heavier lines, so that in fixing the elevation of any high point it will be easier to count up through the lines.

An important feature of contour maps that greatly facilitates their reading is the upstream bend, or notch, where the contours cross a stream valley. Inspection of a contour map indicates at once in which direction each stream is flowing.

QUESTIONS. What is the first step in mapping an area of the earth's surface? If one sighted along an absolutely level line along the earth's surface to an upright pole six miles away on a flat plain, how high on the pole would the sight fall? What is a "projection"? What is the "latitude-longitude grid"? State the four types of distortion that may appear in projections. What names are given to the projections that avoid one or the other of these distortions?

What general type of projection is the Mercator? How does it differ from the basic projection of that type? What is the Gall modification of the Mercator projection? What is the general principle of accuracy in tangent projections? What is the greatest single advantage of the Mercator projection? What is the theory of the gnomonic projection? What is the major advantage of this projection? Describe the use of gnomonic and Mercator projections in navigation. How does the azimuthal-equidistant projection differ from the gnomonic projection? What is the unique feature of the azimuthal-equidistant projection? What is the theory of the conic projection? What is the significance of the standard parallel in the conic projection? How does the Lambert conformal conic projection differ from the standard conic projection? Describe the polyconic projection. What is its greatest advantage? Describe the Mollweide projection? What is its great advantage? What is an interrupted projection?

Define elevation, altitude, height, relief, planimetric, topographic, hypsometric, hachure, contour line, and contour interval. What are the disadvantages of the hachure map? What is the major advantage of the contour map?

CHAPTER 6

The Elements of Weather and Climate

■ INTRODUCTION

There would seem to be little in common between cartography, the subject of the preceding chapter, and meteorology and climatology (the study of weather and climate, respectively), to which this chapter introduces the reader. Yet all three fields concern different aspects of the general study of the world in which we live. A rudimentary knowledge of meteorology and climatology, like that of cartography, is one of the elements of geographic education. In the present instance, moreover, climate is the basis upon which the different regions of the world are discussed in the succeeding chapters. It is essential, therefore, that the student be sufficiently grounded in his knowledge of weather and climate to obtain full benefit from a climatic analysis of the world's regions.

Man lives at the bottom of a "sea" of air, the atmosphere. The physical changes that affect portions of the volume of this "sea," and movements of the affected portions within the "sea" itself, result in the phenomena referred to as "weather" and "climate." Although these two terms are used more or less interchangeably in daily affairs, scientific usage gives each term a distinctive meaning.

Weather is associated with time—it concerns the short-term, day-to-day variations in the physical conditions of the atmosphere. One says, for example, that the *weather* is fine *today*, after the bad *weather yesterday*. The "weatherman," or meteorologist, predicts that the *weather tomorrow* will be fair and warmer. Climate, on the other hand, is associated with place; it is a comprehensive concept that includes the daily, seasonal, and yearly variations in the weather. One says that the Sahara has an arid *climate*, and that the equatorial regions are noted for their generally hot, humid *climate*.

Climate, dominantly, makes natural geography. It is the most important factor of the environment, governing as it does the kind of vegetation, the nature of the soils, and even to some extent the forms of the land. The well-known difference in aspect and utilization between the sections of the western United States which have arid climate and the Northeast with its humid climate illustrates the strong governing effect that climate exerts on man's environment.

To gain a systematic understanding of how this control operates it is necessary first to consider the composition of the atmosphere. The atmosphere consists of a mixture of gases in which varying amounts of dust particles are carried in suspension. The more important constituent gases are: oxygen, which is necessary for animal life; carbon dioxide, essential for plant life; and nitrogen, which comprises four-fifths of the total volume of the air and thus constitutes its "bulk."

Another important gaseous constituent of the air is water vapor, present in amounts up to a maximum of 5 percent of the volume of a given mass of air. A popular misconception is that the water vapor in the air can be seen in the form of clouds. Clouds, however, are condensed vapor; water vapor itself is a colorless gas. The water particles of which clouds are composed are held aloft by the turbulence of the air, for they are actually heavier than air. When such particles coalesce into larger particles that can no longer be held up, precipitation occurs in the form of rain, snow, or sleet, depending on the circumstances.

FACTORS IN WEATHER AND CLIMATE

1. *Temperature and Precipitation.* Temperature and precipitation are the most important factors of weather and climate. They govern "habitability," or the suitability of an environment for man's existence. In a layman's discussion of weather and climate temperature is likely to have first importance, but the geographer finds that precipitation has the greater significance.

2. *Humidity.* The term "humidity" refers to the presence of water vapor in the air. The higher the temperature the greater the amount that *can* be present. It is an important factor: extremes of heat and cold such as plus 130° and minus 90° Fahrenheit can be withstood much more easily under conditions of low humidity; indeed, such extreme temperatures may be fatal if humidity is high. The saying "It isn't the heat, it's the humidity" is the popular and correct explanation of the discomfort that attends high humidity even at relatively moderate temperatures.

3. *Winds.* The strength and persistence of winds are significant elements in determining the nature of weather and climate. Their direction is also a factor, as can be observed at the beach on a hot day. A cool, onshore wind from over the ocean or a hot, offshore wind from over the land spells the difference between comfort and discomfort.

4. *Other Factors.* Factors less fundamental in determining the suitability of a climate for man are: the *length of the days* (hours of sunlight), the *monotony or variability of the weather,* and the *amount of sunshine* (cloudy vs. clear days). However, these factors are also of considerable significance for plant growth because they influence the type of natural vegetation and kind of crop production.

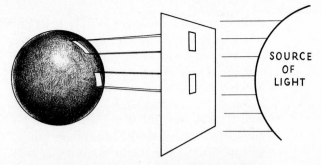

Fig. 6.1—Effect of Latitude on Angle of the Sun's Rays. Two openings of equal size in the screen produce unequal lighted areas on the globe. The farther from the equator, the greater the area over which the rays spread. Thus, a given area far from the equator receives less energy from the sun than an equal area nearer the equator.

THE CONTROLS OF WEATHER AND CLIMATE

The elements of weather and climate listed above are in turn the result of the combination or interaction of circumstances that can be called the "controls" of weather and climate. There are several such controls:

1. *Latitude.* At low latitudes the sun is directly overhead, or nearly so, at noon. A small "bundle" of the sun's rays strikes the earth in these regions over an area equal or nearly equal to the cross-sectional area of the "bundle." As the poles are approached the "bundle" of rays of the same cross-sectional area is spread over a much wider area of the earth's surface, so that in the high latitudes a square foot of surface receives a smaller amount of the energy transmitted in the "bundle" than does a square foot in the low latitudes (Fig. 6.1). The difference in angle of the incoming rays is directly responsible for the low temperatures of the polar regions and the high temperatures of the equatorial regions.

Latitude also governs the length of daylight, which modern investigations indicate to be of significance to all living things. Animals as well as plants seem to respond not only to the amount and intensity of light during the day but also to differences in the length of days and nights.

2. *Distribution of Land and Water.* An important factor in determining the weather

and climate of a particular locality is its position with respect to the land and water masses of the earth—whether it is, at one extreme, an island in the middle of a body of water or, at the other extreme, the center of a continent, surrounded by large areas of land. The air over the island will tend to be humid and have a small temperature range, whereas that in the continental interior will tend to be dry and have great temperature variations.

3. *Wind Belts and Air Masses.* Air moves along fairly well-defined paths, and also tends to move about in more or less discrete masses or "lumps" which differ in their characteristics. The particular wind belt in which a place is situated and the type or types of air masses that pass over it have a profound effect on the weather and climate.

4. *Altitude.* The effect of altitude is most dramatically evidenced in the perpetual snow cover on high mountain peaks even when they are situated on or near the equator. Other, less immediately evident effects are also traceable to altitude, so that discussion of the climate and weather of any region must consider its altitude.

5. *Mountain Barriers.* Mountain ranges, especially those trending generally north-south, may act as barriers and thus to a considerable extent influence the weather and climate of regions adjoining them.

6. *Pressure Areas.* The air masses referred to in 3 above have different densities. The difference in pressures within the atmosphere strongly affects air movements and temperatures—and, therefore, weather and climate.

7. *Ocean Currents.* Surface currents of the ocean transport vast volumes of water across latitudinal lines and in so doing introduce modifications in the temperature of the air along coasts they pass. Thus a cold current coming into a warm region, or vice versa, can have great importance in determining the weather and climate of the adjacent land areas.

8. *Storms.* Storms are disturbances resulting from the contact of air masses or a local pressure and temperature imbalance. Their meteorological importance is attested to by the aviator's use of the word "weather" as synonymous with storms.

■ ATMOSPHERIC TEMPERATURE

The earth seems to maintain what might be called a "body temperature." Moderately deep wells yield water of constant temperature regardless of the season of the year. In New York State, for example, well water has a temperature between 52° and 55° F. throughout the year. Such wells have reached a depth where the outside temperature is not sufficient to influence the temperature the earth is maintaining by its own inner heat. Below this relatively shallow depth the temperature of the earth (and any water present within the rocks) becomes progressively hotter with depth. The origin of the interior earth heat has not yet been satisfactorily explained. It may be due to radioactivity deep within the earth.

Some writers argue that it is this inner heat which keeps the earth from becoming too cold to support life; that the heat received from the sun is insufficient to account for the temperature of the earth as a whole. Regardless of the truth of this contention it is enough for a geographic study to know that the temperature of the atmosphere is important in man's activities, and the atmosphere receives its heat from "outside," that is, from the sun.

Temperature as referred to in a discussion of weather and climate can be either *thermometric* or *sensible.* The former is the temperature recorded by a thermometer; the latter is the temperature as felt by man.[1] The heat in either case is the result of a process known as *insolation*[2]—the delivery of radiant energy from the sun to the earth's surface. Insolation is measured in *thermal days.* Ex-

[1] The sensible temperature is dependent on absolute, or thermometric, temperature, relative humidity, and the movement of the air. The sensible temperature of humid heat and cold is higher and lower, respectively, than that of dry heat and cold.

[2] From the Latin *insolare,* to expose to the sun.

actly at the equator the length of daylight during each day remains constant throughout the year, and so the equator is said to receive 365.2 thermal days a year, equal to the number of days in a year. With this unit it is possible to compare the insolation received by different regions of the earth's surface. The poles, for example, receive only 155 thermal days a year. As one would expect, the number of thermal days varies inversely with the latitude—the higher the latitude the lower the number of thermal days received. It is not a constant rate of decline but decreases faster in the high middle latitudes than elsewhere.

THE PROCESS OF HEATING THE ATMOSPHERE

Of the total energy that reaches the earth's atmosphere from the sun, the earth's surface receives some 40 percent. Approximately 43 percent of the total energy that arrives in the atmosphere is reflected back into space when it strikes water droplets and dust particles in the air. About 17 percent is absorbed by the atmosphere.

The 17 percent of the sun's energy absorbed directly is not, however, responsible for most of the heat the atmosphere acquires. The atmospheric gases are heated mainly by reradiation of the heat absorbed by the land and water, and through conduction—that is, by contact with the earth's surface.

The sequence can be summarized as follows: Light comes through the atmosphere to the earth. This energy is partially absorbed by the earth's surface (heating the land and water) and is partially reradiated from the warmed land and water as heat waves. In this form it is mostly absorbed by the water vapor in the atmosphere, the lower levels of which are thereby warmed. This is known as the "greenhouse effect." The atmosphere acts much as does the glass roof of a greenhouse; it lets the light through but is opaque to the reradiated heat waves.

Thus the three fundamental processes involved in this sequence of heating the earth's atmosphere are *direct absorption, reradiation,* and *conduction.* It is important to understand the difference between them, especially between reradiation and conduction. A hand held over a hot griddle feels the heat being radiated, but a hand touching the griddle gets the heat directly by conduction (and is burned in the process). Similarly, air near the ground receives most of its heat by conduction; however, it does not transfer it freely to higher levels by the same process, for air is a very poor conductor of heat. (Its conductivity is less than $\frac{1}{20,000}$ that of copper.)

HEAT TRANSFER WITHIN THE ATMOSPHERE

In different parts of the world the atmosphere receives varying amounts of heat, depending upon differences in the number of thermal days, the amount of water vapor present, and the degree to which the underlying surface of the earth absorbs and reradiates solar energy. Fortunately, however, there are processes by which the heat is distributed throughout the atmosphere independently of the initial solar radiation. The atmosphere over regions that do not receive much heat directly may obtain it from elsewhere by transfer. The processes of such transfer are as follows:

1. *Convection.* Cigarette smoke rising in a still room illustrates convection on a small scale. The air containing the rising cigarette smoke is appreciably warmer than the rest of the air in the room. Like all gases, air expands on being warmed, its density decreases, and it is, therefore, lighter in weight. The colder, heavier air moves in from the surrounding region to take the place of the air that is rising and in effect helps lift it. In the large-scale atmospheric development of the same phenomenon the air is warmed by conduction from hot land or warm water beneath it and is pushed upward by the neighboring cooler, heavier air that flows in below it from all sides.

2. *Importation.* Importation is a rather complicated process that can be simply, if not precisely, stated as the independent motion of discrete and separate "masses" of air. Despite the seeming complete continuity of

the air gases, separate units develop within the atmosphere and maintain their identity over considerable periods of time, during which they move long distances away from the areas in which they originate. The familiar "hot wave" and "cold wave" of the middle latitudes are due to the arrival of warm or cold air masses over a given region.

3. *Compression and Expansion.* Air moving laterally is forced to rise when it encounters higher land—a mountain range or the edge of a plateau. As it rises the air expands and the pressure falls. The total heat energy originally present does not change but the temperature falls in direct proportion to the amount of expansion. The reverse of this also occurs. Cold air from high places sinks to lower altitudes and is compressed in the process; hence a rise in temperature ensues.

If these interactions seem complicated it must be remembered that thousands of cubic miles of atmosphere are involved and that the several processes may be operating simultaneously in different places. The end result is easily appreciated, but the process is difficult to analyze and there is not yet full understanding of what actually occurs.

■ THE LAND-WATER RELATIONSHIP

A further circumstance of first importance in determining weather and climate is the marked difference in the rate of heating of land surfaces and water masses. Heating of the earth's surface by solar radiation and (by reradiation and conduction) heating of the atmosphere involve on the one hand the top surface of the land and water and on the other hand the bottom surface of the air. In the case of the land it is almost exclusively surface heating, a fact well demonstrated by the coolness of a cellar during hot weather, or the coolness of beach sand only a few inches below the surface on a hot, sunny day. Water, however, is affected to greater depths. For this and the following reasons water heats up much less rapidly than does a land surface.

1. Water has a higher "specific heat" than land. The term "specific heat" is used in physics to denote the ability of a substance to absorb a certain amount of heat without any change in its temperature.

2. As noted above, absorption of the sun's radiation is not so exclusively a surface phenomenon with water as it is with land. On water the sun's rays are not all immediately reflected or absorbed but in part penetrate to a considerable depth below the surface, their energy being gradually absorbed as they go deeper. Thus the total quantity of energy arriving at the surface is not received by a relatively small volume of water but is distributed through a considerable depth. On land the opposite is true.

3. The water at the surface of the oceans, lakes, and rivers of the world is continually changing to vapor at a varying rate. According to a fundamental law of physics the change of a substance from its liquid to its gaseous state without any change of temperature requires the consumption of heat, in this instance obtained from the energy of sunlight. Solar energy used to vaporize water is not, in general, available to raise the temperature either of the water or of the atmosphere.

4. Water reflects more light than land. A certain amount is reflected by both, and the difference in amount between them is actually not too significant, even though this was at one time regarded as a factor of first importance in their differential heating.

5. Water is constantly kept in motion by convection, by currents, and by waves, so that a surplus of heat cannot easily be built up at any one place. Cold water rises to take the place of warm; the heated water flows away to cooler areas where it loses its surplus heat by conduction.

■ THE HEAT BALANCE

Attention must next be given to the general "balance sheet" of temperature, that is, the outcome of the plus and minus effects of the total heat received and lost by the earth and its atmosphere. For not only is energy continually being received; it is also continually being lost to space. If more energy is being received at any place than is being lost, the temperature rises, and vice versa. A surplus is built up during the summer and during the day and is expended during the winter and at night. This is the reason for the daily and seasonal temperature changes at any one place. A hasty consideration of this relation would lead to the conclusion that the point of change from accumulation to loss occurs at the time when the energy received reaches the maximum and starts on the downward curve. Actually, heat accumulation continues as long as the receipts are greater than the losses. The hottest part of the summer in the Northern Hemisphere is not around June 21, the day when the sun is highest in the heavens, the day is longest, and insolation is greatest; it is in July and August, for until then the total energy received still exceeds that given off. And it is in August, depending on the conditions of any given year, that the weather begins to get cool again as the surplus is progressively depleted, as the daily losses normally begin to exceed the daily gains.

In like manner the point of change during the day is not noon, when the sun is highest and the most energy is being received, but sometime in the afternoon (the hour depending on the season and weather conditions), when the surplus has ceased to build up. The delay in the time of highest seasonal and daily temperature behind the time of greatest receipts of heat is called the *seasonal* and *diurnal lag* of temperature. This sequence is not, of course, always in effect. An overcast sky, the movements of wind, and change in the wind's direction are typical major reasons for a departure from the normal daily and seasonal lag.

To persons living in the middle latitudes the daily and seasonal give-and-take is the ordinary course of events. But it will not serve as a complete explanation of planetary temperature adjustments. In the tropical and near-tropical belt between 37° north and south latitudes more heat is received during the *year* than is lost, whereas the opposite is true in latitudes higher than 37°. (See discussion of thermal days above.) It is obvious that if the "lag" bookkeeping applied without further qualification, the equatorial regions would continually become hotter, the higher latitudes colder.

This has not happened because the surplus heat of the equatorial regions is transferred on a large scale to other parts of the world by (1) the movement of air masses, (2) winds, and (3) the movement of ocean currents. The two major examples of ocean currents are the well-known **Gulf Stream** and the **Kurosiwo**, "Japanese" or "Black" Current, which warms the east coast of Asia and the southern coast of Alaska. Both currents transfer tremendous amounts of heat from the tropics to the higher latitudes, although the Gulf Stream has by far the greater volume and is better defined (more easily discernible). The major effect of ocean currents on land temperatures is due to the movement inland of air warmed or cooled over their waters.

QUESTIONS. Distinguish between weather and climate. Name the three major elements of weather and climate. Name the eight contributing factors of weather and climate and explain how each contributes to the development of weather and climate. Define "insolation" and explain its importance in weather and climate. What is the "greenhouse effect"? What roles do absorption, reradiation, and conduction play in connection with this effect? What are the three means by which heat is transferred within the atmosphere? Explain each. Why does water heat more slowly than land? In what way is this important in weather and climate? Explain the occurrence of both "seasonal lag" and "diurnal lag."

■ PRESSURE DIFFERENCES

The shifting of air as winds or in masses is a result of differential pressures. The normal pressure of the atmosphere on the surface of the earth at sea level is 14.7 pounds per square inch, sufficient pressure to support a column of mercury 29.53 inches high. The latter measurement is now more commonly expressed by the metric system of science, in which normal pressure equals one *bar*. This measure is divided into thousandths, or *millibars*, and provides for measurement of differences in atmospheric pressure much more scientific than fractions or hundredths of inches.

The excess of heat continually received in the tropics results in an increasing expansion of the air that is being heated there. This increase in volume without change in mass results in a "bulge," or excess of air volume at the top of the layer of air over the equatorial regions. The bulge is a disturbance of equilibrium, so under the influence of gravity it overflows to the north and south (not east and west, as conditions are similar all around the equatorial belt). In consequence, the *mass* of air over the equator is reduced, whereas that over the belts to the north and south is increased. Thus, unequal pressures are developed.

As a result of this imbalance a convectional circulation is established. There is an excess of pressure on each side of the equatorial belt and a deficit in the center, so that a huge double cycle (both north and south of the equator) of rising, outflow, sinking, and inflow of air is maintained.

At the poles the same principle is in effect, but in reverse. There excessive cooling produces contraction, more air flows in at the top, and a high pressure results, from which air tends to flow out in all directions along the surface of the earth.

Some authorities think that the polar imbalance and the air movements resulting from differences in pressure there are the dominant factors in the development of air circulation on a planetary scale. It is probable that both polar and equatorial imbalances contribute in about the same degree. Since the excess of energy is received at the equator it may well be asserted that this is fundamentally the motivating power.

Fig. 6.2—The Planetary Wind Belts. The diagram shows the generalized latitudinal belts and directions of the planetary winds.

■ THE PLANETARY WIND BELTS

However initiated, there exists a world-wide, integrated system of wind and air mass movements known as the *planetary wind belts* (Fig. 6.2). These belts, listed in order from equator to poles, are as follows:

1. *The Doldrums, or Equatorial Calms.* The doldrums, or equatorial calms, extend from 5° to 10° north and south of the equator. These are the regions of rising equatorial air. Since there is no appreciable lateral air movement, conditions of calm prevail.

2. *The Trade Winds.* The trade winds extend on either side of the doldrums between 10° and 30° north and south latitude. They are the inflowing movement of air along the earth's surface to take the place of the rising air of the doldrums. These winds do not blow directly north-south; in the Northern Hemisphere they are called the *northeast trades* and in the Southern Hemisphere the *southeast trades*.[3] The trade winds acquired

[3] Winds are named by the direction from which they come. The northeast trades move southwesterly, the southeast trades, northwesterly. Contrariwise, ocean currents are named by the direction in which they are moving.

their name from first being encountered in the West Indies during the exploration and discovery which began in the late fifteenth century. Their constant, dependable southwesterly direction was ideal for the outward voyage from Europe of West Indies shipping.

3. *The Horse Latitudes.* The horse latitudes extend in both hemispheres between 30° and 35° latitude. This is the region where the air of the high-altitude "anti-trades," moving out from the equatorial bulge, has become sufficiently cooled to descend somewhat abruptly to the bottom of the atmosphere. Such predominantly vertical motion of the air results again in a condition of calm. The name "horse latitudes" also derives from early experience in ocean navigation. In the seventeenth century, so the story goes, there was a considerable trade in horses and cattle carried from New England to the West Indies. The southward-bound sailing ships were often becalmed in this region. When conditions became serious the horse cargo was thrown overboard because of the tremendous quantities of precious fresh water the animals consumed. The name was later applied to the similar belt in the Atlantic of the Southern Hemisphere, and to like regions of the other oceans.

4. *The Prevailing Westerlies.* The prevailing westerlies are belts between 30° and 60° latitude in both hemispheres. These winds blow around the earth in an almost due west-east direction. In the Southern Hemisphere the general absence of continental lands to obstruct the flow of the westerlies permits them to develop high velocities. The early mariners who were compelled to round Cape Horn referred to them according to the latitudes where they were encountered as the "roaring forties," the "howling fifties," and the "screaming sixties." These winds are part of the convectional system.

5. *The Polar Highs.* The polar highs are the high-pressure areas over the poles. Here again predominantly vertical movement of the air produces conditions of calm.

6. *The Polar Easterlies.* The polar easterlies are winds that theoretically blow out from the edge of the polar highs in the reverse of the manner in which the trade winds blow into the equatorial calms.[4]

7. *The Subtropical Highs and Subpolar Lows.* The centrifugal force of the prevailing westerlies tends to force air to their low-latitude edges and to pile up in the horse latitudes, thus supplementing the high-pressure conditions there and giving rise to the subtropical high belts. At the high-latitude borders of the westerlies there is a corresponding pulling away of air that gives rise to the subpolar lows.[5] These two wind belts are less distinct and of less importance than the preceding six.

■ ROTATIONAL DEFLECTION

The departure of the trades, westerlies, and polar easterlies from the north-south movement that would result from a circulation governed solely by convection needs to be explained. This deviation from a strictly convectional system of circulation is due to the phenomenon of "rotational deflection," that is, an effect resulting from the rotation of the earth on its axis. Because of this rotation any body moving over the earth's surface, including a wind or air mass, is under the influence of a force known, after its discoverer, as the *Coriolis force.*

As a result, any moving body has a tendency to move to the *right* in the Northern Hemisphere, to the *left* in the Southern Hemisphere. The greater the weight, speed and latitude of the body, the greater the deflecting effect.

Unlike animate objects or the motive inventions of man, winds and air masses have only friction to counteract rotational deflection. Thus it is that atmospheric movements (and to a lesser degree ocean currents) exhibit the most pronounced effect of rota-

---

[4] Increasing knowledge of the polar regions has not produced any evidence of these winds.

[5] The subpolar low is an "average" condition, i.e., the weather map for a single day may not show it, but the average pressures over a week or month reveal such a low-pressure belt.

tional deflection. The trades in the Northern Hemisphere are an attempted north-south movement that is deflected toward the right; the winds therefore blow southwest—hence the name "northeast trades." The westerlies are the "residue" of the air that rose from the equatorial regions and flowed farthest north and south. Rotational deflection shifts its course to northeasterly-southeasterly directions (above the trades, as antitrades), but where the air descends from its high altitude the deflection, being cumulative, has produced the westerlies as circular winds around the earth.

■ MONSOONS

Finally, there is a type of wind, the *monsoon*,[6] that is not planetary but nevertheless has a large-scale development. Monsoon winds occur in India, southwest China, south of the western bulge of Africa, and have a slight development in the lower Mississippi Valley. They result from excessive land heating; during the summer months in the Northern Hemisphere excessive heating of the land results in an updraft, and a consequent inrush of cooler air from adjacent oceanic areas. This air comes from the southwest for India, the southeast for China, the southwest for Africa, and the south for the Mississippi Valley. The opposite effect (i.e., outflowing air from the cooler land masses to the warmer oceans) is produced in the winter season, although it is not so pronounced.

■ THE PHENOMENA OF WEATHER AND CLIMATE

ATMOSPHERIC HUMIDITY

Weather and climate include specific phenomena not directly apparent from consider-

ation of their general origins. The first of these is the effect produced by atmospheric humidity, the water vapor present in the air. The maximum volume of vapor a given mass of air can contain is roughly 5 percent of the total volume of that mass. The moisture is transferred to the air by evaporation, chiefly from the ocean but also from lakes, rivers, and other bodies of water, from moist rocks and soil, and from the leaves of trees. The energy or heat required to bring about the evaporation is, in effect, stored in the vapor. Accordingly, when condensation occurs this heat is released to the atmosphere. Such stored-up energy is known as "latent heat," or "latent energy."

The rivers of the world return to the sea approximately 30 percent of the total amount of water precipitated. The remaining 70 percent is again evaporated before it reaches the sea, and is transported to the equatorial regions in discontinuous "surges" of cold air masses moving from the polar regions.

The humidity of the atmosphere is measured and stated in various ways. *Absolute humidity* is the total quantity of water vapor present in the air, measured in weight of water per unit *volume* of air. *Relative humidity* is the ratio between the amount of vapor actually present (the absolute humidity) and the maximum amount that could be present in a given volume of air at a given temperature. It is usually expressed in percentage terms; i.e., if the absolute humidity is only one-quarter the amount that could be present the relative humidity is 25 percent. *Specific humidity* is the weight of water vapor present per unit *weight* or mass of air. This measurement is used to tag or label specific air masses as they move about in the atmosphere. The temperature and volume of a given air mass may change as the mass moves from place to place, thus changing the relative and absolute measurements. But the relationship between the weight of the water vapor and that of the air remains constant and can serve as a label that identifies that air mass (unless appreciable amounts are lost by precipitation or gained by evaporation).

[6] From the Arabic *mausim*, a time or season. Strictly speaking, the monsoon is the season, not the wind that blows during it. Usage has made it the accepted name for the wind, however.

CONDENSATION

The air under a given temperature condition can include only a certain finite amount of vapor in its mixture of gases. This amount varies directly with temperature; the higher the temperature the more water vapor can be included in the air. It follows, then, that if at a given temperature the relative humidity is 100 percent, any lowering of the temperature will result in the condensation of the amount of the vapor that exceeds 100 percent relative humidity at the new temperature. And as a corollary of this, with a relative humidity of any figure above zero a sufficient drop in the temperature can bring about condensation. The temperature of condensation for a specific mass of air with a certain relative humidity is known as the *dew point*.

Temperature Reduction. Reduction of air temperature in a given mass of air can take place in three ways:

1. *By contact with cold ground* (conduction). On a calm night the ground reradiates the heat it absorbed during the day and is thereby cooled (Fig. 6.3). The air immediately above the ground is also cooled by conduction of its heat to the ground. If the relative humidity of the air is sufficiently high the temperature drop will cross the dew point and dew, fog, or frost will result. Under exceptional winter conditions with exceedingly cold, clear air (usually at night) it is possible for snow to form in the lowest 15 to 20 feet of air.

Fig. 6.3—Condensation by Contact of Air With Cooler Ground.

2. *By the motion of air from over warm ground or water to cooler ground or water.* Again, conduction of heat from warm air to the cooler substratum can cause the temperature of the incoming air to fall below its dew point (Fig. 6.4).

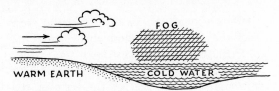

Fig. 6.4—Condensation by Movement of Air to Cooler Substratum.

This is a common cause of widespread ground fogs, often observed on summer evening cross-country automobile trips. The formation of fog over water is a familiar sight during spring, when the water is still colder than the land.

3. *By the rise of air.* The rise of air is the most effective means of temperature reduction. It occurs most simply through *convection*, where warm air rises, cools, and reaches the dew point (Fig. 6.5). The daily afternoon showers of many tropical regions are due to this convectional rise, while the summer thunderstorms of the middle latitudes are a more complicated manifestation of the same phenomenon.

Fig. 6.5—Condensation by Convectional Rise of Air.

An *orographic* rise of air occurs when air moves against mountains and is raised by being forced to ascend the mountain slopes as it continues its lateral motion. The rise causes expansion and cooling, which, if the dew point is reached, results in condensation and precipitation on the windward side of the mountains (the side on which the air mass is rising) (Fig. 66). Since condensation brings about the liber-

Fig. 6.6—Condensation by Orographic Rise of Air.

ation of heat, the air arrives at the crest of the range in a relatively warm state. Then, as the air moves down the farther (lee) slope of the range it is heated by compression, so that at the base of the range it is hot and dry. Such hot, dry, descending winds can have their temperatures raised as much as 60° Fahrenheit.

In *air mass contacts* there is a meeting of a cold with a warm air mass. The heavier cold air pushes like a wedge under the warm air (or conversely, the warm air rides up over the cold air), again with condensation and precipitation as the consequence (Fig. 6.7).

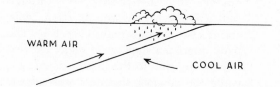

WARM AIR

COOL AIR

Fig. 6.7—Condensation by Rise of Air in Air-Mass Contacts.

In all of these developments the salient feature in bringing about condensation is the *rise* of the air; this is the only means by which *large-scale* condensation can be brought about.

PRECIPITATION

Precipitation, the third specific phenomenon in the development of weather and climate characteristics, refers to the descent of all forms of moisture from the atmosphere.

Important Aspects of Precipitation. There are three important aspects of precipitation, each of which greatly affects the nature of the weather and climate of a given locality:

1. *The annual amount of precipitation,* measured in inches. This is the depth of a hypothetical layer of water which would cover a given area if all the precipitation that fell on it during a year were to remain on its surface. Annual precipitation ranges from a few inches or less in extremely arid regions to 300 or 400 inches in certain equatorial lands.

2. *The seasonal distribution of precipitation,* the most important characteristic of which is whether adequate rainfall is available during the growing season in a given region. (In different regions of the earth the growing season is of varying duration and occurs in different months.)

3. *The dependability of precipitation,* which refers to the relative constancy of the amount of rainfall received from year to year. In general, *the less the annual precipitation the less its dependability.* This is, unfortunately, the worst possible relationship from man's viewpoint, for the agriculture of areas with scant rainfall is completely dependent upon what little can be expected, and the failure of the precipitation to meet the average of a previous period of years can cause a total crop failure. The famines of India and China are in part due to this fact. In these countries the monsoon is depended upon to bring the rain; famine results when no rain falls. In China famine may also come about when the monsoon brings too much rain and the resulting floods destroy the crops.

STORMS

In the middle latitudes storms most commonly occur as a phenomenon associated with cold front-warm front contacts of air masses. Air that comes to rest or is slowly moving across the surface of the earth tends to acquire the temperature-humidity characteristics of the area in which it is present. Areas in which air thus acquires particular characteristics are termed "source regions" (Figs. 6.8 a and b).

In each source region two kinds of surface, *continental* and *marine,* are present from which supplemental characteristics may be derived. As the properties so acquired will be retained for a considerable time after the air moves away from the source area, the air can be recognized by its special characteristics. Such a body of air of approximate homogeneity is termed an *air mass* and is named for its particular source region.

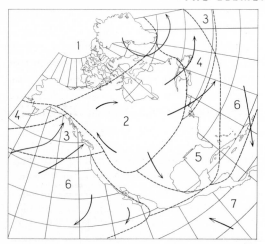

Fig. 6.8a—Source Regions of Air Masses in the North American Winter. Arrows show generalized movement of the air masses. Source regions: (1) arctic; (2) polar continental; (3) polar maritime, or transitional; (4) transitional; (5) transitional, or tropical maritime; (6) tropical maritime; (7) equatorial. (After Sverre Petterssen, *Weather Analysis and Forecasting*, McGraw-Hill, 1940.)

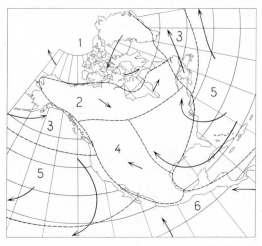

Fig. 6.8b—Source Regions of Air Masses in the North American Summer. Arrows show generalized movement of the air masses. Source regions: (1) arctic; (2) polar continental; (3) polar maritime; (4) tropical continental; (5) tropical maritime; (6) equatorial. (After Sverre Petterssen, *Weather Analysis and Forecasting*, McGraw-Hill, 1940.)

"Polar continental" air masses, for example, develop through the cooling and contracting of air which is stationary, or very nearly so, over polar continental areas. Its contraction draws in air from surrounding areas in order to sustain the general atmospheric depth (air, being fluid, conforms to the earth's spherical shape on its top surface, as do the oceans). High-pressure conditions develop because of the higher density of cold air and the weight of the additional air flowing in at the top. For a time the high-pressure mass is pocketed by surrounding air masses, but eventually it surges out into the westerlies belt, to invade the lower latitudes. If the season is winter the migrating air mass gives rise to the familiar cold wave.

Similarly, but under the opposite conditions, the calm belt of the horse latitudes give rise to masses of high-pressure warm air containing large amounts of moisture. When these move north over the land a heat wave results (in summer).

One writer has characterized the North American continent, where the cold air mass-warm air mass cycle is well developed, as a region of perpetual struggle between the two types:

The contest between the warm tropical and cold polar air, which occurs during all seasons but is most evident during the cooler parts of the year, may be thought of as a continuous battle of weather along a shifting line known in meteorology as the polar front. The attack of the polar forces is held close to the ground. When the opposing tropical breezes, constantly trying to reach the Canadian border, find their way blocked they rise and overrun the polar mass, thus continuing the northward movement. The battle line therefore becomes not a vertical wall but an inclined surface sloping upward toward the north. The two armies rarely battle to a standstill; rather, each southward thrust of cold air is balanced by a northward push of warm air. Thus the polar front is not normally a straight line but develops a series of large-scale waves. Because the polar front is in the region of prevailing west-to-east winds, the waves normally move eastward and bring alternating periods of warm and cold weather.[7] [Fig. 6.9.]

Since World War II the use of new techniques for investigating the upper atmos-

[7] S. F. Markham, *Climate and the Energy of Nations*, Oxford University Press, 2nd American ed., 1947, pp. 164 f.

Fig. 6.9—An Air-Mass Contact. The break in the layer of clouds indicates the boundary between a mass of warm air on the left and of cold air on the right. The cold front is moving eastward over Indianapolis, Indiana. (Courtesy, United States Weather Bureau.)

phere has demonstrated that this wave development is an important phenomenon at high altitudes, between 20,000 and 40,000 feet. At these levels the winds actually follow a wave pattern in their east-west motion. It appears that the *planetary wave*, as it has been termed (Fig. 6.10), is directly responsible for the daily weather and storms of the middle-latitude regions.

In the science of meteorology storms are one of several manifestations of the same

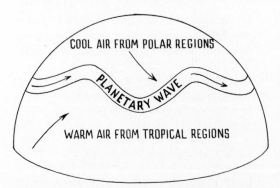

Fig. 6.10—The Planetary Wave. This high-altitude phenomenon occurs in the westerlies belt, in the "battleground" area of cold and warm air masses. High winds from west to east follow a wavelike path, here shown symmetrical and idealized. At the same time, the wave itself moves slowly eastward, "crest" and "trough" varying in their respective reach north and south. It is the location of the "crests" and "troughs" at a given time that exercises a direct determining influence on the weather.

conditions that occur in varying degrees of magnitude but are all included under the generic term *cyclone*.[8] The smallest-scale expression of these conditions is the dust whirl, the familiar small whirlwind which races across dusty fields during the summer months or lifts dead leaves high into the air during the fall. Next in size is the tornado, known erroneously as a cyclone; its winds are destructively violent—400 miles per hour or more. Still larger is the standard variety of cyclone, also formerly called by this name but now known usually as a "low" because of the low air-pressure conditions prevailing within it. It is the ordinary storm of the middle latitudes and extends over thousands of square miles. Its winds may attain a velocity of 40 to 60 miles an hour as they move in toward the vortex of the storm.

There is also a special cyclonic development known as a "hurricane" in the Atlantic and a "typhoon" in the Pacific. These cyclonic storms are halfway between a tornado and a true cyclone in dimensions. They result from the seasonal lag in temperature (see above, p. 93), which develops an unusual combination of atmospheric circumstances in the oceanic areas of the low latitudes in the Northern Hemisphere. In the Atlantic this combination of circumstances occurs during the late summer and early fall months of the year; in the Pacific during both fall and spring.

Because of the seasonal lag and the concentration of land in the Northern Hemisphere the region of the earth with the most heat during the late summer and early fall is not over the equator but a few degrees north of it. This hot belt is known as the *heat equator*. The heat equator phenomenon is not so strongly developed in the Southern Hemisphere during its summer, owing to the smaller amount of land area south of the true equator. As the heat equator moves north and south across the true equator, however, the entire planetary wind system shifts with it.

It will be recalled that the air movement

[8] From the Greek *kyklos*, a circle.

of trade winds serves to replace the rising air over the hot equatorial belt. When the heat equator is north of the true equator the southeast trades blow beyond the true equator to the line of the heat equator, where the maximum rise of air occurs. When they pass over the true equator they enter the Northern Hemisphere, and the effect of rotational deflection changes from left to right. Thus the southeast trades at this juncture develop an abrupt bend at the end of their path which causes them to be known as the *hooked trades.*

The hooked trade phenomenon may be a contributory cause to the genesis of hurricanes, which develop from eddies in the trade winds. The warm oceanic air of such eddies includes a high concentration of water vapor, so that as the air rises in them it expands and its moisture condenses. This releases the latent heat of the moisture, which, added to the temperature of the air, intensifies the rise and further lowers the pressure. The result is the development of tremendous, self-perpetuating, and intensifying atmospheric swirls which move along a path of their own (generally northwestward) and cause shipwreck, death, and destruction when they reach the islands and mainlands which lie in their course. Since the difference between land and water heating interferes with the steady development of the phenomenon, hurricanes and typhoons always form over water (where topographic influences are also absent).

Modern meteorological investigations have shown that rather similar circumstances attend the development of the ordinary cyclone or middle-latitude storm. The emphasis in meteorology is now on air masses rather than on the high- and low-pressure areas of this belt. It has been learned that the movement of the air masses is responsible for the cyclonic development that occurs when a warm and cold air mass come into contact, and further, that the degree of cyclonic development depends on the sharpness of differentiation between the two air masses.

If the cold air mass is the "active" one, and is underthrusting a warm one, the development is not so intense as when a warm mass is actively overriding a cold mass. The reason is that a cold air mass tends to spread out and to dissipate its energy by distributing it. A warm air mass, on the contrary, tends to focus its energy on a small central region. Without the influence of rotational deflection the wind directions in the overriding warm mass would be directly centripetal, but the right-hand deflection of the Northern Hemisphere brings about a swirling motion. Since the deflection is always at right angles to the actual motion of the wind, and since the wind is due to a pressure gradient or difference which increases as the center is approached, the resultant path of the wind is a counterclockwise upward spiral.

The similarity to hurricane-breeding conditions is obvious. The mechanism needed to raise the warm air is that of overriding the wedge-front of the cold air mass. Again there is the sequence of expansion, condensation, release of latent heat, further upward motion, and expansion—in short, another self-exciting, self-intensifying process. Of course, conditions rarely get as extreme as those of a hurricane because of the lower temperatures and lower humidity of the air in the higher latitudes.

These typical storms are known as "cyclonic storms of the west wind belt." They occur so frequently that the average weather cycle of the westerlies belt during the winter alternates between storm and fair weather conditions about every three days (see quotation, p. 99 above). The average storm is some six or seven miles thick, may be 1000 miles in diameter, and moves forward about 20 miles an hour during the summer, 30 miles an hour in the winter.

QUESTIONS. What is fundamentally responsible for the existence of the planetary wind belts? Name the planetary wind belts, describing and naming the causes of each. What is the rule for rotational deflection in the Northern Hemisphere? The Southern Hemisphere? What is a "monsoon" wind? Why does it occur? What countries or regions of the world experience it?

Distinguish between absolute humidity,

relative humidity, and specific humidity. Define the term "dew point." What relationship does it have to precipitation? Explain the ways in which the temperature of a given air mass can be reduced. Name the three important aspects of precipitation. What is the significance of each? If the air masses which invade the middle latitudes tend to move north and south, why does the typical storm move from west to east? Distinguish between "cyclone," "tornado," "hurricane," and "low." How do hurricanes and typhoons develop?

Tropical Rainy Climates:
The Rainforest Climate

CHAPTER 7

The Rainforest Climate in South America and Africa

■ TROPICAL RAINY CLIMATES IN GENERAL

There are two types of tropical rainy climates, the *rainforest* and the *savanna*, which together occupy a belt around the earth 20° to 40° of latitude in width centered on the equator. Variation in the width of the belt is due to the presence or absence of mountain ranges and the disposition of land and water areas within it. This belt corresponds approximately to the "zone" between the Tropics of Cancer and Capricorn, which mark the northern and southern limits, respectively, reached by the sun's vertical rays during the year.

The two types of tropical rainy climates have several characteristics in common. First and most obviously, there is never any frost —the coolest month averages 64° Fahrenheit. This makes possible such practices as the harvesting of sugar cane after a continuous growing period of 14 months.

The rainfall is high, between 30 and 100 inches a year (hence the designation "rainy"). It occurs commonly in thunderstorms and downpours rather than in the steady, three- or four-day drizzles characteristic of middle-latitude "frontal" conditions. In the rainforest climate the rain falls throughout the year, whereas the savanna climate experiences seasonal rains and hence has distinctively wet and dry seasons.

■ GENERAL ASPECTS OF RAINFORESTS

The average annual temperature of rainforest climates at sea-level stations ranges between 77° F. and 80° F. The "seasonal fluctuation," accordingly, is less than five degrees, although during the year the highest temperature may reach 96° F. The daily range, however, is regularly much greater. Night temperatures may be as much as 25° F. below day temperatures; hence the expression "Night is the winter of the tropics." The debilitating effect of the rainforest climate on middle-latitude peoples is due not so much to extreme heat (the heat is actually not extreme) as to other factors—the slight air circulation, the high relative and absolute humidity, and, because of the humidity, the low cooling power of the atmosphere, which results in a high sensible temperature. It is the inability of the body to lose heat through evaporation of perspiration that is so enervating.

The vegetation of the rainforest is chiefly a luxuriant growth of tall, closely spaced, thick-trunked trees that rise devoid of limbs or foliage for many feet until they spread out at the top. Individual "umbrellas" of the taller trees form a continuous canopy from 100 to 200 feet above the ground, and smaller trees usually form a sub-canopy slightly beneath the first. Isolated giants of the forest

Fig. 7.1—Rainforest in Equatorial Africa, with Clearing. (Courtesy, Belgian Government Information Center.)

break through to tower above the general canopy (Fig. 7.1).

The canopies are so dense and tightly thatched with leaves that there is eternal gloom beneath them. The absence of light prevents the growth of the underbrush or scrub associated with other kinds of forests and fosters the development of vines as the subordinate vegetation. By climbing the trunks of the trees the vines reach the light and add their foliage to the mantle above. Like the trees, the vine growth is luxuriant and gigantic; the stems are commonly several inches through. Along with the vines, known as *lianas*, there are parasitic plants which feed on the great trees, and orchids, which get their nourishment from the atmosphere.

The internal appearance of one of these rainforests may be likened to the interior of a great cathedral. In the still, twilight atmosphere great columns adorned with twisting lianas and soaring "aerial roots" rise on all sides, arching to form the roof a hundred feet or more overhead.

A unique characteristic of the rainforest is the extreme variety of trees within it. Unlike the typical middle-latitude forest, which may consist solely of one variety such as oak or pine, the rainforest has as many as 200 to 300 different species of trees to the square mile. There is, accordingly, no one predominant shade of green determined by a particular species of tree, but a mosaic of brown, gray, and yellow along with various greens, and perhaps spotted with brilliant red flowers. There is also a difference in that the horizon line of the rainforest is jagged, owing to the presence of giants of different heights, whereas that of a middle-latitude forest is rather uniform.

Because of the great number of species the tropical rainforest is not the great timber reserve it might at first be thought. Logging is not ordinarily practicable when the desired species must be searched for among a wide assortment of woods for which there is no market. However, the high value of mahogany, teak, and ebony may make profitable the selective logging necessary to obtain such woods.

The unique conditions of the rainforest affect the animal life as well. One assemblage inhabits the forest floor; it lives adjusted to the dampness and gloom. Another fauna lives in the canopy, where more of the fruits, flowers, nuts, and other edible portions of the plant growth are found. Snakes and in-

sects are found in abundance in both environments.

Plantation cultivation in regions of rainforest climate is confined to coasts, islands, and peninsulas, lands situated only a short distance from the sea, where the transportation problem is minimized. The products are all low-latitude crops—rubber, bananas, sugar cane, cacao, coconuts (which flourish only near the coast), palm oil, spices, and in the higher regions tobacco, coffee, and tea.

■ RAINFOREST CLIMATIC TYPES AND THEIR DISTRIBUTION

Three types of rainforest climate can be distinguished on the basis of the duration and cause of precipitation: the *constantly wet type,* the *monsoon type,* and the *windward coast type.*

The major regions of the world with the *constantly wet type* of climate are (Fig. 7.2): (1) the **Amazon Basin** and the contiguous

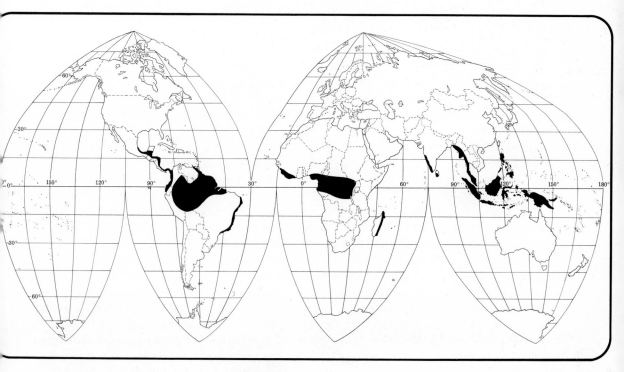

Fig. 7.2—World Distribution of Rainforest Climatic Regions.

region of the Guianas, the largest such climatic region; (2) the **Congo Basin,** slightly less wet than the Amazon because it is at a somewhat higher elevation; (3) the **Guinea coast** of Africa; (4) the **Malay Peninsula;** and (5) the **West coast of Colombia,** a small, less important region.

The *monsoon type* differs from the constantly wet type in that precipitation, although continuous throughout the year, is greatly augmented during the monsoon season, so that the seasons might be termed "wet" and "wetter." The main regions of this type are: (1) the **southwest coast of India (Malabar coast)** and **southwestern Ceylon;** (2) certain coastal portions of **Burma, Thailand,** and **Indochina;** and (3) **Indonesia,** although, strictly speaking, the monsoon climate there prevails only in the lower altitudes, as the mountains exhibit climatic zoning. But because population and agriculture in Indonesia are concentrated in the lower altitudes, the monsoon climate is the most significant of the region.

The *windward coast type* of rainforest climate occurs in the trade wind belt, where the regular, dependable trades blow onto land from the sea and are thus laden with moisture. If the land is low, nothing happens. But if the winds encounter a rising coast, the orographic rise (see Chapter 6, p. 97) causes them to precipitate their moisture in a heavy, more or less constant rainfall. Regions of this type include: (1) the **southeast coast of Brazil,** where the southeast trades rise over highlands a short distance behind the coast; (2) the **east coast of Central America,** where northeast trades provide the rain (this includes parts of southern Mexico and the northern side of the islands of the West Indies); and (3) **eastern Madagascar,** where again the southeast trades meet a rising coast. The windward coast development of rainforest climate is not present in northern Africa because there the northeast trades have been blowing across land and are devoid of moisture by the time they reach northeastern Africa.

■ RAINFOREST REGIONS AND COUNTRIES

A. THE AMAZON BASIN

General Aspects. The tropical rainforest of the Amazon Basin, or "Amazonia," as it is also called, comprises roughly one-third the area of Brazil, yet only 2 million of Brazil's population of 55 million live in the region. The local population is mostly Indian. Living conditions are primitive, disease is prevalent, and literacy is extremely low. What agriculture there is produces only enough for subsistence, for the clearing of land involves toilsome and unremitting struggle with the luxuriant natural vegetation. Some fruits and nuts can be gathered from wild growth; fish may be caught in the streams and a little game obtained in the rainforest. These minimize the dependence of the natives on cultivated produce.

The Amazon (Fig. 7.3) is the key to an understanding and appreciation of the region. The Brazilians call it the *Rio Mar,* or "River Sea." Its matchless size and its function, together with its tributaries, as almost the sole transportation system of the region have been noted (see Chapter 2, p. 36). Yet despite the relatively easy access to the region the river provides, the Amazon Basin is almost completely undeveloped. Because of its constantly wet rainforest climate and poor soils this vast basin, larger than all the United States east of the Mississippi, and all of it a plain, is little utilized. The seasonal flooding of the lower reaches of the Amazon results in the annual deposition of a layer of sediment over the region that replenishes the soil and renews its fertility. On the other hand, during that time the land is under water, unavailable for cultivation or habitation.

Products. The rainforest is the sole source of the important products of the region, the best known of which is **natural rubber.** "Para" rubber, as the Brazilian product is known (after the main seaport of the region, from which it is shipped), is the finest natural rubber in the world. It will probably retain a very small portion of the market de-

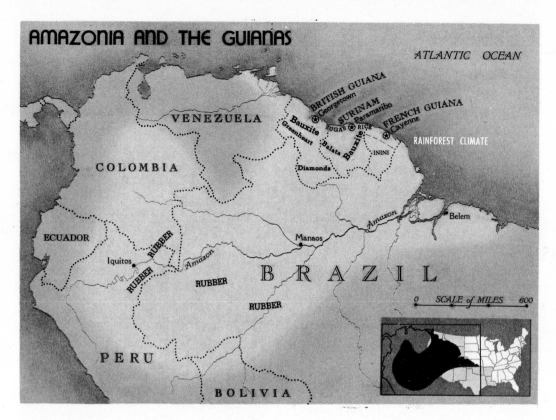

Fig. 7.3. Amazonia and the Guianas. The inset compares the area of the region with an equivalent area of the United States (states in white).

spite the fact that plantation, or cultivated, rubber and synthetic rubber now provide almost all the world's annual supply of this commodity. Physically it is quite possible to have rubber plantations in Amazonia, but the high cost of transportation, taxes, and lack of the required large labor supply make it unlikely that large plantations will ever be successfully developed there.

Large quantities of the rainforest's **timber** are marketed despite the handicaps that beset the industry. The lack of a concentrated stand of any particular species has already been mentioned. Although a tropical rainforest has a due proportion of softwoods along with its hardwoods, the softwoods must compete with the lumber from the middle-latitude forests in the European and North American markets; hence the hardwoods are better known. Another handicap is that the denser woods, for which there is

a demand in the northern lands, will not float in water. They cannot be rafted to the sawmill but must be carted overland through the forest. This greatly increases costs. Mahogany is an exception in that it may be floated in the "dry" season, when most of the sap is in the roots. This perhaps explains why mahogany is much more widely used and is better known than the wood of other species that have equally desirable qualities.

A third handicap to rainforest logging is the excessive hardness of many species—hardness so extreme it dulls the finest tools in a short time. The recently developed technique of power chain-sawing may be useful in overcoming this difficulty.

The future of the Amazon lumber industry may be bright owing to the possibility that with the increasing exhaustion of timber resources of the Northern Hemisphere much of the timber of Amazonia, regardless of species, may eventually find a market for its cellulose, a basic raw material in the rapidly expanding plastics industry.

Extreme Western Amazonia. Although by

far the greater part of the Amazon Basin is Brazilian territory, the western portion of the watershed, comprising the eastern foothills and lower slopes of the *Andes*, is divided between four countries—Colombia, Ecuador, Peru, and Bolivia. The region resembles the main portion of the basin to the east. The problem of transportation is more acute, however. The long water haul to the east is slow and expensive; moreover, with the exception of Bolivia the countries face the Pacific coast, and the normal trend of trade is to keep within the respective national boundaries, oriented toward the west. But because the high, rugged Andes rise between this part of Amazonia and its appropriate political-commercial outlets, the resulting isolation prevents any large-scale economic development.

CITIES OF AMAZONIA

Name	Type	Population (1950)	Country
Belem	Seaport	230,000	Brazil
Manaos	Seaport and governmental	90,000	Brazil
Iquitos	River port	40,000	Peru

Cities. **Belem** is the largest and most important city in northern Brazil, and the port of entry for the entire Amazon Basin. It is located not at the mouth of the Amazon proper but on a separate stream, linked with the Amazon by one of its distributaries. Belem was formerly known as Para, whence the name for Brazilian rubber.

Manaos is an isolated provincial capital located at the junction of a large tributary with the main stream. It exists because of its commerce in forest products.

Iquitos, 2500 miles up the Amazon from Belem, is the second ranking port of Peru. It has many small industries which manufacture products ranging from soap to rum.

B. THE SOUTHEAST COAST OF BRAZIL

Strictly speaking, the southeast coast of Brazil from just south of the Tropic of Capricorn

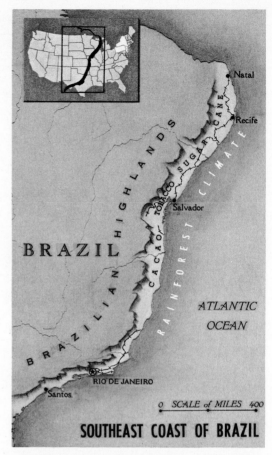

Fig. 7.4. Southeast Coast of Brazil. The inset compares the area of the region with an equivalent area of the United States (states in white).

to the easternmost point of the continent is not all in a rainforest climate. This narrow strip of coastland is, however, everywhere backed by the **Brazilian Highlands** (Fig. 7.4), which force the southeast trades into an orographic rise and give the entire coast a minimum yearly rainfall of 40 inches, with certain regions receiving more than 80 inches. The normal unpleasantness of such a humid tropical climate is greatly mitigated by the winds, which provide a steady sea breeze for the coastal cities.

Products. One of the major products of the region is **cacao**, the production and export of which was nationalized in 1943. This product, the "bean" of the cacao tree (Fig. 7.5), is the raw material for chocolate. "Cocoa," as the product is also known, is a corruption of the word "cacao," and is likely to be confused with the manufactured product of that name.

The cacao tree, besides needing the heat and moisture typical of the rainforest climate, also requires protection from the sun and wind and is, therefore, grown in the shade of larger trees. Brazil ranks among the leading producers of cacao.

The second major product is **sugar cane,** the plant from which two-thirds of the world's sugar is obtained. It is grown mostly in the northern section of the coast. Brazil is approximately the fifth ranking country in its production.

The third product is **tobacco,** in the production of which Brazil is also about fifth. It is the second major crop of the central portion of the region, which produces more than one-third of Brazil's total output.

All three of these products are "cash crops." That is, they are not grown for local consumption but are marketed as raw materials which must be refined and processed before they are useful. Wherever the agricultural products of a region are predominantly cash crops there exists a potential danger to that region's economy, as any large decline in the price of those products may have catastrophic results. Usually such re-

Fig. 7.5—Cacao Bean on Tree. (Courtesy, Brazilian Information Bureau.)

gions raise little food for domestic consumption, all effort being expended on raising a maximum amount of the cash crops. The proceeds of the sales are then used to buy food elsewhere. But if there is a great loss of income from the cash crop and no local food production, starvation in the midst of potential abundance may result.

It so happens that the southeast coast of Brazil does not run these risks. Large-scale, plantation-type agriculture is not well developed because of the scarcity of labor. Cultivation is therefore carried on by individual landholders, who are able to raise enough food for their own needs in addition to working on the cash crop.

The result of this type of development, however, is to handicap Brazil in the world markets for its cash crops. The work of the small-scale, individual producer is inefficient; the quality of the product when harvested is likely to be inferior. And, since products such as tobacco and cacao go through a preliminary processing or screening before shipment to market, carelessness and inefficiency at this stage still further reduce the final quality.

Thus this region illustrates the dilemma of the tropical cash-crop regions—either engage in large-scale, scientific plantation agriculture, with its attendant economic dangers, or take the competitive loss in value of the product when it is grown by many small, independent producers who raise the food they need.

CITIES OF THE EAST COAST OF BRAZIL

Name	Type	Population (1950)
Rio de Janeiro	Seaport, resort, governmental	2,300,000
Recife	Seaport	500,000
Salvador	Seaport	400,000
Santos	Seaport	400,000

Cities. The southeast coast is the site of many of Brazil's largest cities, ports which handle the numerous products of the plateau country behind them, as well as centers of manufacturing for the production of such things as beverages, wearing apparel, and furniture, a considerable industrial development that supplies Brazil with consumers' goods.

The concentration of population and industrial activity in these cities has led to the development of what is, for South America, a good transportation system. The cities are interconnected by a railroad paralleling the coast, with spurs inland to facilitate the movement of produce to the ports. It is the second best rail net of the continent.

Rio de Janeiro is by any test one of the world's great cities. It is the capital and metropolis of Brazil and the second largest city of South America. Not only is it the center of Brazilian culture and finance; it is also a world-famous resort, and the scenic beauty of its harbor makes it the most beautiful city in the world (Fig. 7.6). Architecturally Rio is a city of wide vistas and boldly designed apartment and office buildings. It is also the scene of the continent's greatest traffic jams in its too narrow, overcrowded streets.

Recife, Salvador, and **Santos,** in contrast, have little glamor. Recife is a local center of industry as well as a port, located near the eastern tip of the continent. Salvador is an export city and center of light industry in the cacao district, about two-thirds of the way between Rio de Janeiro and Recife. Santos, 225 miles southwest of Rio, is the world's greatest coffee port, kept busy shipping the tremendous outpouring of coffee from the inland plateau behind it, in another climatic region.

Fig. 7.6—Rio de Janeiro, Brazil. The scenic beauty of the city is well shown in this picture. (Courtesy, Brazilian Government Trade Bureau.)

C. THE GUIANAS

General Aspects. In the center of the northern coast of South America, bounded by Venezuela on the west and Brazil on the south and east, lie the Guianas (Fig. 7.3), the only remaining colonial possessions of the European nations on the continent. The mother countries are Great Britain, the Netherlands, and France; the total area of the colonies is 175,000 square miles, somewhat larger than the state of California.

The Guianas have three topographic divisions: a low, coastal area, the site of large-scale agricultural activities; a middle area of higher elevation containing most of the mineral and forest resources; and an interior, mountain region, containing some minerals, but remote and inaccessible.

The wet, hot climate is very trying. Only the coastal areas get a little relief because of the sea breezes. From April to August the shift of the heat equator brings the region into the belt of equatorial calms and gives it its "rainy season." There is, however, abundant rainfall throughout the rest of the year because of the orographic rise of the northeast trades as they blow upslope into the interior highlands. The yearly rainfall is between 90 and 120 inches on the coast; portions of the interior are somewhat drier.

The population of the region is a mixture of many tropical laborers, brought in by the governing countries to work on the plantations, plus a small number of colonial whites and a scattered, unnumbered native Indian population. The latter live in the inaccessible forests and are practically free from any control by the colonial powers.

British Guiana, the westernmost colony, is the largest and most densely populated, contains the most resources, and is the best developed of the three. This British colony furnishes more than three-quarters of all Guianan exports. The leading commodities are **sugar** and its derived product, **rum.** The East Indian laborers introduced the cultivation of **rice,** which has now developed so that there is an exportable surplus. The remaining nonmineral exports are all forest products, the most important of which is the **greenheart** tree, a wood of exceptional water-resistant qualities much used in marine construction, and of which British Guiana has the world's major supply. In addition to these exportable products such foods as bananas, cassava, and yams are grown by the population for local consumption.

Of the mineral resources, **bauxite**[1] is the most important if not the greatest in value. This mineral, the ore of aluminum, is found close beneath the surface, is easily mined in open pits, and is shipped abroad for refining. British Guiana is one of the leading producers of this important ore.

Diamonds constitute the second commercial product of the colony. They are found in its most inaccessible regions, where production is carried on under extraordinary difficulties. Nevertheless, British Guiana is a significant producer of diamonds.

Surinam, or Dutch Guiana, is smaller than British Guiana and has fewer resources. It is an irony of history that the Dutch, faced with the capture of Manhattan Island (site of New York City) by the British in 1677, renounced their claim to the future most valuable piece of real estate in the world, in return for which the British gave up their claims on Surinam.

The products of Surinam are in general the same as those of British Guiana but in smaller volume. Thus **sugar, rice, bauxite** and **gold** are the principal exports. In addition, **coffee** is also shipped abroad as the crop of second importance. Balata gum[2] takes the place of the greenheart of British Guiana as the colony's principal forest product. In developing sugar and rice plantations the Dutch made good use of the knowledge gained in their homeland in reclaiming considerable areas of coastal lowland.

French Guiana is the smallest, least developed, and least populated of the three colonies. Its population density of 1.3 per square mile is the lowest of any South American country. The low state of development is due as much to the extreme difficulty of communication with the interior and to unhealthful climate as to poor management of colonial enterprise. So remote is the interior that it has been separated from the coastal portion of the colony and established as a separate territory, **Inini.**

For many years the colony was in evil repute because of its penal establishment at Cayenne, the capital, and on Devil's Island, off the coast. These notorious institutions are, happily, a thing of the past. Criminals have not been sentenced to them since 1946.

Rice, beans and sugar cane are cultivated for local use. The chief export is gold; most of the other exports are forest products.

CITIES OF THE GUIANAS

Name	Type	Population	Country
Georgetown	Governmental and seaport	87,000 (1953)	British Guiana
Paramaribo	Governmental and seaport	86,000 (1952)	Surinam
Cayenne	Governmental and seaport	13,000 (1954)	French Guiana

Cities. **Georgetown** is notable for its cosmopolitan population—Negroes, East Indians, Chinese, and whites. Its residential quarter has an unusual aspect in that each dwelling is hidden within its own private jungle of tropical shrubs and trees. **Paramaribo** is an unhealthful town where the water from wells is so germ-laden that drinking water is obtained from the roof drainage. **Cayenne** is a sleepy French colonial outpost in which unpleasant reminders of the penal settlement still linger.

QUESTIONS. What is the major shortcoming of the "tropical-temperate-arctic" scheme of climatic classification? What climatic factors are used as the basis of the Köppen system of climatic classification?

What are the two types of tropical rainy climates, and what is their general world dis-

[1] Bauxite is a mineral of unusual geographic interest. It is the only major ore whose occurrence is governed by climatic factors. Bauxite requires a humid tropical or subtropical climate for its formation. It is, accordingly, found only in those countries that have such climates now or have had them in the geologic past.
[2] A rubber-like substance with special uses, such as material for endless belts.

tribution? What is the major difference between them? How does the precipitation of the tropical rainy climates differ from that of the middle latitudes? What are the temperature and humidity characteristics of the rainforest climate? Describe the typical rainforest. How does it differ from middle-latitude forests? Name the three types of rainforest climate. In what way do they differ from one another?

Describe the following features of the Amazon Basin: the population, the kind and status of agriculture, the general economic level of utilization of the region. How does the Amazon rubber industry differ from that in other parts of the world? How important is it now in the world rubber supply? What are the difficulties of the logging industry in Amazonia? What is the greatest handicap to the development of extreme western Amazonia?

Why is the southeast coast of Brazil a center of population and economic activity despite the rainforest climate and the low altitude? What are the major products of the region? Why is cacao a product of rainforest regions? What do the major products of the region have in common? What problems does this create for Brazil?

What is the unique political condition of the Guianas among South American countries? Which is the most important country in terms of its development and economic activity? The least important? What are the major agricultural and mineral products of each?

D. THE WEST COAST OF COLOMBIA

General Aspects. A short distance inland from the Pacific a small spur of the Andes, the **Cordillera Occidental** (Fig. 7.7), borders the western coast of Colombia. These mountains extend almost to the shores of the Caribbean Sea, ending west of the base of the Panama Isthmus. Between this range and the Pacific there is a narrow strip of lowland with an especially oppressive tropical rainforest climate. A small river, the *Atrato*, which drains this lowland, empties into a bay of the Caribbean just east of Panama; its course is almost due north from a source some 200 miles to the south. Its valley is a low, marshy plain. South of the valley the lowland continues as a strip of deltas formed

Fig. 7.7—Central America and the West Coast of Colombia. The inset compares the area of the Central American countries and the west coast of Colombia with an equivalent area of the United States (states in white).

by numerous small streams off the western slopes of the Cordillera.

From the colonial period until the building of the Panama Canal this region was one of great strategic value and utility. It was the most convenient and only lowland route between the Atlantic and the Pacific. Since the construction of the canal this virtue no longer exists; on the contrary, the low altitude accentuates the unpleasant features of the climate.

The climate is exceptionally bad even for its type. The region receives the heaviest rainfall of all South America—one locality experiences an annual deluge of 331 inches! There is no dry season; every day brings its rain. When the sun beats down the air is like the inside of a steaming teakettle. Human activity is profoundly discouraged under such conditions, and, as one might expect, the rainforest is unusually verdant and luxurious. Tropical trees and plants like the bamboo, the coconut palm, the rubber tree, the toquilla palm (from whose fiber Panama hats are made), the ceiba tree (which furnishes kapok), the tagua tree (whose nut is the source of imitation ivory), the banana tree, plantains, mangoes, breadfruit, cacao, coffee, and others all flourish abundantly.

But because of the climatic conditions the population is very sparse. The climate is too severe even for the Indians; 90 percent of the population is Negroid. The standard of living is extremely low; even the little agriculture necessary for subsistence is neglected. The soils are sterile in many areas and the inhabitants find it easier to live off the foods obtainable in the forest.

Products. The most important products of the region are **platinum** and gold. These minerals are found in "placers" (concentrations of the metals in gravel deposits) and are mined at many places on a small scale. As both are of high value, most of the population—men, women, and children—work the placers. The difficulties of production are extraordinary: the enervating climate reduces human labor to its lowest efficiency. Entire working crews have been wiped out by fever in one season. Transportation is limited to boats on small streams, pack horse, or even human porterage. Nevertheless, the production of platinum is sufficiently large to make Colombia the world's number two source of that metal.

What with the universal preoccupation with mining, and the primitive transportation situation, the forest wealth has been left almost untouched. Plantation cultivation of balata and rubber has begun, however, on a small scale.

CITY OF THE WEST COAST OF COLOMBIA

Name	Type	Population
Buenaventura	Seaport	55,000 (1951)

City. **Buenaventura** is a flourishing tropical seacoast city, the leading port of the country. It was destroyed by fire in 1931 and has since been rebuilt under the impetus provided by its having the best transportation route of any coastal town to the economically active interior of Colombia.

E. CENTRAL AMERICA

General Aspects. The narrow isthmus of Central America, extending from Mexico on the north to Colombia on the south, is divided politically into six independent republics and one colony (Fig. 7.7). The total area of this group of countries is almost 200,000 square miles, about midway between Texas and California in size. The population of over 9 million is larger than that of either of those states. The countries are strung along the isthmus from British Honduras on the north, through Guatemala, Honduras, El Salvador, Nicaragua, Costa Rica, and Panama on the south.

The Central American isthmus has a highland core throughout its length, but its height and lateral extent vary, as does the relative proportion of highland and lowland along the isthmus. In Guatemala the highland peaks reach to almost 14,000 feet; Costa Rica, with 10,000- to 12,500-foot peaks, contains another strong mountain development. Along the west coast is a relatively narrow lowland strip. The east coastal lowlands are widest in Nicaragua, eastern Honduras, and northeastern Costa Rica.

Fig. 7.8—Indian Girl, Guatemala. (B. Eichenberger.)

The population is in general sparse. For any one country it is proportional to the area of plateau within the country. Racially the range is from 80 percent white in Costa Rica to 60 percent Indian in Guatemala (Fig. 7.8). In the other countries the largest group is comprised of *mestizos,* or persons of mixed Indian-Spanish ancestry.

The inhabitants generally shun the low eastern coast in favor of the more agreeable climate of the central highlands, where the capitals of most of the countries are located. The lowland population is extensively infected with the two tropical diseases malaria and hookworm.

Products of the East Coast. The major crop of Central America is **bananas** (Fig. 7.9). The banana is predominantly a rainforest climate growth; 90 percent of the present world production is in rainforest regions, and some 70 percent of the total output comes from the Caribbean area. The climatic requirements of the banana are very exacting: the temperature must remain high and rainfall must come throughout the year; the land must be low but not swampy; and the composition and chemistry of the soil may vary only within narrow limits. These requirements are best fulfilled on the low-lying deltas and flood plains of the eastern coast of Central America.

The cultivation and marketing of bananas on a profitable basis is possible only through plantation agriculture on a scale large even for that type of enterprise. The hazards and difficulties are great, and the necessity for

large capital investment to overcome these handicaps is demonstrated by the size of the corporations engaged in the industry. Chief among these is the United Fruit Company, one of the great agricultural enterprises of the world. It employs 70,000 workers and cultivates over 2 million acres of land. As a consequence of the activities of such companies in Central America the term "Banana Coast" is now applied to what was formerly known as the "Mosquito Coast"[3] (not that the mosquitoes have been eliminated).

With the increasing realization that diversification of products is as much conducive to profits as it is to the enhancement of the economy of the country concerned, the corporations have been promoting the turning out of other products of the rainforest climate. Wartime shortages encouraged the undertaking of rubber and abaca (also known as "Manila hemp") projects.

Other products secured from the Central American rainforest are: **mahogany,** found in special abundance in the Honduras forests; **chicle** (the base of chewing gum); and **cacao,** which is of good quality here because of more careful cultivation and processing than elsewhere. Sugar was formerly important but is fast declining because of the irregular profits from its production in Central America.

Products of the Central Highlands. Although the climate of the other regions of Central America is not the rainforest type, the regions are included here to complete the discussion of Central America as a whole. Technically, the central highlands area has no specific type of climate, and the west coast is a region of minor economic significance.

As the east coast is known for bananas, so the highlands are associated with **coffee** (Figs. 7.10, 7.11). Indeed, except in Honduras and Panama, coffee is the leading export crop of all the Central American countries. The coffee is a mild variety for which there is a special demand. It is not as im-

Fig. 7.9—Banana Plantation With Drainage Channel. Two near-ripe "stems" of bananas are shown as they grow "upside down" on the banana tree.

[3] The original term was a corruption of the name of the former inhabitants, the *Misskito* Indians.

Fig. 7.10—Picking Coffee Berries in Costa Rica. (Courtesy, Embassy of Costa Rica.)

portant in the world market, however, as are the banana exports.

The occurrence of coffee on the higher ground is typical of the plant. Depending on the latitude, conditions for coffee growing are found within the tropics on plateaus or slopes between 1000 and 6000 feet in elevation. There middle-latitude crops such as potatoes, wheat, and barley can be grown. The agriculture is very primitive, however, and is at the subsistence level (i.e., sufficient only to provide for the farmer and his family). At the lower altitudes Guatemala and Costa Rica are especially favored for coffee production by the volcanic nature of the uplands. The lava and volcanic dust emitted during the erruptions of the local active volcanoes make exceptionally fertile soil when subjected to the weathering action of a tropical rainy climate.

Products of the West Coast. The Pacific coast of Central America differs from both the other two regions. It is alternately wet and dry, for it receives rain only when the heat equator moves north between April and November. Since it is seasonally dry the trees are fewer and there is more grass;

hence cattle raising becomes important. Some coffee is grown on the higher slopes, and sugar cane in the lowlands. Production is small, however. The west coast in general is more healthful than the east, and as a result communication between the interior and the sea is mainly on the Pacific side.

From the foregoing it is apparent that the seven Central American countries all produce the same things; therefore they compete with one another and trade between them is minor. Their trade instead shares the common characteristic of being almost exclusively with the United States, both in imports and in exports. But perhaps the oddest fact about their economies is the regional independence within each country. It was noted that bananas dominate the eastern regions under foreign plantation capital. Coffee dominates the central sections under individual planters with smaller holdings, and the Indians are in general on their own (rather poorly) in the west. The distinctly different populations, products, and climates of the three regions combine to make them separate and quite independent of each other in each country. This is developed to the extreme in Nicaragua, where there is so little communication between east and west that eastern Nicaragua imports its food from the United States, whereas western Nicaragua grows its own.

Fig. 7.11—Drying Coffee Beans, Seeds of the Berries, on Cement Platforms, Costa Rica. (Courtesy, Embassy of Costa Rica.)

CITIES OF CENTRAL AMERICA

City	Type	Population	Country
Guatemala	Governmental	294,000 (1950)	Guatemala
San Salvador	Governmental	195,000 (1953)	El Salvador
Belize	Governmental and seaport	22,000 (1946)	British Honduras
Tegucigalpa	Governmental	100,000 (1950)	Honduras
Managua	Governmental	110,000 (1950)	Nicaragua
San Jose	Governmental	300,000 (1952)	Costa Rica
Panama (City)	Governmental and seaport	128,000 (1950)	Panama

Cities. **Guatemala, San Salvador, Tegucigalpa, Managua,** and **San Jose** are all exotic, picturesque cities, with both Spanish and Indian aspects. Except for Managua they have plateau sites. As the capitals of their respective countries they completely dominate national political, economic, and cultural activity.

The two other cities are also national capitals, but differ in character. **Belize** is a stagnant backwater of the British Empire. **Panama** is an exciting, cosmopolitan "sailor's city" owing to its proximity to the Pacific end of the Panama Canal.

Fig. 7.12—Southwest Coast of African Bulge and Western Equatorial Africa. The inset compares the area of the region with that of the United States.

F. THE SOUTHWEST COAST OF THE AFRICAN BULGE

General Aspects. A small area of rainforest climate occurs on the southwestern coast of the bulge which the continent of Africa makes into the Atlantic Ocean. It includes the political divisions of **Sierra Leone, Liberia,** and the coastal portion of the **Ivory Coast**—a total of some 100,000 square miles, about the size of the state of Colorado (Fig. 7.12). The first-named country is a British colony, the second is an independent republic founded in 1847 by repatriated slaves from the United States, the third is a portion of French West Africa. The name Ivory Coast is retained from the early days of exploration and development when the traders named the sectors of the coast in this region for the products they obtained from them. Sierra Leone and Liberia together were known as the "Grain Coast."

This African region is perhaps the most unhealthful and disease-ridden occurrence of the rainforest lands. The rainfall in Liberia, which is typical of the region, is between 160 and 180 inches a year. In addition to the many tropical diseases with which the very dense native population is endemically ridden, tuberculosis, brought by the white race, takes its toll of the Negroes in the same measure that the tropical diseases affect the whites.

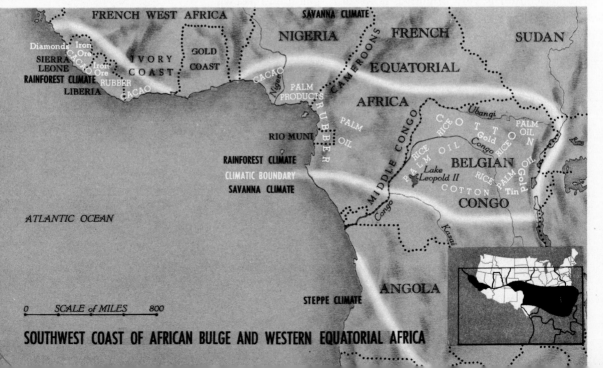

SOUTHWEST COAST OF AFRICAN BULGE AND WESTERN EQUATORIAL AFRICA

Products. In Sierra Leone the policy has been to let the local inhabitants cultivate their own lands rather than to develop plantation agriculture. The result has been a modest production of **cacao** and **palm products** (the country is one of the three leading producers of palm kernels). Sierra Leone is also one of the important sources of **diamonds**, although the first discovery was made as recently as 1930, and is an even more recently developed source of high-grade **iron ore**, which is shipped to England.

In Liberia major developments have been undertaken by two American companies, one in **rubber**, the other in **iron ore**. These two products, the leading exports, are shipped to the United States. Small amounts of forest products are also sent abroad.

In the Ivory Coast the natives have been taught to grow **cacao** in addition to carrying on their subsistence agriculture.

G. WESTERN EQUATORIAL AFRICA

General Aspects. From the apex on the west coast of Africa where the coast turns from a north-south to an east-west trend on the south side of the continental bulge, a rectangular area of rainforest climate, roughly 1.5 million square miles in area (about one-half the size of the United States) extends eastward (Fig. 7.12). This region resembles Amazonia in South America in the intensity of development of the rainforest climate, in the luxuriance of rainforest growth, and in the presence of a great river dominating most of the area. It differs from Amazonia, however, in that it is much more densely populated and is not chiefly within a single political unit.

The extreme western portion of the area is the coastal section of the British colony **Nigeria**, where the Niger River reaches the sea. The rainfall is extreme—over 150 inches yearly. East of this region is **French Equatorial Africa**—specifically, that portion of the colony known as the **Cameroons** and the **Middle Congo**— an area covered with almost unbroken rainforest. A short distance south of the coastal apex is the little-known

and unimportant Spanish possession **Rio Muni**. Under 10,000 square miles in area, it is a tiny tract of land on the coast of French Equatorial Africa.

The remaining portion of this rainforest area comprises about one-half the territory of the **Belgian Congo**. This colony practically coincides with the drainage basin of the Congo River. The heavy precipitation and large tributaries, such as the **Ubangi** and the **Kasai**, so swell the waters of the Congo that its volume is exceeded only by the Amazon. The Congo Basin, like Amazonia, is flat, with numerous swamps, and includes one large lake—**Lake Leopold II.** The Congo area, however, is almost 1000 feet above sea level. It is a "basin" in the sense that it is a depression in the larger, higher African plateau (see Chapter 2). Unlike the Amazon region, this area is not dependent on the Congo as its sole line of transportation into the territory. Although the impenetrability of the rainforest does compel the use of the river system, its defects, the marshy banks and rapids and the impossibility of direct boat connection between the interior and the coast, have led to railroad construction. Rail routes around barriers serve materially in overcoming the transportation handicaps.

Products. In the rainforest portion of French Equatorial Africa the products are **wild rubber, palm oil** and **coconuts**. In the similar portion of the Congo Basin the products are **palm oil** and **nuts** (the Congo is the second-ranking producer of the former), **cotton, rice,** wild rubber, lumber, and some sugar. Ivory is also exported.

H. THE EAST COAST OF MADAGASCAR

General Aspects. The world's fourth largest island, Madagascar (Fig. 7.13), is a French possession some 250 miles east of southeastern Africa which parallels the continental coast for about 1000 miles. The island is divided topographically into three regions: a low-lying western belt approximately one-third the width of the island, a central plateau averaging 5000 feet in altitude with

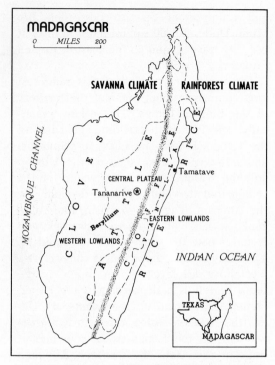

Fig. 7.13—Madagascar. The inset compares Madagascar with Texas, which has approximately the same area.

isolated mountain masses rising above it to nearly 10,000 feet, and a narrow belt of lowland on the eastern coast 10 to 15 miles wide. The drop from the plateau to the western lowlands is a series of gentle steps; to the east it is abrupt and precipitous.

The rainforest climate of Madagascar is due to the year-round orographic rise of the southeast trades against the central plateau and mountains. This climate is thus restricted to the eastern lowlands along the coast and to the steep eastern slope of the plateau. The rains average over 100 inches a year.

The chief agricultural product of the plateau and eastern slopes is **rice.** The east coast is also a major source of **vanilla.** Indeed, Madagascar and its neighboring islands are responsible for three-quarters of the world's supply of natural vanilla. **Coffee,** grown on the higher, eastern slopes of the highlands, is an important export to France.

CITIES OF MADAGASCAR

City	Type	Population (1953)
Tananarive	Governmental	187,000
Tamatave	Seaport	40,000

Cities. **Tananarive,** a truly governmental city with little commerce, is an unusual mixture of native huts with European dwellings and public buildings. Its location on a high ridge bespeaks its original defensive site. Large wooden palaces in the city are relics of the former era of native kings.

Tamatave, the chief port of the island, is crowded on a narrow peninsula and faces a harbor protected by a coral reef. It is aided in serving the island as a whole by a canal dug along most of the length of the east coast, allowing coastal shipping to move protected from the southeast trades.

QUESTIONS. Why is the lowland portion of the west coast of Colombia sparsely populated? What is the most important industry of the region? Explain the special significance of the important products in view of the climatic difficulties.

Name the countries of Central America. What is the general topography of Central America? What racial elements constitute the population? What is the most important crop? Why is the agriculture carried on by large American companies? What is the chief product of the highlands? Of the west coast? Why is there so little trade either among or within the Central American countries compared with the trade with the United States?

What is the most important agricultural product of Sierra Leone and the Ivory Coast? The most important mineral product of Sierra Leone and Liberia? Compare the degree of development of the Belgian Congo with that of Amazonia. Madagascar is the chief world source of what agricultural product?

CHAPTER 8

The Rainforest Climate in the Far East

I. THE MALABAR COAST

The term "Malabar Coast" refers in the strict sense to the southern third of the west coast of India. It is sometimes used, however, to refer to all the southern half of the west coast, a narrow lowland strip backed by mountains 5000 feet or more in altitude (Fig. 8.1). The heavy rainfall essential for the development of the rainforest results from the orographic rise over the mountains of the winds from the ocean, especially the monsoon winds.

The Malabar Coast is good plantation country. Its alluvial soil is continually renewed through deposition by west-flowing streams descending from the highlands to the east, thus counteracting the leaching due to the heavy rains, a factor which generally affects crop production adversely in rainforest lands.

The region contains large, valuable forests. The staple crop is **rice,** grown in large quantities. Coconut palms are abundant along the coast. The most valuable export products are **spices;** the climate is exceptionally well suited for the **pepper** plant. Other spices produced here are cinnamon and nutmeg.

J. CEYLON

General Aspects. The country of Ceylon, an island of 25,000 square miles (about one-half the size of Alabama), lies just off the southeast tip of India (Fig. 8.1). It is only 22 miles from the mainland to the nearest point of Ceylon, and the island is almost connected to India by a chain of low islands and reefs known as **Adam's Bridge.** The pear-shaped island has a central nucleus of mountains of over 8000-foot altitudes. This higher portion intercepts and forces an orographic rise of both the southwest and northeast monsoons (i.e., the monsoon of summer and the antimonsoon of winter). The rainfall from the summer monsoon is much the

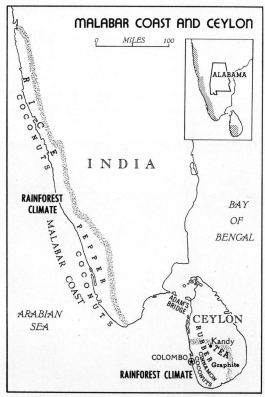

Fig. 8.1. Malabar Coast and Ceylon. The inset compares the region with Alabama, which has approximately the same area.

heavier; hence the south and west slopes of the highlands are by far the more productive. The rainfall exceeds 200 inches a year in some parts of this region. On the northern plain and extreme southeast coast there are no mountains to produce the rain, and only about 40 inches falls each year.

Products. Ceylon is an agricultural country. The largest acreage is in coconuts, sufficient to make the island the fourth-ranking country in the production of **copra** and number two in the production of **coconut oil.** Some **rubber** is also produced.

The southeast portion of Ceylon is the source of almost the entire world supply of **cinnamon.** This spice consists of the bark from shoots of a small evergreen tree indigenous to Ceylon and neighboring parts of India. Cinnamon cultivation has spread to other regions, but not widely enough to subject its home country to serious competition. The prime requirement for successful cinnamon production is cheap labor to cultivate the trees, gather the bark, and prepare it for marketing.

In bulk, the ranking agricultural product of Ceylon is **tea** (Fig. 8.2), of which the island is the second-ranking producer. The

Fig. 8.2—Picking Tea Leaves, Ceylon. In the distance tea plantations cover all the sloping land. (Courtesy, Embassy of Ceylon.)

mountainous areas of southern Ceylon are the best site ever discovered for tea growing. The shrubs are grown on slopes so steep that it is difficult to understand how the laborers, even though barefoot, can keep from sliding off. Erosion is prevented by terracing and drainage ditches. Tea is grown mostly at an altitude of 3000 feet, but extends as high as 7000 feet. The best teas are those from the higher slopes and picked during the months of least rainfall.

Like cinnamon, tea cultivation requires an exceptionally large labor force. One person is needed for every acre under cultivation. (On a farm in Iowa, by contrast, one man can grow 50 acres of corn.) The laborers come from India, work a short time, save a little money, then return home. With the population density that exists in this part of the world there is no danger of a labor shortage. When tea cultivation was first introduced the Ceylonese were reluctant to work on the plantations, but monsoon failures and consequent rice famines so impoverished them that they were compelled to accept employment or starve.

The coastal plains on the south and west produce the local foodstuffs—breadfruit, rice, and mangoes. The dry northern area has a barren soil, and even the forest is of the scrub type.

Most of Ceylon is composed of rocks rather rich in mineral deposits. Certain veins contain **uranium** and **thorium** in significant amounts, as do certain beach sands. **Graphite** of excellent quality has long been a well-known export of Ceylon, as well as many kinds of **gems,** found in the river gravels. Most of these minerals come from the southwestern part of the island.

CITIES OF CEYLON

Name	Type	Population (1953)
Colombo	Governmental and seaport	425,000
Kandy	Religious	57,000

Cities. **Colombo,** the capital and chief commercial city of Ceylon, has an excellent artificial harbor with modern port facilities.

Various parks and recreation facilities built by the British throughout the city and its suburbs give it a pleasing aspect. **Kandy,** an exotic religious city, contains the most sacred of all Buddhist shrines—the Temple of the Tooth (Fig. 8.3)—which houses a reputed tooth of Buddha.

Ceylon as a Whole. Ceylon became in 1948 an independent country within the British Commonwealth, having been for a century and a half a part of British India. Within its short life as an independent country Ceylon has distinguished itself by the political maturity of its government, both in internal stability and in its voice among the councils of the new nations of southern Asia. Although an agricultural country, Ceylon must import two-thirds of its food needs. The achievement of a stable economy despite this circumstance is the country's greatest problem.

Fig. 8.3—Temple of the Tooth, Kandy, Ceylon. (Courtesy, Embassy of Ceylon.)

K. SOUTHERN BURMA

General Aspects of Burma as a Whole. The rainforest climate in Burma is restricted to the southern, coastal, and deltaic portions of the country (Fig. 8.4). Burma is nevertheless considered as a whole at this point because the rainforest region is the political and cultural heart of the country.

Burma comprises some 260,000 square miles, an area somewhat smaller than Texas. It is situated between India and China and extends down the Malay Peninsula to the west of Thailand. Burma can be divided into three distinct topographic regions. On the west along the Indian border is the **Arakan Highland,** which causes an orographic rise in the southwest monsoon and a rainfall of almost 200 inches a year. The dense rainforest that originally covered the windward slopes was removed and is now largely replaced by bamboo thickets. The region is sparsely inhabited.

In the center is a low-lying block drained by the **Irrawaddy River.** The alluvial plain and delta of this stream constitute most of the agriculturally productive land of Burma. Most of Burma's population resides in this area.

A southern projection of the country constitutes the base and northeastern portion of the Malay Peninsula and is known as the **Tenasserim District** of Burma. Its appearance is much like that of the Arakan region.

East of the Irrawaddy and roughly parallel to it flows Burma's second river, the **Salween.** Its delta and valley are also foci of population and agriculture, though on a smaller scale than along the Irrawaddy.

Burma is thus sharply separated from its neighbors on both east and west. Its climate and topography are quite distinct from those of India in general and are so similar to those of the countries to the east that Burma was formerly called by some "British Indochina."

Timber Resources. Burma is richly endowed with such timber resources as are common to the rainforest countries. Unlike the other regions, however, Burma has made

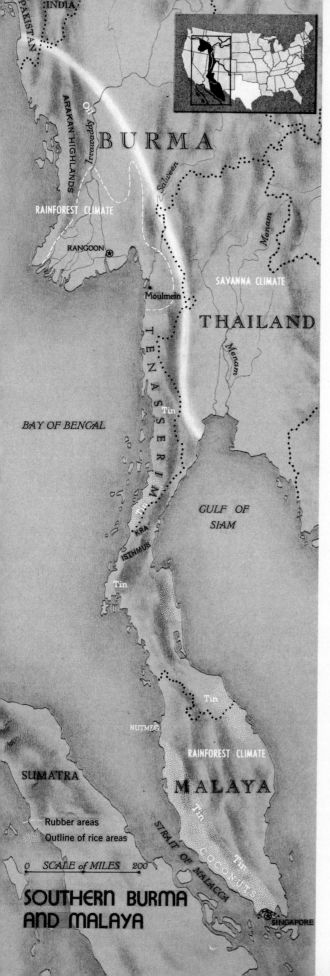

SOUTHERN BURMA AND MALAYA

extensive use of the timber itself rather than the forest products. More lumber is exported from this country than from all the rest of Asia except Siberia. All the valuable forest lands are preserves in which logging operations are permitted only under license.

The timber resources include **mahogany, sandalwood, rosewood,** and especially **teak.** Sandalwood and rosewood take special finishes and are highly prized in cabinetmaking and carpentry. The renown of Burma in lumber production, however, is for its teak.

Teak is a highly valuable wood because it is extremely durable and does not warp or crack. It is also the most prized of all woods for shipbuilding, as it contains an oil that serves to protect metals in contact with it from corrosion, a valuable property where exposure to salt air or water must be withstood.

Agriculture. Farming is centered on the deltas and valley lowlands. About two-thirds of all cultivated land is devoted to **rice,** by far the most important crop. The areas of chief production are the deltas of the Irrawaddy and Salween rivers (which receive over 100 inches of rain yearly) and the Tenasserim and Arakan coastal areas. Burma's total yield is not large when compared with the rice crop of the world but is sufficient to place the country third in rank of producers of this grain. The significant circumstance, however, is that the normal production per inhabitant is almost one-half ton, so much above the domestic requirements that Burma is able to export half its crop in normal years. The importance of this fact for the Oriental economy is very great. Rice is the staple food of hundreds of millions of people in the Eastern Hemisphere. Most of the Oriental countries do not grow enough to supply their populations; imported rice must make up the difference between sufficiency and famine in bad years.

Sesamum is next after rice in volume of production. Sesame oil is extracted from the

Fig. 8.4. Southern Burma and Malaya. The inset compares the area of the region with an equivalent area of the United States (Texas).

seeds of this plant. The oil is not well known in the United States but is of considerable commercial importance elsewhere in the world. It is similar to olive oil, and its uses are the same.

Transportation. The transportation arteries are the two large rivers. The Irrawaddy is navigable for 900 miles upstream, and in the absence of an extensive road system this long water route is an important means of access to the interior. There has been some railroad development, mostly in a north-south direction. Overland east-west connections are so poor, on the other hand, that the Arakan district, for example, must depend upon marine transportation between it and the rest of Burma. There is no railroad connection with any neighboring country.

The People. The 19 million inhabitants of Burma speak 126 different native languages and dialects. They are racially Mongolian and are divided in such tribes as the Burmans, Karens, Shans, Chins, and Kachins, with minority Indian and Chinese groups numbering in the hundred thousands. The ambition and strong sense of independence of the Burmese have caused them to be labeled the "Irish of the East."

The religion is strongly Buddhist, and Burma has begun a Buddhist revival in southeast Asia. Moslems, Christians, Hindus, and others each constitute less than 5 percent of the population. The Karens have their own form of spirit worship. They have not forgotten that they were the slaves of the Burmese in early times, and strive to preserve their own customs and traditions distinct from those of the Burmese.

The unusual status of Burma—a relatively underpopulated and underdeveloped country situated between the densely populated lands of India and China—has made it attractive to immigrants, especially those from India, who have been lured there by higher wages. These immigrant Indians perform the menial, "coolie" work in Burma; the Chinese immigrants are mostly artisans and merchants.

Cities. **Rangoon,** the capital of Burma, is dominated by a great golden pagoda rising

CITIES OF BURMA

Name	Type	Population
Rangoon	Governmental and seaport	700,000 (1952)
Moulmein	Seaport	71,000 (1941)

more than 500 feet above the city. Its chief industries of rice milling and teak working are carried on in the suburbs. The bulk of the city's commerce is in those products. **Moulmein** is a secondary rice and teak port which is suffering from a slow silting up of its harbor.

Burma as a Whole. Burma achieved independence in 1948 along with Ceylon, as part of the British relinquishment of India, but Burma's severance of empire ties was complete. In contrast to the calm progress of newly independent Ceylon, however, the first few years of Burma's independence were chaotic and bloody. No less than five rebellions raged separately but simultaneously during the early years, and assassination and political chaos all but toppled the new nation. Gradually, however, order was achieved, and the alert, ambitious Burmese have provided the beginnings of a potentially important nation in southeast Asia.

L. MALAYA AND LOWER THAILAND

General Aspects. The Malay Peninsula extends for some 750 miles in a south-southeasterly direction from the Tenasserim District of Burma, varying from 60 to 200 miles in width (Fig. 8.4). Although the northern half of the peninsula is Thai territory it can be considered here as a topographic and economic extension of "British Malaya," as the southern half of the peninsula is known.

British Malaya includes the **Federated Malay States,** the **Unfederated Malay States,** and the **Straits Settlements,** all part of the complex political and administrative system that is the British Empire. The "Malay States" term is indicative of a certain degree of autonomy for the native rulers, each of whom has his British adviser.

Topography and Climate. The backbone of the peninsula is a range of mountains with peaks of 7000 feet or more in altitude. The mountains divide the country unequally: the larger and wider plains area is on the west, where the climate is much like that of Burma. For a rainforest climate, however, it is not too unhealthful. Humidity is high, but sea breezes along the coast help mitigate the discomfort this causes. The rainfall averages 100 inches on the west, 120 inches on the east. The east coast receives greater precipitation because the northeast monsoon adds to the rain brought by the regular southeast monsoon.

The heavy rainfall and short distance from the mountains to the sea have given rise to a dense network of streams, which, in the absence of roads, serve as transportation routes. There is also a limited railroad system. Over 70 percent of the country is a dense rainforest, much of it unexplored.

Resources and Products. Malaya, although a small territory, leads the world in the production of two highly important commodities—**natural rubber** and **tin.** Rubber trees

Fig. 8.5—Tapping a Rubber Tree in Malaya. (Courtesy, British Information Services.)

require a constant high temperature, plentiful rainfall evenly distributed throughout the year, and rich, well-drained soil (Fig. 8.5). Shortly after rubber cultivation was started in the Orient it was found that the climate of Malaya was exceptionally well suited for the most productive varieties of rubber tree. In the Amazon region there is a season of lower rainfall, whereas the rainfall of the Malay country is almost unchanging from month to month. The unusually uniform climate insures a steady yield of latex (the milky sap from which rubber is made) the year round.

The significance of the Malayan rubber production in the country's economy is indicated by the fact that 10 percent of the total area is planted to rubber, over three-fifths of all the land under cultivation in the peninsula. Although Malaya supplies large fractions of the world total output of several other commodities, the value of yearly exports of rubber surpasses the value of all the others.

Tin, the other chief product, is a relatively scarce metal in terms of the geographic distribution of its deposits. As tin ore is heavy it tends to be concentrated at the bottom of gravel beds, in placer deposits. The largest tin placers are found on the western plain, between the mountains and the Strait of Malacca. The placer mines were originally operated by Chinese with manual labor. When the rich deposits exploitable through such methods were worked out, heavy machinery in the form of dredges became necessary, and the British became dominant in the industry. The lower-grade gravels are now worked profitably on a large scale (Fig. 8.6). It is said that the dredging, oddly enough, improves the land for agriculture.

In addition to rubber the agricultural products of Malaya are **copra** (Fig. 8.7), in which the region ranks third or fourth, and **nutmeg.** Rice is grown for local consumption.

The People. Like Burma, Malaya is a region of relatively sparse population between two overpopulated areas, but with this great difference: the tin and rubber industries require great amounts of labor. It has been

Fig. 8.6—Hong Fatt Tin Mine Near Kuala Lumpur, Malaya. (Courtesy, British Information Services.)

Fig. 8.7—Dehusking Coconuts for Copra, Perak, Malaya. The nuts are brought from the groves to the dehusking area in shallow-draft boats. (Courtesy, British Information Services.)

said that except as the tremendous labor supply of India and China was available at low cost and susceptible to easy adjustment with changes in demand the two great industries could never have developed as they did. This situation is directly reflected in the composition of the Malayan population. Of a total population of over 5.3 million, native Malayans comprise not quite one-half, Chinese are almost as numerous, and there is an Indian minority of 10 percent. The Chinese

work in the tin mines, the Indians on the rubber plantations. In boom times both are brought in by the thousands; in depression periods they return home. The Malays themselves are Moslems; the imported laborers retain their own religions.

CITY OF MALAYA

City	Type	Population (1949)
Singapore	Seaport	700,000

City. **Singapore,** an island off the southern tip of the Malayan peninsula, is a British colony quite distinct from the Malayan Union both physically and politically. The city (Fig. 8.8) is the commercial capital of Malaya, however, and is one of the world's great strategic, commercial crossroads. It has long typified the glamorous, exotic, cosmopolitan, Oriental trading center as developed by the former great imperial powers of Europe. In an era when empire everywhere is on the decline this colonial jewel still gleams brightly, as fascinating, exotic, and valuable as ever.

Fig. 8.8—Harbor and City of Singapore. (Courtesy, British Information Services.)

M. INDONESIA

General Aspects. The thousands of small islands of the **East Indies** (Fig. 8.9) comprise a belt some 1000 miles wide centered slightly south of the equator. This belt extends over 3000 miles from east to west, and from south of Burma almost to the east coast of Australia. The main islands are **Java, Sumatra, Borneo, Celebes, Timor,** and **New Guinea.** Aside from these six the islands are of relatively minor size and significance.

The East Indies were under Dutch rule from the seventeenth century until World War II. In the wake of the Japanese occupation several separate native states sprang into being. In 1949 and 1950 these states achieved formal independence and merged into the Indonesian Republic.

Topography and Climate. The larger islands all have mountainous interiors; they are the tops of a "drowned" mountain system, an extension of the circumpacific system that swings down through Kamchatka, Japan, and the Philippines, and of the Himalayan system that bends south through

Burma and is continued through Sumatra and Java. Many of the islands have volcanoes, some of which are still active, and fertile flatland margins—shelves attached to the slopes of the submerged mountains, developed from erosion of the mountains and deposition in the sea of the debris brought by the streams that course down the mountains.

The climate is similar throughout most of the area—low pressure, high humidity, and more or less constant rainfall—in other words, that of the equatorial doldrums. The rainfall in many places is over 100 inches a year, and rainforests cover most of the islands.

The People. The total population of Indonesia is almost 80 million, the bulk made up of native Indonesians. The largest nonnative group is Chinese, and there are now also present thousands of Japanese who came to the islands during the conquest of World

Fig. 8.9—East Indies, Including the Philippines. The inset compares the area of the region with an equivalent area of the United States (states in white).

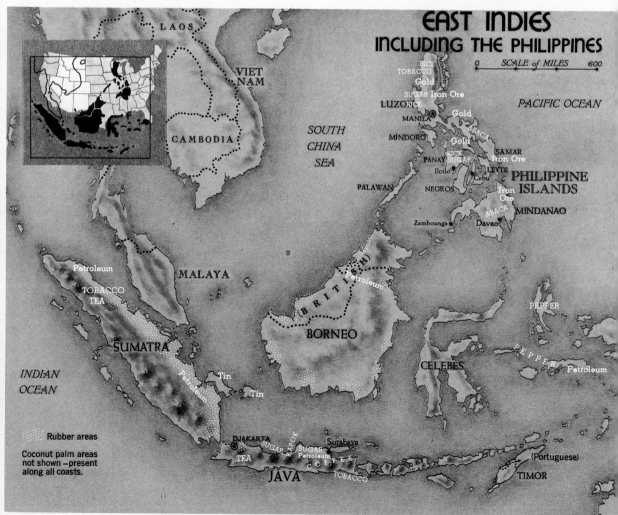

War II and who will never return to their homeland, having found refuge in the wild interior rainforests. Another group, known as "Eurasians," are a result of the Dutch colonial regime. The Netherland colonials regularly became permanent residents of their colonies, not temporary adminstrators as is true of the English colonial system. The Eurasians are the progeny of extensive intermarriage with the Indonesians by the Dutch, and formerly constituted the subordinate administrative class under Dutch rule.

Some 60 languages are spoken throughout the islands, but Malay is understood in most of the territory. The prevailing religion is Islam (Mohammedanism), but there are large minorities of Christians, Brahmans, and Buddhists.

Resources and Products. The East Indies are unusually rich in mineral resources and produce vast yields of tropical agricultural products. A group of islands off the east coast of Sumatra is geologically a continuation of the Malay Peninsula; the tin deposits also continue into them, making them the second-ranking area of world production of this metal. **Tin,** accordingly, is the major mineral product of the East Indies as a whole.

The second mineral product is **petroleum,** found in Borneo, Sumatra, and Java in that order of importance. Although the oil fields do not rank high in volume of output, their location gives them immense strategic and economic value, as they are the only significant source of oil in the Far East.

The East Indies are leading exporters of an astonishing number of tropical agricultural products. The islands rank first as exporters of **copra.** The ubiquitous coconut palm (Fig. 8.10) bears a cash crop on even the smallest islands, and the yield is everywhere collected by the local inhabitants. East Indian dominance in copra production has not resulted from exceptional suitability for the coconut palm, for the tree thrives along seacoasts everywhere in the tropical rainy climates, but from the use of cheap labor and efficient methods of preparation and handling. Nor does the rank of the is-

Fig. 8.10—Coconut Palm.

lands as the premier exporter mean they are the greatest producer. It has been estimated that about two-fifths of the total coconut crop of the world is used within the producing countries.

The East Indies are the second-ranking **tobacco** exporter. This crop is raised on Java (Fig. 8.11) and Sumatra, the latter island producing a leaf of very high quality. The excellence of Sumatran tobacco is the result

Fig. 8.11—Tobacco Field in Central Java. (Courtesy, Embassy of Indonesia.)

of painstaking care and the scientific methods of agriculture and processing introduced by the Dutch.

The islands are third in world production of both **coffee** and **tea.** Again, Java and Sumatra are the significant islands. The **Molucca Islands** west of New Guinea are **spice** producers, accounting for 85 percent of the world's **pepper. Rubber** is grown in Sumatra, Borneo, and Java; production is about 35 percent of the world total.

Of the six major islands, Borneo and Timor are the least developed and contain the most primitive native cultures. Borneo is held in low esteem because it lacks fertile soils. Sumatra was in the process of intensive development which was cut short by World War II. Java, however, is geographically so richly endowed as to make it chiefly responsible for the impressive production and export standing of the East Indies as a whole. Its geography, therefore, merits extended discussion.

Java. **Java** and **Madura** (a small island off the northern coast) have a combined area of slightly over 50,000 square miles, or a little larger than New York State. Here live over 42 million people, *supported almost entirely by the agricultural yield of the area.* The average density of population is around 1000 per square mile, and in certain areas it reaches 1700. This compares with Iowa, the most densely populated agricultural state in the United States, where the highest density figure is under 500 per square mile. Eighty percent of Iowa's area is farmed, yet less than 50 percent of the total area of Java is under cultivation. Java is smaller than Iowa, which has considerable industry in addition to its agriculture, yet supports 16 times as large a population.

In addition to feeding its millions of inhabitants Java exports more than a dozen major agricultural products. Though the living standard is low judged by the criteria of Western civilization, Java's inhabitants are well off compared to the millions in India and China. Why is there this difference?

From very early times Java has been densely populated and intensively cultivated while the other islands of the East Indies remained regions of savagery. The fundamental reason for Java's productiveness is its fertile soil, derived from volcanic ash. Countless eruptions of the string of volcanoes along the central axis of the island have spread finely divided volcanic dust over the slopes of the cones and the lowlands between. The fresh rock substance from deep below the surface supplies the soluble mineral foods essential for plant growth. When these are not perennially renewed, as is true in most other rainforest regions, they are rapidly depleted by the leaching action of the incessant tropical rains. The ash soil also has the advantage of being porous; thus there is no waterlogging even under the heavy downpours.

The bedrock under much of the island is limestone, which itself yields a productive soil. On the basic fertility of the volcanic and limestone soil the Indonesians, with zeal and energy exceptional in the tropics, developed their agriculture. They constructed an elaborate system of terraces that keeps the heavy rains from washing away the rich soil and permits the use of slopes of 45 degrees (Fig. 8.12).

The final element in this exceptionally successful exploitation of rainforest territory was the enlightened economic policies of the Dutch colonial administration. The Dutch were intelligent and far-seeing enough to realize that effective utilization could be achieved only through encouragement of native agriculture in addition to the traditional plantation development, and through vigorous public health measures to raise the health standard and thus benefit not only the Indonesians but the planters as well. As a consequence most of the land remained under Indonesian cultivation and ownership, a circumstance at the foundation of the island's successful economy. Improvement in public health made possible the rise in population from 5 million to over 40 million in little more than a century. The Dutch measures were not all altruistic, however. Labor-forcing devices were freely used.

A brief recital of the products of this amazing island will make clear how soil fertility, the energy of the Indonesians, and the perspicacity of the Dutch have made possible the agricultural *tour de force* that is Java.

The basic crop of the island is **rice**; it is food for Java's millions, 90 percent of whom are agricultural laborers. The Dutch administration insured enough rice production for subsistence each year by restricting the acreage devoted to other crops. The other main domestic food crops are **corn** and **soybeans.**

Although Java is not unusually well suited to the growing of sugar cane it produces one-sixth of the total world crop and is the second largest exporter of **sugar,** the leading cash crop of the island. High returns are obtained by intensive cultivation (in contrast to that in other major sugar-producing areas), by rotation of crops (cultivation in turn of different crops on the same land to maintain the fertility of the soil), and by the use of cheap but efficient labor. The major sugar area is in the east of the island, where the rainforest conditions are less pronounced.

Fig. 8.12—Rice Terraces. The maintenance of the terraces is itself an enormous task, in addition to the labor expended on cultivation. (Courtesy, Ross Bristol.)

The eastern area is also the site of **tapioca** cultivation. Tapioca is the commercial product obtained from the root of the cassava plant. The tapioca-processing industry of Java provides almost 90 percent of the world supply.

A third product localized in the eastern end of the island is **tobacco.** It is of low quality compared with that of Sumatra and is grown mostly as a rotation crop with rice.

Tea growing is concentrated on the volcanic slopes of the western part of the island. Here the heavier rainfall (150 inches) combined with the high temperature gives a high yield. The tea shrubs are raised in both plantations and home gardens. Mixing the garden product with that from the plantations lowers the quality of the marketed product but contributes to Java's importance among world tea producers.

Roughly one-half the **rubber** output is also non-plantation. **Coffee** is grown along with the rubber, a combination that enables Java to compete successfully with the naturally better coffee lands of the Western Hemisphere. The trees are grown at altitudes between 2000 and 4000 feet, and so yield a good-quality product.

Still another product in which Java leads is **kapok.** This is a light, fluffy substance, the product of the kapok, or ceiba, tree. It can

support 35 times its weight in water, a property which gives it preëminence in the manufacture of life preservers.

Climatic zoning due to altitude, as it affects tropical agriculture, is well illustrated in Java. The rainforest is predominant below 2000 feet, with sugar and rice grown on the flat lowlands, rubber and pepper on the low hills. Above 2000 feet tea and coffee are dominant. Above 12,000 feet on some of the highest peaks middle-latitude crops are grown to a limited extent.

In addition to the foregoing agricultural products, Java produces indigo and teak. For mineral wealth it has oil, coal, tin, and gold. Compared with some of the other East Indian islands, however, its mineral resources are small.

CITIES OF JAVA

Name	Type	Population
Djakarta	Governmental-seaport	4,000,000 (1955)
Surabaya	Seaport	340,000 (1953)

Cities. **Djakarta** (formerly Batavia) is the capital of the Republic of Indonesia. It inherited a fine, modern port from the Dutch regime as well as a section of the city which, with its old Dutch residences, looks in places like an urban district in the Netherlands. The climate of Djakarta fits perfectly all the specifications of a rainforest climate at sea level.

Surabaya, the second port of Java, was formerly the main naval base of the Netherlands East Indies. The naval installations still dominate the city.

Indonesia as a Whole. As another of the new independent countries of southeast Asia created after World War II, Indonesia has experienced early years full of turmoil and troubles. The new nation faced a severe wartime destruction of property and at the same time lost its technical, professional, and administrative class. The lack of opportunity for education under Dutch rule is evidenced by the 7 percent literacy rate, raised to 25 percent by 1955.

As in Burma, the absence of political experience and maturity in the population fostered numerous rebellions, separatist movements, and local political chaos. Gradually, however, Indonesia has made progress despite political shakiness, owing in no small part to the country's basically strong resource position.

N. THE PHILIPPINES

General Aspects. Physically, climatically, and in native population the Philippines are much like the islands of the East Indies. The history of the Philippines has differed markedly, however, from that of the East Indian islands, and their present political status alone warrants their discussion as a separate unit.

The Philippines total 115,600 square miles in area (slightly larger than Nevada), but fewer than 500 of the more than 7000 islands that constitute the group are over one square mile in size. The most important islands, in order of size, are: **Luzon, Mindanao, Samar, Negros, Palawan, Panay, Mindoro, Leyte,** and **Cebu** (Fig. 8.9).

The Philippine chains of mountains and volcanic peaks tend to run north-south, with narrow, interrupted plains between ranges and along the coasts. Rainforests cover the mountains; the plains are the site of the major agricultural activities and the centers of population. The most important and largest plain is that of central Luzon, which runs north from Manila Bay.

The climate of the Philippines is not uniform throughout the islands. Although the islands as a group are included in the rainforest region, local conditions produce many variations, especially in the number and duration of the wet and dry seasons. The Philippines are actually in the trade wind belt and normally would not receive the heavy rainfall of the rainforest type of climate. The summer monsoon is responsible for the added rainfall. An unpleasant feature of the climate and location is the frequent occurrence of typhoons, most of which cross the islands north of Manila Bay.

The People. The Filipinos[1] are not a single race but a group of peoples of Malayan stock. They comprise all but a small fraction of the total population of over 19 million. The most important racial intermixture other than Spanish has been Chinese. Most of the Chinese immigrants were men, who married Filipino women, so that there is a strong Chinese element present in the population of certain urban areas that is not brought out in population statistics. Before 1941 Japanese were numerous on Mindanao.

With the inauguration of the republic in 1947, Tagalog (a Malayan dialect, one of the 64 native languages and dialects of the country) was made the official language. Both English and one of the other native dialects are spoken by a majority of the people, however, and English and Spanish are still the languages of commerce.

The religion of the islands is predominantly Roman Catholic; 80 percent of the population is of that faith. The largest exception is the Moro tribe of Mindanao, which is fanatically Moslem.

Products and Resources. In comparison with Java the land of the Philippines is almost unused. Over 60 percent of the total area is arable but relatively little is actually under cultivation. Almost all of this area is owned by Filipinos. The Philippine rainforests, moreover, are much less exploited than are those of many other such areas. They are mostly under government ownership and there is only a small production of cabinet woods.

As is true of all Oriental tropical lands the major food crop of the Philippines is **rice.** The total production of the islands is not, however, sufficient to place the country among the ranking world producers. Its cultivation is concentrated on the central Manila plain and scattered areas of the other

[1] The name was originally used by the Spanish to mean those of mixed native-Spanish ancestry. The people preferred it as a national designation to the term "Indios" by which they were originally known.

islands. Associated with this rice cultivation is one of the man-made wonders of the Orient. In northern Luzon a tribe known as the *Ifugao* have, through centuries of labor, produced the most perfect terracing in the world, excelling even the intensive development in Java. Entire mountainsides have been transformed into series of steps which hold rice fields, in some instances continuously over an ascent of almost a mile.

The second food crop of the islands is **corn;** other tropical foods, including fruits, are raised in smaller quantities for local consumption.

The leading cash crop in export value has been **sugar,** with a total production sufficiently great to rank the Philippines as one of the first five producers. The crop is grown on the central Luzon plain and the lowlands of the western islands (where the rainfall is not so heavy or continual). Although Java's production has exceeded that of the Philippines, the latter's potential is far greater. The lack of complete development has been due to the smaller labor supply and the fact that there were no Dutch in the Philippines to compel such development.

The next ranking cash crops, grown along the coasts of all the islands, are the products of the coconut palm—**copra,** and **coconut oil.** The Philippines lead in the production and export of the oil and rank second or first in copra production.

The fourth-ranking agricultural export is **pineapples,** the result of great American investment in scientifically managed plantations on Mindanao.

In the production of **abaca,** or Manila hemp, the islands have had until recently a complete monopoly. Manila hemp is a long, tough fiber, the raw material used in the manufacture of the best heavy rope and hawsers. The low yield of fiber per plant and the previous lack of substitutes have made Manila hemp an unusually costly material. The plant needs well-drained soil and high rainfall, and like the banana plant it is weak and top-heavy. It is grown therefore on the south and southeast coasts of Luzon, Leyte, and Mindanao, which are out of the typhoon area and have a rainfall between 80 and 140 inches a year.

The continued Philippine monopoly is mainly the result of an early start and the supply of cheap labor. Exceptional skill is needed to obtain high-quality fiber from the plant, and during the processing for export. These skills were acquired early and passed from generation to generation. Much labor is needed in all stages of the harvesting and processing. No satisfactory machinery has yet been developed to do any of this work.

The islands are also one of the important **tobacco** producers of the world. The best-quality product, which has a high reputation in the Orient, is grown in the **Cagayan Valley** of northern Luzon, where annual floods renew the fertility of the soil. Tobacco is also grown on the central Luzon plain and on Panay, Cebu, and Negros.

Among the mineral products **gold** is the most important, occurring on Luzon and Mindanao. The 1940 output was worth $38 million, but output in the first decade after World War II did not exceed half that amount. The second mineral of the islands is **iron.** Large deposits occur on Mindanao but there is little production because of difficulty in smelting the ore. The main production comes from scattered, small deposits of high-grade ore. **Copper** from domestic ore is also produced and exported.

Industries. Most of the Philippines industries are concerned with the processing of agricultural products. They include **sugar refining, rice milling, cigar and cigarette manufacture, distilling,** and **textile manufacture.** The ranking position of the islands as exporters of coconut oil is due to the lack of shipping space during World War I and the large processing industry established in the islands as a consequence. Once started, the Philippine coconut oil industry possessed the supreme advantage of being on the spot.

In addition to the processing and extractive industries the largest export industry of the islands is **embroidering,** carried on in home workshops rather than in large factories.

CITIES OF THE PHILIPPINES

Name	Type	Population
Manila	Governmental and seaport	1,200,000 (1953)
Cebu	Seaport	168,000 (1948)
Davao	Seaport	111,000 (1948)
Iloilo	Seaport	110,000 (1948)
Zamboanga	Seaport	103,000 (1948)

Cities. **Manila,** with one of the world's finest harbors in Manila Bay, is a leading center of commerce in the Far East. The modern section of the city, especially the public buildings of the national government, has been restored after having been severely damaged during the city's recapture from the Japanese in World War II.

The other cities listed are the chief seaports of their respective islands. **Davao** and **Zamboanga** are export centers for copra and abaca; **Iloilo** is chiefly a sugar port. **Cebu** is historically significant as the site of Magellan's death in the course of the first round-the-world voyage.

The Philippines as a Whole. The Philippines differ from the other Asiatic nations which achieved independence after World War II in that this status had long been planned for and was due at the time it was voluntarily granted by the United States. Thus the Philippine Republic was from the beginning politically more stable than Burma or Indonesia. There is ample indication that the nation will be successful in developing its resources and achieving a healthy, self-sustained prosperity.

QUESTIONS. Locate the Malabar Coast. What is its most important product? What is the cause of the heavy rainfall in the Malabar Coast? In Ceylon? What are the three most important agricultural products of Ceylon? Why is the high population density an important factor in the tea industry? Why is Burma relatively isolated from its neighboring countries? What is the major axis of commerce and communications in Burma—north-south or east-west? Why? What is unusual about the economic use made of Burmese rainforests? Where is agriculture concentrated in Burma? What is unusual about the rice output? Describe the people of Burma. Name the two important products of Malaya. What is Malaya's rank as a world producer of these products? Why are the Malays a "minority group" in their own country?

What is the composition of the population of Indonesia? What are the two important mineral products of Indonesia? Which islands of Indonesia are economically important? Name five tropical agricultural products of which the East Indies are among the leading exporters. What is so unusual about the economy of Java? What makes this unusual circumstance possible?

Explain the occurrence of the rainforest climate of the Philippines. Describe the people of the Philippines. Contrast the degree of utilization of resources in the Philippines with that in Java. Where is the center of economic activity in the islands? Name the agricultural product in which the Philippines have almost a monopoly. Explain how this came about.

Tropical Rainy Climates: The Savanna Climate

CHAPTER 9

The Savanna Climate in Africa

■ DEFINITION AND CAUSES OF THE SAVANNA CLIMATE

The savanna climatic regions occur in general on the northern and southern borders of the rainforests, although other climatic controls such as mountain barriers, the distribution of land and water, and altitude can modify this relationship or even prevent the occurrence of the savanna climate. The true savanna climate results from the seasonal shifting of the heat equator (see Chapter 6, p. 100). This causes a seasonal, north-south extension of the tropical rainforest climate, producing rainy seasons in the adjacent regions to the north and south.

Where the monsoon phenomenon is strong it also can create a type of savanna climate. In such circumstances the monsoon winds produce a rainy season as they blow from ocean to land during the summer.

■ GENERAL ASPECTS OF THE SAVANNA REGIONS

The typical transition from rainforest to savanna climate is made evident by the change in vegetation from tall trees with little undergrowth to lower trees with thick undergrowth. The impenetrable mass of such savanna vegetation is the true "jungle," contrary to popular usage, which applies the term to any tropical woodland. The vegetative change continues progressively from jungle to "parklands," or regions of associ-ated jungle and open grasslands, then to uninterrupted grassland—first tall grass, then short grass (Fig. 9.1). All these variations occur within the savanna climatic region.

As has been noted, the distinction between savanna and rainforest climate is based on differences in the distribution and amount of rainfall. The gradation in vegetative aspect is a direct consequence of these differences in precipitation characteristics. Where they border the rainforest the savanna regions experience two wet and two dry seasons a year; their far sides, the short-grass areas, get only one wet and dry alternation.

The vegetative differences within the savanna regions result not only from the total amount of yearly rainfall but also from the duration of the dry periods between the rains. Six months instead of three between the rainy seasons means a drier climate on the average, and less profuse and prolific vegetation. There is also the additional factor that in the border-belt drier climate a greater temperature range is experienced, for high humidity has a moderating effect on temperature similar to that of an adjoining large body of water to windward. (See Chapter 6, p. 96.)

The main commercial crop of the upland savanna in the Western Hemisphere is coffee; and of the monsoon savanna of Asia, rice. Sugar cane is grown on the lower lands in Latin America.

Although there are considerable local population concentrations and areas of high economic activity around valuable mineral deposits, the savanna regions of the world

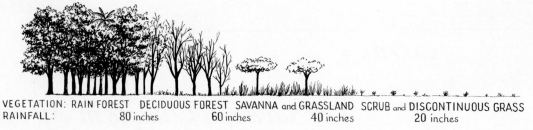

VEGETATION: RAIN FOREST   DECIDUOUS FOREST   SAVANNA and GRASSLAND   SCRUB and DISCONTINUOUS GRASS
RAINFALL: 80 inches   60 inches   40 inches   20 inches

Fig. 9.1—Vegetative Gradation, Wet to Dry Tropical Climates.

are, with the exception of India, sparsely settled. The handicap of a climate inherently less suitable than others for agriculture, and the presence of insect swarms which transmit diseases are serious inhibitors of human activity and progress. India, as the exception, would seem to present a rather extraordinary example of the predominance of human culture over environment as the proximate determinant of the utilization of a region.

■ DISTRIBUTION OF THE SAVANNA CLIMATE

The type region of savanna climate is in Africa (Fig. 9.2). It occurs as a belt surrounding the rainforest climatic region on the north, east, and south. The northern portion extends from the west coast almost to the east coast at the widest part of the continent. This is a region of tall grass between seven and eight feet in height. ("Grass" is here used in the botanical sense, which includes plants as large as corn.) The eastern portion comprises all the land from the border of the Belgian Congo to the coast. This portion is the home of the greatest assemblage of wild animals left in the world. The southern portion covers more than half of that part of Africa situated below the equator and includes also the west coast of the island of Madagascar. Certain areas, known as the *veld* (Dutch for "field"), with a higher average altitude than the grassland, have a

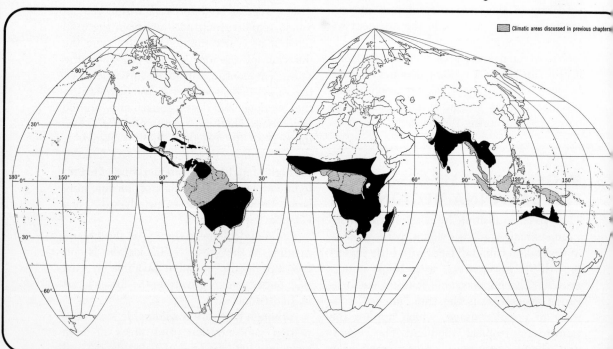

Climatic areas discussed in previous chapters

Fig. 9.2—World Distribution of Savanna Climatic Regions.

slightly different, parkland aspect. Numerous political divisions are wholly or in part within the African savanna region.

In South America a vast region of savanna climate covering most of **Brazil** is known as the *campos* (Portuguese for "field"). It extends on the west into a territory known as the **Gran Chaco** (Great Forest) and includes the northern half of **Paraguay.**

The savanna climate also prevails over most of **Venezuela** and the northern and eastern portions of **Colombia.** The grassy lowland areas of this region undergo extreme wet-dry alternation. The highland areas to the south are plateau country and, like the African veld, have a very pleasant climate because of the ameliorating effects of altitude. The vegetation accordingly is here also the parkland type.

The **Coast of Ecuador** is the third region of savanna climate in South America. Other regions in Latin America include the west coast of Central America and the Yucatan Peninsula of Mexico (not of sufficient importance to merit separate discussion), and the West Indies. Of the latter **Cuba,** the most important island, is described separately.

In Asia the savanna climate occurs in a great arc embracing all of **India** except the Malabar Coast, **East Pakistan,** central and northern **Burma, Thailand,** and **Indochina** (Fig. 11.10). In this Asiatic area the monsoon variety of savanna climate gets expression, and the savanna climatic gradation from wet to dry is poorly developed or is not present. The monsoon comes once a year, and regional differences in climate are due either to different positions relative to the monsoon winds, and thus to the amount of rainfall received, or to topography.

The remaining region of savanna climate is **Northern Australia,** the remote tropical portion of that continent.

■ SAVANNA REGIONS AND COUNTRIES

A. AFRICA

General Aspects. The great crescentic savanna region of Africa covers approximately one-third of that continent's 11 million square miles. This enormous area differs politically from unit climatic areas previously discussed in that it comprises a crazy quilt of political divisions, many of them of minute size and significance. This diversity is a heritage from the period of colonial seizures in the nineteenth century. The various political entities range from colonies and protectorates to independent countries.

Nevertheless the basic elements of climate, topography, and peoples in the majority of these countries are so similar that a description of the region as a whole serves better than a separate account for each of the different political units in presenting an understandable picture of their regional geography.

The most characteristic phenomenon of all the African savanna region is the relatively slight economic development so far achieved there. One of the basic reasons for this backwardness is the presence of the native populations. Unlike tropical South America, Africa south of the Sahara is densely occupied by native peoples. Any modern exploitation of the resources of the region therefore involves some degree of economic and cultural dislocation, or physical displacement of the people. The dense population provides a large potential labor supply for plantation agriculture and mining enterprises, but the Negro inhabitants exhibit (understandably) a great disinclination for such work. Some labor is compelled from the natives by the imposition of a head tax payable in money, which, of course, is obtainable only through work. The ethics of such a procedure, it should be noted, are questionable in the light of currently professed international standards.

The People. There exists a popular misconception as to the homogeneity of the native African peoples. The black population of Africa is actually rather varied. Very primitive types, the Bushmen and Pygmies, have been driven into the protective desert and rainforest habitats of the Kalahari and

Congo, respectively. In the savanna regions, bordering the rainforest, are the true Negroes (Fig. 9.3), the most advanced of the black peoples. The northern and eastern portions of the continent (the Mediterranean border and Ethiopian regions) are inhabited by dark-skinned Hamitic and Semitic racial groups from Asia.

Last to arrive in the African savanna lands were the Europeans, who have been a primary cause of great disturbance in African social stability through the cultural changes they have engendered. European traders broke up the natural economic life of the natives, and missionaries attempted to substitute European for native customs and religions. As a result the more "civilized" natives lost respect for their own standards, while only partially assimilating those of the Europeans.

The French trained the Negroes for military service and employed them in wars in which the natives had no interest or concern. The British educated upper-class Negroes in English universities, then, when they returned to their African homes, denied them

the material and political fruits of their knowledge, leaving them rootless and discontented. In recent years more enlightened policies have been instituted in certain of the British colonies to remedy this situation, but progress in overcoming the initial mistakes has been slow, and a truly satisfactory solution is still in the future.

Communications. A second factor of significance in accounting for the lag in economic development of the African savanna lands is the topographic barrier to their access as this has affected the development of communication lines. The handicap imposed by the steep rise to the interior plateau, and the rapids and falls of the rivers that descend from it was noted previously (see Chapter 2, p. 22).

Although Africa is the second largest of the continents, it has a smaller railroad mileage than all of them save Australia, and it lacks an integrated net. The rail lines in Africa were built for one purpose, namely, to move a particular product from a certain interior locale to a specific port on the coast. There are projects afoot to correct this de-

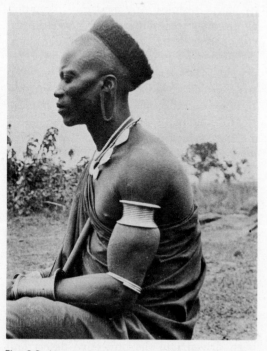

Fig. 9.3—Negro Native of Tanganyika. The ear lobes have been pierced and stretched. (Courtesy, British Information Services.)

Fig. 9.4—Railroads of Africa. Except in the extreme north and south the railroads of Africa serve less to connect places or regions with each other than to provide a route from a single interior point to the sea.

fect, but in general the different railroads do not provide for intercommunication between various regions of the continent (Fig. 9.4). Aside from other considerations, the multiplicity of political units makes it difficult to remedy this situation.

Disease. A third factor that adversely affects the economic development of a relatively restricted area of Africa including part of the savanna lands is the scourge of the tsetse fly and the dire malady—sleeping sickness—it spreads. All the region from the mouth of the Congo River to Tanganyika is afflicted with this pest and the disease (Fig. 9.5). Perhaps nowhere else in the world does a single disease so completely dominate the lives and arrest the activities of the inhabitants of a region as is true here. The chief victims are man and domestic cattle. Wild animals are not only immune but also, according to some students of the problem, act as hosts, or reservoirs, of the disease. The difficulties of eradication are tremendous and no real solution has yet been found. Until the tsetse plague is eliminated there will be little cattle raising or agricultural development in the areas affected.

Fig. 9.5—Tsetse Fly Areas in Africa. (After Fitzgerald, Africa.)

Up to this point the African savanna territory has been considered as a unit. Its diverse political divisions do, however, deserve some individual attention. The following survey is intended to show each country in the light of its present importance as a producer for world markets and its potentialities for development. The list is long but, even so, not exhaustive. Several minor portions of countries and some insignificant possessions are omitted.

1. The Northwestern Lands

The northwestern tip of the crescent of African savanna lands is the colony of **Senegal** (Fig. 9.6), one of several colonial possessions that together comprise French West Africa. The total area of French West Africa is 1.8 million square miles (or three-fifths the size of the United States), and it has over 17 million inhabitants, including fewer than 30,-000 Frenchmen.

The most important products of Senegal itself are **peanuts** (known as "groundnuts" in Africa) and **peanut oil.** The peanut plant was introduced into Africa by the Portuguese slave traders. Peanuts grow and yield a crop on the poor soils which prevail there.

Hides and skins[1] are also exported. The native tribes carry on subsistence agriculture, growing mainly corn, millet (a coarse grain), peanuts for their own use, and a little rice.

South of two minor British and Portuguese colonies is **French Guinea,** which extends to the southeast inland from Liberia and Sierra Leone to connect with the **Ivory Coast.** Both these colonies are also portions of French West Africa. The chief export of the Ivory Coast is **cacao,** the production of which is sufficiently large to make the country a leading source. Cacao was originally grown on the Ivory Coast by Europeans, through plantation agriculture. Expansion of demand for cacao created such a labor shortage, however, that the natives were taught to produce

[1] "Hides" is the term used in connection with horses and cattle, "skins" in connection with sheep, goats, and the smaller animals.

cacao as independent growers. Nevertheless there has been little other economic development. The lack of a natural harbor in both colonies is a further handicap to the development of the essential foreign trade.

East of the Ivory Coast is the **Gold Coast**, a British colony with an area of 92,000 square miles (somewhat smaller than Oregon). As is suggested by the name, one of the leading products in value is **gold.** Other mineral exports include **diamonds,** in the world production of which the Gold Coast ranks high, and **manganese,** for which it is equally important. There are also large deposits of **bauxite,** in connection with which there is a large hydroelectric project on the **Volta River.** Power from the project is primarily for the production of **aluminum** metal at the mine, so the necessity for long-distance shipping of the heavy and bulky bauxite ore is eliminated.

In addition to possessing rich mineral wealth the Gold Coast is the source of over 40 percent of the world's output of **cacao.** This section of Africa—low, yet fairly well drained, with high humidity and, since it is on the "near" side of the savanna belt, supplied with ample rainfall—is a land especially suited for the cacao tree.

Fig. 9.6—French West Africa, Gold Coast, and Nigeria. The inset compares the area of the region with an equivalent area of the United States (states in white).

The cacao industry here is entirely in native hands. On this account the product unfortunately is of inferior quality owing to careless treatment during the harvesting and processing. The native is suspicious of the European administrator and trader, so that it has been difficult to convince him that good care of his product will insure a better return for his labor. The African cacao also differs naturally in quality from that grown in the New World. The processors of cacao have learned, however, to produce from the African cacao a finished product as acceptable as that made from the cacao from other sources. Accordingly, the African material is not so much at a discount as it once was.

But there are still other difficulties. The labor supply is exceedingly short at each of the semiannual periods of cacao harvest. This cannot be alleviated by native ownership of the plantings. The cacao country is in the tsetse fly area, where draft animals cannot survive; hence most of the transportation from the tree to the nearest road is by human porterage. The necessity of good roads for truck transport was shortly realized, and an expansion in the road network has occurred.

The Gold Coast has a population of more than 4 million persons, of whom fewer than 3000 are Europeans. Native aspirations for self-government were encouraged by the

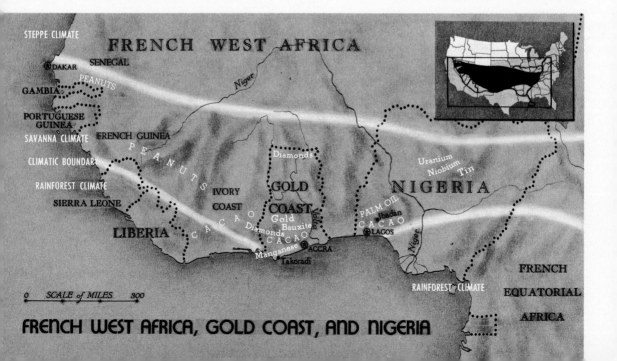

FRENCH WEST AFRICA, GOLD COAST, AND NIGERIA

British in 1949 with an unusual constitution giving the country and its Negro population the greatest degree of self-government of any colony in Africa.

Life even at the subsistence level is barely sustained because of widespread disease, the severities of the climate, and ineffective effort due to low standards of education. Nevertheless the prospects for the Gold Coast appear bright in view of the progress in handling political and social problems, and because of the Volta power-aluminum project. The extensive transportation and port development this requires will promote the establishment of a well-rounded, sound economy. It would not be surprising if some day the Gold Coast were to become one of the leading countries of Africa.

East of the Gold Coast and separated from it by another portion of French West Africa lies **Nigeria,** the largest country of the region so far considered. Its area of 373,000 square miles is equal in size to Texas, Oklahoma, and Louisiana combined. This British colony was mentioned rather briefly in connection with the portion of its territory that is in the rainforest climate (see Chapter 7, p. 119).

Nigeria is an excellent example of the climatic zoning of the savanna land. The southern portion of Nigeria comprises the rainforests, on low and swampy terrain. The northern portion is higher, averaging over 1000 feet, and has a savanna climate. The savanna region receives an average of 43 inches of rainfall annually along its southern border, as little as 25 inches in the extreme north.

The mineral products of Nigeria, like those of the Gold Coast, are of considerable importance but are not so well developed. The most important product until recently was **tin,** found in gravel deposits in the northeast corner of the country. More significant in the age of jets and rockets, however, is **niobium** (also known as columbium), a rare metal of great value for alloying steel so that it will withstand very high temperatures. Nigeria is the outstanding source of this metal.

The major agricultural products of the colony as a whole are **palm oil** (Fig. 9.7)

Fig. 9.7—Palm-Oil Palms. Both the pulp and the kernel of the fruit yield a high-quality oil. (Courtesy, British Information Services.)

and **cacao.** Nigeria is the leading source of the former and one of the three ranking producers of the latter. The shift in production from palm products to cacao, which first occurred in the Gold Coast, came later in Nigeria. A higher grade of cacao is produced than in the Gold Coast because the problem of quality was better presented to the natives. The bean is a product of the wetter, coastal portion of the colony.

Nigeria is much farther from a solution of its problems than is the nearby Gold Coast. Ethnic and hence political disunity within the colony make it more difficult for the population to be brought to grips with the troubles of low productivity, poor diet, and general underdevelopment. On the other hand, Nigeria is sharing with the Gold Coast the political benefits of the British determination not to let the growing political awareness of the Negroes lead to violent consequences. There is a Nigerian "national parliament," although progress is not quite as rapid as in the Gold Coast, which in 1949 already had a Negro prime minister.

2. The Central Region

The second large French possession in Africa included within the savanna lands,

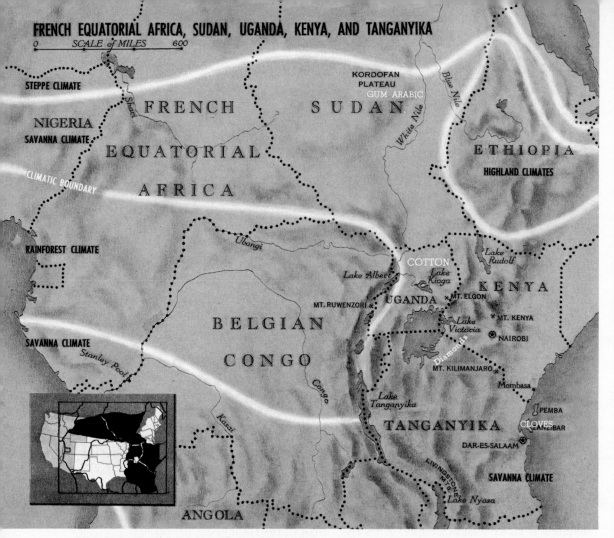

Fig. 9.8—French Equatorial Africa, Sudan, Uganda, Kenya, and Tanganyika. The inset compares the area of the region with an equivalent area of the United States (all except the shaded states).

French Equatorial Africa (Fig. 9.8), comprises territory both north and south of the central rainforest region of the continent. The rainforest portion of French Equatorial Africa, the Middle Congo section, has already been discussed (see Chapter 7, p. 119). The savanna portions are the northeastern, or *Ubangi-Shari* territory (named after its two major streams) and the southern portion of the northern or *Chad Colony* (named after the large lake on its western border).

A vast region stretching from Egypt to the Belgian Congo and from French Equatorial Africa to Ethiopia is known as the **Sudan.** Only the southern third of this region of nearly one million square miles possesses a savanna climate. The name "Sudan" is a con-

traction of the Arabic phrase, *Bilad es Sudan,* or "Country of the Blacks."

The savanna portion of the country is inhabited by Negro tribes. This is the province of the upper reaches of the great **Nile River** —the **Mountain Nile** (the southernmost portion of the main stream), the **White Nile** (the central portion), and the **Blue Nile** (a large tributary of the Nile which rises in Ethiopia and joins the main stream in central Sudan).

The country of Sudan has a virtual monopoly on the world production of **gum arabic,** the product of a tree sap which in turn is the base of mucilage. The best gum forests are along the Ethiopian border, in the south-central portion of an elevated tract known as the **Kordofan plateau,** and along the banks of the Blue Nile.

Directly south of Sudan nearly 100,000 square miles of territory (about the size of Colorado) in the heart of the continent is known as **Uganda,** a British protectorate. Here geologic disturbances have created long, deep trenches known as "rift valleys," many of which are occupied by lakes. The lakes of Uganda are **Lake Victoria,** the source of the Nile and the largest lake of the continent; **Lake Kioga,** into which the Nile drains Lake Victoria; and **Lake Albert,** a smaller lake to the west which also feeds the Nile.

Associated with the rift valleys are the highest peaks of the continent. Under a rainy tropical climate this geologic complex has been carved into a region of stupendous scenery, with great rivers descending over falls and rapids, and with snow-capped peaks occurring almost on the equator. The mountains include **Mount Ruwenzori** (elevation 16,800 feet) on the western border and **Mount Elgon** (elevation 14,100 feet) on the eastern border, the third and fourth highest peaks, respectively, of Africa.

As a British protectorate Uganda is composed largely of self-governing native kingdoms totaling 5 million inhabitants and constitutes an excellent example of creditable colonial administration. Products include **coffee,** sugar, hides and skins, and a new and increasingly important crop, **cotton,** of which Uganda is the second largest African producer. The potential cotton land is of considerable extent, and given improved transportation Uganda may be expected to acquire mounting significance as a cotton producer.

East of Uganda lies **Kenya Colony and Protectorate,** a 225,000-square mile portion of the British Empire. Its share of the scenic beauties consists of **Lake Rudolf** on the north and **Mount Kenya** (elevation 17,000 feet), the second highest peak of Africa, in the center.

The 9000-foot relief of Kenya occasions diverse climatic conditions; accordingly, the agricultural products of the colony are varied. The highlands produce flax (the raw fiber for linen), corn, coffee, sisal, tea, wheat, and pyrethrum (an insecticide). Peanuts, the African stand-by, and such middle-latitude vegetables as potatoes and beans are also grown. The raising of sheep, introduced just prior to World War II, has interesting possibilities for large expansion in the highlands. The mineral resources are not yet fully known.

Kenya is unfortunately plagued, however, by a particularly acute racial problem which must first be solved. Unequal territorial reservations for whites and blacks have led, since World War II, to continued, small-scale rebellion.

South of Kenya is **Tanganyika,** the former colony of German East Africa, now a British Trusteeship under the United Nations. The country's 360,000 square miles (somewhat larger than California, Oregon, and Washington combined) are the home lands of an estimated population of almost 8 million.

The topography of Tanganyika consists of lowlands along the coast, a plateau inland, above which rises **Mount Kilimanjaro** (Fig. 9.9) (elevation 19,300 feet), Africa's highest peak situated on the Kenya border, and the **Livingstone Mountains** on the south. The Congo border on the west is along **Lake Tanganyika,** largest of the rift lakes. South of the Livingstone Mountains is **Lake Nyassa,** completing the roster of the rift lakes.

Forests cover much of Tanganyika. They vary from the typical tropical rainforest to mangrove forests along the coast. Since most of the forests are in government reserve, they will be conserved as a perennial source of timber and forest products.

Tanganyika's leading agricultural product is **sisal.** This fiber is the basis for most cheap cord, especially binder cord in reaping combine machines. In a spectacular rise during

Fig. 9.9—Mount Kilimanjaro, Kenya. Africa's highest peak. (Courtesy, British Information Services.)

the period prior to World War II Tanganyika became the leading producer of sisal and now accounts for approximately one-third of the world production.

Coffee has large possibilities for expanded production in both Tanganyika and Kenya. The plantations are well located on slopes, the labor supply is satisfactory, and recent improvements in transportation will facilitate growth of the industry in both countries.

Like the products of Kenya, those of Tanganyika are varied. The country produces among other things cotton, hides, pyrethrum, peanuts, rubber, copra, tea, rice, and sugar. The islands of **Zanzibar** and **Pemba** (see Chapter 1, p. 12) off the northern coast are the source of 85 percent of the world's **clove** supply.

Just before World War II a new **diamond** discovery was made in Tanganyika that has subsequently been developed into one of the world's largest diamond producers.

One of the unusual features of both Kenya and Tanganyika is the amount of land available in them for potential utilization by white settlers. The highland areas possess the most healthful climate for whites in all Africa (although women, strangely enough, age prematurely under its influence). Since, however, large reserves of such lands have been set aside for native ownership, the total number of whites that could find homes here is too small to be of significance as an outlet for the overpopulation of certain European lands. Moreover, as the need for capital in this region is great, nothing could be gained from a large influx of impoverished settlers.

Both colonies, together with Uganda, also present large possibilities for extensive cotton plantations. Realization of these potentialities must, however, await the elimination of the tsetse fly scourge at lower altitudes—Tanganyika has the most severe infestation of any country in Africa.

QUESTIONS. What is the fundamental cause of the savanna climate? How does monsoon development bring about the occurrence of a savanna climate? What is the general world distribution of the savanna climate? Describe the typical vegetative transition between rainforest and savanna climatic regions. Why is the African savanna region considered the type development of the savanna climate? Name the major crops of the savanna regions.

Why is the native population a major problem in the development of the African savanna region? Describe some of the major social problems created by the European colonization of Negro Africa. Why are the railroads of the savanna region of Africa ill suited for its general economic development? What is the significance of the tsetse fly in Africa?

Name the two most important countries, in terms of value of output, of the northwestern portion of the African savanna region. What are their important agricultural and mineral products? What unfavorable feature of the southern coast of the "African bulge" is a deterrent to commerce there? What is a significant feature of the government of the Gold Coast? What important basis for further economic development exists there?

What important topographic difference between the northwestern and east central (Kenya and Tanganyika) portions of the African savanna region influences the climate of those portions? Why is there not likely to be a significant future white colonization in the latter countries?

3. The Southern Countries

West of Tanganyika is the **Belgian Congo,** part of which is situated in and has been discussed as a section of the African rainforest region. The southern third of the Belgian Congo is in the savanna climatic region (Fig. 9.10). Utilization of the entire area is affected by the nature of the Congo River drainage system. The defects of these streams as transportation routes have been pointed out earlier (see Chapter 2, p. 35). Beyond the head of ocean navigation some hundreds of miles of unnavigable water extend to a lake, **Stanley Pool,** beyond which a stretch of 1000 miles is again navigable. The total length of the navigable portions of the drainage system (including tributaries to the main river) is more than 6000 miles.

In the more than 900,000 square miles of the Belgian Congo (over twice the combined

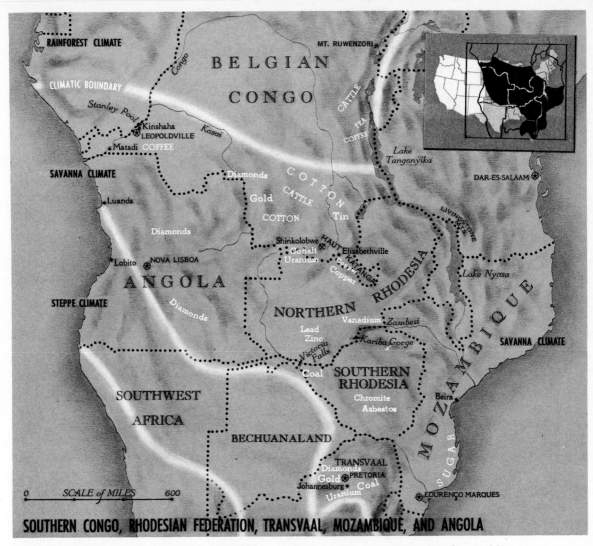

RAINFOREST CLIMATE
CLIMATIC BOUNDARY
BELGIAN
CONGO
MT. RUWENZORI
Congo
Stanley Pool
Kasai
Kinshaha
LEOPOLDVILLE
Matadi COFFEE
CATTLE
TEA
COFFEE
Lake
Tanganyika
SAVANNA CLIMATE
Luanda
Diamonds
Gold
COTTON
CATTLE
COTTON
Tin
DAR-ES-SALAAM
Diamonds
NOVA LISBOA
Lobito
Shinkolobwe
Cobalt
Uranium
Elisabethville
Copper
HAUT KATANGA
RHODESIA
LIVINGSTONE
Lake Nyasa
ANGOLA
Diamonds
NORTHERN
Vanadium
Zambezi
STEPPE CLIMATE
Lead
Zinc
Victoria
Falls
Kariba Gorge
SAVANNA CLIMATE
SOUTHWEST
AFRICA
Coal
SOUTHERN
RHODESIA
Chromite
Asbestos
Beira
MOZAMBIQUE
BECHUANALAND
SCALE of MILES
0   600
TRANSVAAL
Diamonds
Gold PRETORIA
Johannesburg
Uranium
Coal
SUGAR
LOURENÇO MARQUES

SOUTHERN CONGO, RHODESIAN FEDERATION, TRANSVAAL, MOZAMBIQUE, AND ANGOLA

Fig. 9.10—Southern Congo, Rhodesian Federation, Transvaal, Mozambique, and Angola. The inset compares the area of the region with an equivalent area of the United States (states in white).

area of Texas and California) lives a native population of 11.8 million and only 82,000 white persons. This disparity is typical of the composition of population in all Africa south of the Sahara.

The chief agricultural export from the savanna region of the Belgian Congo is **cotton.** Scattered plantations in the east raise **coffee, tea,** and **cacao.** Most agriculture, however, is of the native subsistence type. In the higher regions, where there are no tsetse flies, **cattle** are raised. The Belgian colonial government, in a rather successful effort after World War II to lift the native out of the slough of subsistence agriculture, brought native farming under close control with a system that not only determines what cash crops shall be

planted but also eliminates the middleman and so insures the native grower a better return for his produce.

The savanna region in the Congo comprises the higher portion of the country, where the land rises from the low elevations of the Congo basin to the highlands on the southern border. This region, especially the area in the southeast corner of the colony known as the **Haut Katanga,** is the chief source of the country's wealth. It is one of the major mineral regions of the world; the variety and quantities of mineral raw materials it produces are truly amazing. Few areas of comparable size anywhere can boast such a concentration of important mineral resources.

Thus the Belgian Congo is the world's largest producer of **industrial diamonds** (used for all sorts of cutting and grinding purposes), accounting for some 70 percent of the total output. These are recovered from gravel deposits along the upper **Kasai River.** This production is of vital importance to the world's manufacturing industries.

In the atomic age the Congo has become especially significant as one of the outstanding world sources of **uranium.** The mine at **Shinkolobwe** was also for many years virtually the only important source of **radium.**

Other, less glamorous but equally important mineral products are: **cobalt** (three-quarters of the world output), **copper** (one of the five leading producers), **tin** (recently developed to give the Congo a rank equal to that it has in copper), and, less important but still significant, gold, silver, manganese, and zinc.

All in all, the surge of development and economic expansion in the Congo since World War II holds great future promise. Although political and social problems remain, the native's material welfare has vastly improved in the last decade.

South of the Belgian Congo is a large country known as the **Federation of Rhodesia and Nyasaland,** a virtually self-governing member of the British Commonwealth. The Federation was established in 1953 by the union of Northern and Southern Rhodesia, two British colonies, with the adjoining Nyasaland Protectorate. The new country is almost 500,000 square miles in area and has a total population of nearly 7 million, of which some 200,000 are Europeans.

Northern Rhodesia, the largest of the three member territories, is about three times the size of New England. Its topography is mostly high plateau surface, the home of almost 2 million natives and fewer than 20,000 whites. The agricultural products are tobacco, raised for export, and corn and wheat, grown for local use.

The agricultural activities of Northern Rhodesia are, however, comparatively unimportant. A large portion of its northern area is geologically a part of the Katanga region of the Congo, hence Northern Rhodesia is also an important producer of metals, notably **copper, lead, zinc,** and vanadium.

The Rhodesia-Congo mineral belt as a whole measures 280 by 50 miles. Two-thirds of this area is in the Congo, but the copper deposits of Rhodesia are three and one-half times as large as those of the Congo and are considered to be the largest concentration of copper reserves in the world.

The occurrence of this great mineral wealth in the center of Africa has been of extraordinary significance in furthering the general development of that region. The necessity of bringing in the equipment and supplies required for its exploitation, and the need for moving the mineral products to their markets in the industrial centers of Europe and the United States, has stimulated the provision of adequate transportation facilities. The mining and smelting of the ores has led to the development of the exceptionally large hydropower resources of the region. And the large demand for labor has brought about a concentration of population in the mining areas, providing a market for the expanded agricultural production of a large portion of southern Africa.

So great are the mineral resources of the region that a considerable expansion of the already large output is possible. After World War II the pace of expansion was stepped up in both the Congo and Rhodesia. Realizing their past mistakes, the Belgian authorities (and to a lesser extent the British) are endeavoring to make certain that the expanded economic development is a balanced one. The expansion program is therefore not limited to mineral output but is aimed at a balanced economy in which the natives have a share in the benefits through measures to insure more healthful conditions and higher standards of education and living.

East of Northern Rhodesia is Nyasaland, a narrow strip of territory along the west shore of Lake Nyassa. In contrast to the colonial character of the other two members of the Federation it is a little-developed territory in which the native African people live much as they always have and the few whites are there for purposes of administration.

Southern Rhodesia, the third member of the Federation, is slightly larger than Montana in area, with a total population of 2 million, including fewer than 70,000 Europeans. The northwest and southern boundaries of the country are, respectively, the **Zambezi** and the **Limpopo,** the two largest rivers of southeastern Africa. The Zambezi leaves the central African plateau at **Victoria Falls** (Fig. 2.13), one of the natural wonders of the continent—a waterfall over 300 feet high (almost twice as high as Niagara). Farther east along its course is the site of the **Kariba Gorge** power and flood control project, center of hopes for future economic growth and development of the Federation.

Southern Rhodesia is well suited, because of its high altitude, for white settlement and European-type agriculture. In consequence, cultivation of the soil is the chief economic activity. Although it is possible to grow a wide variety of crops, only **corn** and **tobacco** are important. One-half the yield from European farms is available for export; the native production is used locally for human food and fodder. The pitfalls of dependence on one or two cash crops are beginning to be realized, and attempts are being made to diversify the farm output. The establishment of a considerable citrus industry appears to be a good prospect.

In view of the main dependence on agriculture Southern Rhodesia surprisingly has only a small fraction—about one-quarter— of its white population engaged in farming. The Europeans have congregated in the colony's small cities, which have under 15,000 European population. This urban concentration seems to be due to the fact that so many of the whites are temporary residents, either merchants or government officials. Nevertheless, two-thirds of the land has been reserved for the sole use of the whites.

The chief mineral products of Southern Rhodesia are gold and silver, which have been mined for centuries, and **chromite** and **asbestos,** in the production of which the country ranks as one of the two leading world producers. **Coal** from the southwest has been important in the development of the Katanga-Rhodesia mining and smelting industries.

South of the Federation is the **Transvaal,** a province of the Union of South Africa. The Transvaal is some 110,000 square miles in area, or about equal to the size of Nevada. Its total population is 4.8 million. Unlike the previously discussed political divisions of Africa, the Transvaal has a European population about one-third of the total rather than the small fraction present elsewhere.

The large white population is present mainly because of the development of **gold** mining in a small area of the province. Gold was discovered there in 1884; since then it is estimated that the gold-producing area—the *Witwatersrand* (White Waters Ridge), or "Rand" for short—has yielded one-quarter of all the gold mined in the world since the discovery of America by Columbus! At this prodigious rate of output it is, of course, the leading gold producer of the world. More than one-third of the world's yearly output comes from the Rand mines.

At one time it was thought that the Transvaal's position as premier gold producer was threatened by the exhaustion of the mines. These fears were allayed, however, when extensions of the gold-bearing formations were discovered, and were all but banished with the announcement, in 1952, that **uranium** could be recovered as a by-product from the gold ore. The uranium comprises only a small fraction of one percent of the ore, but the returns from its recovery make possible the processing of what would otherwise be waste material. Because of the large scale of the gold-mining operations the Transvaal thus becomes a front-rank producer of this source of atomic energy.

Even if neither gold nor uranium were found in the Transvaal it would still be a glamorous mining region because of the presence of the world's greatest **diamond** deposits. Diamonds are recovered not only from the gravel deposits that are the type source elsewhere in the world but also from mines located in the original rock in which the diamonds were formed.

Less glamorous but nevertheless of considerable importance are the **coal** beds of the Transvaal. Although not of very high quality, this coal, because of its availability, has been

Fig. 9.11—Cattle in South Africa. A native "Nguni" breed which is being improved for better milk production. (Courtesy, Union of South Africa Government Information Office.)

an essential factor in the development of the power needed for the gold-mining operations.

The chief rural activity in the Transvaal is stock raising, mostly of cattle (Fig. 9.11) and sheep, with smaller numbers of goats and pigs. It is possible to grow both middle-latitude and tropical crops in the Transvaal, as in Kenya and Tanganyika. Agriculture in general, however, has a secondary role because of the overwhelming importance of the gold fields. Production is directed more to provision of food for the resident population engaged in mining than to growing crops for sale elsewhere in the world.

The east coast of Africa opposite the island of Madagascar is the site of the old Portuguese colony of **Mozambique,** or Portuguese East Africa. This region was discovered by Vasco da Gama in 1498 and was settled by Portuguese colonists only a few years later. The colony comprises almost 300,000 square miles (about twice the area of Montana), and has a population of nearly 6 million, more than 98 percent of which is Negro.

Mozambique is a clear example of the Portuguese colonial policy of minimizing national administration. Until 1942 one area of Mozambique remained still under the absolute rule of the original colonizing company. Such companies were once organized by all the European colonial powers as the appropriate agencies for the development of colonial lands. By the early part of the twentieth century, however, colonizing companies had all but disappeared elsewhere. Although there is some indication that since World War II the pace of development in Mozambique is being accelerated, Mozambique is still little known or exploited.

Sugar is the single agricultural commodity produced in large volume, but even it is cultivated only in great enough quantity to satisfy the home demand. Despite its own lack of exportable products the colony participates in large-scale commercial enterprise, as its ports provide the most economical shipping points for the exports and imports of the Rhodesias and the Transvaal. Such functioning has been made possible by linking up the Mozambique ports by rail routes with the railroad systems of the three neighboring states. It must be added, however, that this development came about through the initiative of the interior states.

One more African political division lies within the savanna climatic region: **Angola,** or Portuguese West Africa, situated along the Atlantic coast south of the Belgian Congo. Like Mozambique, it was discovered and colonized just prior to the sixteenth century; indeed, it is the oldest of all the European "colonies" on the continent. Angola is a good deal larger than Mozambique (480,000 square miles—equal to all the coastal United States from Maine to Alabama), but its population is only 4 million, like Mozambique more than 98 percent Negro.

The economic aspects of Angola are strikingly similar to those of its sister colony Mozambique, on the eastern coast. There are no important agricultural products, but the country does rank high as a source of **diamonds.** Despite the lack of local economic development Angola is the scene of significant commercial activity, for it serves as the outlet for the great mineral production of the Katanga-Rhodesia mineral belt.

Summary

The mention of hides among the products of the savanna countries of Africa in the preceding discussion is a somewhat ambiguous indication of the important place of cattle raising in the savanna regions. As the age-old occupation of many African tribes, cattle raising is more a custom than an industry. In some places, indeed, it is a kind of semi-religious activity. In other places wealth is measured in terms of the number of cattle owned, so that cattle are a form of money. The price of a wife, for instance, is quoted in terms of cows. A superior bride may bring as high as 80 cows.

In addition to this peculiar relation between the native and his cattle holdings, such factors as the lack of any modern techniques or knowledge of animal husbandry, the climatic difficulties and prevalence of insect pests, and the fact that the savannas in general are only second-rate grazing lands combine to limit the export products of the cattle "industry" chiefly to hides of poor quality. In the twentieth century European management in the south and east highlands has brought some improvement, but even with modern, scientific techniques it is doubtful if the cattle industry of the African savanna land will ever be really significant for the world market in meat or dairy products.

From the foregoing account it will be appreciated that savanna Africa is a region of tremendous potentialities, both agricultural and mineral—and in the far future even industrial. Its development is handicapped, however, by the nature of the climate, by topographic factors, and, most important, by the fact that it is populated by millions of the black race under the control of a small number of resident Europeans.

Further utilization of the region involves solution of the problem how to reconcile the conflicting interests and desires of the two races.

Cities of Savanna Africa

Dakar is the capital, largest city, and chief seaport of French West Africa. Located on the *Cape Verde* peninsula, the extreme western tip of Africa, it is sometimes called "the African Gibraltar" because of its commanding cliffs and strategic location. It has a fine harbor and well-developed port facilities. It enjoys a pleasant climate and so possesses a large European population; indeed, it is the most European of all the cities in West Africa. Since World War II it has become a major terminus for transatlantic air travel in addition to its older status as an important port of call for Atlantic shipping.

Accra is the capital and chief city of the Gold Coast. Originally a native fishing village on a low cliff at the water's edge, it is still largely a native city with only about 1000 European residents. **Takoradi** is the site of an artificial harbor built to take care of the cacao trade. It is the only decent harbor along the entire length (some 1300 miles) of the southern coast of the African bulge.

Ibadan (in southern Nigeria in the rain-

CITIES OF THE SAVANNA REGION OF AFRICA

Name	Type	Country	Population
Dakar	Governmental and seaport	Senegal	185,000 (1951)
Accra	Governmental and seaport	Gold Coast	135,000 (1951)
Takoradi	Seaport	Gold Coast	45,000 (1951)
Ibadan	Commercial	Nigeria	460,000 (1953)
Lagos	Governmental and seaport	Nigeria	267,000 (1953)
Nairobi	Governmental	Kenya	186,000 (1954)
Mombasa	Seaport	Kenya	85,000 (1951)
Dar-es-Salaam	Governmental and seaport	Tanganyika	100,000 (1952)
Matadi	Seaport	Belgian Congo	22,000 (1948)
Leopoldville	Governmental	Belgian Congo	280,000 (1954)
Elisabethville	Mining and commercial	Belgian Congo	120,000 (1953)
Johannesburg	Mining and commercial	Transvaal	884,000 (1951)
Pretoria	Governmental	Transvaal	285,000 (1951)
Lourenço Marques	Governmental and seaport	Mozambique	95,000 (1950)
Beira	Seaport	Mozambique	43,000 (1950)
Lobito	Seaport	Angola	25,000 (1950)
Luanda	Seaport	Angola	141,000 (1950)
Nova Lisboa	Governmental	Angola	15,000 (1950)

forest climatic region) is the largest native city in Africa. It is the center of a highly developed native farming industry. The farmers commute from its suburbs as much as 10 miles to work on their farms. It is also the site of numerous handicraft industries. **Lagos,** also in the rainforest climate, is the capital of Nigeria and is connected by railroad to Ibadan. Originally a pesthole, it is now much improved and is the chief port of the colony.

Nairobi (Fig. 9.12), the capital of Kenya, is located in the highlands about 300 miles inland from the coast. Its mile-high altitude gives it a delightfully cool climate. It is a clean-looking city of pleasant aspect owing to good city planning and its excellent view of Kilimanjaro and Mount Kenya. It is an outfitting point for hunting and movie expeditions. **Mombasa,** its port, is the leading harbor on the East African coast by reason of its good rail connections with Kenya, Uganda, and a large portion of Tanganyika. Located on an island in Kilindi Harbor, it is the modern successor to Zanzibar (see Chapter 1, p. 12). Like that city it is very Oriental in appearance, with a network of twisting, narrow streets which is a heritage

Fig. 9.12—Nairobi, Kenya. Despite its modernity lions from the surrounding wild lands occasionally wander into the streets of the city. (Courtesy, British Information Services.)

from its original status as an Arab colony.

Dar-es-Salaam, the capital and chief port of Tanganyika, is a vigorous rival of Mombasa. Its name, meaning "Haven of Peace," refers to its small but ideal harbor. It contains a free zone for the transit of goods to and from the Belgian Congo, although traffic between it and the Haut Katanga involves four transshipments.

Fig. 9.13—Leopoldville, Belgian Congo. (Courtesy, Belgian Government Information Center.)

Matadi, at the head of the Congo estuary, is the port of the Belgian Congo and the site of the first transshipment of river and rail traffic on the route inland. It is of minor importance in the trade of the colony because of the transportation difficulties involved in its use. **Leopoldville** (Fig. 9.13), the capital of the Congo, is located on the south bank of Stanley Pool alongside its industrial twin city, **Kinshasa.** Both are well-developed, modern-looking cities. **Elisabethville** is the commercial and industrial metropolis of the Katanga mining region and capital of the province. It is a center of copper smelting.

Johannesburg (Fig. 9.14) is the real metropolis of South Africa and the second largest city on the continent. It is dominated by its gold mines and the great mountains of waste rock from the mines that mar the landscape. The waste dumps will not support vegetation and are the source material of frequent, annoying dust storms. The city is also the center of the railroad system of South Africa, a reflection of the importance

Fig. 9.14—Johannesburg, Transvaal. The vast dumps of the Rand gold-mine tailings appear in the background. (Courtesy, Union of South Africa Government Information Office.)

of the gold mines in South African economy. **Pretoria**, 40 miles to the north, is the capital of the Union of South Africa; it owes this status to sentiment, as it was the original capital of the South African Republic, the independent nation that became the Transvaal. It is 1000 feet lower than Johannesburg and has a considerably warmer climate.

Lourenço Marques, the capital of Mozambique, possesses very good port facilities and the best natural harbor in southern Africa. As the major port for the Transvaal and the city of Johannesburg it is a good example of how the trade routes in southern Africa cut across the tortuous artificial boundaries man has drawn in this part of the world. Although a Portuguese port, its commerce is mainly in British hands. Local trade is carried on largely by Indians, who reside there in considerable numbers. **Beira**, on the coast of central Mozambique, is the port of land-locked Southern Rhodesia, and to a lesser extent of Northern Rhodesia. Its business is also taken care of by a resident British community. Because of its pleasant climate the port is a popular resort for the European inhabitants of the Rhodesias.

Lobito, the main port of Angola, is a competitor with Beira for the Katanga-Rhodesia copper belt trade. It owes its existence to the fact that it is the terminus of the railroad from the Katanga to the west coast. **Nova Lisboa** (New Lisbon, originally Huambo) is the new capital of Angola, chosen because of its healthful, highland site in the center of the colony and the fact that it is on the railroad. **Luanda**, a port on the northwest coast of Angola, was the former capital, but in the absence of a through rail connection with the interior it has lapsed into desuetude.

B. MADAGASCAR

The region of savanna climate in Madagascar is restricted to the western half of the island (Fig. 7.13). The eastern half, it will be remembered, possesses a rainforest climate (see Chapter 7, p. 120). The total population of Madagascar and its neighboring islets is almost 4.5 million, including fewer than 85,000 nonnatives. The native people are known as the *Malagasy,* the descendants of original settlement by Polynesian (Pacific) immigrants and an ensuing constant admixture of African slaves of the Bantu tribe. The Malagasy are afflicted with a strange, inexplicable physiological defect: 30 percent of the women are unable to bear children. As a consequence some tribes are actually dying out.

One of the chief export commodities from the savanna portion of the island is **hides,** the product of the extensive cattle raising carried on by the natives. The number of cattle, almost 6 million, is greater than the number of people. As the cattle are of the humped variety used throughout the tropics, and as little attempt is made at selective breeding, the quality of hides is not high and the volume is a minor item in world production.

Rice, manioc (tapioca), and corn are the chief staple crops of the island, and a small exportable surplus of each is usually available. Sugar cane is a good potential crop on the western plain. A significant agricultural product is **cloves,** as the island is one of the few world producers of that spice.

The mineral products include **graphite** (the island is the major producer of a special variety), mica, some gold, and small but significant quantities of **beryllium.**

Madagascar as a Whole. Madagascar is another example of an undeveloped colony. Although politically the French adminstration has been excellent in permitting a good deal of local self-government, preservation of native cultures, and retention of native landownership, the overall economic policies in force have been a great deterrent to development. Trade would naturally flow between the island and the cooler, middle-latitude climatic region of South Africa because of the difference in agricultural produce, but the French have persisted in confining trade as much as possible to the mother country.

The greatest need of the island is increased population. Only 2 percent of the island is under cultivation, and it has been estimated that an additional 2 million people engaged in agriculture could raise the output as much as 15 to 20 times above its present level. With competent supervision such an expansion in population and wider utilization of the resources of Madagascar would result in a comparatively high standard of living for all the island's inhabitants. This would be possible, however, only if the colony were allowed to market its surplus production in the world at large.

QUESTIONS. What is the chief agricultural product of the savanna portion of the Belgian Congo? Name the region that is the chief source of the colony's mineral wealth. Name the major mineral products.

Why are many of the mineral products of Northern Rhodesia the same as those of the Belgian Congo? What has the occurrence of this mineral wealth meant to the development of central Africa? What is unusual about the distribution of white population in Southern Rhodesia? Name the major products of the colony. What is the outstanding product of the Transvaal? What by-product has recently become highly significant? Why is agriculture of minor importance as a source of exports in the Transvaal?

How does the level of development in Mozambique differ from that of the British colonies that are its neighbors? Explain the existence of a large commerce in Mozambique despite the fact that the colony is a negligible source of exports and a small market for imports. Describe the points of similarity in the economic and commercial status of Mozambique and Angola. If there were no railroad connections between these colonies and central Africa, what routes would have to be followed to export the products of the latter region?

Describe the peculiar features of the native "cattle industry" in the savanna regions of Africa.

Name the major products of the savanna portion of Madagascar. What French colonial policy has hampered its development? What is the greatest need of the colony for further development?

CHAPTER 10

The Savanna Climate in the
Western Hemisphere

C. BRAZIL

General Aspects. The savanna climate of Brazil extends over all that portion of the country not within the rainforest climatic region with the exception of the extreme southern projection and a few isolated areas in other parts of the country (Fig. 10.1). The savanna region is a vast plateau, the **Campos** (see Chapter 9, p. 141) comparable in extent to Amazonia but with an average elevation of 2000 feet. On the east it begins with an abrupt rise to this height immediately behind the coast. Toward the interior the plateau surface presents a gently rolling topography. Still farther west is the **Mato Grosso** ("Great Woods"), a continuation of the plateau region around the headwaters of the **Paraguay River** and the southern rim of the Amazon Basin. On the western border is the lowland of the upper reaches of the Paraguay River.

Despite the seasonal wet-dry alternation, the climate of savanna Brazil is, on the whole, relatively dry. As a result of the orographic rise of the southeast trades as they cross the plateau edge on the east they have already lost a good deal of their moisture before they even reach the interior. In the Campos to the west and northwest, typical savanna, the borderland of the rainforest, is encountered. Here the wet-dry alternation is rather pronounced; the rainfall is less than one inch during the dry season (June to August) and nearly 30 inches during the height of the wet season (December to February). The 2000-foot altitude causes a reduction in temperature over the entire plateau to a 70° F. average from 80° F. at sea level. It also becomes cooler at night—so cool, in fact, that frost occurs in the higher parts on very clear, calm nights.

There are two distinctive regions within the plateau, alike in climate and similar in topography but complete opposites with respect to their use by man, their development, and their importance and significance to Brazil. The difference between them is so pronounced that they are here discussed separately despite their climatic and topographic unity.

The Western Campos. The western portion of the plateau, much of it in the state of Mato Grosso, is a huge tract of grassland representing one of the largest potential cattle-grazing grounds of the world. (Lowlands on the edge of the Amazon Basin and in the Paraguay River Basin which have a forest cover give the region its name.) The most important local industry is **cattle raising**, but its present state of development is negligible compared with the full possibilities. Large areas of grazing land—in fact, most of Mato Grosso—are completely unutilized. The entire area has a population density of less than one person per square mile. Nomadic Indians constitute what sparse population there is.

The mineral potentialities of this region are, in general, unknown. The largest de-

Fig. 10.1—Brazil. The inset compares the area of the region with that of the United States.

posits of **manganese** in the Western Hemisphere occur, however, on the Bolivian border in the southwestern corner of Mato Grosso state. Mining of these deposits has been sporadic and on a small scale during the past several decades because of the remoteness of the site.

The prime handicap of the western Campos region is lack of population.[1] The failure of settlement to occur is at least partly due to an almost complete absence of transportation facilities. The region is in the interior of the continent and there are no direct natural lines of communication with the coast. Available routes to the seaboard are extremely devious and roundabout. The cattle and mineral industries, the two great potentials, cannot develop without a good transportation system to supply

an adequate connection with markets. To provide even an initial trunk route such as first spanned the western United States will require much capital expenditure, which, as long as Brazil suffers from a general capital shortage, will not be applied to the development of remote, sparsely settled land when nearer, richer, and more populous regions are clamoring for development. The overall utilization of the western Campos must wait for the general growth of Brazil and all of South America, at which time a larger population will provide a ready market for the products of a Campos cattle industry, and domestic capital will be more available for investment in the region.

The East Central Plateau Region. In contrast with the lagging development of the Campos the eastern portion of the plateau has experienced a developmental boom comparable to the great industrial expansion of the United States between the Civil War and

[1] A commission of the League of Nations once reported that western Brazil could support a population of 900 million!

World War I. Competent observers have asserted that this territory possesses the greatest potentialities of all South American regions; indeed, some have said that without the eastern plateau area Brazil would be but a hollow shell.

The factors in combination which have caused this phenomenal growth, and which make this region one of such great possibilities, are rich mineral resources, large hydropower potential, good soil, a healthful climate, and a growing population. There also exists in the people living there an intangible quality that spurs to enterprise, something that seems to be needed in addition to the material resources if the developmental process is to be started and maintained. Other regions have comparable advantages but lack the necessary human spark that gives rise, in this eastern portion of the plateau, to frantic hustle and bustle in bringing about a spectacular growth.

Products. In the eastern plateau region, just inland from the low coastlands, is an area about the size of the state of Indiana where almost half of the world's **coffee** is produced. The coffee tree will grow almost anywhere in the tropics, but if the beans are to have a fine flavor certain environmental conditions must exist which are best fulfilled in highlands with a savanna climate. The rainfall alternation for the "coffee plateau," as this district is sometimes called, is that of heavy precipitation during the spring and summer, with the dry season in autumn and winter. This distribution provides rain during the growing season, clear skies during the picking and drying season. The temperature requirements—warmth but not tropic heat—are met by growing the trees on slopes and hillsides where they escape frost damage (Fig. 10.2). Cold air, with frost, settles into the valleys during the coldest nights, while on the slopes the coffee trees are not affected by cold winds that blow across the tops of the hills. Moreover, this district has a rich volcanic soil, one that is exceptionally thick and allows the coffee trees to extend their roots deep into the earth for mineral plant food.

Fig. 10.2—Coffee estate in Brazil. The coffee trees extend up the hill slope in the foreground. (Courtesy, Brazilian Government Trade Bureau.)

Harvesting and marketing the coffee crop is a complicated procedure that involves selective picking of the berries and careful drying of the coffee beans. Both operations require a large amount of manual labor. Although Brazilian coffee dominates the world market, it is not a quality product. Its low repute is due partly to the careless, haphazard handling the beans receive during the harvest and processing, and partly to the fact that the higher the growing altitude the better the flavor of the coffee. Thus several other coffee regions of the world produce, at higher altitudes than those of Brazil, better, so-called "mild" coffee.

The coffee industry of Brazil first gained importance in the late nineteenth century and has since grown to become a dominating factor in the Brazilian economy. As a popular song asserts, "There's an awful lot of coffee in Brazil." In the past Brazil has had great trouble, as a one-crop country, with overproduction of coffee and great fluctuations in prices. The coffee-growing industry before 1953 had, however, already begun to decline in relative importance within Brazil, as other industries expanded and new ones arose. Nevertheless, Brazil's economy appears destined to remain dangerously dependent on coffee for some years to come.

Part of the relative decline in the importance of coffee in Brazil has been due to the growth in the production of **cotton,** which now rivals coffee in value of the crop and is second to it as an export product. Brazil is now among the six largest cotton producers in the world. The modest yield of former years was chiefly from the northeast corner of the country, south of the Amazon's mouth, but between 1930 and 1950 there was a large expansion in volume from the southern states, particularly the state of Sao Paulo.

A third important agricultural product is **corn,** the leading crop in terms of acreage. Most of the corn comes from the southern portion of the savanna region. Total output, the bulk of which is consumed domestically, is sufficient to rank Brazil as the third corn country of the world.

Other important food crops of the savanna region are **beans,** the staff of life in Brazil, and **rice,** which is grown under drier conditions than elsewhere in the world and is termed "upland rice."

The east central plateau lands are the basis of a large **cattle** industry, a use for which they are even better suited than the lands of the Mato Grosso district. The cattle population of Brazil is the largest of any country in South America, and fourth largest in the world. Despite the poor quality of the stock the value of meat output alone is greater than that of any crop, and Brazil is the second-ranking exporter of **hides** and **skins.** It also leads the continent in its output of **milk** and is second in **butter** production.

Although the state of **Minas Geraes** is the site of important agriculture, its name, "general minerals," attests to its resources of greatest value. **Iron ore** is found in a belt 100 miles long and 60 miles wide, the greatest single deposit being an entire mountain containing some of the richest ore on earth. There are also extensive, rich deposits of **manganese,** and sufficient deposits of **gold** to result in the precious metal's first rank among Brazilian mineral products in terms of value of output. Other important minerals are **bauxite** and **quartz crystals,** the latter

of great value in radio and radar, and **beryllium** and **tantalum,** for which Brazil is the source of two-fifths and one-half, respectively, of the world supply. Still another leading mineral product is the variety of **industrial diamond** known as "carbonado" (because of its black color).

Industries. Although still predominantly an agricultural country (farming accounts for two-thirds of the economic activity), Brazil is making steadily accelerated progress in developing industrial strength based on its domestic resources and products. In terms of value of output the leading industry (aside from food processing) is **textiles,** centered in the state of Sao Paulo and based on the country's cotton production. There is also an infant **steel** industry (Latin America's largest), hampered by a lack of fuel and transportation difficulties, and a considerable **cement** industry. Various other industries produce consumers' goods ranging from shirts to refrigerators and automobiles. The growth of an industrial center in Sao Paulo state has been greatly spurred by large-scale utilization of the huge hydropower potential of the eastern plateau edge to develop large quantities of cheap electricity. The power is obtained through a 2400-foot drop off the plateau-edge of water from dammed-up streams flowing on the plateau surface.

CITIES OF SAVANNA BRAZIL

Name	Type	Population (1950)
Sao Paulo	Commercial and governmental	2,000,000
Belo Horizonte	Governmental	340,000
Cuiaba	Commercial	24,000
Corumba	River port	13,000

Cities. **Sao Paulo** (Fig. 10.3), capital of the state of that name, is one of the world's most amazing cities. It was in 1953 the third largest city of South America. In 1890 it had 64,000 inhabitants; in 1920, about 580,000. At its 1946 rate of growth of 80,000 a year it is planning for a population of 4 million in 1966! This extraordinary boom town has

Fig. 10.3—Sao Paulo, Brazil. (Courtesy, Brazilian Information Bureau.)

moved one writer to the following eloquent description:

> The town library is twenty-two stories high. The main street, ten miles long, cuts through mountains, runs on three levels. . . . Street vendors sell more books on accounting, office management and manufacturing than almost anything else and courses in fifteen lessons on how to establish your own company often outdraw the movies. Every hour of the working day more than four new buildings are finished. . . . The hemisphere's fastest-growing metropolis, Latin America's foremost manufacturing center, larger in area than even Los Angeles . . . Sao Paulo, booming, building and breaking records—the only metropolis in the Americas never to have known a depression. . . .[2]

[2] Ray Josephs, *Latin America: Continent in Crisis,* Random House, 1948, pp. 442 f.

Belo Horizonte, the capital of the state of Minas Geraes, is an excellent example of a governmental city. It was founded and completely planned (to the extent that all public buildings and utilities were finished before the seat of government was transferred) around the turn of the century. Its street plan is similar to that of Washington, D.C., and in a country noted for its excellent city planning, Belo Horizonte is considered one of the better examples.

Cuiaba and **Corumba**—the former the capital of Mato Grosso state, the latter the Brazilian port of the upper Paraguay River— are the only two cities of consequence in the western Campos. They are 500 miles apart, typical of the large distances and small population of the region.

Brazil as a Whole. The full title of the

country is the United States of Brazil. The "U.S.B." is the fourth largest nation in the world in extent of territory, exceeding that of the "U.S.A." by some 250,000 square miles. The republic was established in 1889 and consists of 20 states, a Federal District, and several federal territories disposed as a belt around the borders of the country.

The Federal District corresponds to the District of Columbia in the United States. It is now a tract of country surrounding Rio de Janeiro on the coast but will eventually be set up in the center of the plateau region, on the western border of Minas Geraes. Thus the site of the future federal capital will be ideally located in the heartland of a fully developed Brazil.

The population of Brazil is 57 million, largest on the continent and second in numbers only to the United States in the Western Hemisphere. The language is Portuguese and the religion Roman Catholic, both heritages from the days when Brazil was a Portuguese colony. Although Portuguese culture prevails, the population contains large elements of native Indian and African Negro stock. Only 35 percent of the inhabitants have all-white ancestry. The three races are well blended through constant intermarriage, for it is the considered policy of the government to encourage a thorough mixture of the races into a homogeneous "Brazilian people." As one Brazilian official has put it, "In the United States, many people are afraid that racial intermarriage will take place. Here we are afraid it won't!" Accordingly, Japanese immigration was halted when it was found that the Japanese were intent on preserving their distinctive traits by not intermarrying with the other racial elements in Brazil.

In view of the impressive list of natural advantages Brazil possesses, the question arises, Why has Brazil not made further progress in its development? The answers are several.

First is poor communication, as epitomized in the Mato Grosso region. No country can develop industrially without trade, both internal and external. The country must be-

come integrated and mutually interdependent in its various regions if it is to achieve economic maturity. Brazil is well situated for participation in international overseas trade but has great natural difficulties (i.e., the eastern plateau rise, the Amazon lowland, etc.) to overcome in developing its domestic transportation and communication lines. Greatest progress in solving this problem has been made along the southeast coast and in parts of the east central plateau.

Secondly, Brazil needs capital, one of the essentials in overcoming the lack of communications facilities. The capital required for the construction of an adequate railroad net, or even a highway system, cannot be raised domestically, as available domestic capital is poured into real-estate speculation or hoarded in the banks of other countries. Foreign capital is easier to attract for the development of natural resources than for public works and industrial needs. Moreover, there is a traditional distrust in Brazil of all foreign investment.

Thirdly, Brazil has no easily developed energy resources. Adequate supplies of coal, the basis of all industrialization, are lacking. This deficiency is to some extent offset by the existence of the large hydropower developments such as those in Sao Paulo. In addition, minor known occurrences of oil in the southwest appear to presage more significant discoveries in the future. Brazil as a whole, however, remains an energy-poor nation.

Finally, the people as a whole lack industrial initiative. Brazilians are confident of the country's great destiny but do not feel any responsibility for its immediate realization. The general health level is very low—one-third of the rural population has malaria, one-fifth is infected with hookworm; tuberculosis and syphilis are rampant in the large cities. Brazil is a rich country, but the general standard of living does not reflect its riches. Approximately two-thirds of the people are illiterate. Improvement of living standards is thus necessary to create the demand so vital to sound industrialization.

Despite all these handicaps the potential

of Brazil is great. United States aid during World War II advanced development at a much faster pace than previously. Through this assistance Brazil has already become the chief rival of Argentina as the industrial power of the continent. The wartime stimulus to development has persisted in subsequent years, and it is possible that the process of self-sustaining development has at last been started.

D. VENEZUELA

"The United States of Venezuela," as the country is officially known, consists of 350,000 square miles (equal to all the states east of the Mississippi, north of the Ohio and west of the Hudson) on the southern shore of the Caribbean Sea (Fig. 10.4). It is divided politically into 20 states, a Federal District, and two territories. The language

is Spanish, as it is in all the independent South American countries except Brazil. The religion is Roman Catholic. The population is about 5.5 million, of which two-thirds is mestizo, some one-fifth of European descent, and the remainder Negro and Indian.

Climate and Topography. Venezuela is divided into four well-defined regions, all of them more or less disconnected and economically independent. The heart of the country is composed of an eastern prong of the Andes that crosses Venezuela near its eastern end as the **Sierra Nevada de Mérida** and continues in an east-west direction along the coast as a series of lesser highlands. Because of the altitude (2000 to 6000 feet) the daily temperature range is between 90° F. and 60° F., so that the oppressiveness of even the hottest days is compensated for by cool nights. As might be expected, this re-

Fig. 10.4—Venezuela, Colombia, and Ecuador. The inset compares the area of the region with an equivalent area of the United States (states in white).

gion contains most of the population, is the site of all the major cities but one, and contains most of the domestic industries and what transportation system the country possesses.

Between this and another projection of the Andes farther to the west lies the **Maracaibo Basin.** This is one of the hottest places in all South America, and the humid climate (it experiences two rainy seasons) is extremely debilitating. Lake Maracaibo (see Chapter 2, p. 34), its center, is nevertheless the focus of great activity.

Running east-west through the length of Venezuela, from the Sierra Nevada de Mérida to the sea, and south of the coastal highlands, is the valley of the **Orinoco River.** The lowlands of the river basin are known as *llanos* (Spanish for "plain, even") and constitute one of the three major plains regions of South America. The llanos are characterized by the wet-dry extremes in the alternation of the seasons. From April to October, during the rainy season, 30 to 50 inches of rain falls; from November to March, none. These climatic extremes have precluded more than a sparse settlement of the 100,000 square miles of the llanos.

The remaining division of Venezuela is the southeastern section, 200,000 square miles of territory topographically part of the Guiana Highlands. It is a remote, unutilized region, with a savanna climate in general but bearing tropical rainforests on the northern slopes because of exposure to the northeast trades. Except for native Indians the region is practically uninhabited and largely unexplored.

Transportation. Most of the cities and concentrations of population in Venezuela are on or near the coast, and transportation between them is relatively adequate. Nevertheless, transportation is Venezuela's chief problem. The Orinoco is navigable for 1500 miles upstream from its mouth but flows through such sparsely settled country that the great advantage of a natural highway it provides is largely to no purpose. The major need is for transportation between the different regions. The lack of either a road or railroad

net for the country as a whole greatly increases the cost in one region of the products of another.

Products. The outstanding product of Venezuela is **petroleum.** The oil fields on the eastern shore of Lake Maracaibo and under the lake itself (Fig. 10.5) constitute one of the major oil regions of the world, the most important in the Western Hemisphere outside the United States. Other fields occur in the llanos.

Fig. 10.5—Oil Wells in Lake Maracaibo, Venezuela. (Courtesy, Creole Petroleum Corporation.)

Venezuela produces about 15 percent of the world's oil, accounts for some 40 percent of world oil exports, and has about 12 percent of global reserves. The occurrence of the oil with convenient water transportation at hand has greatly facilitated and hastened its exploitation. Neither long pipelines nor roads needed to be built. The oil is transferred directly to tankers which carry it to the local refineries and those on nearby Caribbean islands.

The second major mineral resource of Venezuela is **iron ore** (Fig. 10.6). Large, high-grade deposits that can be mined on the surface occur in a belt parallel to the Ori-

Fig. 10.6—General View of Mining Operations at Cerro Bolivar, Venezuela. (Courtesy, United States Steel Corporation.)

noco River and about 50 miles south of it along its lower reaches. American companies developed these deposits for large-scale production during and after World War II as an important source of raw material for the American steel industry.

In contrast with the thriving petroleum and iron ore industries is the declining **cattle** industry of the llanos. The wet season in the llanos brings out lush and prolific vegetation on which cattle can be fattened rapidly, but it also creates vast areas of swamp in which the cattle can get mired and may drown. During the dry season the grass becomes so coarse and unnutritious that cattle cannot feed on it and must be driven elsewhere for further pasturage or for sale. These circumstances plus the prevalence of disease have made the cattle industry of the llanos chiefly remarkable for its futility.

Some 20 percent of Venezuela's popula-

tion is engaged in agriculture. This is a low figure for a South American country and is explained by the large number of workers in the oil industry, to which they are attracted by the high wages.

The most important crops are **coffee** and **cacao,** both supplying a moderate yet significant volume to the world production of these two commodities. Both crops are subsidized by the state. Venezuelan coffee is of medium quality; it is grown on the slopes of the northern highlands and would be of much higher grade because of the altitude if proper care were taken in its harvesting and processing. The cacao is grown mostly in the eastern extension of the highlands.

Many additional crops are raised for domestic consumption in the northern and western highlands and in the Maracaibo Basin. The former exhibit typical altitude zoning: on the highest slopes grazing is carried on; below that middle-latitude crops such as wheat, beans, tobacco, corn, and cotton are grown; farther down come coffee and cacao, which grade in turn into sugar cane, rice, and bananas at the bottom.

Fig. 10.7—Caracas, Venezuela. At the center left is a twin 30-story office building, part of a development much like, but larger than, Radio City, New York. (Courtesy, Hamilton Wright.)

CITIES OF VENEZUELA

Name	Type	Population
Caracas	Governmental	900,000 (1955)
Maracaibo	Seaport	235,000 (1950)
Barquisimeto	Commercial	105,000 (1950)
Valencia	Commercial	90,000 (1950)

Cities. **Caracas,** the capital and largest city of Venezuela, is situated in a mountain-rimmed basin nine miles inland from the sea at about the mid-point of the country's coastline. In the 1940's and early 1950's the city experienced a construction boom that has transformed its appearance; skyscrapers, fancy hotels, and spectacular apartment developments give it an exciting aspect (Fig. 10.7). The city's altitude of 3400 feet is enough to give it an agreeable climate, and its broad streets and many flower gardens further contribute to a good general impression.

Maracaibo, on the northwestern shore of Lake Maracaibo near its connection with the sea, is the country's second city and chief port by reason of its large petroleum export

trade. When the Spanish explorers first reached this region they found native villages built on stilts over the lake, whence Venezuela, or "Little Venice," gets its name.

Barquisimeto, Venezuela's third largest city, is about 150 miles west of Caracas on the edge of the llanos. It is a local commercial center.

Valencia, the most industrialized city of Venezuela, and the center of its most developed agricultural region, is located in a lowland area about halfway between Caracas and Barquisimeto. It has a decidedly Spanish air and, like Caracas, a pleasant climate.

Venezuela as a Whole. The royalties and taxes paid by the oil industry make Venezuela one of the richest of the South American countries as measured by revenue poured into the treasury. (In 1955 tax payments from the oil industry provided 65 percent of total government revenue.) This money, together with the many facilities and improvements in sanitary and living conditions made by the oil companies themselves, provides the basis of all modern developments in Venezuela. On the other hand, because of the abundance of money the cost of living is high. Because of the high degree of dependence on its oil resources Venezuela faces potentially very serious problems when production begins to show the effect of exhaustion of the reserves. Happily, that time is still some distance in the future, and the development of iron ore and other resources begun since World War II may mean that the anticipated problems will not be serious after all.

QUESTIONS. Identify the *Campos* and *Mato Grosso.* What are the important differences between the western Campos and the east central plateau region in Brazil? Name the two potentially significant industries of the western Campos. What is the major need of the region? What factors have been responsible for the development of the east central plateau district? Why is the production of coffee concentrated in a small area of the district? What important nonfood crop is a competitor of coffee for land use in Brazil? What products and exports come from the cattle industry of the east central plateau? Name four important mineral products from Minas Geraes. What industries are important in the state? What is unique concerning the language and cultural background of Brazil? What is the racial policy of the country? Discuss the four major handicaps to the future development of Brazil. Why is Sao Paulo one of the world's most amazing cities?

What are the four topographic regions of Venezuela? Which contains most of the population and industry? Why? The Orinoco in Venezuela is one of the major rivers of South America; why, nevertheless, is transportation one of the chief problems of the country? What product dominates the economic activities of Venezuela? Describe Venezuela's world position in this product. What problem does this raise for the country in the future? What is the second-ranking mineral resource of Venezuela? Where is it found? Why are both of these resources specially significant to the United States? What are the two ranking crops of Venezuela?

E. COLOMBIA

General Aspects. The Republic of Colombia, situated in the northwestern corner of South America, comprises a territory of almost 500,000 square miles (about equal to Texas, Oklahoma, Louisiana, and Arkansas combined) (Fig. 10.4). It has the distinction of being the only South American country bordering on both the Atlantic and the Pacific. Its coastline of some 1200 miles is about equally divided between the two oceans.

Colombia represents the core of the original Spanish colony of New Granada, which won its independence in the early nineteenth century but in 1858 split into several independent states, including Colombia and Venezuela. The two countries are similar in many respects. Both have large areas of savanna climate, rainforest climate, and Andean highlands with their climatic zoning. Both have large, partially navigable rivers. Both have similar agricultural products and at least one common mineral product.

The People. The population of Colombia is over 12 million. The whites, who consti-

tute only 10 percent of the population, live in the highlands where the climate is pleasant. The Indians and mestizos who form the majority live in the highlands and along the lower slopes. The Negroid elements of the population comprise about 35 percent of the total (highest of any South American country) and live in the lowlands.

Topography. Like Venezuela, Colombia is a country of diverse topographic and agricultural regions. The economic activities of the country are dominated by the mountain topography of the Andes, which here, at their northern limit, break up into three ranges, known as the **Western, Central,** and **Eastern Cordilleras.** All three ranges are typical lofty Andean ranges with peaks over 17,000 feet in elevation.

Between the three ranges two major north-south valleys extend, that of the **Magdalena River** and that of its tributary, the **Cauca.** In the north the lower course of the Magdalena is across an extensive plain to its mouth in the Caribbean.

Roughly one-half of the country lies to the east of the Eastern Cordillera. This section is a large plain divided between the rainforest climate of the Amazon Basin and the savanna climate of the llanos. Almost uninhabited and quite undeveloped, it has little significance for the Colombian economy. The other lowland area of Colombia, the Pacific coast, has been discussed previously. (See Chapter 7, p. 114.)

Highlands constitute almost one-quarter of the total extent of Colombia, and because of their altitude about one-third of the highlands possesses pleasant and healthful middle-latitude climates, even though these regions are situated almost on the equator. As a result almost 99 percent of the population is found there. This concentration gives a density of 30 to 60 persons per square mile—the highest anywhere in the Andes. The Western Cordillera is the most rugged and lacks mineral deposits, so that it cannot compare in importance with the other two ranges, which are the centers of population. The Eastern Cordillera is the wider and includes the greater expanse of land with middle-latitude climates. The northeast extension of this Cordillera forms the Sierra de Mérida of Venezuela.

Transportation. In Colombia transportation is dominated by the Magdalena and its tributary. Because the country is creased by its three great north-south Cordilleras the parallel trend of the rivers provides two natural highways to the Caribbean coast. East-west traffic is, however, almost impossible; few roads are better than mule trails. Such railroads as exist are mostly feeders to the navigable Magdalena. The beginnings of a road system are being made, however.

Unfortunately, even the major Magdalena route has great defects. The river is clogged throughout its course by sand bars and snags due to uprooted, submerged trees. No attempt has ever been made to improve the channel; the difficulties are just endured. These handicaps are experienced throughout the year but come to a climax during the dry season. Low water then may stop all navigation for a time, and freight piles up at docks, where it may be ruined by exposure. Passengers spend days or weeks en route. In view of these difficulties it is not surprising that air transport has had an early and vigorous development in Colombia.

The general inadequacy of transportation has resulted in a strong growth of regionalism centered on the various cities. For this reason Colombia has been referred to as "a nation of city states."

Products. The major agricultural product and leading export of the country (some four-fifths of total exports by value) is **coffee.** Although the crop does not dominate the economy of the country, as it does in Brazil, nevertheless Colombia is one of the three major world producers of this commodity. It leads in the production of mild coffee, and much attention is given to maintaining the high quality of the crop.

There is a small area of coffee-growing in the narrow highlands just east of the Magdalena's mouth, but the major producing areas are in the Central and Eastern Cordilleras. There are almost no flatlands, but the steep slopes are ideal for coffee. As in Java (see Chapter 8, p. 130), a rich volcanic soil under ample rainfall yields a bounteous harvest.

Bananas are the chief product of the level plains east of the Magdalena delta, where physical conditions for banana growing are among the best to be found. Again, production is chiefly for export.

Tobacco is grown in most parts of the country for local use, but in a few districts a surplus is produced for export, most of which goes to the United States along with the coffee and bananas.

The remaining crops are all consumed at home. Sugar cane is grown chiefly in the Cauca Valley but also on the coffee estates up to an altitude of 6000 feet. Cotton is produced along the lower Magdalena. Its quality is low because of careless picking and unscientific methods. Rice for domestic consumption is becoming increasingly important in the northwestern lowlands.

The great altitudes of the Andean mountains and their location so near the equator result in a marked zoning of agriculture on their slopes. Such food crops as corn, wheat, and barley are grown at their respective temperature levels. The yields are small, however, owing to poor cultivation.

As in Venezuela, the savanna lands are utilized for the raising of generally scrubby **cattle** under the handicaps of disease, poor breeding stock, and careless husbandry. The important savanna grazing lands are the northwestern lowlands. The Colombian grasses are coarse and not too nutritious because of the savanna seasonal alternation but are somewhat better than those of the Venezuelan llanos. Plantings of better grasses have been undertaken.

The market for the meat products of the cattle industry in all three Colombian localities is in the highlands of the country. The quality is far too poor to find an export market. Hides can be sold abroad, since their quality is less adversely affected by the low efficiency with which the industry is conducted. The western and river valley savannas are in a relatively good position with respect to the domestic market compared with the isolation of the eastern llanos, where, as in Venezuela, driving the cattle to market causes them to lose much of their weight.

The major mineral product, second in value among the country's exports, is **petroleum.** The volume is far less than that of Venezuela, but good quality, high yield from the wells, and a good labor supply have been important favorable factors in the extension of the country's petroleum output.

The main oil fields are along the Magdalena, and it is indicative of the state of Colombian transportation that despite the riverside location of the fields the oil companies preferred to build a 300-mile pipe line at high cost from the interior to the coast rather than entrust transportation of the crude oil to the uncertainties of Magdalena shipping. In 1940 a field was opened farther in the interior, where the hostility of the forest Indians has been a great hazard. As the oil workers go about their jobs they are targets for heavy, barbed arrows that can penetrate clear through their bodies.

Gold follows platinum (see Chapter 7, p. 115) in value as a Colombian export. Although Colombia is the ranking South American gold producer it accounts for only a small fraction of the world output. **Emeralds,** on the other hand, are almost a monopoly of Colombia, as the country is the world's chief source of that costly gem.

Industries. Despite its topographic and climatic handicaps and the many difficulties that lie in the way of any underdeveloped country in its attempts to industrialize, Colombia has made good progress in building up its manufactures, especially during and since World War II. Home needs for textiles, building materials, beverages, footwear, and certain chemicals are met almost entirely from domestic production. Most of the industries are small but thriving. The chief handicap to further growth is lack of power, but this is being remedied through development of the large potential hydropower resources.

Cities. **Bogota,** the capital and first city of Colombia, is situated in a large basin in the Eastern Cordillera at an altitude of 8700 feet. Bogota is one of the most attractive cities of South America; its climate is pleasant, the scenery of the surrounding mountains is magnificent, and it is a noteworthy cultural center. It is said that the purest Spanish spoken in South America may be heard in Bogota. The maintenance of this sophisticated cultural center in the mountains is, however, expensive. Goods double in price through the transportation charges incurred in moving them from the Caribbean coast to the capital. The city, moreover, is situated to the east of the Magdalena River, whereas the industry and economic activity of the country are centered west of the river. Air transport is in some degree remedying this situation.

CITIES OF COLOMBIA

Name	Type	Population (1951)
Bogota	Governmental	48,000
Medellin	Commercial and industrial	358,000
Cali	Commercial	284,000
Barranquilla	Seaport	280,000
Cartagena	Seaport	129,000

Medellin, the second city, is on the east side of the Cauca Valley at the northern end of the Central Cordillera. Medellin resembles Sao Paulo in that it is the center of an almost explosive economic expansion and a building boom with modern architecture. The city contains several score factories. The concentration is on textile production but other products range from mineral waters to zippers. Medellin is, as well, the center of coffee and mineral production. The rapid industrialization is the work of the energetic people of the state of Antioquia, of which Medellin is the capital. The rugged topography of the state preserved the Antioquians from the debilitating influence of the colonial feudal system that prevailed elsewhere in Colombia under the Spanish rule.

Cali, the commercial center of western Colombia, is located on the upper reaches of the Cauca 90 miles inland from the Pacific, in the center of a rich agricultural region. It is also the site of many light industries.

Barranquilla is located on the Magdalena River 11 miles from its mouth. Until just before World War II, however, it was a port that was not a port, for the river channel below the city was so shallow as to be unusable. An 18-mile railroad connected the frustrated city with Puerto (Port) Colombia, a small town on the Caribbean that served as the actual seaport. Puerto Colombia has now become a bathing resort and Barranquilla, through dredging of the river channel, has taken its rightful place as the major port of Colombia. It is also the chief international airport of the country.

Cartagena is another seaport about 65 miles south of Barranquilla on the Caribbean coast and also serves, through a canal, as a port for the Magdalena Valley. Its picturesque harbor is dominated by many forts dating from the buccaneering days of the Spanish Main.

Colombia as a Whole. The great need of the country is improved transportation, including flood control and channel improvement on the Magdalena so that it will be navigable the year round over all its 900-mile course. Construction of roads and railroads for adequate east-west communication, and to unify the country's development, is next in order. It is no coincidence that the chief exports of the country, aside from petroleum (which uses the foreign-built pipe line) are those that have high value in small bulk and can stand the cost of transport by human porterage, which is commonly resorted to during the dry season.

Aside from the transportation problem Colombia has good prospects. Its economy is not dominated by a single crop or mineral product. It has large, unexploited natural resources, and, equally important, a significant portion of its population is vigorous and capable, determined to develop the country as fully and rapidly as possible.

F. ECUADOR

General Aspects. On the west coast of South America, fitting wedgelike between Colombia and Peru, is the second smallest of the countries of that continent, the Republic of Ecuador (Fig. 10.4). Ecuador is a country of political, economic, and physical contrasts. Astride the equator in one direction and the stupendous Andes in the other, it experiences almost the full gamut of world climates in its relatively small area. This area cannot be stated precisely, as it has never been measured. Estimates range between 175,000 and 275,000 square miles.

The population numbers nearly 3.5 million people. Only 8 percent of the inhabitants are white; the great majority are Indians and mestizos. The official language is Spanish, but the language of the Indians is predominant. The poverty-stricken life of the Indians differs little in manner or substance from that prevailing when the Spanish conquistadors appeared on the scene. The white population centers around a few ruling families with great landholdings. These families are descended from the Spanish aristocrats of the colonial period and maintain the traditions of their ancestors.

Topography and Climate. The physical regions of Ecuador are similar to those of Colombia but simpler in pattern. The Pacific borderland on the west is a segment of the coastal plain that extends almost the length of South America and is here at its widest (some 100 miles across) and most productive. As a site for cash crop production it constitutes Ecuador's sole developed resource. The climate of the plain varies from desert conditions in the south to rainforest conditions in the north. A wet-dry alternation over most of the area warrants its classification with the savanna lands. And, as this area is the one most significant for Ecuador as a whole, the country is appropriately considered as part of such lands.

The Andean highlands contain the bulk of the population and produce the local food crops. The Andean climate is pleasant in comparison with that of the steaming coastal plain. Here too there is a gradation in rainfall from high in the north to low in the south.

East of the Andes there is included in Ecuador a small area of the Amazon Basin known as the **Oriente** region, with a typical rainforest climate. Like the equivalent region in Colombia it is inhabited only by native

Indians and is completely undeveloped and only partially explored. It figures not at all in the life of the country as a whole.

Products. The crops of Ecuador vary from tropical products for export, grown in the coastal lowlands, to products for domestic consumption typical of the middle latitudes, grown on the slopes and in the mountain valleys of the Andes. Ecuador thus presents the unusual phenomenon of a country that exports tropical agricultural products and lives on middle-latitude crops, all grown within its own small area.

The dominant agricultural product is **cacao.** The central coastal region, especially that part around the **Gulf of Guayaquil,** has almost ideal physical and climatic conditions for cacao growing; but because of ineradicable plant diseases production is under that of the former peak years, the while total world output has increased many times.

Other crops of the coastal plain include rice, which is assuming increasing importance as an export product; bananas, grown for export to Peru and Chile; cotton, sugar, and tobacco in minor amounts.

Almost all of Ecuador is forest covered save for the higher mountainous regions and the areas of cultivation along the coast. The scant use made of the forests in the Oriente is in sharp contrast with the yield of the forests on the western slope. Ecuador is a major source of **balsa** wood, which is obtained chiefly from the coastal lowlands, with minor amounts coming from the Oriente. The demand for this very light wood is rising so rapidly that the production, from wild forest trees, is insufficient.

Ecuador is also the major source of **Panama hats,** manufacture of which involves a tremendous amount of hand labor, supplied by women and children.

The highland agriculture, already referred to as the source of food for the populace, is carried on at altitudes between 7000 and 11,-000 feet. The crops are middle-latitude grains and vegetables.

Ecuador's mineral resources are almost unutilized. There is very little mining because of political instability and the physical inac-

cessibility of the ore deposits. Both of these factors are effective deterrents to investment in mine development, a risky business under the best of circumstances.

CITIES OF ECUADOR

Name	Type	Population (1950)
Guayaquil	Seaport	260,000
Quito	Governmental and commercial	210,000

Cities. **Guayaquil,** the largest city of Ecuador and only significant seaport, lies 35 miles inland (on the Guayas River) from the head of the Gulf of Guayaquil, one of the few indentations on the west coast of South America north of the fiord coast of Chile (see Chapter 1, p. 15). The application of modern public health and sanitation practices under the auspices of the Rockefeller Foundation in 1915 proved such a stimulus that the city was virtually rebuilt in subsequent years.

Quito, the capital, is situated at an altitude of nearly 10,000 feet in the northern part of the Andean highlands. Although it is only 15 miles from the equator its altitude insures a pleasant climate of warm days and cool nights. Because of its isolation it has remained a haven of Old Spanish culture and contains many fine specimens of Spanish colonial architecture.

The two cities, practically equal in size, are representative of the disunity that has plagued Ecuador in the intense rivalry between them. Quito and its environs stand for the attitudes and customs of the highland inhabitants, Guayaquil those of the lowland people.

Ecuador as a Whole. Ecuador is an unusually poor country, even by South American standards. Illiteracy is the common condition of the inhabitants and they are everywhere disease-ridden. Economically the country has never fully recovered from the effects of the cacao blight. Like Venezuela and Colombia, Ecuador also suffers from the lack of transportation facilities and the consequent tendency toward regionalism and disunity. Relics of the Spanish feudal system, moreover, persist even more strongly in Ecuador, constituting formidable obstacles in the way of improving the standard of living. Something new has been added, however, in the presence of several thousand European refugees from totalitarian persecution. They began coming just before World War II and have since injected a spirit of enterprise and activity that may provide the necessary spark to kindle Ecuador's development.

G. THE GRAN CHACO

General Aspects. In central South America in the region where Bolivia, Paraguay, and Argentina meet is a territory some 200,000 to 300,000 square miles in extent known as the **Gran Chaco** (Fig. 10.1). The name is Spanish for "great hunting ground"; this designation dates, however, from before the Spanish conquest. It is said to derive from the fact that invading Inca armies were able to scatter the local savages before them like so much wild game. The respective political portions of the Gran Chaco are of very unequal size; by far the largest area is Paraguayan territory.

Topographically, the Gran Chaco is a vast, low plain, almost all of which is less than 500 feet in altitude, with considerable portions under 200 feet. Largely unexplored, the plain extends from the foothills of the Andes on the west to outliers of the Brazilian Highlands on the east, and from the low divide south of the Amazon Basin on the north to the flood plains of the **Pilcomayo** and **Paraguay** rivers on the south.

On every square mile of this vast, level plain of low altitude and remote interior location tons of water are dumped each rainy season, which extends from November to April. The sluggish rivers are quite incapable of draining off the great excess of water. As a consequence enormous swamps and shallow lakes are formed in which countless millions of insects breed.

The dry season gives rise to the opposite extreme. Between May and October so little rain falls that the major rivers are reduced to mere trickles and grass grows in their beds. At this time swarms of locusts, so huge that they may darken the sky for days at a time, fare forth from their breeding grounds to bring devastation to neighboring regions.

The interior location also results in extremes of temperature (see Chapter 6, p. 90). The thermometer reads above 105° F. at times during the summer (this in a *humid* climate!); during the winter months temperatures below freezing are recorded.

Because of local variations in the depth of the permanent water table (and the consequent difference in the effect of the severity of the dry season on the vegetation in different places) the Gran Chaco is a patchwork of swamps, forests, grasslands, and palm groves. West of the Paraguay River there are scrub forests, and certain areas contain extensive tracts of continuous grassland.

The People. This unpleasant, isolated region is mainly the abode of primitive Indians whose lives are dominated by the weird superstition that the Chaco is peopled by ghosts. However, Paraguay, encouraged by the League of Nations, permitted a few thousand whites (members of the Mennonite sect) to settle in the area during the period between the two World Wars. It is a tribute to their religious convictions and steadfastness that these Mennonites are successful and contented settlers in this inhospitable region. The total population of Indians and whites is impossible to gauge accurately but has been estimated to be 135,000. The few towns and settlements are all found on the borders of the region.

Products. **Meat** and **hides** are the major products of the Paraguayan portion of the Chaco. The region possesses a distinct advantage over other savanna grazing lands, such as the llanos, in having nutritious and succulent grasses, but the handicaps are crushing. First, the Gran Chaco water holes are commonly bitter because of the accumulation of salt in the soil through aridity and inadequate drainage. Second, the alternation between flood and drought makes impossible the uninterrupted use of a large part of the land throughout the year. Third, the region's isolation is heightened in that facilities for land transportation are almost nonexistent and unrestricted water transportation is limited to the wet season. Finally, human frailty has led to a serious deterioration of the quality and numbers of the livestock. For possession of the territory the neighboring countries fought a series of wars that lasted into the 1930's. During the fighting the herds went untended, and the armies lived off them.

What might be called a lumber industry ranks next to the cattle industry in importance. It consists in the felling of the *quebracho*[3] tree and the extraction of **tannin** from its wood. Tannin is a substance commonly used to convert hides into leather. The quebracho tree contains over twice as much tannin as the bark from the best middle-latitude trees (e.g., hemlock and oak) used in the leather industry. The Gran Chaco, accordingly, is the world's most important source of the compound.

The most extensive quebracho stands are found in a belt extending along the west bank of the Paraguay River and upstream on the north side of the Pilcomayo River where

[3] From the Spanish *quebrar*, "to break"; *hacha*, "ax." The wood is so hard that specially tempered steel is needed to cut it.

Fig. 10.8—Cuba. The inset compares the area of Cuba with Pennsylvania, which is approximately equal in area.

it joins the Paraguay. This concentration near the rivers is a great advantage for logging operations, as the streams can be used as highways.

Originally the logs were exported to Europe for processing, but now large corporations have factories along the rivers and own reserves of quebracho forests. Though modern methods of extraction are used, numerous difficulties remain. The local Indians are a poor and undependable labor source; diseases and insects plague even the Indian workers; the climatic extremes force complete work stoppage when it is too hot, too wet, or too dry.

The third product of the Gran Chaco, as yet of only minor volume, is petroleum. Exploitation progresses slowly in the western part of the region along the Andean foothills in the Bolivian Chaco. Indications point to the occurrence of oil all through the northern part of the Gran Chaco, and it was this possibility that caused the warfare of the 1930's between Bolivia and Paraguay. The Bolivian section in general is the most isolated and least known of all the Gran Chaco.

H. CUBA

General Aspects. Cuba (Fig. 10.8), the largest and by far the most important one of the West Indies, well exemplifies the climatic conditions of those islands. Thus eastern

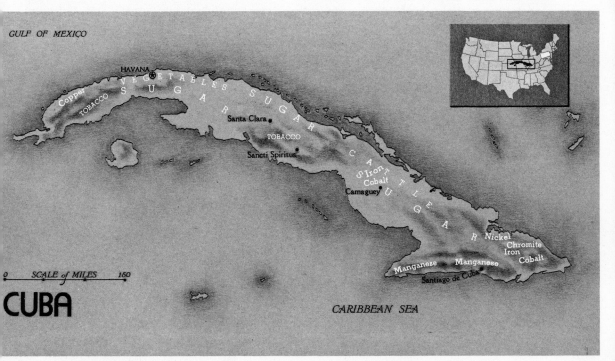

Cuba has a climate approximating the windward coast type of rainforest (see Chapter 7, p. 108) because it is in the path of the northeast trades the year round. In this respect it is representative of the northeastern coasts of all the islands. Similarly western Cuba, which does not have a typical savanna climate because it has no true dry season, rather merely a season of less rain, is climatically representative of the western sides of all the other large islands. Total rainfall and temperature characteristics, however, as well as savanna vegetation make appropriate the inclusion of Cuba with the regime of savanna climate.

Cuba lies some 200 miles south of Florida and extends east-west as a narrow strip of land for approximately 700 miles. The total area of the Republic of Cuba, including small surrounding islands and islets, is just under 45,000 square miles (about the size of Pennsylvania). The population is 6 million (versus Pennsylvania's 10.5 million).

The island was a Spanish possession almost uninterruptedly from its discovery by Columbus in 1492 until the Spanish-American War, at which time it was finally relinquished by Spain. After a brief period of American military governorship an independent republic was established in 1901. Spanish is the official language of the island, but English is much used commercially.

The people of Cuba are mostly descendants of the Spanish colonizers. The Negro and mulatto population is concentrated along the coasts and in certain provinces. Because of the geographical closeness of Cuba to the United States the people have adopted many aspects of the American way of life, yet remain thoroughly Latin. Professional baseball (*beisbol* to the Cubans), for example, is a popular sport; on the other hand, almost everyone indulges in the noontime siesta.

Topography. The topography of Cuba is quite different from that of the other large islands of the West Indies. Whereas most of them have east-west mountainous ridges, or backbones, that produce an orographic rise in the trades (rainforest conditions on the northeast and comparatively arid conditions

on the southwest slopes), Cuba is in general low and level, the least rugged of the West Indies. Mountains in the extreme southeast rise to 7500 feet and produce the rainforests of that region; other highland areas are scattered in minor ranges throughout the island.

The elongated shape of Cuba is economically significant because it permits access to the sea over a short distance from any point on the island. Moreover, the location of the island so near the United States means the close proximity of a great market for whatever tropical and subtropical commodities Cuba can supply. Cuba is, in effect, a tropical garden in the United States backyard.

Products. As Malaya is identified with rubber and Brazil with coffee, so Cuba connotes **sugar** (Fig. 10.9). Cuban production accounts for less than one-fifth of the world yield but contributes more than half of the sugar sold on the world market. Domestically, the dominance of the sugar industry is indicated by the fact that one-quarter to one-third of the total national income is derived from it. Over one-half the cultivated land in Cuba is in sugar cane.

Sugar cane has always been an important crop in the West Indies, one which, at the time when Europe was without other sugar sources, was responsible for the high esteem in which the islands were held as colonies. (The British government, for example, at one time considered Jamaica a richer and more

Fig. 10.9—Sugar Cane Cutting. The leaves are stripped from the stalks before the latter are carted to the mill. (Courtesy, Sugar Research Foundation, Inc.)

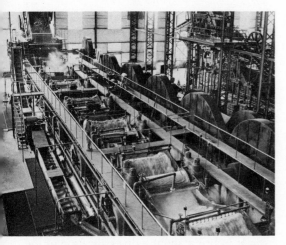

Fig. 10.10—Interior of a *Centrale*, or Sugar Mill. The cane enters the mill in the far background and is passed between rollers until 98 percent of the juice is extracted. (Courtesy, Sugar Information, Inc.)

valuable possession than Canada.) Sugar is still raised on many of these other islands.

Cuban conditions are ideal for sugar cane. The temperature ranges between 75° F. and 80° F. throughout the year, and rainfall is at least 40 inches. These climatic circumstances are very close to perfect for the plant. Another favorable factor is the rich, well-drained soil on generally level land. Cuba's climate further fits the sugar cane industry because 40 to 70 inches of rain falls during the long wet season from April to December. During this time the cane grows rapidly. The dry season that follows is also cooler—perfect weather for harvesting and processing the cane.

The cultivation of the cane and the processing of sugar from it are usually separate enterprises. Most of the cane is grown by *colonos*, independent farmers who work the land (much of which is owned by the processing mills) and who range from poor to wealthy, with the majority of "middle-class" status. The mills, or *centrales* (Fig. 10.10), are large-scale and, as their name implies, centralized operations, mostly American owned.

The second-ranking agricultural activity in terms of combined value of products is raising **livestock,** and the associated **meat** and **dairy** industries. The Cuban climate is well suited to cattle, and pasturage is abundant. There is, however, no export trade in these products, as the output is not sufficient to satisfy domestic needs.

Second to sugar in importance as a single product is **tobacco.** Cuban tobacco has an excellent reputation for cigar manufacture; "Havana leaf" in a cigar signifies quality in a brand. The most important of the five tobacco regions on the island is the **Vuelta Abajo** region, located on the south slopes of a low range of hills in the western end of the island. The reason for the exceptionally high quality of the tobacco from this region is a mystery. Such tobacco cannot be grown anywhere else on the island.

Fruits and **vegetables** are next in importance after tobacco. Production is mainly for export to the United States. Because of its low latitude Cuba is able to supply the United States market with these commodities during the winter, when production to the north is low. **Tomatoes** are the chief vegetable product; **pineapple** is the leading fruit.

For its small area Cuba has remarkably large and varied mineral resources. Such deposits are of unusual strategic value by virtue of their proximity to the United States, the world's largest consumer of mineral raw materials. Unfortunately, many of the ores are on the margin of economic usefulness, but as this defect is due to their mineral composition (and consequently difficulty of extraction) rather than to their being of too low grade, they will be of great significance as improvements in processing are achieved.

Cuba's most important mineral products by value are **copper, chromite, manganese,** and **nickel,** in that order. The country has about the same world status in each—a comfortable position among the smaller producers. Ores of **iron** and **cobalt** (together) constitute the potential resources referred to above. Cuba has produced appreciable amounts of these in the past, but full-scale development of the large reserves is being held up pending the necessary improvements in technology. In 1955 petroleum possibilities also began to receive consideration.

Industries. As is true of so many of the Latin-American countries, the industries of Cuba are light industries. They are, however, many and varied and account in sum for somewhat more than a third of the total national income. Those based on domestic raw materials range from furniture and cement to rum and soft drinks. Those using imported materials include textiles, rubber tires, and tubes.

CITIES OF CUBA

Name	Type	Population (1953)
Havana	Seaport and governmental	783,000
Camaguey	Commercial	204,000
Santiago de Cuba	Seaport	167,000
Santa Clara	Commercial	145,000
Sancti Spiritus	Commercial	2 ,000 (1943)

Cities. **Havana,** capital and commercial center of Cuba, is the metropolis of the West Indies. It is located on the north coast of the island near the point where it approaches closest (100 miles) to Key West, Florida. The city is in many respects like Rio de Janeiro, a center of commerce that is at the same time a cosmopolitan, sophisticated resort because of its beauty and the ample facilities for entertainment. The harbor is large and attractive; its entrance is dominated by *Morro Castle,* a sixteenth-century Spanish structure of world-wide fame. It is perhaps not too much of an exaggeration to say that, romantically, Havana *is* Cuba.

Camaguey, Cuba's second city, is located on the central axis of the island, about one-quarter of the way from the eastern end on the Central Highway that runs almost its full length. Camaguey's medieval Spanish buildings make it a picturesque city. It is an important commercial center in an agricultural district.

Santiago de Cuba is the second port and commercial city of the country. Lying in the center of the southeast coast, at the eastern end of the island, it is the outlet for the products of that district. Like Havana it has a large, beautiful harbor, and even a Morro Castle at its entrance.

Santa Clara is almost at the exact center of the island, on the Central Highway. It is a commercial city dealing in the sugar and tobacco produced in the surrounding countryside. **Sancti Spiritus** is also a center of the sugar and tobacco trades, located 60 miles east of Santa Clara on the Central Highway.

Cuba as a Whole. In 1950 a thorough survey of the Cuban economy was made to provide a basis for planning the future development of the country.[4] Cuba was found to be a one-crop country confronted with all the dangers and problems this status implies. It was found that the major goal to be striven for was to bring about a diversification of the country's production. The resources exist: the land is rich, the climate is good, and the country's geographical position on important trade routes, primarily its proximity to the enormous market of the United States, provides an excellent opportunity for profitable commerce. There are, to be sure, drawbacks. Cuba has no adequate supply of fuel, and the forests have been badly depleted. Nevertheless, the major obstacle to the kind of development envisioned was found to be a lack of confidence in the country's future, a great deterrent to the investment of capital on a large scale. If this can be overcome, the prospects for Cuba are good indeed for a country of its size at its stage of development.

QUESTIONS. List the similarities between Venezuela and Colombia. Describe the major topographical features of Colombia. How is the distribution of population related to the topography? Outline the transportation situation in Colombia. What is the significance of the phrase, "a nation of city states," as a description of Colombia? Why is Colombian coffee of better quality than Brazilian coffee? Name two other important export crops of Colombia. Compare the petroleum industries of Venezuela and Colombia. What is the greatest need of Colombia in its further development? Name the center of commerce and industrial activity in Colombia.

Describe the main physical regions of Ecuador. What is the country's chief crop? Dis-

[4] International Bank for Reconstruction and Development, *Report on Cuba,* Washington, 1951.

cuss the reasons for Ecuador's poverty. How do Ecuador's major cities typify the country's problems?

Name the countries whose territories are in part within the Gran Chaco. Describe the region during each of its two seasons. Why is the climatic range so extreme? What are the major products of the Gran Chaco? What is quebracho? For what is it used?

Describe the people of Cuba. Describe the island's topography. What advantages does it derive from its topography and location? Describe the sugar industry in Cuba. What special use is made of the best Cuban tobacco? Describe the unusual features of Cuba's mineral resources. What is the chief problem facing the Cuban people? What characteristic of the people is a major disadvantage in the country's development? Discuss the advantages and disadvantages of Cuba as a basis for that development.

CHAPTER 11

The Savanna Climate in Asia and Australia

I. INDIA

General Aspects. The historic country of India was roughly coextensive with the great triangular peninsula (so large it is often called a "subcontinent") that projects south of the Himalayas from the main mass of Asia. This India until 1947 was a collection of individual states, some of them outright possessions of Great Britain, others independent princely states ruled ostensibly by a rajah (prince) or maharajah (great prince), but with a British adviser present at the court. Historic India as a whole was considered part of the British Empire.

On August 15, 1947, as one of the most dramatic and significant changes occurring in the aftermath of World War II, this India was divided between two independent states, the Republic of India and a new nation, Pakistan, created from two separate portions of historic India. For a time the earlier independent princely states continued to exist as such, but they were gradually absorbed by the Republic of India. Thus the republic is bordered by West Pakistan on the west, and its projection east to the Burma border is not quite severed from the main body of the country by East Pakistan, which extends from the Bay of Bengal almost to the base of the Himalayas.

India is 1,200,000 square miles in extent, or over one-third the size of the United States (Fig. 11.1). The population is approximately 360 million, equivalent to 15 percent of the total population of the world. India is the second most populous country on earth.

Topography. The subcontinent of which India constitutes the greater part could scarcely be more isolated from the main portion of Asia if it were an island. On the north is the mighty Himalayan barrier, averaging 19,000 feet in altitude and almost completely impassable for 1000 miles in an east-west direction. On the east the Himalayas project southward in a series of lower ranges that form a rugged country along the India-Burma border. On the west there is also a Himalayan projection reaching to the sea. The only gap in this natural defensive barrier is the 33-mile-long **Khyber Pass** in the northwest, between Afghanistan and what is now West Pakistan (Fig. 2.10). This famous landmark is the ancient overland route into India, through which poured from the north successive invasions by peoples of the same racial stock as that from which the modern west European peoples are descended.

South of the mountain wall is the vast **Plain of Hindustan,**[1] on which flow the **Indus, Ganges,** and **Brahmaputra** rivers. These rivers are unusual in that they do not occupy valleys, as do most rivers, but flow rather over the surface of the plain. This is because the plain is composed of sand and silt washed down from the Himalayas and accumulated in immense thickness. No boring has ever reached the bedrock beneath this material, and estimates of its thickness

[1] Hindustan was the Persian name for India. It has since been variously applied to different parts of the country or to the country as a whole. The names "India," "Hindu," and "Indus" are all from the same root as Hindustan.

run into the tens of thousands of feet. The plain is also remarkable for the fineness of the sediments of which it is composed. It is difficult to find a large-sized pebble

Fig. 11.1—India and East Pakistan. The inset compares the area of the region with the approximately equivalent area of the United States (states in white).

throughout the whole extent of this area.

The Hindustan plain comprises some 250,000 square miles. It stretches east to west for 1500 miles—from the Bay of Bengal to the Arabian Sea—with a north-south width varying between 150 and 200 miles. The flatness of this large area is as fantastic as the thickness and fineness of the sediments. The eye

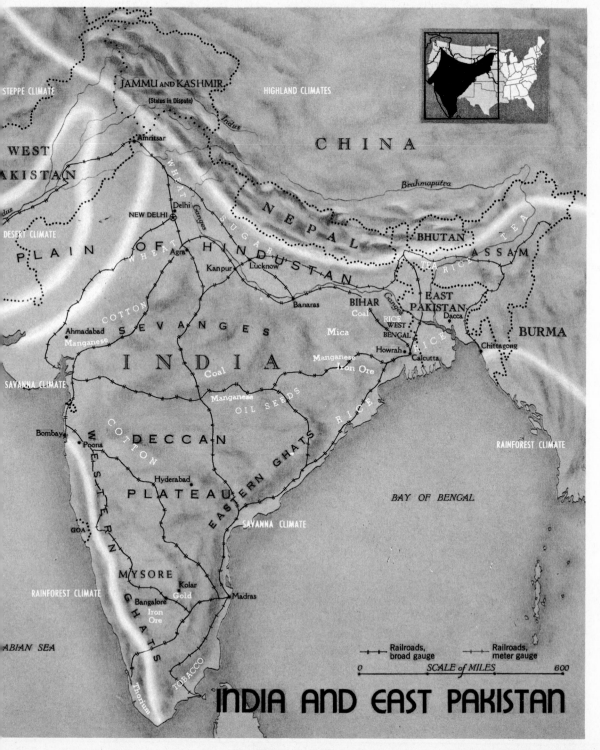

INDIA AND EAST PAKISTAN

cannot detect any slope to the land, which is so low that 1000 miles from the oceans it is only 500 feet above sea level. This plain is one of the world's most densely populated and agriculturally most productive areas. It has supported intensive agriculture for 5000 years.

South of the Hindustan plain is a group of of east-west mountains—the **Sevanges**—between 1500 and 4500 feet in elevation. Although comparatively low these mountains were formerly an effective barrier to invaders that regularly restricted the latest newcomers to the Hindustan plain. Peoples to the south of this barrier were thus insulated from contact with undiluted foreign influences, and while the successive invasions brought new, progressive ideas and customs into northern India, the people of the south remained less advanced culturally than those of the north.

India south of the Sevanges can be described as a plateau that slopes gently to the east and breaks up into low hills at the tip of the Indian peninsula. The plateau rises westward to altitudes of 3000 or 4000 feet, attained only a short distance inland from the west coast to form a continuous north-south wall known as the **Western Ghats** (gates). On the east a lower acclivity, about 1500 feet in elevation, forms the **Eastern Ghats** behind a wide coastal plain. The Eastern Ghats are not continuous but are interrupted by the river valleys, which are wide at their mouths.

The plateau as a whole is known as the **Deccan** (meaning "south"). Approximately 200,000 square miles of the west central section of the Deccan is an area of lava outpourings piled one layer on another (see Chapter 2, p. 24). Weathering of the lavas has developed a rich black soil over their extent. The soil over the remainder of the plateau is poor, but these non-lava regions are rich in minerals.

Climate. Except for drier regions in the northwest and the rainforests at the base of the Western Ghats, India is dominated by the monsoon variety of savanna climate and can be considered as the type country for that

climate. June to October is the season of the southwest monsoon, during which moisture-laden air from the Indian Ocean rushes in toward the central Asiatic land mass at a steady rate of almost 20 miles an hour. This does not mean that the country is uniformly supplied with rainfall or that the rainfall from one year to the next is the same. Indeed, it is the unreliability of the monsoon and the amount of rain it brings that constitute one of India's sorest problems.

From March to May it is hot and dry as the land warms up under the northward-moving sun. Temperatures of 125° F. in the shade have been recorded during this season. So unbearable is the heat that all who can afford it (in the days of British administration even the government) move to the highlands to the north, in the Himalayan foothills. Before independence this seasonal migration was described by the saying "India is ruled from 7000 feet above sea level."

From November to February is the cool season, when the northeast monsoon, or "anti-monsoon" occurs. It is not so strong as the true monsoon, its velocity being only two to three miles an hour. In Madras state the wet-dry seasons are reversed as to time of year, for here it is the northwest monsoon that picks up moisture in its passage over the Bay of Bengal and loses it on the Eastern Ghats.

As might be expected, the temperature variations from one season to another are least in the south of India, greatest in the north. It is also, in general, drier in the north than in the south. East to west across the Ganges plain the rainfall varies from 100 inches annually on the river's delta to less than 30 inches in central northern India.

Vegetation. The native vegetation of India varies with the amount of rain received. Where the annual rainfall is more than 80 inches, as in the Western Ghats, there are evergreen forests. Most of the Ganges plain and the northwest part of the Deccan plateau receive between 40 and 80 inches a year, a moderate rainfall. Here the hill slopes are covered with "monsoon forests," so called because of the seasonal shedding of leaves to enable the forest to survive the annual drought.

On the north-south line through the center of India there is a belt of land of varying width which has, on the average, low precipitation because of its interior location. It receives only what is left of the monsoon moisture after the Western Ghats have been drenched. In this belt the vegetation is scrub or thorn forests.

Although the natural vegetative cover has been removed in most parts of the country, uncleared land that cannot be utilized because it is too rough or barren exists in broad tracts throughout. There is thus a remarkable juxtaposition of jungle wild life and a dense human population. Tigers are found throughout India, and their menace to both domestic animals and humans is a real one. The depradations of leopards and wolves are equally serious. The bears, rhinoceroses, and elephants found in various parts of the country are a lesser menace, but snakes, crocodiles, and scorpions are responsible each year for many deaths.

The People. To a demographer (one who studies the statistics of population) India is a subject of fascination and wonder. The birth rate is among the highest in the world, not far from the theoretical limit. The death rate is also extraordinarily high, especially in the early years of life. As a result, the life expectancy for the average Indian at birth is 27 years (compared with 70 in the United States), and two-thirds of the population is under 30 years of age.

Such statistics are inadequate, however, to indicate the grim balance that is maintained between population and available food supply. India is notorious for its famines, the natural means by which such equivalence is maintained when the harvest is poor. It has been estimated that only two-fifths of the population get enough to eat; one-fifth live their lives in a constant state of semistarvation. Under such conditions it is inevitable that serious diseases are prevalent at such a rate that they would be considered raging

epidemics in the United States. Tuberculosis, dysentery and diarrhea, typhoid, smallpox, and similar diseases are the major causes of death.

The poverty of the average Indian peasant is difficult for Americans to comprehend. He lives in a windowless mud hut built around a courtyard. Cow dung, after being plastered on the outside walls to dry in cakes, is used for cooking fuel. There is almost a complete lack of furniture and utensils; the Indian sits on the floor and eats with his hands. The country peasant, nevertheless, is well off compared to the poor city dweller. Living conditions in the crowded tenements of the large cities defy description, and there are many city dwellers—the "pavement sleepers" —who have no place at all to live.

The population of India is equally fascinating to the ethnographer (one who studies the races of man), because of its extraordinary complexity. There are six distinct racial types representing three of the main racial divisions of the world: white, black, and yellow. The white *Indo-Aryans* or *Aryans* are the true Indians (Fig. 11.2). They are tall,

Fig. 11.2—Aryan type, North Indian (Rajput) from Udaipur. (Courtesy, Government of India Information Services.)

Fig. 11.3—Dravidian Types, South Indians. Itinerant minstrel dancing under village banyan tree. (Courtesy, Government of India Information Services.)

with fair skin, and inhabit the northern part of the country. The dark *Dravidians* (Fig. 11.3) represent the original population of India. They are short, and make up the principal population element in southern India. Culturally they are the most primitive of the Indian peoples. The poorer Dravidians are the coolie class of India and many Oriental ports. *Mongoloids* (Fig. 11.4) inhabit the Himalayas and bordering regions. As members of the yellow race they have a typical Oriental aspect. The other racial groups represent mixtures of mongoloids and the primitive tribes living in isolated hill and jungle areas.

The complex racial composition of India has produced a complicated language pattern. The total number of different languages

in India has been estimated at from 179 to 250, depending on what definition of a distinct language is used. They can all be classified, however, into four main groups, which include the 14 official languages of India. Eight of these fourteen are in the *Indo-Aryan* group; these are spoken throughout the north of the country and also part of the way down the axis of the peninsula. The most important single Indo-Aryan language is *Hindustani*, spoken by some 150 million people. The Indo-Aryan languages all together are spoken by some 70 percent of the population, and are of the same degree of similarity as are French, Spanish, and Italian. The *Dravidian* group, once the language of all the subcontinent, is now restricted to the southern peninsula area and is spoken by about 70 million people.

The written language situation is even more involved but this complication is of less importance because of the low literacy rate —about 20 percent. The English language

Fig. 11.4—Mongoloid Types from Assam in Their Tribal Dress. (Courtesy, Government of India Information Services.)

occupies a special place among the educated classes, serving as a common means of communication among men of different Indian languages. If the Indians can carry out their intentions, however, English will decline in importance. The Indian constitution provides that Hindi (the form of Hindustani whose written language is Sanskrit) becomes the national language in 1962.

The racial and lingual diversity in India is matched by a similar multiplicity of religions. There are some eight major religions, the most important being *Hinduism*. Islam is the second important religion, followed by Buddhism, Animism, and Christianity, in that order. The three last taken together are, however, fewer in number than the Moslems.

Although India has no official state religion, Hinduism is more important in the conduct of the government and in affecting the daily lives of its citizens than is Roman Catholicism in many of the countries where that religion is the officially declared state religion. India has been termed "a land saturated with religion,"[2] a situation stemming from the character of Hinduism. Hinduism is more than a set of beliefs and mode of worship; it is a way of living. There is scarcely a single activity of a Hindu's life that is not governed by his religion. His job, his eating, and his social position are all prescribed by Hinduism in addition to the events of birth, marriage, and death with which all religions are concerned.

The most significant feature of Hinduism is the *caste system*. The caste system classifies society into a series of levels, one above the other. A person born within a particular caste is by custom destined to remain within that caste. He must follow a certain occupation, cannot marry outside the caste, can have no social contact except with members of his own caste. There are over 3000 distinct castes in present-day Hinduism, and the proliferation of traditions, customs, unwritten laws, and regulations over the cen-

turies has contributed to the complexities of a religion that recognizes hundreds of deities, has no single creed, and is an esoteric philosophy. Hinduism, as such, is a strong, thriving religion, but the caste system it engendered is slowly breaking down under the impact of self-government, industrialization, and the adoption of Western technology.

Transportation. The rivers of India were the traditional means of transport but are little used now. Extensive diversion of the water for irrigation has so reduced the volume of the large streams as to make them unsuitable for navigation. On the other hand, road building has always been difficult in India owing to the lack of highway materials in many regions, to the floods on the plains, and to the lack of incentive for maintaining a road network.

The stimulus these circumstances imparted to railroad construction in India was notably effective. Yet when allowance is made for the difference in the areas of India and the United States, the rail network of India is only one-quarter as dense as that of the United States. Further, although India's railroads are connected with those of neighboring Pakistan, both networks are isolated from the other rail systems of Asia. Moreover, there are four different gauges, or track widths, in India, with consequent transshipment problems. Despite its limitations, however, India's rail net is the best in all Asia, and as a coördinated transportation system is a credit to the British, who were responsible for its construction.

Farming in India: (1) Irrigation. One of the unfortunate characteristics of India's climate is the extreme variability and undependability of the rainfall. Not only is there a wide range of the average annual rainfall among different regions, but at any given place the amount of rain brought by the monsoon is subject to erratic, extreme fluctuations from year to year. Thus farmers in some districts, such as the Ganges delta, are sure they will get the monsoon; in other districts they are equally sure rain will not come. And for a large area of India the reli-

[2] T. W. Wallbank, *India in the New Era,* Scott, Foresman and Co., 1951, p. 23.

ability is neither one way nor the other. One year in five is likely to be dry and one in ten brings a severe drought. As a result, irrigation is an absolute necessity for continued successful cultivation of the land in those regions where the average annual rainfall is less than 50 inches.

Irrigation is thus an ancient feature of Indian agriculture. One-fifth of all cultivated land is under irrigation of some form or other. Although this is not a high proportion compared to other countries, because of the great size of India it is equivalent to one-half of all the irrigated land in the world.

In the twentieth century, under British rule, there was a great expansion in irrigated area through the construction of large dams and development of projects requiring the application of modern engineering methods for their completion. The Indian government has continued with similar large-scale projects. Northern India is especially suitable for such works, for large, snow-fed streams from the Himalayas debouch onto a fertile plain and provide an unfailing year-round supply of water.

In other areas less ambitious solutions are resorted to. Thus, where streams have seasonal floods, irrigation is by "inundation canals." During high water the streams can be diverted into ditches and led overland to water the crops. About one-half of Indian irrigation is by either this or the preceding method.

At certain places great deposits of sand and gravel up to 1000 feet thick and 20 miles wide have accumulated at the foot of mountains. Here tunnels, known as *karez*, are dug into the deposits, providing "horizontal wells" in which the water accumulates and runs out, to be directed where needed.

Still another method is the use of "tanks," the Indian word for the ordinary farm pond in the United States, one that is made by scooping out a depression or damming a small stream. Standard wells are also used. As mechanical power is unavailable much animal and manual labor is expended in lifting the water from underground to the level of the fields. Nevertheless such wells are the

source for about one-quarter of all the irrigation water used.

2. Domestic animals. One of the extraordinary features of Indian life is the very large number of domestic animals relative to human population. According to the Hindu religion cattle are sacred.[3] The "sacred cows" of India wander at will through the streets, obstructing traffic and foraging at stalls. Hindus, moreover, are forbidden to kill or injure any living animal. Buddhists, also, will not take the life of any animal, and the Moslem religion forbids the eating of pork. Domestic animals in India, therefore, mostly die of old age.

Thus it is that India supports 135 million cattle, or between one-quarter and one-fifth of all the cattle in the world, and 40 million water buffaloes. None of the religions forbids the use of animals for dairy products or draft purposes (Fig. 11.5), so much of this large animal population is available for use in agriculture. With the spread of cultivation to new land the area available for grazing has decreased, and sufficient fodder crops are lacking. Consequently much of the cattle population is underfed and rather ineffective. The greatest concentration of the cattle population is on the drier portions of the Deccan, where the animals can be maintained on land unfit for agriculture.

India also has an estimated 36 million sheep and 44 million goats—it is the greatest goat country of the world. The sheep and goats are found mostly in the drier uplands of the southeast. India is the major exporter of goat and kid skins. More than 50 million pounds of wool are produced annually, but the quality is very poor. The yield per sheep is also low, so that, if successful, efforts by the Indian government to improve the breed could raise India to one of the leading wool producers of the world.

3. Crops. India is definitely an agricultural country; over 70 percent of the popula-

---

[3] This veneration dates back to the time in ancient India when oxen were so scarce there were not enough for plowing. To kill one was thus a crime against the community. This proscription later became a religious law.

Fig. 11.5—Cattle in India Lifting Water for Irrigation. (Courtesy, Press Information Bureau, Government of India.)

tion is engaged directly or indirectly in agricultural pursuits. Yet the country is not self-sufficient in food despite the subsistence level of existence of most of the population. Yields are low—one-quarter to one-fifth those of other producing countries in the same crops—because of poor seed stock, insufficient fertilizing (only 40 percent of the large supply of animal dung is used as fertilizer, the bulk of it serving as fuel), primitive equipment and methods, and the extremely small size of the individual farms.

Mechanical implements are being introduced as rapidly as possible, and the steel plow has become standard equipment in many areas. But sowing and harvesting by hand remain all to prevalent practices (Fig. 11.6). The small size of farms is due to centuries of successive partitioning of the land as it is handed down from one generation to the next. In many instances the resultant individual farm is insufficient (less than an acre in size) to support a family even at the Indian standard of living, and the able-bodied members of the family must hire out as laborers or do piecework on some handi-

Fig. 11.6—Indian (Bihar State) Farm Worker With the Primitive Hoe He Uses for Crop Cultivation. (Courtesy, Government of India Information Services.)

craft at home. A final deterrent factor is the exactions of the village moneylender, to whom the farmers are forced to turn in order to meet unexpected expenses due to droughts, weddings, or funerals, which are a social compulsion that cannot be economized on. Interest rates of 25 percent or more keep the farmers in virtual slavery to the moneylenders.

The great crop of India, the importance of which as a food staple overshadows all other crops, is **rice**. More than one-quarter of all the cultivated area of India is devoted to rice. The size of India as a unit in the world's population is vividly illustrated by the fact that, merely for the purpose of supplying the local population (and this with a deficit of up to 10 percent of needs), India raises yearly one-fifth of all the rice grown on earth, ranking as the second rice producer.

The place of rice in the world's total food production is statistically most impressive. Rice is by far the world's largest food crop. The value of the annual harvest is roughly equal to that of wheat and corn (the two chief middle-latitude crops) combined.

Rice is ideally suited for production in the tropical rainy climates. Of all the grains, it is best fitted for storage in hot, humid conditions because of the heavy protective husk in which the seed grain is encased. The plant needs year-round high temperatures and an annual rainfall of at least 50 inches, five inches a month during the growing season. It requires several inches of standing but not stagnant water during the growing season, which in turn means level land surrounded by dikes, or terraces on hillsides. These requirements can also be met through irrigation. Deltas and flood plains make ideal sites for rice paddies, especially as they have underlying clay layers which prevent the water from soaking into the ground and draining off.

Rice is also suited to production in areas where human labor is cheap. All steps in its production, from planting to harvest, involve endless hours of backbreaking physical toil. It is sprouted in nurseries, then transplanted by hand into wet fields whose soil has been cultivated to the condition of a soupy mud. (Rice can also be sown in such fields without transplanting, but the yield is poorer.) During the growing season continual cultivation is necessary.

Because of its dependence on rains during its growing season (when not grown under irrigation) rice is *the* monsoon crop. One of the most noteworthy geographic circumstances of man's distribution on the face of the earth is the utter dependence for existence of hundreds of millions of people, nearly half of humanity, on the annual monsoon in southeastern Asia. In India the great center of rice production is on the parts of the Indo-Gangetic plain where the rainfall is sufficient. It is grown on a smaller scale over most of the country. The average yield is low, only 723 pounds to the acre compared with 2350 pounds in Japan.

Wheat ranks second among the cereal crops of India. It is grown mostly in the north as a winter crop and accounts for almost 10 percent of the total crop acreage. In areas of moderate rainfall corn is grown as a secondary grain. Most production is from the Ganges plain. Where the rainfall is between 20 and 40 inches annually, especially in the central Deccan, millet[4] provides the food for the poorer classes and for the animals. This coarse grain is little used in Western countries.

The second major food crop in terms of value is **sugar cane**. Again, India's production, entirely consumed by the enormous population, is actually insufficient for her needs, yet is enough to rank the country among the world's three or four leading producers. The bulk of the crop is grown in the irrigated portions of the upper Ganges plain, with some on the southeast coast. In addition to refined white sugar a low-cost, soft, brown sugar known as *gur* is also produced in large quantity.

Another important food crop, constituting the second- or third-ranking export item, is **tea**. India produces about one-half the total

[4] From the French *mille*, "one thousand"; an allusion to the 1000 grains reaped for every grain sown.

world output, consuming 20 to 30 percent of the crop domestically, and is also the leading exporter. The chief tea region is northeastern India, especially Assam and West Bengal. The tea plantations are on the slopes of the north-south mountain ranges. The monsoon rains make the trees extremely vigorous, so that the tea leaves can be picked every 10 days during the harvest season. Processing is done by the most advanced methods, and it is this tea that the British consume in such vast quantities. Tea of lower quality is grown in Travancore, at the tip of the peninsula.

A number of crops have significance because they are the source of vegetable oils. Taken together the **oilseeds,** as they are called, are the third-ranking crop in value terms. The most important of the oilseeds is the **peanut.** India is the leading producer, accounting for about one-half of world production. It will be recalled that the peanut is well adapted to poor soils, and the large acreage devoted to it represents a triumph of government campaigning for its introduction and wide cultivation. Other important oilseeds are **rape, mustard, linseed, sesamum,** and **castor beans.** Linseed comes from the flax plant, which in Europe is used to make linen. India is second in the world in its output of castor beans.

Tobacco is also an important crop in terms of both value and volume of output. Poor seed quality, careless cultivation, and inferior processing result in a product of very low grade that is practically all consumed domestically.

Cotton is another leading crop, in which India ranks third among world producers. The major cotton region is on the Deccan lava plateau. The monsoon rains supply the necessary moisture at the beginning of the growing season, and the unusual "black cotton soil," as it is known, derived from the lava, holds enough moisture to supply the plants during the following dry season. So rich is the soil that cotton has been produced on it year after year for centuries. The yield is low, however (90 pounds per acre compared with 270 pounds in some parts of the United States), and the quality is poor. Elsewhere, in the north central part of the peninsula and on the Ganges plain, cotton of better quality is raised under irrigation.

Mineral Resources. For its size, India is not richly endowed with minerals. Nevertheless the mineral resources the country does possess are outstanding in one respect: the occurrence of **coal** and **iron ore** deposits in close association and in significant quantities. These two minerals are found in an area just west of the Ganges delta. The noteworthy feature of the coal deposits is not their size, which is small in comparison with those of the United States, Russia, and Europe, but the low mining costs and the suitability of about one-third of the reserves for the smelting of iron. The iron ore deposits constitute a reserve about three-quarters the size of those in the United States and have the great advantage of being rich and minable at the surface. This occurrence of high-quality, easily obtainable raw materials near together (there is also adequate limestone in the vicinity), together with cheap labor, provides geographically for the potentially cheapest pig iron production in the world.

India is also one of the two countries in the world that possess in addition to the above-named requirements for steelmaking substantial deposits of **manganese,** another essential element in the process. The country is one of the leading world producers and exporters of this metal.

India is the predominant source of the world's high-grade **mica,** an important material used in the electronics industries. Production is mainly from a 60-mile belt of deposits in the state of Bihar.

The third-ranking mineral product in terms of value is **gold,** produced from some of the oldest and deepest mines in the world. The **Kolar** gold fields are in the state of Mysore in the southern part of the peninsula.

Newly important are the large **thorium** deposits in Travancore, at the southern tip of India. It has been estimated that these deposits constitute the major portion of the total world reserves of potential atomic fuels.

Industries. In terms of workers employed

and value of output the leading industry of India is the **textile** industry. Most of the large cities are the sites of cotton mills. The industry is based on the domestic production of cotton and, although it is small compared with the similar industries of Europe and America, nevertheless it supports one of the leading textile export trades of the world, a position attained only since World War II.

Of ever increasing significance is the **steel** industry. India is the only country within the savanna climatic regions that can be said to have a steel industry of any consequence. The industry is centered near the coal and iron deposits outlined above, with a smaller concentration in Mysore. Its special pertinence is that it supports a noteworthy development of heavy industry (with production of such large equipment as locomotives) and a variety of special alloys and machinery. The steel industry is, moreover, entirely the product of domestic capital and enterprise and is able to supply the bulk of the country's needs.

Other important industries are chemicals, cement, glass, motion pictures, paper, plastics, nonferrous metal products, and vegetable oils, an impressive and diversified array. In addition to these is a group known as the "cottage industries." These activities, carried on by individual artisans and their families, account for a considerable portion of the textile production as well as the major output of leather, wood, pottery, and miscellaneous small articles. The importance of the cottage industries lies not only in their output but also in the fact that they provide gainful employment to the millions engaged in agriculture who require a supplementary occupation.

Cities. **Bombay,** the largest city of India and capital of the state of that name, possesses the finest harbor on the west coast of the country. It is the traditional port of entry into India for travelers from Europe and is known as the "Gateway to India." It is a major center of cotton textile manufacturing and is the most modern of India's large cities. Since independence it has undergone a tre-

CITIES OF INDIA

Name	Type	Population (1951)
Bombay	Seaport and industrial	2,800,000
Calcutta	Seaport	2,500,000
Madras	Seaport and governmental	1,400,000
Delhi and New Delhi	River port and governmental	1,200,000
Hyderabad	Commercial and governmental	1,000,000
Ahmadabad	Commercial	790,000
Bangalore	Commercial and industrial	780,000
Kanpur	Commercial and industrial	700,000
Lucknow	Commercial	500,000
Poona	Commercial, resort, and educational	480,000
Howrah	Commercial	435,000
Amritsar	Commercial, religious	390,000
Agra	Commercial	375,000
Banaras	Religious, commercial, and educational	355,000

mendous population expansion and has large slum areas.

Calcutta is situated on the Ganges delta some 80 miles upstream on one of the distributaries. It is the trade outlet for both the Ganges and the Brahmaputra regions, although it is hampered in this function by the fact that a good deal of its hinterland is now part of another country. Its western suburb, **Howrah,** is also one of the major cities of India. Located across the river from Calcutta, it is the rail terminus for all roads to the west. Calcutta's outstanding physical feature is a large park two square miles in extent at its center. The city also contains many large government buildings, as it was the center of British rule until 1912.

Madras is the only significant port on the east coast of the peninsula and is the capital of the state of the same name. Its harbor is wholly artificial. Its industries include textile mills, cigar factories, and iron foundries.

Delhi and **New Delhi** are located in north central India at the head of navigation on the Ganges River system. Delhi has a long history as a trading center at the intersection of mountain and river trade routes, and as the ancient capital of India. In 1912 the

British established the administrative capital of India at a new location five miles south of Delhi which they named New Delhi. The new city has been retained as the capital of the Republic of India. Old Delhi is studded with ancient monuments and great mosques; it typifies the true Indian city. New Delhi, by contrast, is a completely planned modern city. It is beautifully laid out around a central eminence and consists of a collection of magnificent government buildings as well as palaces built by the native princes, all situated along broad, tree-lined avenues.

Hyderabad, the capital of the state of that name, is situated on the Deccan plateau about in the center of the peninsula. It contains 32 palaces and numerous other government buildings erected by the former princely ruler.

Ahmadabad is located in the northern part of Bombay state. It is known for its many examples of Indian architecture, including mosques, temples, tombs, and houses. It is a trade center and also the site of cotton mills and many light machine and handicraft industries.

Bangalore, the capital of the state of Mysore, is on the Deccan plateau in the southern part of the peninsula. Its elevation of 3000 feet gives the city a healthful climate, and as a consequence it is the site of considerable heavy industry such as the manufacture of machinery, as well as textile mills and tobacco factories.

Kanpur (also known as Cawnpore) is on the Ganges about 250 miles southeast of Delhi. It is known for its leather goods of all sorts and for its cotton and woolen products.

Lucknow is in the central part of the Hindustan plain 40 miles northeast of Kanpur. It contains many palaces and other monuments of former regimes and is known for the products of its gold- and silversmiths.

Poona is located in the Western Ghats about 75 miles southeast of Bombay. Its elevation of 1800 feet is sufficient to give it a summer so much drier and cooler than that of the lowlands that it is a resort and the summer capital of Bombay state. It is the

Fig. 11.7—The Taj Mahal. (Courtesy, Government of India Information Services.)

site of a number of governmental educational institutions and also many industries.

Amritsar, in the northwest near the Pakistan border, is the commercial center for trade across the Himalayas. It is the holy city for a Hindu sect known as the *Sikhs*. The city derives its name from the holy *Amrita Saras* (Pool of Immortality) within its confines.

Agra lies south of Delhi in the western portion of the Ganges plain. It was one of the great cities of the Mogul Empire and the capital of India under that regime. It is now famous for its outstanding examples of Mogul architecture, especially the world-renowned *Taj Mahal* (Fig. 11.7). This memorial to a Mogul empress, erected in 1630, is considered to be one of the most perfect architectural masterpieces of all time. The name comes from one of the empress' titles meaning "Crown of the Palace."

Banaras (also known as Kasi) is farther east, on the middle course of the Ganges. It is the sacred city of the Hindus, who believe that the sacred river Ganges has special

Fig. 11.8—Ghats at Banaras, India. (Courtesy, Press Information Bureau, Government of India.)

cleansing properties, both material and spiritual. The river flows through the city at a level below the surrounding land, and its banks are a solid course of walls and staircases (ghats) (Fig. 11.8). The ghats are used for bathing purposes and for cremating the dead, who thus gain eternal peace. The city itself has the amazing total of 1500 temples (including those of the Buddhists, for whom the city is also a religious shrine), and is a maze of narrow, winding streets that only foot traffic can negotiate. The streets are jammed with a colorful, teeming mass of pilgrims from all over India, and with beggars, who are attracted by their charity. The nature of Indian life and philosophy, so exotic and difficult for the Western mind to comprehend, is here visibly exemplified.

India as a Whole. The presence of the combination of raw materials necessary for a steel industry provides India with the same basis of strength as that on which the modern great powers rest. Its resources for industry are exceeded only by those of the United States and the Soviet Union. Thus *India is potentially one of the great industrial nations of the world.*

It is generally agreed that the failure of India to make any significant progress previously toward realization of its great industrial possibilities may be directly attributed to British imperial policy with respect to customs duties. The aim of the government then was to promote, through tariffs, the production of raw materials in India and to hold back industrialization. In this way India was preserved as a market for British manufactures. The success of this policy was implied in Churchill's reference to India as "the brightest jewel in the British Imperial crown."

World War II forced the British to expand and utilize the industrial capacity of India to the limit as an arsenal in the Orient. Consequently industrial development, long overdue, was given a great impetus, and the momentum thus attained has been avidly accelerated by the independent Indian nation.

On the other hand, the British may be credited with the construction of the railroad system and the many irrigation and reclamation projects which were provided through their initiative and enterprise. In this connection a British official once wistfully remarked in answer to criticism of the British rule in India: "India adds an Egypt to its area every five years, but the world takes little note."

Industrialization is not easy, however. There is as yet no industrial labor force such as exists in the Western countries. The country has, on the other hand, everything to gain by industrialization. The present occupational distribution of 70 percent in agriculture is an anomalous development. It was only 58 percent in 1881. Such an increase in the percentage of the population engaged in agriculture is contrary to the experience of most other countries, notably the Western industrial powers. This indicates, significantly, that industrialization may well be able to bring about a rise in the standard of living despite the tremendous population growth, with the important proviso that food production is also increased.

The proviso poses no small problem. To offset the growing pressure of population increases on local food production it is planned to utilize higher-yielding crops such as sweet potatoes, to get higher yields of present crops through better farming techniques, and to increase the acreage of arable land through reclamation projects. Substantial increase in the volume of food production will not be easily achieved. It is a good omen, however, that this and all other problems are being met by the Indians aggressively and confidently, with full appreciation of both the possible rewards and the pitfalls that beset the path of progress.

J. EAST PAKISTAN

General Aspects. East Pakistan is a geographical oddity resulting from the partition of India in 1947 and the establishment of two independent countries. The sole reason for the separate existence of East Pakistan is the fact that the population is predominantly Moslem (about 71 percent). Geographically an integral part of the hinterland of the great Indian port of Calcutta, the region was confronted by great problems owing to its political separation from that city.

The area of East Pakistan is 54,000 square miles (about the size of Arkansas), and comprises most of the low reaches and the combined deltas of the Ganges and Brahmaputra rivers (Fig. 11.1). At the eastern end of the Hindustan plain, it is a low, wet country, the deltaic portion of which is interlaced with innumerable waterways and canals. The fertility of the land is high, as is that of the inhabitants. The total population is 42 million, with a density in some areas of 1200 to the square mile. Such a density is extraordinary in view of the completely agricultural character of the economy.

Products. The leading crop in terms of value is **jute,** a coarse fiber used in making burlap and gunnysacking, as well as carpets, linoleum, and other products. It is the cheapest of all commercial fibers because of the yield per acre and its suitability for machine processing. The Ganges-Brahmaputra delta country has a virtual monopoly on the world's jute supply, with East Pakistan accounting for almost 80 percent. The identification of jute with this area is a consequence of the early start in its production, the almost ideal growing conditions for the plant, and the vast amount of cheap labor available.

The heavy rainfall (100 inches) insures high yields of jute and provides, as well, the large amount of water necessary to process the fiber. The yearly inundations of the land, however, make it necessary for the people to live on mounds, which become islands during the rainy season. The network of waterways and canals serves to transport the product to market (Fig. 11.9).

Among the economic problems created by the partition of India the most serious was probably that of the reorganization of the jute industry. About one-half of the raw fiber produced in the delta country went to supply the jute mills of Calcutta. As a result of partition India was left with a jute manufacturing industry and no source of supply; Pakistan had the raw material with no industry to convert it. What were formerly purely internal commercial transactions have now become international trade, with all the problems of currency exchange, customs duties, and the like that this entails. Sheer necessity has forced the continuance of a certain amount of such trade, but India has attempted to become self-sufficient in jute production, whereas Pakistan has subsidized the establishment of a jute-milling industry. The economic absurdity of this duplication does not need to be elaborated.

The second crop of East Pakistan is **rice**, of which two crops are harvested yearly, so fertile is the soil. Despite this advantage the yield per acre is very low owing to poor farming practices. Consequently East Pakistan, although an agricultural country, does not feed itself, and rice must be imported.

Fig. 11.9—Baled Jute Loaded on Boats for Shipment. (Courtesy, Embassy of Pakistan.)

Other crops of some importance are tea and tobacco. The former is produced in the portion of East Pakistan previously part of the tea province of Assam. The latter is exported in large quantities.

CITIES OF EAST PAKISTAN

Name	Type	Population (1951)
Dacca	Governmental and commercial	400,000
Chittagong	Seaport	290,000

Cities. **Dacca,** the new capital of East Pakistan, is located on the delta in the center of the jute- and rice-growing area. It has a long history as a local administrative center. Its chief commercial activities are the processing and marketing of jute and rice.

Chittagong, the chief port of East Pakistan, is located 10 miles upstream on a small river on the east side of the Bay of Bengal below the Ganges-Brahmaputra delta. It is the best harbor and port east of Calcutta but because of its location is not well suited to serve East Pakistan. It is probable that eventually a new port on the delta proper will be developed to serve the region.

QUESTIONS. Explain the difference between the Republic of India and "India" as it formerly existed. Why is the Indian subcontinent so isolated from the rest of Asia? Describe the unusual features of the Hindustan plain. Describe the major topographic features of the peninsula of India south of the Hindustan plain. What are "monsoon forests"? Why is the wild life of India of unusual significance? Discuss the significance of the birth and death rates in India. Describe the living conditions of the country and city dwellers. What racial elements make up the bulk of the population? Describe the language situation. What are the main features of the Hindu religion? What is the caste system? Summarize the transportation situation.

What features of the rainfall in India are undesirable from the farmer's viewpoint? Describe the five methods of irrigation used in India. What is the economic significance of the "sacred cow"? What other domestic animals are present in very large numbers? Why is India incapable of feeding its own population despite the large proportion of the people engaged in agriculture? Describe the main features of rice cultivation. Why is rice *the* monsoon crop? What other cereal crops supplement rice in the Indian diet? What is *gur*? Why is India the leading tea producer of the world? What are oilseeds? List some of the oilseeds produced in India.

What circumstances provide the potential in India for the cheapest pig iron in the world? What is the largest industry in India? What are "cottage industries"? Why is India potentially one of the world's great industrial nations? What circumstance was responsible for the former lack of industrialization? What handicaps to industrialization still exist?

What are the contrasting features of Delhi and New Delhi? What unusual class of cities is Banaras an example of? Describe the aspect this gives the city.

What is jute? Why is its production concentrated in East Pakistan and the Ganges-Brahmaputra delta? Describe the effects of political partition on the jute industry.

K. CENTRAL AND NORTHERN BURMA

Central and northern Burma is a region of north-south trending hills and valleys, including the **Shan Plateau** (3000 to 6000 feet in elevation) in the east (Fig. 11.10). This topography not only makes east-west communication within the region all but impossible; it also effectively isolates it from neighboring China, India, and Thailand. The region is sparsely inhabited but of strategic importance because of the resources it contains.

Petroleum is produced from oil fields between 300 and 400 miles up the **Irrawaddy River.** The fields constitute the largest petroleum resources on the mainland of southeast Asia. The oil is sent downstream by pipe line and barge to Rangoon at the mouth of the River (see Chapter 8, p. 125) for refining and export.

The major metallic products are **lead** and **silver,** produced from a mine on the Shan Plateau just south of the China border. This mine is one of the largest and most important single mines in the world, as the deposit is unusually rich.

CITY OF CENTRAL AND NORTHERN BURMA

Name	Type	Population (1941)
Mandalay	Commercial	163,000

Mandalay, the second city of Burma and its former capital, is located on the Irrawaddy 400 miles upstream from Rangoon, with which it is connected by railroad. It is a famous city because of Kipling's poem "On the Road to Mandalay," although the author used considerable poetic license in representing the character and location of the city.

L. THAILAND

General Aspects. Thailand is a country of 200,000 square miles (a little larger than Arizona and Utah combined) situated between Burma on the west and Indochina on the east (Fig. 11.10). In 1949 the Kingdom of Siam became known officially as the Kingdom of Thailand, and the people asked to be known by the rest of the world as the *Thai,* or "The Free People," as they call themselves.

The Burma border and northern portion of Thailand is mountainous. In the center of the country a wide plain extends from north to south, and on this plain flows the principal river, the **Menam.**[5] On both sides of the central plain there is a low plateau between 3000 and 4000 feet in elevation. In the extreme east is a basin whose bottom is a plain 200 to 300 feet above sea level. This plain resembles the llanos of South America (see Chapter 10, p. 164) in the extremes of its wet-dry alternation.

The middle plain, comprising about one-fourth of Thailand, is the center of population and economic heart of the country. The eastern basin is inhabited by people as poverty-stricken as any in the world. The plateau is a region with poor soil cover and a long dry season. It supports little more than scrub forest.

The seasons are like those of India. Mountains to the east prevent Thailand from re-

[5] *Menam* means "The River." The full name is *Menam Chao Phya,* or "The River Chao Phya."

ceiving the rains of the northeast monsoon (antimonsoon). The southwest monsoon brings plentiful rains, however, from May to October.

The population of Thailand is over 18 million. The preponderant majority are Buddhists, with Moslems and Christians constituting very small minorities. There is a considerable Chinese minority that handles most of the country's commerce.

Roads and railroads are few, but the latter are important. A line to the south connects the capital city at the mouth of the Menam with the Malay Peninsula and Singapore.

Fig. 11.10—Central and Northern Burma, Thailand, and Indochina. The inset compares the area of the various countries and portions of the region with the state of Texas.

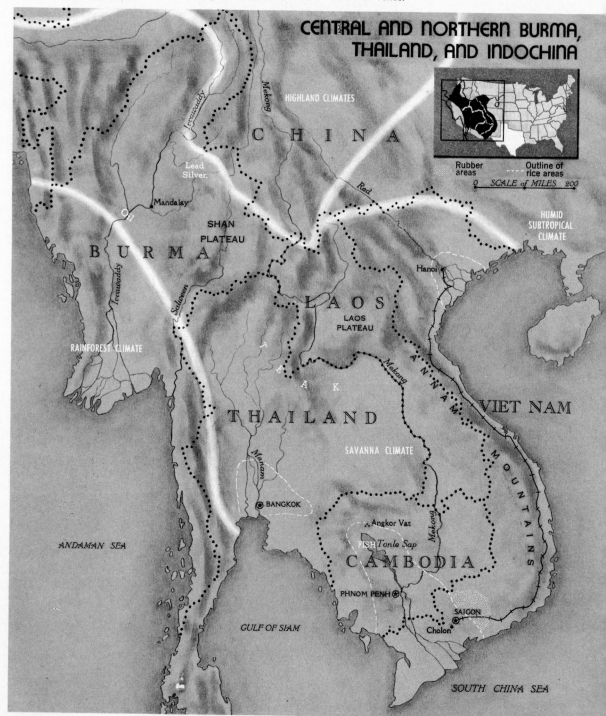

CENTRAL AND NORTHERN BURMA, THAILAND, AND INDOCHINA

HIGHLAND CLIMATES

C H I N A

Rubber areas   Outline of rice areas

SCALE of MILES   200

Lead Silver.

Mandalay

Irrawaddy

Mekong

Red

Hanoi

HUMID SUBTROPICAL CLIMATE

SHAN PLATEAU

OIL

B U R M A

Irrawaddy

Salween

L A O S

LAOS PLATEAU

A N N A M

RAINFOREST CLIMATE

T H A I L A N D

VIET NAM

SAVANNA CLIMATE

Menam

Mekong

M O U N T A I N S

BANGKOK

Angkor Vat

ANDAMAN SEA

FISH Tonle Sap

C A M B O D I A

PHNOM PENH

SAIGON

GULF OF SIAM

Cholon

SOUTH CHINA SEA

Another line runs into the north of the country.

Products and Resources. Nearly 85 percent of the population is engaged in agriculture and fishing. **Rice** is the largest crop, grown everywhere on the central plain. Some 90 percent of the population carries on its cultivation, milling, and trade. Thailand is one of the few Oriental countries with a perennial rice surplus, and is a large exporter. Other Thailand crops are of only minor importance in comparison with rice.

The mountains in the north are covered with dense forests from which **teak** (Fig. 11.11) is obtained in large quantities. Thailand is one of the leading exporters of this timber wood. The teak industry is dominated by British capital.

From the southern extension of the country down the Malay Peninsula comes **tin,** of which Thailand is an important producer. From the northern hills tungsten, antimony, and gold are extracted in commercial quantities. Ores of zinc, molybdenum, silver, lead, copper, and other metals are also reported.

CITY OF THAILAND

Name	Type	Population (1947)
Bangkok	Governmental and commercial	885,000

City. **Bangkok,** Thailand's capital, port, and only city of any size is located on the Menam 20 miles upstream from its mouth. It is a city interlaced with so many canals and natural waterways that it has been termed "the Venice of the East." Bangkok is given a very exotic look by the Thai architecture, best exemplified by the royal palace in the center of the city and by the many Buddhist temples scattered throughout its area. These are characterized by brightly colored tile roofs and ornate spires of unusual design. Bangkok is probably the "most Buddhist" city of the world. Under the influence of Buddhism on its population the city has a serenity unusual for one its size.

Fig. 11.11—Teak Log Rafts on a River in Thailand. (Courtesy, Public Relations Department, Thailand.)

Bangkok's trade is hampered by a bar at the Menam's mouth, but a deep channel has been dredged to a new, modern port developed five miles south of the city.

Thailand as a Whole. Thailand has long been an obscure country known chiefly as the only independent state in southeast Asia. It owed its independence solely to the rivalry between France and England during the colonial period in Asia. These great powers found it to their mutual interest to maintain a buffer state between their colonies in that part of the world.

Thailand was an absolute monarchy until 1932, when a coup d'état changed the government to a constitutional monarchy. Even though independent, the country was economically almost a British possession before World War II. Foreign capital controlled all commerce and industry; the British ports of Hong Kong and Singapore handled the bulk of the trade; Chinese investments in the rice and fishing industries were large; and Chinese labor was the mainstay of the teak, tin, and rubber industries. Since World War II Thailand has striven for economic independence. Lack of domestic capital (which prefers investment in land and usury) and of technical and managerial skill is a great impediment. Industrialization, the dream of all underdeveloped countries, is out of the question because of an almost complete lack of fuel. Some of Thailand's power plants operate entirely on rice husks as fuel.

Thailand is now a country of great strategic importance, owing to its position relative to the commerce of southeast Asia. Before World War II the British were badly frightened by a Thai-Japanese proposal to cut a canal through the **Kra Isthmus** (the narrowest portion of the Malay Peninsula, near its northern end). A canal there would put Bangkok on the direct route between India and China—cutting 1000 miles off the shipping distance—and would seriously threaten Singapore's position as the commercial center of that part of the world.

M. INDOCHINA

General Aspects. Indochina occupies the eastern rim of the great peninsula of which Burma, Thailand, and Malaya comprise the remainder (Fig. 11.10). The country forms a rough crescent reaching from China on the north and partially encircling eastern Thailand. It is larger than France, with which it is loosely associated, with a total area of 286,000 square miles (somewhat larger than all the American Atlantic coastal states from Delaware south).

Politically, Indochina is composed of three autonomous states: **Viet Nam** ("Land of the South") runs the entire length of the eastern coast. The **Kingdom of Cambodia** covers the southwestern portion of the country. The **Kingdom of Laos** comprises the interior central and northern portions, inland from Viet Nam.

Topography and Climate. The northern portion of the country consists of the lower reaches and delta of the **Red River.** To the southwest is the **Laos Plateau,** which extends into the **Annam Mountains,** a range paralleling the eastern coast almost to its southern tip. A narrow, discontinuous coastal plain lies between the Annam Mountains and the South China Sea. The southern portion of the country comprises the delta and lower reaches of the **Mekong River.** This river, whose length of 1900 miles makes it one of the longest streams in southeast Asia, rises in Tibet behind the Himalayas and forms the Thailand-Indochina border for more than 1000 miles.

The annual overflow of the Mekong, due to the monsoon rains, is caught in a natural reservoir in a lowland to the west of its lower course in central Cambodia. Known as the **Tonle Sap** ("Great Lake"), the outflow of the lake waters stored during the wet season maintains the Mekong during the dry season. The watercourses connecting the Mekong and Tonle Sap thus reverse their flow with the seasons.

The climate is typical monsoon savanna. The west and south have the monsoon season from April to October, brought by west winds from the Indian Ocean, whereas the Annam mountains and the east coast have their rains between September and January, because of the orographic rise of the northeast monsoon.

The People. The population of Indochina is almost 30 million, some 80 percent concentrated in the river deltas. About three-quarters of the inhabitants are *Annamese,* a people apparently resulting from a mixture of Chinese, other Mongols, and perhaps Indonesians. The Annamese live in the lowlands of Viet Nam. The *Cambodians,* occupying the Kingdom of Cambodia, comprise about 10 percent of the population. They are a mixture of Aryans, Malays, and Mongolians. Thai people and Indonesians account for another 10 percent, and there are smaller minorities of Chinese, Malays, and Europeans. The prevailing religion is Buddhism.

Products and Resources. **Rice,** the monsoon cereal, dominates the agriculture of Indochina. Five-sixths of the land is devoted to its cultivation, and it constitutes the bulk of total exports. Indochina is normally the world's leading exporter of rice despite a yield that is low even for Asia. The largest center of rice culture is the Mekong delta and the lowlands around the Tonle Sap; the delta of the Red River is a second concentration. This has prompted the Chinese to describe Indochina as "two baskets of rice balanced on a pole" (the pole being the Annam Mountains).

The country is also an important source of **rubber,** its second-ranking export product. Large plantations developed by the French in the south are responsible for this production.

Another large export is **corn,** grown in all sections of the country. This is an unusual product for a region of tropical climate.

Fish (dried and smoked) is a large export item as well as a diet staple for the inhabitants. The industry thrives on the Tonle Sap, one of the world's great fishing grounds, and in the swamps and marshes which dry up during the dry season and concentrate the fish for easy catching.

Luxuriant forests cover most of Indochina, supplying a variety of hardwoods, notably the ubiquitous **teak** of this part of the world.

The major mineral resource is **anthracite,** or hard coal. This is found in northern Viet Nam and forms a large, valuable export item.

Transportation. Transportation in Indochina is considerably handicapped by the coastal mountains that bar access to the interior, and the rapids of the rivers. A railroad runs the entire length of the east coast and there is a connection in the southwest with Thailand. The lower few hundred miles of the rivers carry considerable traffic, and a good network of highways was built under the French rule.

CITIES OF INDOCHINA

Name	Type	Population (1953)
Saigon-Cholon	Seaport	1,600,000
Phnom Penh	Governmental and river port	375,000
Hanoi	Governmental and river port	298,000

Cities. **Saigon,** the leading city and port of Indochina, was the capital of the country under the French administration. It retains a very French atmosphere, with wide boulevards and sidewalk cafés similar to those of Paris. It is located on the eastern edge of the Mekong delta about 40 miles inland. It is a seaport by virtue of a 40-mile canal connecting it with the main channel of the Mekong. **Cholon,** its large suburb, is a center of light industries.

Phnom Penh is the capital of Cambodia. It is located on the Mekong River at the place where the Tonle Sap connects with it. The city is the commercial center of the surrounding agricultural district.

Hanoi, the chief city of the north, is the northern capital of Viet Nam. It lies on the Red River 75 miles inland. Its name means "having river boundaries," from the fact that the Red River flows on two sides of the city. It is below the river level and is protected by dikes 45 feet high.

Indochina as a Whole. Indochina was assembled by the French through piecemeal conquest extending over the last half of the nineteenth century. It was a deliberate territorial expansion undertaken in part to counteract the British extension northward from Singapore which was then going on. Until World War II the country had been one of the most thoroughly exploited of the French colonies.

Indochina is well equiped for industrialization on a modest scale. It has an abundance of mineral and agricultural resources to provide raw materials, along with hydropower resources. The great handicap, on the other hand, is the legacy of years of maladministration under French rule—the absence of any traditions of responsible self-government.

Burma, Thailand, and Indochina as a Whole

It is appropriate at this point to give attention to the geographic circumstances common to all three of the countries of the "Indochinese peninsula." They are sparsely populated in comparison with the other countries of the Orient, perhaps on account of the history of the region. The original inhabitants of the territory were Negritos, a dwarfish Negroid race of the same primitive status as the Pygmies of Africa and the Bushmen of Australia. The Malays, a people of Mongolian stock, drove the Negritos into the seclusion of the mountains as they took over the area. About 2000 years ago settlers from India, the Khmers (Cambodians), came into the region. They built up a remarkable civilization in what is now Cambodia. Their capital, *Angkor Vat,* (Fig. 11.12), is one of the great ruins of the world—a city 800 years old, profusely decorated with magnificent stone carvings, rising in the midst of the

Fig. 11.12—Angkor Vat, Ancient Temple (800 A.D.) of the Khmers, in Cambodia. The savanna jungle that had completely overgrown it and which can be seen in the background was cleared by French scientists and Cambodian workers. (Courtesy, Arienne Française.)

jungle just north of the Tonle Sap. About 1000 years later the area was invaded by another Mongolian people, the forebears of the present Thai and Indochinese peoples. Lastly, an Arab-Mohammedan invasion occurred in the thirteenth century.

The great single similarity among the three countries is topography. All three have a great north-south river that dominates the life and economy; all three have a large city located on the delta of their respective rivers; and all three owe their position as rice exporters partly to their rivers as water sources and the yearly fertilizing of the flood plains. It should be pointed out, however, that it is the combination of fertile land *and* a low population density that permits a surplus of rice to be grown for export. Per capita production of all three countries is actually less than that of India or Japan.

N. NORTHERN AUSTRALIA

General Aspects. The savanna climate in Australia extends along all the northern coast including, from west to east: a portion of the

northwest coast known as **Kimberley** (a ria coast—see Chapter 1, p. 14); a wide projection of land on the north central coast known as **Arnhem Land;** and to the east, on the other side of the **Gulf of Carpentaria,** the **Cape York Peninsula** and its base (Fig. 11.13). These areas are part of **Western Australia,** the **Northern Territory,** and **Queensland,** respectively.

The savanna climate is partly the result of a monsoon development over the Australian continent, but owing to low altitude the shifting of the heat equator is also a contributing factor. On the east the Cape York Peninsula is the northern expression of a range of highlands and mountains running the entire length of the east coast of the continent. In the Southern Hemisphere winter the southeast trades bring orographic rainfall, making the southeast portion of the savanna climatic belt more humid than the remainder.

The volume of rainfall, except on the east coast, is not typical for a savanna climate. It averages between 20 and 60 inches a year, is highest along the north coast, and falls off rapidly to less than 20 inches toward the interior. Practically the entire amount falls during the three summer months of the rainy season. During the rest of the year the precipitation is only a few inches at most. This combination results in a very unpleasant climate; the worst features of the rainforest climate are experienced during the wet season, followed by parching, searing dryness. The region is also noted for its continual high temperatures. Wyndham, a small settlement at the eastern end of the Kimberley region, has an average yearly temperature of 85° F., one of the hottest places on earth.

The combination of light rainfall, prolonged drought, and sterile soil over most of northern Australia limits natural vegetation to extremely sparse growths. Along the coast there may be a thin fringe of jungle or mangrove swamp; inland these growths rapidly give way to short, scrubby grass.

Except for the east coast the region is also thinly populated. The settlements are small and scattered, and the families on the iso-

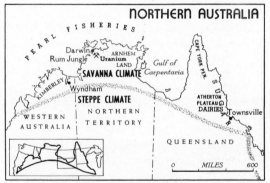

Fig. 11.13—Northern Australia. The inset compares the area of the region with an equivalent area of the United States (the five states outlined).

lated ranches—or "stations," as they are called—keep in daily touch with each other and consult the family doctor by radio, depending on this means of communication much as American farm families do on the telephone.

Products and Resources. In the 20- to 40-inch rainfall belt that forms a large arc through northern Australia the cattle industry struggles to survive against great odds. Poor-quality forage and the need for additional food during the dry season are two of the greatest handicaps.

The major pest of the region illustrates the manner in which man can unwittingly upset natural geography with dire results. In the 1860's a large rabbit farm in eastern Australia was destroyed by a fire which set the rabbits free. By 1930, in the absence of any natural check, the animals had spread over practically all of the continent by the millions, despite expensive, large-scale preventive action by both individuals and the government. The damage the rabbits do is to consume vegetation that would otherwise be available for domestic animals. It is estimated that 40 rabbits consume as much as one sheep. The rabbits are now under control, but only at the cost of constant warfare.

Another major handicap of the cattle industry is the remoteness of northern Australia from the markets to the south. So desirous is the government of developing this portion of the country that it has built and maintained a 1000-mile cattle trail through the central desert, with feeding stations and

water supplies at suitable intervals, along which the cattle may be driven to market.

At the base of the Cape York Peninsula a short distance inland from the east coast is a small area known as the **Atherton Plateau.** Here, where the rainfall is greater, a **dairy** industry is becoming increasingly important.

The east coast itself is the only place with savanna climate in Australia where crops are of any importance, or are even possible. The main product is **sugar cane,** which gives the name "Sugar Coast" to the region. The sugar industry is unusual in that it is based entirely on white labor, the direct result of the government's deliberate policy of excluding all nonwhite immigrants from the continent in an attempt to avoid the race problems that plague those countries with racial minorities.

Enough time has now passed to settle the argument that formerly raged so heatedly as to whether the white man could do heavy labor in a tropical climate. He can, but not at the same low standard of living as can the nonwhite tropical laborer, and so Australia pays for its all-white sugar industry with government subsidies and tariffs. Australia is a sugar exporter in the world market, but the cost of production is at least twice as great as in Cuba.

Nonagricultural resources are in general equally meager throughout the savanna region. Until 1952 the operation of **pearl fishing** along practically the entire northern coast was the only nonagricultural activity of any account. In that year, however, **uranium** deposits were discovered in the **Rum Jungle** area near the northwest coast of Arnhem Land. Except for the Queensland area, the future of northern Australia can be said to be dependent on the future importance of these deposits.

CITIES OF NORTHERN AUSTRALIA

Name	Type	Population (1952)
Townsville	Seaport	38,000
Darwin	Seaport and governmental	2,500

Cities. **Townsville,** the largest town of the more populous east coast in the savanna region of Queensland, is the commercial center of the northern portion of that state. With rail connections to the interior, it is the major shipping point for the products of the region.

Darwin, named after the great scientist Charles Darwin, is the capital of the Northern Territory. It is an isolated, primitive little town, the only settlement of more than a few hundred inhabitants on the entire northern coast of the continent. The "uranium rush" has increased its importance but cannot be said to have improved its character.

QUESTIONS. Why is communication so difficult in central and northern Burma? What mineral products does the region produce? Describe the major topographic features of Thailand. What is the major religion? What are the major products? To what does Thailand owe its continued independence? What are the handicaps to its development?

Name the political components of Indochina. Describe the major topographic features of the country. What is the Tonle Sap and what unusual function does it perform? Explain the meaning of the description of Indochina as "two baskets of rice balanced on a pole." What handicaps to transportation exist? Compare Burma, Thailand, and Indochina as to topography, people, and products. What accounts for the exportable surplus of rice?

What feature of the savanna climate in Australia is unusual? What unusual pest exists in Australia, and why is it of economic importance? What are the major handicaps to agriculture in most of northern Australia? What is the chief product of the savanna portion of Queensland? What important mineral resource is found in the Rum Jungle area of Arnhem Land?

Warm Dry Climates

CHAPTER 12

Warm Deserts and Steppes—Africa and the Middle East

■ DEFINITION AND CAUSES OF WARM DESERTS AND STEPPES

Warm regions with less than 20 inches of precipitation yearly, and cool regions with less than 10 inches are classified as territories with dry or arid climates. The distinction between warm and cool regions must be made because of the greater evaporation at higher temperatures, so that for plant growth 10 inches of rain in a cool region suffice as well as 20 inches in a warm region. Since areas of dry climate grade imperceptibly from warm to cool, the establishment of climatic boundaries separating the warm-dry from the cool-dry must be done arbitrarily. In this section, however, the discussion relates to those arid lands that have distinctively high temperatures.

In general, such warm or low-latitude dry climates are associated with the trade wind and horse latitude planetary wind belts (see Chapter 6, p. 94). Within the average limits of these two belts—15° to 30° north and south latitudes—more than one-half the total land area is under a desert or steppe climate. Small areas of such climate do occur locally, however, beyond those limits.

This wind belt association is a cause-and-effect relationship. The warm, dry, settling air of the horse latitudes is not conducive to precipitation. The trades, starting at the low-latitude border of the horse latitudes, blow from cooler to warmer regions, hence their capacity for water vapor is raised by the progressively higher average annual temperatures of the regions they cross. Moreover, any region reached by the trades after they have given up (on a windward coast or on mountains) what moisture they may have collected by passing over the sea will be exceptionally dry. As the trades in both hemispheres are easterly winds, the west side of continents in their belts is regularly arid. This relationship between deserts and the trade winds is well expressed in the saying "The trade winds are the desert makers."

Where cool ocean currents are found off the west coasts in the low latitudes, arid conditions exist even beyond the trade wind belt. Onshore winds from over these currents come from the cool sea to the warm land and are, accordingly, evaporating, not precipitating, winds. Such currents commonly intensify the aridity caused primarily by the trades.

Arid climates may also be defined in terms of plant cover. As was pointed out in the discussion of typical (non-monsoon) savanna regions, distance away from the equator is marked by a progressive change in the character of the vegetation (see Chapter 9, p. 139). The typical sequence begins with the heavy tropical rainforest. The tree jungle succeeds it; then trees interspersed with grass—the parklands. The trees then disappear and give way to typical savanna with its tall grass, and finally to short grass on its arid border. Still farther poleward the short grass cover becomes discontinuous; it occurs only in clumps separated by barren rock and earth. This is the steppe. The space between clumps becomes wider and wider until the extreme of aridity is reached and plant life vanishes almost completely. This is the absolute desert. The line where the plant cover becomes discontinuous may be considered to mark the boundary between humid and arid climates.

Dry climates can also be defined as those in which evaporation exceeds precipitation. This is a more technical definition, as it can be applied only where appropriate weather records have been kept over a long period of years.

Since climatic regions do not as a rule have sharply defined boundaries it follows that most desert, or truly arid territory, is surrounded by a belt of varying width that has an intermediate, or semiarid climate. This is the steppe country. For practical purposes the arbitrary boundary between steppe and desert has been assumed to be the line where the precipitation is half that which separates humid from arid regions. Thus, with 20 inches of rain the measure of the outer limit of the warm arid region, the line of 10-inch rainfall marks the division between warm steppe and desert.

Although this distinction is useful to climatologists, it is not significant enough to warrant the separation of steppes and deserts in this discussion; the important thing is that they are both arid climates, and the difference between them is only one of degree. Accordingly, the warm deserts and their respective surrounding steppes are considered jointly.

■ DESERT CHARACTERISTICS

Probably no other type of climatic region is misconceived in so many ways by the average person as is the desert. This is because its unusual and extreme conditions have been unduly emphasized and romanticized in literature and in motion pictures. An essentially false picture of its nature has been created.

Contrary to popular opinion, for example, rain does fall in deserts, if only sporadically and at extremely irregular intervals. It occurs in convectional showers—the sudden violent downpours of large volumes of water in a short time referred to as "cloudbursts."

The lack of vegetation and the torrential nature of the rain permit most of the water to run off at once. Hardly more than the upper inch or so of ground is wet through. At the time of a cloudburst the ordinarily dry valleys and canyons (known as *wadis* in Africa, *arroyos* in America) of the desert territories are, within a few hours, filled tens of feet deep with roaring torrents of water that sweep everything before them and then subside as quickly as they rose. The French army regulation forbidding overnight encampments of the Foreign Legion in low places in the Sahara was doubtless dictated by bitter experience with this phenomenon.

The tropical or low-latitude desert does conform to the popular notion of great daytime heat in deserts. Cloudless skies, the absence of a vegetative cover, and low vapor content of the air combine to induce rapid heating up of the land and cause extreme air temperatures to be attained by conduction. Over 130° F. has been recorded in several places. As the heat is dry, temperatures of 100° F. are not, however, unbearable.

Less well known is the fact that deserts not only heat up rapidly under the sun but cool off just as quickly during the night. Day-night temperature ranges of 30° F. are common, and they may reach 50° F. or more. The annual temperature ranges of 20° F. to 30° F. are also large. These ranges are due not so much to excessively low temperatures during the night, or to the low-sun seasons, as to the high extremes of the day, most pronounced at the season when the sun is highest in the sky.

These statements concerning temperatures must be qualified with respect to the deserts past which cool ocean currents flow. Such currents tend to modify the temperature extremes; there is less seasonal range, and in general, lands so situated are somewhat cooler than other arid lands of the lower latitudes.

Fig. 12.1—A Small Oasis With Date Palms. Qatif, Saudi Arabia, near the Persian Gulf. (Courtesy, Arabian American Oil Company.)

A characteristic, though not universal, feature of desert regions is interior drainage. Such regions are basins more or less completely enclosed by mountains or highlands. The water that descends into them as rain or in streams does not escape to the sea. In humid lands interior drainage is a temporary condition, lasting only until enough water accumulates to fill the basin to overflow level. Then the outflow stream cuts a channel through the barrier and the basin is drained. But where evaporation equals or exceeds precipitation and inflow, no wide and deep basin can be filled to overflow level.

Despite the surface aridity there is an underground water supply in deserts, although not necessarily easy of access or of large volume. In basin regions this water is more potable when tapped near the base of the enclosing mountains. Near the center of the depression it is likely to be salty from losses by evaporation. In the Sahara there are indications of a general movement of ground water from the equatorial belt to the Mediterranean. Nevertheless, the belief that there is danger of dying from thirst in the desert is one popular concept that is definitely warranted.

Another common misconception is that deserts are vast, monotonous wastes, or "seas," of shifting sand. In reality sandy areas, especially those with sand dunes, are the exception rather than the rule in deserts. By far the major extent of desert tracts is bare rock or a gravel-covered surface. The topography likewise varies from broad, flat basins to mountains and plateaus.

Lastly, most of the desert territories of the world are in some degree occupied and utilized, contrary to the popular notion of deserts as completely uninhabited, useless areas. The Old World deserts have from time immemorial been the home of nomads, wandering peoples who roam the desert expanses and the bordering steppelands subsisting on their herds of domestic animals which graze on the sparse vegetation.

At scattered, isolated points in deserts underground water rises to or near the surface.

These are the sites of *oases* (Fig. 12.1), agricultural centers, mostly small, whose chief products in the Old World are dates and barley or wheat. Typical desert commerce in Asia and Africa consists in trading the nomad's animal products (wool, meat, and hides) for the agricultural products of the oasis peoples.

■ STEPPE CHARACTERISTICS

By definition the characteristics of the low-latitude steppe are transitional between those of the desert on which it borders and those of the climatic type on its other, "far" side. All *steppes between a low-latitude desert and the equator* merge into savannas on the equatorial border, for such steppes are the north and south margins of the belt affected by the movement of the heat equator as it follows the vertical rays of the sun (see Chapter 6, p. 93). They begin, in other words, at the poleward margin of the savanna's rainfall.

In some years the steppes share slightly in the savanna's rain, but in other years and in the dry season they lack any precipitation. The total rainfall averaged over the years is always less than that of the savanna, its occurrence is less certain, and the length of the dry season is greater. Temperatures in such steppes are usually like those of the desert they border. They are the steppes of "high-sun," or "summer" rainfall.

Contrariwise, the *steppes on the poleward side of the low-latitude deserts* have their "rainy season" in the winter. They mark the transition zone between the westerlies and the trades. In the summer all the planetary wind belts shift toward the (respective) poles and these belts are then situated within the trades and the horse latitudes. They thus experience the aridity characteristic of those winds. In winter the equatorial shift brings these regions under the influence of the low-latitude margin of the westerlies. Some of the great cyclonic storms characteristic of the westerlies belt in winter then extend far enough toward the equator to bring rain to the steppe areas. The steppes of "low-sun" rainfall tend, therefore, to reflect middle-latitude rather than tropical climatic conditions.

In both types of steppe the important fact is that the rainfall is deficient, undependable as to volume, and irregular in occurrence. Grass growths, unlike trees, can survive a long drought period; hence the predominance of that type of vegetation. There is, of course, considerable variation of vegetation with difference in altitude and depending on whether the rainfall is "high-sun" or "low-sun." The higher elevations of "low-sun"

commonly pastoral—their economic activity is almost exclusively the tending of flocks and herds of sheep and goats, and perhaps cattle. As the grass is not the thick, lush cover of the savanna lands nomadism is the necessary way of life. Sparse vegetation can support more sheep than cattle in a given area; on the other hand, cattle can stand heat better. Goats subsist on even less forage than sheep and can stand heat better than cattle. Accordingly, the proportion of these three kinds of animals varies with the intensity of one or the other of these factors in the different regions.

Fig. 12.2—Steppe Country in Northern Australia, Summer Rainfall, High-Sun Type. The solitary automobile traveler, (see road, right center) has stopped to light a fire for a midday meal. (Courtesy, Australian News and Information Bureau.)

steppe regions are commonly forested owing to higher precipitation and lower evaporation, and zones between forests and the grassy lowlands have scrub, bush, thorn, and cactus growths (Fig. 12.2).

The wild animals of the warm steppe are the grazing kinds and carnivorous beasts which prey upon them. Birds are also abundant, as the grass provides seeds for food and material for nests.

The human populations of steppes are

The undependable rainfall both lures and defeats agricultural settlers. A few years in succession of ample rain convinces newcomers that a steppe region is as suitable for cultivation as are the farm lands outside its borders. Succeeding normal or subnormal years bring about the ruin of the venturesome intruders. Nevertheless, the application of dry-farming methods (special techniques that conserve moisture in the soil, thus lessening dependence on rainfall to supply the plants) or irrigation have made some steppe regions permanently productive.

Steppe lands in the Old World are in general sparsely populated and commonly little known or even unexplored. Until the advent of the air age lack of water was a greater deterrent to exploration than the densest jungle or most unhealthful rainforest.

■ DESERT AND STEPPE REGIONS AND COUNTRIES

The major warm desert regions of the world are (Fig. 12.3): The **Sahara**,[1] the largest and

sociated steppe country is discussed as a unit.

A. THE SAHARA

General Aspects. The Sahara extends completely across North Africa, with a total area of approximately 3.5 million square miles, or almost one-third of the entire continent. Even without its surrounding steppe lands it equals the combined area of the continental United States and Alaska. Portions of the Sahara are designated by separate names, e.g., the **Libyan** and **Nubian** deserts.

This vast area is a land surface of marked diversity. Although its average elevation is

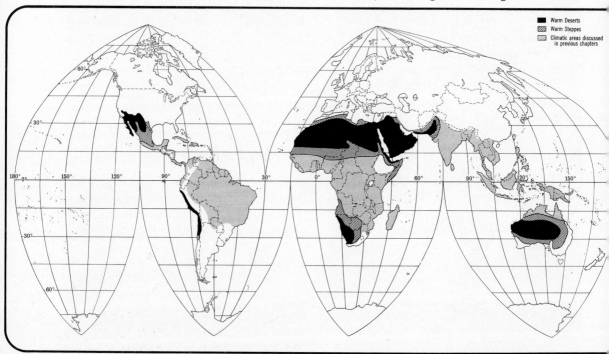

Fig. 12.3—World Distribution of Warm Desert and Steppe Climatic Regions.

most famous; the **Southwest African Desert,** on the coast of Africa; the **Arabian Desert,** regionally an extension of the Sahara; the **Thar Desert** of Pakistan and northwest India; the **Australian Desert,** in the center of that continent; the **Atacama-Peruvian Desert** on the west coast of South America; and the **Sonora-Chihuahuan and Southwestern United States Desert.** Each desert and its as-

---

[1] "Sahara" is from the Arabic for great desert, so the term "Sahara Desert" is equivalent to saying "Great desert desert."

1500 feet and it consists in the main of different-sized basins, the basins are separated by higher plateaus, some of which are over 5000 feet in elevation. Various types of desert surfaces occur: sand, salt, hard clay, gravel, and rock. The sandy tracts constitute about one-third the total area.

The Sahara is bordered on the northwest by the **Atlas Mountains** and on the southeast by the **Ethiopian Highlands** (Fig. 12.4). Only two mountain areas are found within it: the **Ahaggar Mountains,** located almost in the center, and the **Tibesti Massif,** some hundreds of miles to the east. The Tibesti block is over 11,000 feet in elevation and is surmounted by active volcanic cones.

Only two rivers of any size have part or all of their courses within the Sahara. The **Niger** makes a great, sweeping bend northward into the desert, but leaves the arid country before emptying into the Atlantic. The **Nile** crosses the entire width of the desert, from north to south, on the eastern side.

The Oases. An authority on Saharan geography lists 43 important oases. These are so irregularly distributed that some areas of the Sahara are comparatively well populated because of their existence, whereas other areas are completely uninhabited. Oases have often been likened to islands in the sea in that they are small, isolated, habitable spots in a barren waste without permanent occupants.

The chief product of the Saharan oases is the **date.** It is difficult to exaggerate the importance of the date palm to the oasis dweller. Even the phrase "bread of the desert" fails to convey the idea of the full value of the tree and fruit. Dates can be eaten in various ways and in any form are a highly nutritious food. The date is a source of sugar and wine and is fodder for the domestic animals. The palm itself is the source of lumber,

Fig. 12.4—Sahara Region. The inset compares the area of the Sahara region with that of the United States.

fiber (for mats and screens), leaves (for thatched roofs), seeds, and stumps (for fuel). The Saharan oasis is the optimum environment for the tree. As long as water is available to its roots it thrives in the dry air and high temperatures, which serve to ripen the fruit. The date palm is said to do best "with its feet in water and its head in the sun."

In the shade of the date palms smaller fruit trees are grown, such as **olives, peaches, oranges,** etc., with perhaps **grapevines** trellised between them. And on the ground **barley** is the chief crop, sown everywhere in the shade of the trees. Wheat sometimes takes its place. **Vegetable** gardens, with **melons** as the chief item, are regularly present. Under irrigation, four or five crops are harvested yearly.

This intensive, "three-story" agriculture is indicative of the tremendous efforts the oasis inhabitants expend to maintain themselves. In some places a never-ending struggle is waged against encroaching sand. Ingenious devices are used to insure maximum returns from use of the precious water. The date palm, not the land on which it grows, is property. Unless the owner immediately replaces a tree that dies with another, anyone is free to make use of the spot to plant his own tree. This system provides for maximum use of the limited productive land.

The present oasis agriculture goes back

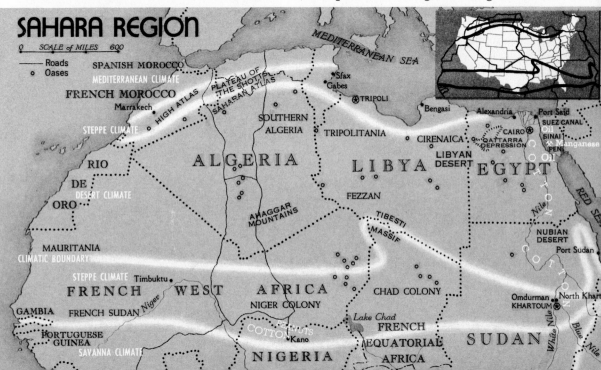

SAHARA REGION

SCALE of MILES   0   600

— Roads
o Oases

SPANISH MOROCCO
MEDITERRANEAN CLIMATE
FRENCH MOROCCO
Marrakech
STEPPE CLIMATE
RIO
DE
DESERT CLIMATE
ORO
MAURITANIA
CLIMATIC BOUNDARY
STEEPE CLIMATE   Timbuktu
FRENCH   WEST   AFRICA
GAMBIA   FRENCH SUDAN
PORTUGUESE
GUINEA
SAVANNA CLIMATE
NIGERIA

HIGH ATLAS
PLATEAU OF
THE SHOTTS
SAHARAN ATLAS
SOUTHERN
ALGERIA
ALGERIA
AHAGGAR
MOUNTAINS
NIGER
NIGER COLONY
PEANUTS
COTTON
Kano
Lake Chad

MEDITERRANEAN SEA
Sfax
Gabes
TRIPOLI
TRIPOLITANIA
FEZZAN
TIBESTI
MASSIF
CHAD COLONY
FRENCH
EQUATORIAL   AFRICA

Bengasi   Alexandria   Port Said
CIRENAICA   CAIRO   SUEZ CANAL
SINAI
QATTARRA   PEN
LIBYAN   DEPRESSION   Manganese
LIBYA   DESERT   Oil
EGYPT
Nile
RED SEA
NUBIAN
DESERT
Port Sudan
COTTON
Omdurman   North Khart
KHARTOUM
SUDAN
White Nile   Blue Nile

only to the eleventh century, when the date palm was introduced from lands to the east. Before that time the struggle for subsistence in the oasis tracts was even more severe than now, as only cereal crops were cultivated. Furthermore, oases are not now limited to those that occur naturally. The French have created oases by sinking deep wells where no water was previously available at the surface.

Modern communication and transportation systems have largely broken down the age-old isolation of the Saharan oases. Their inhabitants have been brought into contact with the many products of Western civilization. As a consequence their desires have been increased but not the means with which to satisfy them. It is not yet clear what changes in the mode of life at the oases will result.

The People. The line of separation between the regions inhabited by the Negro peoples of South Africa and the non-Negroes of North Africa is roughly the same as that marking the southern border of the Sahara. The primitive desert people are the *Tuaregs.* Their total number is not great, but they are scattered over the central and western portions of the Sahara. The Tuaregs were formerly a fierce, warlike people who traditionally feuded among themselves and raided caravans and oases, but under the French regime they have been forced to accept the role of peaceful nomads. The French policy of creating new oases and enticing some of these aggressive wanderers into becoming peaceful, sedentary agriculturalists seems to have been rather successful. This would indicate that the Tuaregs were nomads from necessity and not by choice.

Arab tribes inhabit the Sahara border. During the more humid months they move into the desert with their flocks to take advantage of any pasturage available there. As arid conditions return they retreat into the steppe country, or to their "home" oases. In the northwest the Atlas Mountains afford good summer pasturage.

Transportation. The popular conception of

the desert trade route with its picturesque camel caravan is quite correct in so far as it portrays the traditional method of Saharan transportation. But such transport was not always in existence, and for some time it has been declining in importance. Like the date, the camel is not native to the Sahara but was introduced from the east at about the same time as the date palm. Dates then became the chief item of the caravan trade, the camel the means of transportation.

"The ship of the desert," as the camel is often called, is the perfect desert animal (Fig. 12.5). Its eyes and nostrils are of such structure as to afford natural protection against wind-blown sand; it carries extra nourishment and water in its hump and stomach; its tough lips enable it to feed on the harshest desert plants; its large, padded feet do not sink into loose sand and are insensitive to heat. It is also a fast traveler by comparison with other beasts of burden in the same environment. On the other hand, it is expensive to maintain compared with the humble ass or donkey. In fact, it has been said that except for long, arduous journeys the donkey serves more desert transport than does the camel.

Fig. 12.5—Camels Feeding on Sparse Vegetation of a Sand Dune Area. Note the padded feet. This dromedary type is the swiftest and hardiest of the camel varieties. (Courtesy, Arabian American Oil Company.)

Now, however, the caravan is being replaced by buses and trucks. Motor buses are well adapted for travel over non-sand desert surfaces. Their use has reduced to hours and days trips that formerly took weeks. In the western Sahara the French have established two routes across the entire north-south width of the desert. In Libya, Italy under Mussolini went so far as to build hard-surfaced roads through the desert, although the motivation was military rather than commercial.

Railroads have often been suggested as the best solution to desert transportation problems. This is an error. Long stretches of track through barren wilderness are expensive to build and maintain. A single sandstorm can bury miles of track, and even ordinary desert heat necessitates excessive maintenance costs for tracks and ties. This expense is difficult to meet when the traffic is all between terminals, with no business along the route. The conclusive argument against a trans-Saharan railroad is that ocean transportation between north and south on the continent is cheaper.

The Sahara is still an unexploited region in terms of mineral exploration and development. **Salt** is at present the only mineral product of commercial significance. It is recovered from small salt lakes or found as a crust on the ground in certain areas. It is also mined in the west. Petroleum is a possibility, as the types and ages of the underlying rocks are favorable for its occurrence. Mineral exploration is now being expedited by aerial surveys, which are excellent in such barren country, where the geology is exposed.

The Nile Valley and Delta. Although the typical Saharan oasis is of the nature described above, it is customary to apply the term "oasis" to any tract of watered, fertile land within a desert region. The long oasis comprising the valley and delta of the Nile River is, however, unique, and of such importance as to merit separate description. The delta is approximately 100 miles on each side of its roughly triangular outline; the valley is some 900 miles long and varies in

width from a few hundred yards to some 30 miles.

The Nile oasis is unique in that nowhere else on earth is a major desert crossed from border to border by a major river. The Nile maintains its course and its identity for hundreds of miles of desert country despite the excessive evaporation to which it is exposed. This is possible because of the enormous volume of the equatorial rains of the highlands to the south which are its sources. As these regions are subject to the tropical wet-dry alternation the Nile exhibits a seasonal volume change—a flood stage and a low stage.

The seasonal flooding provides an annual soaking of the low flood plain and delta ground, and replenishment of the surface soil by a cover of new sediment. As the water recedes the crops are planted in the moist earth. In consequence of these conditions high agricultural yields have been obtained for thousands of years without the use of fertilizers supplied by man.

The early predominance and preëminence of Egypt in the development of civilization, and its national continuity for thousands of years, is thus seen to be no mere coincidence (Fig. 12.6). (Written records go back to 3500 B.C.; Egyptian national power lasted until Rome's greatness.) Nor should Egypt's ancient greatness be attributed to historical accident or to the ethnological background of the Egyptians. If geographical factors have been a major determinant of human progress anywhere in the world, they have been in Egypt.

1. Egypt was isolated and protected. Deserts guarded both flanks; the marshy Sudan and Nile rapids protected the south; the Mediterranean, until overseas navigation developed, was a barrier on the north. Civilization could evolve and flourish here with little danger of interference or destruction by invading barbarians.

2. Geographic conditions—the soil, climate, topography, and resources—were uniform throughout the land. This fostered a unified development of civilization among the inhabitants, as the interests of all were

Fig. 12.6—Egypt's Ancient Greatness. Sphinx and pyramid, near Cairo, date back nearly 5000 years (2900 B.C.). (Courtesy, Egyptian State Tourist Administration.)

the same. The forces were all for unity and against the development and preservation of petty states.

3. The placid lower Nile provided a ready-made transportation route and facility extending across the whole width of the country. It was a simple thing to float down the river, then sail back up with the help of the steady trade winds. Transport of bulk goods and communication between the upstream and downstream areas would be and was primitively achieved early on a large scale.

4. Geographic conditions necessitated coöperative effort for success. (a) Irrigation early called for the development of engineering, planning, and organization. (b) Alternation of harvest and nonproductive seasons compelled the storage of grain and required social control of food for the population in general, along with the provision of work during the slack period. This in turn meant

the management of large labor forces in coöperative effort.

Countries of the Sahara Region

1. EGYPT

General Aspects. Although the country's areal extent is 387,000 square miles (about the size of Texas and New Mexico together), most of Egypt's territory is desert wasteland inhabited only by nomads. Egypt as a nation is limited to the oasis of the Nile Valley, an area equal to that of Massachusetts, Rhode Island, and Connecticut combined.

The chief topographic feature of Egypt is the Nile Valley. The northeastern portion of the country is the **Sinai Peninsula,** between the Red Sea and the Mediterranean Sea, the land bridge between Africa and Asia and the site of the Suez Canal (Fig. 12.4). Most of the country, except for the mountainous Sinai region, is low and flat. A portion of the northwest, near the Mediterranean coast, is an area below sea level.

The People. The population of Egypt is over 20 million. Some 60 percent are peasants, or *fellahin* (Fig. 12.7). There is a small middle class (the *effendi*) and a much smaller wealthy class (the *pasha*). Other elements of the population are the desert nomads, or *Bedouins,* and a highly diverse collection of foreign peoples in the cities. Modern Egyptians are a mixture of the ancient Egyptian race with Arab and Negro stocks.

Egypt is a Moslem country. Islam is the state religion and practically all the *fellahin* are Moslem. The largest minority group is that of the *Copts,* whose religion is a variety of Christianity that established itself very early in the Christian Era. The language of Egypt is Arabic.

Egypt, like India, is a land in which most of the inhabitants live in extreme wretchedness and poverty. And, as in India, birth and death rates are both high, sanitary conditions are lethal and diseases are everywhere, the life expectancy is short, and the population density presses heavily on the food supply. When England took over the rule of Egypt in the nineteenth century the population density of the country was 500 to the square mile of settled land. After World War II, when Egypt became independent, it had risen to 1200. In the last 100 years the population has increased sevenfold. The total acreage of arable land is only one-fifth that of Iowa, yet the population that must be supported is almost eight times greater in Egypt.

Agriculture. As an agricultural nation, the country's dependence on the Nile is absolute. Without the river's water not a single crop could be grown. The traditional method of utilizing the water from the time of early Egyptian civilization was to enclose each field with a dike so as to make it a basin. The waters of the flood season (June to October) were thus retained long enough to soak the ground thoroughly, after which the planting was done. This provided for only a single crop a year, however.

Under the British one of the most intensive irrigation systems in the world was developed. Many dams were built, some for storing water for the dry season, others to raise the stream level and divert it into distribution canals. As a result, two or three crops can be obtained yearly. The chief food crops are **wheat, millet, rice,** and **barley,** in order of harvest size.

Although irrigation has been modernized, the farming techniques remain generally the same as those of the ancient Egyptians. The handicaps are the same as in India—primitive equipment, use of dung for fuel rather than for fertilizer, dependence on human labor, and the small size of individual farms.

The major Egyptian crop is **cotton,** of which it is the world's fourth largest producer. Egypt—that is, the Nile Valley and delta—has been called "the best cotton field in the world." The yield per acre is almost double that of any other cotton country, and the variety produced is one of the best.

Egyptian cotton is the long-fiber or "long staple" type, and Egypt accounts for a large portion of the world output of this type. A single fiber measures one and a half inches; such a long staple makes a stronger thread and is regarded as a premium product. Indeed, the cotton is too expensive to be used in Egypt; it is all exported to the great textile mills of Europe and the United States. Cotton comprises four-fifths of Egypt's exports.

Fig. 12.7—Nile Delta and an Egyptian Peasant Farmer, a *Fellah.* (Courtesy, Egyptian State Tourist Administration.)

The cultivation of cotton is made possible by modern irrigation controls. Under the old "basin" system it was impossible to grow any crops during the summer. Now, however, with irrigation, cotton is planted in March and harvested at the end of August—independent of the Nile flood season. About 90 percent of the crop is grown on the delta lands.

Mineral Products and Resources. **Petroleum** and **phosphate rock** are both found along the Red Sea coast. Production is modest, but Egypt is able to provide about one-half its needs for each. **Manganese,** although of poor quality, is exported for use in European steel mills. Iron ore is found near the Nile in the south, and with the combination of iron, manganese, and limestone, the potential (except for coking coal) exists for a modest steel industry.

CITIES OF EGYPT

Name	Type	Population (1947)
Cairo	Governmental and river port	2,100,000
Alexandria	Seaport	920,000
Port Said	Seaport	178,000

Cities. **Cairo** is the capital of Egypt and the largest city in Africa. It is on the east bank of the Nile at the head of the delta, about 140 miles from the Mediterranean. Although it became the capital of Egypt in 1863, Cairo owes its preëminent status chiefly to its history as a great commercial center. It stands where the Nile River, the major north-south route of northern Africa, is crossed by the ancient overland trade routes to both east and west. Cairo is also one of the great centers of Moslem culture and learning, with many mosques and the foremost Arab university. The city is a teeming, cosmopolitan center, with fashionable residential districts on islands in the Nile and a warren of slums on the mainland to the east of the river. Despite its large population Cairo occupies only eight square miles of land (and this for a city with few multistoried buildings). Some idea of the degree of congestion in the city is had

by comparison with Philadelphia, a typical United States urban center of equal population, which covers 128 square miles.

Alexandria is the second city and chief port of Egypt. It is located on the shore of the Mediterranean on the western edge of the Nile delta. Its history is long and colorful. Founded by Alexander the Great in 332 B.C., it was for most of the time until the nineteenth century the capital of Egypt. It was also for a long time the chief center of learning and culture of the civilized world during the first centuries of the Christian Era.

Port Said, at the northern end of the Suez Canal, is also a cosmopolitan city, more important than its size would indicate. It serves as the main way station on the Europe-Asia shipping route.

Egypt as a Whole. Egypt is a country whose major contemporary problems are of more than ordinary interest to the rest of the world because of Egypt's high strategic significance. A poor, overpopulated country in a remote corner of the world is one thing; a country similarly handicapped within which is the Suez Canal is quite another matter.

Egypt suffers from the combined effects of two very serious woes: overpopulation and a one-crop (to make it worse, a cash-crop) economy. Nothing has been done concerning the population problem, but there has been some progress toward diversification of agriculture. Because of the higher income obtainable from cotton the incentive to grow it is irresistible, and in consequence Egypt does not produce enough food for its own population.

The mineral resources of the country give some hope of progress through the diversification of economic activity, but there is no prospect of effective industralization on this basis. The country's resources are too meager and not sufficiently varied to provide the base, and the lack of any immediate prospects for improvement in the lot of the *fellahin* means a continuing lack of home markets.

The one great hope of the nation is the so-called "high dam" at **Aswan.** Conceived by the Egyptians in 1952, this project, the largest of its kind in the world, will ultimately both increase the irrigable acreage by about one-third and expand the power supply by eight times in fuel-short Egypt. In the meantime, more than 20 million people must be supported by the irrigated croplands of the Nile Valley—an area not much larger than Vermont.

QUESTIONS. What is the distinction between dry and humid climates? With what two planetary wind belts are the warm dry climates associated? Explain the reason for this association. How do cool ocean currents also contribute to the existence of a warm dry climatic region? Define dry climates in terms of vegetative cover. Distinguish between deserts and steppes on the same basis. What is the difference between deserts and steppes in terms of rainfall?

Discuss the frequency, amount, and character of rainfall in the warm desert regions. What are *wadis* and *arroyos?* What factors are responsible for the extreme heat reached under desert conditions? Why is there such a great day-night temperature range? What is "interior drainage"? Why is it commonly associated only with conditions of dry climate? Why is the popular idea of a desert as a flat, sandy waste a misconception? Define "oasis."

Distinguish between the steppes on the "equator side" and the "poleward side" of a warm desert and discuss the characteristics of each. What is the most significant feature of the rainfall of the warm steppe?

Give a brief topographical description of the Sahara. Why is the date palm indispensable to the oasis dweller? What is "three-story" agriculture? Describe the people of the Sahara. Why is the camel so ideal for desert transport? Why then are donkeys used more than camels? What is the current most important means of desert transport?

Why is the Nile oasis unique? What is the agricultural significance of the annual flooding of the Nile? Discuss the factors that aided the early development of civilization in the Nile Valley. Describe the people of Egypt as to social strata, religion, language, health, and level of income. What effect has the building of dams had on irrigation and farming in Egypt? What is the chief crop of Egypt? Why is the Egyptian variety of this crop of premium quality? Discuss Egypt's major problems. Why is Cairo a great commercial center?

2. THE NORTHERN SUDAN

The term "Sudan" refers both to the savanna belt that stretches across all Africa south of the Sahara, previously discussed (see Chapter 9, p. 146), and to the more northerly steppe belt here under consideration (Fig. 12.4). In general this steppe belt is a country of native farmers and cattle raisers. In the more humid sections subsistence agriculture is practiced. The steppe is also the site of trade centers, where the products and culture of the Arab country to the north meet those of the tropical jungle and rainforest on the south.

Countries of the Northern Sudan. The most important country of this belt is **Sudan.** Steppe and desert climate prevail over the northern two-thirds of this country of almost a million square miles. Like Egypt, Sudan is dominated by the Nile.

For many years Sudan was a "condominium," a country ruled by two other countries —Egypt and Great Britain—together. In 1953, however, an agreement was reached providing for an eventual choice by the Sudanese between self-government and union with Egypt, and at the beginning of 1956 the country declared itself independent. The population of nearly 9 million is a mixture of Hamitic and Negro stock considered as "Arab" because their culture is Arab and their religion Islam.

The chief crop is **cotton**, grown under irrigation along the stream valleys. Both Egyptian and American varieties are produced, but both are long staple and of high quality. The output is only a small fraction of the world total but is of great value.

West of Sudan is the French colony of **Chad,** the northern portion of French Equatorial Africa. Its area of 460,000 square miles (about three times that of California) contains a population of more than 2 million. The Chad Colony extends north to the Tibesti Massif, but the valuable region is around **Lake Chad,** on the western border of the country. Here native agriculture is carried on during the dry season. The fields are the fertile lake bottom, exposed as the shallow lake shrinks by evaporation. In both Chad Colony and Sudan large areas of good land for cotton and tobacco are still unused.

West of Chad Colony are the Northern Provinces of **Nigeria,** about two-thirds of the total area of the country. Most of this region is a plateau between 1500 and 2000 feet in elevation. Cotton, peanuts, hides, and skins are the products.

North of Nigeria is the French colony of **Niger,** the eastern portion of French West Africa. Its population is roughly equal to that of Chad Colony and its area of 500,000 square miles is almost equal to that of Alaska. It is mostly uninhabited desert. Only in the southwest and southeast, near the Niger River and Lake Chad, respectively, is there sufficient water for agriculture. Products are millet, manioc, beans, peanuts, and dates (the last-named from oases).

West of Niger Colony is the **French Sudan,** another portion of French West Africa 600,000 square miles in extent, with a population of 2 million. Most of the colony is desert, except where the great bend of the Niger River passes through the country and provides the water for some modest irrigation projects initiated by the French. The products are cattle and peanuts.

Still farther west is the coastal colony of **Mauritania,** with an area of 320,000 square miles (equal to the combined area of the Pacific coast states) and a population of 4 million. The products of this sparsely populated country are cattle, gum, and salt.

Cities. **Khartoum, Omdurman,** and **North** **Khartoum** are a tri-city complex located at the juncture of the White and Blue Niles which forms the Nile itself. Khartoum, the present capital, is located on the neck of land between the two tributaries. Omdurman, on the west bank of the Nile, is the former capital and still the great trading center of the country. North Khartoum is located across the Nile from Omdurman.

Port Sudan, on the Red Sea coast, was built in 1908 to relieve Sudan from the handicap of trading through Egypt with the rest of the world. With rail connections to the Khartoum center and to other points along the Nile, it now provides a fully adequate port for the country.

Kano (Fig. 12.8) is a little-known but very important trading center in northern Nigeria. It is not just a local market but has a large portion of the continent as its hinterland. It is the southern terminus of a trans-Saharan caravan route to the Mediterranean, and a 700-mile railroad connects it with the coast to the south. In addition to its commercial significance Kano is a center of manufacturing. For 1000 years its weaving, leather, and sandal industries have supplied a large part of Africa with household articles. It is the original source of the famous "Moroccan leather." The native city, within which Europeans are not allowed to live, is surrounded by a wall 12 miles long.

Timbuktu is the opposite of commercial Kano—it is a city whose name is linked with romance, slaves, the Foreign Legion, and exotic life in the African desert, yet one whose fame derives largely from its past grandeur. Located on the edge of the desert near the Niger River, it is now a town of minor importance functioning as a local

CITIES OF THE NORTHERN SUDAN

Name	Country	Type	Population
Omdurman	Sudan	River port	130,000 (1954)
Khartoum	Sudan	River port and governmental	83,000 (1954)
North Khartoum	Sudan	River port	44,000 (1954)
Port Sudan	Sudan	Seaport	61,000 (1954)
Kano	Nigeria	Commercial	130,000 (1953)
Timbuktu	French Sudan	Commercial	7,000 (1949)

Fig. 12.8—Kano, Ancient Market City of Northern Nigeria. (Courtesy, British Information Services.)

commercial center where people gather during the market season.

3. THE NORTHERN SAHARA

General Aspects. The northern steppe border of the Sahara is somewhat narrower than its southern counterpart, the northern Sudan. On the east it reaches the shore of the Mediterranean, but on the west it is limited to the southern flank of the Atlas Mountains and a plateau just to the south of them (Fig. 12.4). This is a steppe with "low-sun" rain, hence it differs from the Sudan in that its vegetative aspects are middle latitude rather than tropical.

The political divisions of the northern Sudan meet those of the south roughly along the center line of the desert. This boundary is no doubt due to the gradual extension into the desert from each side of the more valuable populated territories along both borders.

Countries. On the west coast north of Mauritania is a portion of the Sahara known as the **Rio de Oro,** a Spanish colony with an area of more than 100,000 square miles. This country, the size of Nevada, is as empty and valueless a piece of colonial territory as could be imagined.

Northeast of the Rio de Oro the Atlas Mountains begin their course across the northwest corner of Africa. The western half of the chain, the "High Atlas," is in **Morocco.** Only the southern border of the country is in a steppe climate. It is somewhat more habitable and useful than the Rio de Oro by reason of several important oases.

East of Morocco is a French possession, **Algeria.** Again only the southern portion of the country is desert or steppe, but in this instance the 750,000 square miles of Southern Algeria (almost three times the size of Texas) is 90 percent of the entire country. The population is concentrated in the oases, which are large and numerous. Dates form the single large export of the region.

The southernmost range of the Atlas Mountains here is known as the "Saharan Atlas." Between this range and the main mountain chain is the **Plateau of the Shotts.** (A "shott" is a lake which evaporates to dryness during the summer.) Nomadic herders of sheep and goats use the poor pasturage the plateau affords.

East of Algeria is **Tunisia,** the southern two-thirds of which are within the Saharan climatic region. **Olives** are the chief product of the northern portion; **dates,** of the oases in the south.

The remaining country within the northern boundary of the Saharan region is **Libya,** between Tunisia and Egypt on the Mediterranean coast. The Kingdom of Libya is exceedingly young, having been created by the United Nations in 1951 from three territories—Tripolitania, Cirenaica, and the Fezzan—that constituted the beginning of the ill-fated Italian Empire. Its 680,000 square miles are mostly empty desert. The non-desert portion, some 17,000 square miles along the coast, is some of the richest agricultural land in all North Africa. Oranges and olives are grown by a few thousand Italian colonists who have remained. The total population of over one million is mostly mixed Arab-Negro.

Libya is an extraordinarily poor country. About 80 percent of the people are nomadic herdsmen, but the country can scarcely support its population even with that way of life.

4. The East African "Horn"

The dry climatic region of North Africa continues in a southeastern extension along the shore of the Red Sea and around the eastern projection, or horn of Africa, to Kenya (Fig. 12.9). This coastal strip of some half-million square miles is divided into four political divisions, all nearly as valueless as the Rio de Oro.

Eritrea extends along the southwest coast of the Red Sea below Sudan. Forcibly

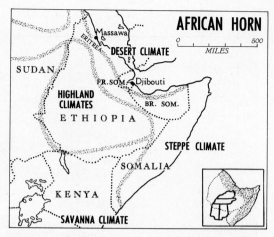

Fig. 12.9—African Horn. The inset compares the area of the region (stippled) with that of Kentucky, Tennessee, Mississippi, and Alabama.

wrenched from Ethiopia during the days of Italian empire building, it was reunited with that country in 1952. **French Somaliland,** at the end of the Gulf of Aden, is the smallest country; it is the size of New Hampshire. **British Somaliland,** on the northern coast of the "horn," is a British Protectorate. The Somali tribes are self-governing. **Somalia,** the largest of the four countries, is south of British Somaliland, an Italian trusteeship under the United Nations.

The region as a whole is of little significance as to present economic life or recognizable future possibilities.

Marrakech, the largest city of Morocco, is located on a plateau at an elevation of 1500 feet, about 15 miles south of the Atlas range and 125 miles inland from the Atlantic coast. It is an important local market center and at times in the past was the capital of the country. It is a very picturesque and beautiful city, with many groves and gardens, and good examples of Arab architecture such as mosques, tombs, and fountains. It is in the center of a large palm grove of almost 100,000 trees. The city has remained practically unaffected by European influences and is noted for its leather and metal handicraft products.

Sfax is the leading seaport of southern Tunisia and is the export outlet for phosphate rock, a fertilizer material produced in-

CITIES OF THE NORTHERN SAHARA AND EAST AFRICA

Name	Country	Type	Population
Marrakech	Morocco	Commercial	245,000 (1952)
Sfax	Tunisia	Seaport	55,000 (1946)
Gabes	Tunisia	Seaport	23,000 (1946)
Tripoli	Libya	Seaport and governmental	145,000 (1955)
Bengasi	Libya	Seaport	62,000 (1951)
Massawa	Ethiopia (Eritrea)	Seaport	25,000 (1947)
Djibouti	French Somaliland	Seaport and governmental	28,000 (1953)

land to the west. **Gabes,** a lesser port 70 miles southwest of Sfax, is an oasis town on the coast, and a date export center.

Tripoli, the capital of Libya, has a good harbor and is adjacent to an oasis on the east some 25 square miles in extent. **Bengasi** is the second city of Libya, an isolated port serving the coastal portion of Cirenaica. It is much reduced in population and activity since the days of heavy subsidization of the region under Mussolini.

Massawa has a good harbor developed by the Italians into an ample port to serve their colony. Unfortunately, it is a strictly Eritrean port, as it lacks a rail connection with Ethiopia proper.

Djibouti, the capital and port of French Somaliland, has a good harbor and a highly strategic location at the restricted entrance to the Red Sea. Despite its desert situation it suffers under excessively high humidity because of its position on the Gulf of Aden. As the seaward terminus of the only railroad in Ethiopia it serves as that country's major port.

B. THE SOUTHWEST AFRICAN DESERT

Climatic Relationships. The discussion of the other large desert region of Africa (Fig. 12.10) is complicated by a confused use of the term "desert." In southwest Africa the driest portion of the region, along the coast, is known as the **Namib** desert, and a large portion of the bordering steppeland is also known specifically, even to geographers, as a desert—the **Kalahari.** The situation is further complicated by the use of the term "Southwest Africa" for one of the political divisions of the region. Only about half the

territory of Southwest Africa is true desert.

The trade winds are responsible for the dry climatic region of South Africa in that they precipitate their moisture as they rise over a high southeast coast. As a consequence the rest of the continent in those latitudes is progressively drier to the west. A true desert strip, accordingly, is developed along the west coast from central Angola on the north to midway between the Orange

Fig. 12.10—Southwest African Desert. The inset compares the area of the region with an equivalent area of the United States (states in white).

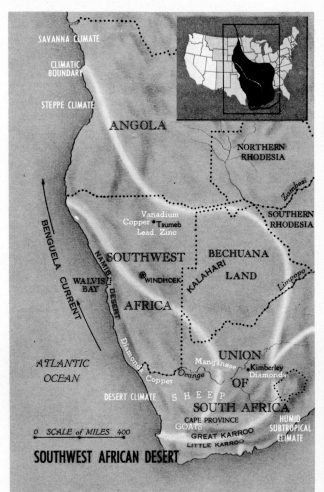

SOUTHWEST AFRICAN DESERT

River and the Cape of Good Hope on the south. It is between 60 and 100 miles wide, bulging inland directly west of the highlands of the southeast coast. The aridity of this coastal desert is intensified by the cold **Benguela Current,** but the high temperature extremes are moderated by its presence off the west coast.

The belt of country with steppe climate parallels the desert on the east and is narrowest on the north and south. To the north and northeast it grades into the savanna climate (like the Sudan). On the south the steppe becomes much cooler and is technically not a warm dry climate. In view of the confusion in terminology, however, all the steppe area is here presented as a unit.

Fig. 12.11—Bushmen Making Bows Which They Still Use for Hunting in Southwest Africa. (Courtesy, South African Government Information Office.)

Countries of the Southwest African Desert Region

1. SOUTHWEST AFRICA

The territory of Southwest Africa is a former German colony 318,000 square miles in area (about equal to the combined area of the Pacific coast states) mandated to the Union of South Africa by the League of Nations, the mandate renewed by the United Nations.

The major portion of the true desert region of Southwest Africa is within this territory. Except for the **Orange River** along its southern boundary and smaller streams on its northern boundary the watercourses are ordinarily dry. Like the wadis of the Sahara they flow only after the infrequent rains. The annual rainfall along the coast is only one inch.

The territory is inhabited by several Negro tribes totaling almost 400,000 in number. The original inhabitants are the *Bushmen* (Fig. 12.11), the most primitive tribe in Africa, often cited as one of the least advanced human groups in existence. The Bushmen were driven into this barren country in past times by the more capable Negro tribes which occupy the rest of southern Africa. Later, many of the superior Negroes also became inhabitants of the desert,

driven there from the better land by the encroachment of the white race. The center of the desert region is also the home of a partly self-governing group of 5000 half-breed Hottentots officially known as "The Bastards."

The principal industry is the raising of **cattle, sheep,** and **goats,** carried on chiefly in the southeastern portion of the country. **Fishing** is also important at certain points along the coast.

The mineral products include **vanadium,** of which the territory is the third-ranking producer; **copper, lead,** and **zinc**—all produced from a single large deposit at **Tsumeb** in the north central region; and **diamonds,** found in the surface gravels along the coast.

2. BECHUANALAND

To the east of Southwest Africa lies the British Bechuanaland Protectorate, 275,000 square miles named after the Bechuana tribes who inhabit it. The southwestern portion of the country, about 120,000 square miles in extent (equivalent to the area of New Mexico), is the so-called **Kalahari Desert.** Actually, the country has more a steppe climate. The aridity increases both from north to south and from east to west. Beyond the savanna that borders it on the north the rainfall of the Kalahari declines from 13 inches to about 8 inches on its southern border.

Bechuanaland is another of the elevated

basins (the average altitude of the country is over 3000 feet) characteristic of the interior plateau of Africa. The **Zambezi** and **Limpopo** rivers on the north and south are the only drainage outlets to the sea, but much of the area is not in their watersheds. During the rainy season (January and February) depressions on the surface become shallow lakes, or "pans." At this time mosquitoes and other insects breed in great numbers and spread disease. With the onset of the dry season the pans evaporate, leaving a white crust of salt. The name Kalahari means "salt pans" in the Bechuana language.

It is probable that the occurrence of the salt pans and small tracts of sand dunes, together with the fact that surface water is unobtainable during the dry season, was responsible for the designation of the region as a desert. Actually, most of the country is not barren. The northern savanna border has thick forests, the west has a thick scrub cover, and the south has grasses of medium height. Just after the rains the country abounds in game of all sorts, which comes in from the savannas to "enjoy the season" by taking advantage of the temporarily good feeding conditions.

The whole of Bechuanaland has a population of almost 300,000, made up almost entirely of native tribes, including the Bushmen. The main occupation is, as in Southwest Africa, the raising of **cattle, sheep,** and **goats.** Corn, sorghum, and beans are the native crops; they succeed or fail as the erratic rainfall varies from year to year.

3. THE CAPE PROVINCE— NORTHERN PORTION

South of Bechuanaland and Southwest Africa the desert and steppe country continues into the **Cape of Good Hope Province**

of the Union of South Africa. The northern portion of the province is relatively uninhabited and of little importance. Still farther south the great interior plateau drops off to the southern coast of the continent in two large steps—the **Great Karroo**[2] and the **Little Karroo.** The former is the higher and wider of the two.

Here also the vegetation is scrub or grass, depending on the rainfall; trees are present only along the watercourses. This is the great grazing land for "small stock" in South Africa. The raising of **sheep** is the principal industry, with **goats** less important. The sheep are the merino breed, noted for its high-quality wool but by the same token poor for meat. Merinos are adapted to a dry environment and so are found in the center and west. The goats are raised for their *mohair,* a fine, wool-like product. The region is one of the leading producers of both wool and mohair.

Corn is the chief crop, consumed by both animals and man, but the total acreage suitable for cultivation is small. Less than one percent of the land on the Great Karroo is farmed. **Alfalfa** is increasing in importance as a forage crop.

The land is rich in minerals. **Diamonds,** from the north central region of the province, are the leading mineral product. **Copper** is produced in the desert just south of the Orange River, and **manganese** is shipped from large deposits to the north, some 100 miles west of the diamond district.

Windhoek, the capital of Southwest Africa, is located at about the center of the country at an elevation of slightly over one mile. Its climate is cool and dry. It is a pleasant, well-planned town of some commercial import-

[2] *Karroo* is a Hottentot term meaning "waterless."

CITIES OF THE SOUTHWEST AFRICA DESERT-STEPPE REGION

Name	Country	Type	Population
Windhoek	Southwest Africa	Governmental and commercial	30,000 (1951)
Walvis Bay	Southwest Africa	Seaport	7,000 (1952)
Kimberley	Cape Province, Union of South Africa	Mining	62,000 (1951)

ance by virtue of its rail connection with the Union of South Africa.

Walvis Bay, the port of Southwest Africa, is located at about the center of the coastline. It has one of the finest harbors of all

Fig. 12.12—Saudi Arabia and Iraq. The inset compares the area of the region with an equivalent area of the United States (states in white).

Africa. The town is the center of a thriving fishing and canning industry.

Kimberley is one of the great mining towns of the world (see Chapter 3, p. 44), the site of the original large diamond mines of South Africa and still the leading diamond-mining center of the world. It is dominated by the "Big Hole," the abandoned pit

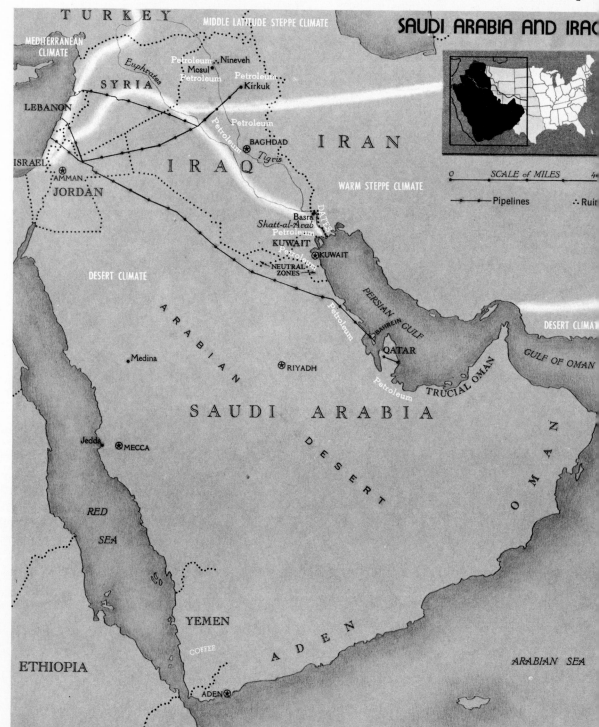

of the Kimberley Mine, 1200 feet deep. The diamonds are now recovered from underground workings.

C. THE ARABIAN DESERT

General Aspects. The Arabian Desert is coextensive with the Arabian peninsula of Asia (Fig. 12.12). It juts southward between the Red Sea and the Persian Gulf. Arabia, as has been noted, is a climatic extension of the Sahara; its desert expanses are created by the dry trades that blow in from the wide Asiatic land mass extending off to the northeast.

Topographically the Arabian peninsula is a plateau sloping gently to the east. The western border is rimmed with uplands that rise to peaks of 10,000 feet at their southern extremity. A smaller mountainous area in the far eastern corner of the peninsula attains 9000-foot altitude.

Save for the highland and mountain areas that cause sufficient orographic rainfall to make them regions of steppe climate, the desert expanses of the peninsula are uninterrupted and cover roughly a million square miles. The southern portion of the area is sandy desert; on the central west coast there are rough lava fields that are completely desolate and impassable.

Arabia is the home of the Arab, of the date palm, and of superior, thoroughbred camels and horses (Fig. 12.13). Large oases scattered in the interior support a consider-

able population. Until World War I the region was remote, unknown, and inhospitable to foreigners. Even now there are large areas that have not yet been visited by Europeans or Americans, regions where the nomadic tribes live each under its own sheikh, independent of outside influences, much as their ancestors did a thousand or so years ago.

Countries of the Arabian Desert

1. SAUDI ARABIA

The major part of the Arabian peninsula lies within the Kingdom of Saudi Arabia. As boundaries of this kingdom have never been exactly defined, its precise area is indeterminate. It does, however, comprise something over 900,000 square miles of territory, with an estimated population of 7 million. The name of the country refers to Ibn Sa'ud, an Arab chieftain who single-handedly built the unit nation by absorption or conquest of the several previously existing small kingdoms of the peninsula.

The outstanding characteristic of Saudi Arabia is its role as the stronghold and holy land of Mohammedanism, or Islam. As the cradle and birthplace of the religion, and the site of its greatest shrines, the country is a leading nation in the Moslem world. It is one of the chief religious duties of all good Moslems to make a pilgrimage sometime during their life to the birthplace of Mohammed, the founder of the religion. Arabia for centuries thus derived its main income from the hordes of pilgrims who came there from all over the Moslem world.

Fig. 12.13—Arabs and Camels on Desert Rock Floor, Saudi Arabia. In the distance are black tents, made of strips of coarse cloth, of the Arab encampments. (Courtesy, Arabian American Oil Company.)

The export of fine camels to other desert countries was formerly another leading source of income. The return from this source is now, however, almost nil owing to the increasing use of buses and trucks in deserts everywhere.

Such loss of revenue has been more than offset since the 1930's by the development of the country's **petroleum** resources. Saudi Arabia contains one of the richest oil provinces in the world, the yield from which may eventually exceed that from all those of the United States. Exclusive rights to petroleum recovery from 440,000 square miles of land have been obtained by American oil companies. Oil pools along the shore of the Persian Gulf have already been developed, and their yield is processed at a local refinery. The oil is easily obtained from shallow wells, but is produced remote from Europe, which is the nearest market. Accordingly, a 1000-mile pipe line to the Mediterranean has been built to carry the output to this seaboard. From there it can be economically transported by tanker to European customers.

Except for its oil Saudi Arabia is a poor country. Its inhabitants are mostly nomads, and the agricultural yield from the few oases is insufficient to provide the grain and dates they need over and above the milk, cheese, and meat supplied by their flocks and herds. Unfortunately, only a minor part of the royalties from oil production have found their way into development and construction programs; most have accumulated in the private fortunes of the ruling family.

The significance of the oil—its occurrence in quantity, its development by American companies, and its influence in the life of the country—is enormous. Oil makes Saudi Arabia a strategic region of first importance in world politics. The influence of American ways of thought and action which results from training Arabs to drill wells and operate refineries is fast changing old traditions and customs. Rather surprisingly, the nomadic Arabs have readily adapted their lives to employment in the oil industry and have proved to be competent workers.

2. MARGINAL ARABIA

Although Ibn Sa'ud succeeded in unifying central Arabia under his rule, he was unable to extend dominion over certain border areas and coastal stretches of the peninsula, because years earlier Great Britain had either taken these over or given official protection to local chieftains. Hence, except for the Red Sea coast and a small section of the Persian Gulf coast, Arabia is ringed around by small independent or quasi-independent local states and British protectorates (Fig. 12.12).

Yemen is an independent kingdom the size of South Dakota in the southwestern corner of the Arabian peninsula. The country is best known for its **coffee**, a variety called "mocha" much prized for its good quality. Arabia is the original home of the coffee tree.

East of Yemen is the British colony and protectorate of **Aden**, about the size of Arizona. It is of strategic importance because of its control of the entrance to the Red Sea.

The remainder of the southern and southeastern coast of the Arabian peninsula is the independent sultanate of **Oman**, roughly the size of Kansas.

The northwestern border state of Saudi Arabia is **Jordan**, an independent kingdom about the size of Indiana, with a population of some 1.5 million. The western portion, comprising the Arab part of Palestine and the adjacent part of the kingdom proper, contains most of the population and agricultural resources. **Cereals** are the chief products. **Potash** is produced from the **Dead Sea**, on the Israel border. The present kingdom is the successor to a British mandate set up after World War II. Devoid of any significant resources, it still must be subsidized by Great Britain.

Other minor bordering states include **Kuwait**, a shiekhdom under British protection at the northeastern corner of Saudi Arabia, and **Bahrein**, a small shiekhdom consisting of a group of islands in the Persian Gulf. They are important far out of proportion to their size because of their prodigious **oil** production. Bahrein is also the site of a large refinery.

CITIES OF ARABIA

Name	Country	Type	Population
Mecca	Saudi Arabia	Religious	200,000 (1952)
Medina	Saudi Arabia	Religious	50,000 (1952)
Riyadh	Saudi Arabia	Governmental	60,000 (1952)
Jedda	Saudi Arabia	Seaport	50,000 (1952)
Aden	Aden	Seaport	96,000 (1955)
Amman	Jordan	Governmental and commercial	200,000 (1955)

Fig. 12.14—Mecca, Saudi Arabia. The cubicle in the center foreground draped with black cloth is the "Ka'ba," which houses the sacred black stone. This is the holiest shrine of Islam. (Courtesy, Arabian American Oil Company.)

Mecca (Fig. 12.14) is located in west central Arabia, 45 miles inland from the Red Sea coast. It is in a barren valley surrounded by well-watered slopes, a sort of oasis center. Its importance is not agricultural, however, but religious, for Mecca is the birthplace of Mohammed. It is to the Moslem what Bethlehem and Jerusalem combined are to the Christian. As the shrine to which Moslems must make their pilgrimage, the name "Mecca" has come to mean any goal to which a pilgrimage is made. It is considered so holy that no infidel, or non-Moslem, is allowed near it, and only a few adventurous nonbelievers have risked their lives to visit it in disguise.

Medina, about 200 miles to the north, is also a religious shrine, revered as the place of Mohammed's death.

Riyadh, in east central Saudi Arabia, and Mecca are the twin capitals of the country. Jedda, at about the mid-point of the Red Sea coast, is the port of Mecca and the only port of the country. Its inhabitants are almost entirely dependent on the pilgrim trade for their livelihood.

Aden is located near the southwestern tip of the Arabian peninsula in the crater of an extinct volcano whose walls formerly provided an excellent natural defense. It is important as a fueling station for Europe-Asia commerce and as a strategic control point for what is left of the British Empire in the Orient.

Amman, the capital of Jordan, is located on the edge of the Arabian plateau at an altitude of 2700 feet. Its position between the populous Mediterranean coast and the desert Arabian peninsula gives it some commercial importance as a desert "port of entry."

3. IRAQ

General Aspects. The Kingdom of Iraq consists of some 175,000 square miles of lowland (about the size of Idaho and Wyoming together) between the two plateaus of Arabia and Iran (Fig. 12.12). Across this lowland from northwest to southeast the **Tigris** and **Euphrates** rivers flow in roughly parallel courses, uniting about 100 miles from the Persian Gulf to form the **Shatt-al-Arab.** The northern part of the country is occupied by the foothills of the mountains north of Iraq. South of the foothills there is a rolling, stony, barren stretch which merges southward into the very level alluvial plain built up by the two rivers. In these lower reaches the overflow of the rivers creates wide marshes.

Climatically the southern half of the country is part of the Arabian Desert. North from the course of the Euphrates it is a steppe country of low-sun, or winter, rains. The summers are hot, the winters in general are mild—recorded temperature extremes are 19° and 123° F. Still farther north the climate gradually becomes cold steppe. Most of both the warm and cold steppe areas is covered with scrub growth or coarse grass.

Mesopotamia. Mesopotamia means "land between rivers" and refers to the plain and its twin river system that form roughly half of Iraq. Like the Nile Valley, this region was the site of one of the earliest recorded civilizations. Ur of the Chaldees, referred to in Genesis, was on the lower Euphrates; it dates back to 3800 B.C. Later came the Assyrian civilization with its capital Nineveh, on the upper Tigris, followed by Babylonia and the city of Babylon on the middle Euphrates.

Again, as in the case of the Nile Valley, it is no coincidence that early civilizations arose in this region. The similarity of environment to that of the Nile Valley is marked. Indeed, here not one but two streams pass through a dry country. The Tigris and Euphrates are, however, swifter, more turbulent streams than the Nile. Consequently, flood plain and deltaic deposits are built up very rapidly along their courses and on the delta. Man in this region, accordingly, was early confronted with the problem of river control and drainage.

Unlike the single, uniform resource that was the arable land of the Nile Valley, Mesopotamia had diverse possibilities for production, and hence a broad basis for "international" commercial development. The northern highlands provided timber that could be rafted down the twin rivers; the steppe and desert provided cattle, wool, and hides; there was asphalt that could be used to strengthen bricks and help build the great cities. The absence of natural barriers permitted easy expansion of trade with the surrounding regions. Thus the eastern shore of the Mediterranean was early brought into the Mesopotamian sphere of activities.

Again it is evident that the necessity for organization and planning aided in the advancement of a culture. The irrigation works of this region were more elaborate than those of the Egyptians, rivaling modern projects in size. But the absence of natural barriers which facilitated trade also meant a lack of protection against invasion, and diversity fostered disunity. The surrounding land was inhabited by barbarous, nomadic tribes to whom the prosperous river civilizations were tempting prey in times of drought. Armies established for defense by the separate units turned on each other eventually in self-destroying wars.

The decline of the early great civilizations was followed by the Arab (nomad) conquest, a disaster from which the region never fully recovered. The farmers were driven off and the great irrigation works lapsed into decay and disrepair. The rivers ran uncontrolled and spread into marshes. What had been a fruitful, productive land became once more a semidesert. During the past few centuries there was little to suggest a basis for the legend that this land was the site of the Garden of Eden.

Until World War I the country was under the Turks, who up to then had no interest in restoration of the irrigation works. But, as in Arabia, Turkish defeat provided the opportunity to gain independence. The country was a British mandate until 1927 and has since been independent. Interest in restoring the irrigation works was then revived.

The People. The Iraq of the present is a nation of some 5 million people who are a racial mixture of Indo-European and Semitic stocks. About 80 percent are Arab (Fig. 12.15), 16 percent are Kurds (an Indo-European people), and there are small minorities of Iranians and Turks. The Kurds live mostly in the mountainous northeast, near Iran. The Iranians live along the border district proper. The Turks inhabit a belt between the Kurds and the Arabs, who occupy by far the largest area of the country. The farming portion of the population is concentrated in the Shatt-al-Arab region. Many nomads roam the desert south of Mesopotamia and the higher steppe lands to the north. The religious make-up of the country is predominantly Moslem. Many small Christian sects are also present.

The condition of the Iraqi is generally wretched. The literacy rate is about 10 percent. Disease is rampant. The nomads barely eke out an existence in their harsh environment, and the farmers are in perpetual debt and bondage to the moneylenders.

Transportation. Ancient river travel on the Tigris has already been mentioned; the Euphrates was and is little used. Both rivers are swift, with shifting channels that make them unsuitable for large-scale navigation. The large cities of Iraq are, however, all connected by railroads that run to Turkey and the eastern shore of the Mediterranean, and transportation by motor truck in caravans is becoming increasingly important between the Mediterranean and Iraq.

Agriculture. The contrast between Egypt, whose agricultural productivity has remained high for 5000 years, and Iraq, which has not yet recovered from the deterioration of its irrigation works, is marked. Nevertheless the essential fertility of Iraq's soil remains. It has been estimated that 7 million acres of productive land (equal to that of Egypt) would result from the full restoration of the ancient irrigation systems.

At present less than 10 percent of the plain is irrigated, mostly by taking advantage of the difference in character of the two rivers. The Tigris is fast in its upper, slow in its lower reaches, where it has built up its bed higher than the Euphrates. The Euphrates, contrariwise, has a higher bed than the Tigris in its upper valley. It is thus possible to lead irrigation water by gravity from the Euphrates to the Tigris in their upper reaches, from the Tigris to the Euphrates in their lower reaches.

The outstanding agricultural product is the **date.** An estimated third of all the date palms in the world are in Iraq and produce 80 percent of the world output. About half the trees are concentrated along the Shatt-al-Arab in one oasis 100 miles long and one to two miles wide, forming a great, green carpet on the drab desert. Irrigation here is

Fig. 12.15.—Arab couple on the desert southeast of Baghdad, Iraq. (Courtesy, A. H. Detweiler.)

operated by the tides, which back up the river water and send it into the date groves. **Fruits,** melons, and **vegetables** are grown in the shade of the date palms.

Other crops are barley, wheat, millet, sesame, and corn, grown in the winter to take advantage of the rains from the cyclonic storms. Cotton production is not very large, but many authorities consider that the similarity of the country to Egypt indicates great future possibilities.

Wool is a product from the large numbers of sheep and goats in the herds of the nomads.

Mineral Resources. The asphalt for which this region was known to the ancients was merely the surface indication of great **petroleum** resources underground. Iraq is the second of the three great oil countries of the Middle East. The output of Iraq's three producing fields, one in the north and two along the eastern border, is transported by pipe lines to the eastern Mediterranean coast. The concessions here are operated jointly by British, American, French and Dutch interests.

CITIES OF IRAQ

Name	Type	Population (1947)
Baghdad	Governmental and commercial	552,000
Mosul	Commercial	340,000
Basra	Seaport	206,000
Kirkuk	Commercial	148,000

Cities. **Baghdad,** the capital and largest city of Iraq, is located on the Tigris at the point where the distance between it and the Euphrates—25 miles—is least. The ruins of several large ancient cities nearby testify to the importance of the site. The old city of Baghdad, romantically famous as the city of the "Arabian Nights," is on the west bank, connected by a pontoon bridge with the modern city on the east bank. It is at the crossing of the ancient, east-west trade routes with the route to Mecca from the north. Although the city suffered a great decline along with the general misfortunes of the Mesopotamian region there are good prospects that

Baghdad will partly regain its old place with the growing importance of air and motor caravan transportation. Baghdad is a center of silk and woolen goods manufacturing.

Mosul is the second city of the kingdom, located on the west bank of the Tigris about 230 miles north of Baghdad, at the upstream limit for small-boat travel. Across the river from Mosul is the site of ancient **Nineveh.**

Basra is the chief port of Iraq and the center of the large oasis district of the south. It is located on the Shatt-al-Arab 60 miles upstream from its mouth. The city is thought to have been the home port of Sinbad the Sailor. It is mostly a collection of mud huts and large mosques, a dirty city with a very unpleasant climate. It is newly important as an airport on the Europe-Asia route.

Kirkuk, the fourth city of Iraq, is about 150 miles north of Baghdad and 60 miles from the Iranian border. It is a local commercial and market center situated in the major oil field of the country.

Iraq as a Whole. The future of Iraq hinges on the two items that have already been emphasized—oil and irrigation. Restoration of the irrigation works is essential to the recovery of the country from the low economic status it has so long endured. Oil, through the revenue it affords the government, is the source from which such restoration may be realized. Progress, though slow, has been and is being made. There is an increasing use of oil-powered pumps, which permit reclamation of some land without waiting for the full-scale restoration of the irrigation works. Utilization of the wealth from oil revenues (Iraq receives one-half of the total oil revenues from her output) should enable the country eventually to regain the full use of her basic and relatively inexhaustible resource, the soil. The great question is whether the population will have the patience to wait for the results of a long-term development program.

QUESTIONS. Name the chief crop of the Sudan. Describe one of the two major cities of the western portion of the northern Sudan. What are the major products of the northern Sahara border region? Compare the northern

Sahara and East African regions as to climate, population density, and economic importance.

Distinguish between the Namib and Kalahari deserts. Explain the occurrence of the Southwest African desert-steppe region. What is the principal occupation in Southwest Africa? What important mineral commodities are produced? What is the principal industry of the desert-steppe portion of the Cape of Good Hope Province of the Union of South Africa? What is the leading mineral product of the Cape Province? With what product is Kimberley identified?

Describe the general topography of the Arabian peninsula. What is the economic significance to Saudi Arabia of the fact that it is the "holy land" of Islam? What is the major resource and source of income for Saudi Arabia? Why are some of the minor countries of marginal Arabia important out of all proportion to their size? What is the special significance of the city of Mecca? Of Aden?

What is the meaning of the name Mesopotamia? Compare the geographic features of Mesopotamia with those of the Nile Valley with respect to the early development of civilization in each of the regions. What is the racial composition of the people of Iraq? How does the presence of the Tigris and Euphrates contribute to the success of irrigation in Mesopotamia? What is the major product of Mesopotamia? What unusual irrigation possibility exists along the Shatt-al-Arab? What is the leading mineral product of Iraq? Explain how this product and the problem of irrigation are interrelated factors in the future development of Iraq.

Warm Deserts and Steppes—Other Parts of Asia, Australia, and the Western Hemisphere

D. THE THAR DESERT

General Aspects. The Thar, or Indian, Desert, together with its bordering steppelands, comprises the western portion of the Hindustan plain known as the **Punjab**,[1] a region dominated by the **Indus River** drainage system (Fig. 13.1). It extends on the north and west to the mountainous lands of the **Hindu Kush** and **Sulaiman** ranges, and on the northeast to the **Himalayas.**

The Thar is mostly a sandy desert with many dunes. The driest region is in the south, where the annual precipitation is 10 inches or less. Rainfall increases to the northeast, reaching 30 inches in the foothills of the Himalayas. From June to September the Thar gets some monsoon rain from an orographic rise, and during the winter it gets slight rains from the westerlies (which marks it as essentially a steppe of low-sun rainfall).

An unusual geographic phenomenon associated with the Thar is the **Great Rann of Kutch,** a salt pan, practically at sea level, that covers thousands of square miles south of the Indus delta. During the monsoon period it is flooded by the small streams emptying into it. When dry it has a glistening white surface of salt. The Rann is actually the abandoned delta of a river that formerly flowed across part of the Thar. A natural rearrangement of the drainage system of north-

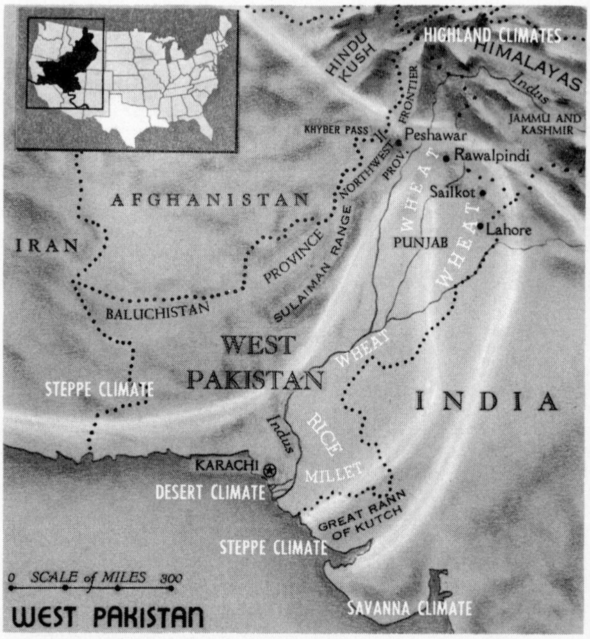

Fig. 13.1—West Pakistan. The inset compares the area of the region with an equivalent area of the United States (states in white).

west India within historical time caused the abandonment of the stream bed and the development of the present area of wasteland.

West Pakistan

The Thar Desert proper lies along the India-Pakistan border. Most of the area of the desert and its surrounding steppeland combined is, however, within West Pakistan, which embraces 300,000 square miles, an area equal

---

[1] The name "Punjab" means "land of the five rivers," referring to the five streams that flow southwest off the Himalayas and unite to form the Indus.

Fig. 13.2—Sukkar Barrage, Sind, Pakistan. This great dam diverts the waters of the Indus for the world's largest unit irrigation project. (Courtesy, Embassy of Pakistan.)

to that of Texas and Louisiana together.

Agriculture. In West Pakistan, as in Iraq and Egypt, an arid territory is traversed by a large river or rivers. West Pakistan has, as a consequence, one of the very large irrigation systems of the world. The five rivers of the Punjab province annually flood in the summer from the melting of the Himalaya snows, so that the inundation canal system of irrigation has traditionally been used. This inefficient method has been and is being supplemented with modern dams and ditch irrigation. The Sind province, in the southeast corner of the country, is the site of the world's largest single irrigation project (Fig. 13.2).

The leading crop of West Pakistan is **wheat,** one-half of which is grown under irrigation in Punjab province. Pakistan is one of the five ranking countries in both production and export of wheat. The irrigation permits "double cropping." The wheat has its green growth in the winter, favored by the cool temperatures and slight rainfall. The spring harvest, in addition to wheat, includes **barley, millet,** and other cereals. Autumn crops are **rice, corn, cotton,** and **sugar cane.**

The industrial side of the Pakistan econ-omy is as yet small, although there is a strong desire to enlarge it. "Cottage industries" and those that can be carried on by small factories still constitute almost the entire industrial establishment. There are small but world-famous industries producing cutlery, surgical instruments, and sporting goods. Light machinery is also manufactured.

CITIES OF WEST PAKISTAN

Name	Type	Population (1951)
Karachi	Governmental and seaport	1,000,000
Lahore	Commercial	850,000
Rawalpindi	Commercial	237,000
Sialkot	Commercial and industrial	168,000
Peshawar	Commercial	152,000

Cities. **Karachi,** the leading city of Pakistan, is the capital and chief port of the country and is located on the western edge of the Indus delta. Its strategic position as the port on the Indian subcontinent nearest to Europe caused it to grow rapidly during World War II, when it was the major transshipment point for war supplies from the west. Karachi is connected by rail with the interior of India and is the terminus of the caravan trade from Afghanistan. It is also one of the leading airports of Asia. Growth after World War II continued to be rapid with the selection of the city as the capital of the new nation and the concomitant large influx of Moslem refugees from Hindu India.

Lahore is the second largest city of Pakistan and the former capital of the undivided Punjab of British India. Though it is only a few miles west of the Indian border, it is the commercial center of Punjab province of Pakistan and is situated in a rich, irrigated agricultural district. It is also a center of light manufacturing and the site of the major Pakistan university and of various technical and other schools.

Rawalpindi is located in the extreme north of Punjab province at the base of the Himalayan foothills. It was formerly the largest British military base in India, an important unit in the defense organization of the Northwestern Frontier against the harassing tribesmen.

Sialkot is a commercial and industrial center 72 miles northeast of Lahore almost on the Kashmir border. It has long been famous for the excellence of the sporting equipment, cutlery, and surgical instruments manufactured there. Special wood and leather go into the making of its tennis and badminton rackets, hockey sticks, and cricket bats.

Peshawar (Fig. 13.3), the capital of the North-West Frontier Province, is just inside the Pakistan border, 11 miles from the Khyber Pass. It is a bazaar and trading city of great strategic importance because of that location. As a holding point in the constant warfare with the Afghan tribesmen it had a good deal of the atmosphere of an old frontier town of the American West.

Pakistan as a Whole. The Dominion of Pakistan was created and took its place in the British Commonwealth on August 15, 1947, along with the newly independent India. It is, literally, a nation created overnight, for there was no preëxisting government, as there was in India. The country owes its existence to religious differences. Its creation came about through the determination of the predominantly Moslem population of the Punjab not to be left to the political mercy of a greatly preponderant Hindu majority in an independent, united India.

The country is the largest Moslem nation in the world; some three-quarters of its 76 million inhabitants are Mohammedans. The racial composition of Pakistan is also somewhat different from that of Independent India. The 20 million inhabitants of the Punjab province are of Indo-Aryan stock, like those of northern India. The 5 million people of the North-West Frontier Province are *Pathans* (Fig. 13.4), inordinately proud, fierce tribesmen who have become through constant practice in harassing the British the world's best guerrilla fighters. **Baluchistan,** a desolate, barren province in the southwest, is the home of one million *Baluchs* (Fig. 13.5), tough fighting tribesmen like the Pathans, to whom they are closely akin. The population of East Bengal is a mixture of Mongoloid and Dravidian stocks (see Chapter 11, p. 182).

Pakistan is a geographical oddity—a state that has no sound natural basis for existence.

Fig. 13.3—Peshawar, Pakistan, Street Scene. (Courtesy, Embassy of Pakistan.)

Fig. 13.4—Pathan Youths, Pakistan. (Courtesy, Embassy of Pakistan.)

Fig. 13.5—Baluchi Shepherd, Baluchistan, Pakistan. (Courtesy, Embassy of Pakistan.)

It is a country of two separate territories 1000 miles apart—one-third the span of the United States—isolated from each other by a belt of foreign territory. Over half the population is concentrated in the small area of East Pakistan, which must depend on West Pakistan to make up the food deficit. The center of national energy, on the other hand, is in West Pakistan, yet it is dependent on the jute exports of East Pakistan for the major portion of all Pakistan's foreign earnings.

It will take a long time to overcome the economic disruption brought about by the emergence of Pakistan as an independent nation. Because of the religious compartmentalization that existed in old India the new Pakistan found itself seriously lacking in technical and skilled labor. This deficiency, plus a power shortage (remediable only through use of the hydropower resources of disputed Kashmir), exerts a strong braking influence on the realization of the ambitious industrialization schemes the Pakistani have projected.

Still, miracles have already been accomplished, and, in general, the outlook is favorable for a modest growth and development. The country has a basic advantage in normally having available an exportable food surplus. Over the long term, however, successful progress would seem to require economic coöperation with India. The logic of such coöperation must eventually prevail between countries geographically so closely interrelated and with complementary economies.

E. THE AUSTRALIAN DESERT

Although desert conditions prevail over large parts of Africa and Asia, no continent is so completely dominated by warm dry climates

as is Australia, for some three-quarters of it is desert or steppe. Indeed, Australia is sometimes referred to as the "dry continent."

Topography. The **Great Australian Desert** is a west-coast trade wind desert that expands eastward over most of the continent (Fig. 13.6). The western portion comprises most of the territory of Western Australia and is a rather level plateau between 500 and 2000 feet in elevation. Here and there isolated mountain groups rise above the general surface, one of these, in the very center of the desert, to nearly 5000 feet elevation. Much of this plateau region is a sand desert and is the driest portion of the Australian desert as a whole. The sand does not occur in typical dunes but in strange, elongate "hills" about 40 feet high, which stretch continuously for hundreds of miles in parallel lines, like gigantic ripples on the land surface. The southern coast in the west central portion is known as the **Nullarbor** (treeless)

Fig. 13.6—Australian Arid Regions. The inset compares the area of the region with that of the United States.

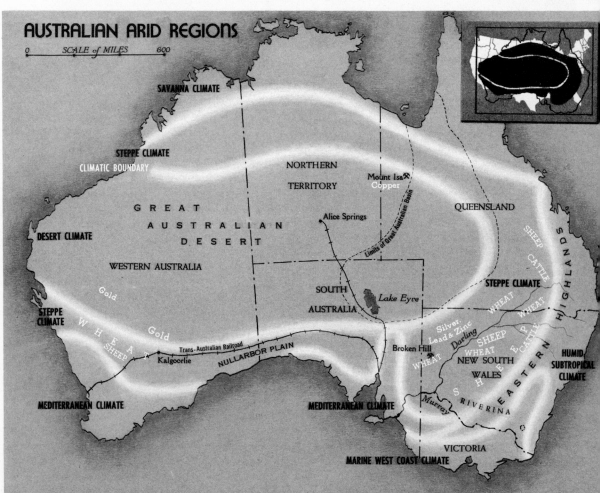

Fig. 13.7—Nullarbor Plain, Southern Australia. The railroad extends in a straight line for 300 miles. (Courtesy, Australian News and Information Bureau.)

Plain, a region of scattered grass clumps (Fig. 13.7).

East of the plateau is a lowland area that extends north and south across the width of the continent. The greater part of both the two political divisions **South Australia** and **Northern Territory** is in this area. Intermittent streams and salt lakes are its characteristic features. The largest lake, **Lake Eyre,** occupies the northern end of a great depression.

To the east of the central lowland the land rises gradually toward the **Eastern Highlands,** which rim the east coast of the continent. Two large artesian basins (i.e., regions with flowing wells due to the pressure of water accumulated underground) occur here. The northern one includes most of the state of **Queensland** and is known as the "Great Australian Basin." It possesses a great underground water supply from so deep a source that the water obtained is hot and in places briny, but not so salt as to be unusable for livestock. The southern basin is in New South Wales and is related to the drainage basin of the **Murray River** and its chief tributary, the **Darling.** The two rivers form the only important drainage system of the continent. The Darling barely escapes classification as intermittent, as it does dry up completely whenever there is a severe drought. The Murray maintains a more uniform flow because it is snow-fed from the mountains to the southeast.

Vegetation and Climate. Australian vegetation is unlike the typical desert types encountered in other continents, for Australia's plant life as well as animal life is peculiar to that continent. The predominant plant form is *Eucalyptus,* which occurs in all forms from scrub growth in the drier regions to forests of large trees in humid areas. The grasses of the Australian steppelands are, however, like those of other deserts.

The steppe borders of the Australian interior desert correspond to those of the deserts previously discussed. The northern side (Southern Hemisphere) gets the savanna rains, the southern side the occasional storms of the westerlies. The central eastern portion of the steppes is an expression of the rain shadow of the Eastern Highlands, as the trades come in from the southeast. Accordingly, the most southerly portions of the steppe are technically cool-climate rather than warm-climate grasslands but are included here with the rest of the Australian steppe in order to simplify discussion.

With so much of Australia possessing an arid climate it is natural that rainfall or the lack of it dominates man's activities and must be the governing geographic factor in the utilization of the continent. The topography and productivity of the soil are quite suitable for the maintenance of a dense population supported by agriculture, but, lacking precipitation, the true desert portion is unoccupied and so barren that it has been referred to as "the dead heart of Australia." Even in the more humid borders of the steppelands the rainfall is so erratic and undependable that severe drought years occur with discouraging frequency, many of them in succession.

Native People. Like the Kalahari and its neighboring desert region in Africa, the Great Australian Desert and its steppelands are inhabited by a primitive people, the Australian aborigines (Fig. 13.8). Although they are often referred to as the "black-fellows" because they are dark-skinned, they are not Negroes. Many authorities consider them to be the most primitive of the living races of man. They are nomadic hunters and collectors who eke out a meager existence from the wastelands. Their numbers were so few

Fig. 13.8—Australian Aborigines. In central Australia they still hunt with spear and boomerang. (Courtesy, Australian News and Information Bureau.)

that they had no effect on the colonization and development of Australia as a white man's continent.

The Grazing Industries. The vast arid regions, despite their barrenness, dominate the economy of Australia. The leading exports all come from the desert and steppe. As might be expected, the steppelands, especially on the east and west, are **sheep** and **cattle** country.

The wide fluctuation in the volume of rainfall is, however, a major deterrent. When there is less than 10 inches of rain a year it is too dry even for sheep; above that figure, the more rain, the more sheep that can be pastured on a given area of land. Early settlers who pushed too far into the arid country lost sheep by the millions in consequence of a series of devastating droughts.

Sheep have many attributes which fit them for existence in the Australian steppelands. They are at home on both rough and level ground; they can travel far (either in search of pasture or to market) without losing weight; they need little water and can feed where grass is too sparse to support cattle. On the other hand, the sheep is primarily a cold-climate animal; when temperatures are

high it tends to lose its wool and grow only hair. In Australia this tendency is counteracted by the constant importation of fresh breeding stock from the cooler regions of the world. Sheep are excellent in general for utilization of lands unsuitable for agriculture, either through deficient rainfall, infertility, or both. (Indeed, if the rainfall is over 30 inches yearly sheep are likely to contract foot disease.) Finally, sheep raising is feasible in remote places because the products of the industry, as wool or as mutton on the hoof, may be profitably transported farther than cattle products.

The size of Australia's sheep industry is impressive. There are some 123 millions of the animals in the country, or approximately one-sixth of all the sheep in the world. **Wool,** of course, is the big product, and accounts for half the total value of exports. Australia's output is more than one-quarter of the world total, and the country is the major wool exporter. **Mutton** is also important but is far overshadowed by the "golden fleece" which brings the country so much revenue.

Almost one-half of all the sheep in Australia are pastured in the Darling River Basin. The other great concentrations of sheep are in the eastern and western steppe regions.

The sheep industry, like the cattle industry, has its pests. Wild rabbits are the chief menace because of the food they eat (see Chapter 11, p. 199). It is ironical that in some years the value of the rabbit skins and meat exported has exceeded that of the wool and mutton! In the central lowland the wild dog of Australia is also a predatory pest.

In a reversal of the relation found in most countries, **cattle** are raised on land unsuitable for sheep. They are found in scattered numbers all through the steppelands, but more on the humid border than elsewhere.

Agriculture. As the yield of the sheep industry dominates the animal production of Australia, so **wheat,** the great grain crop of the steppe, dominates the agriculture of the country. Over two-thirds of the cultivated land in Australia is devoted to wheat, the second-ranking export product. The country is fifth or sixth in world production, third in export. In normal years over one-half the crop is shipped abroad.

The wheat lands are centered on the western slopes of the Eastern Highlands and in southwest Australia, with a special concentration in the Murray-Darling Basin. Like all Australian rural activity wheat raising is perennially subject to the danger of drought. Much of the drier land may be utilized only through careful dry-farming methods. As a consequence, only about one-third of the total wheat land is under cultivation at any one time.

The prize land of the Murray Basin is a tract known as **Riverina** (Fig. 13.9), a fertile flatland farmed with the aid of irrigation. The flow of the Murray as a source of irrigation water has been the subject of frequent disputes between the Australian states competing for the rights to its diversion.

In southwest Australia the wheat land is a belt, some 100 miles broad, inland from the coast and on the edge of the plateau. At its interior margin it merges with the grazing lands.

Mineral Products. **Gold** is the most ubiquitous mineral product of the desert and steppe regions of Australia, as well as of the country as a whole. In the late nineteenth century Australia was the scene of a series of great gold rushes that brought in a flood of fortune seekers from all over the world and gave the Australian his national nickname of "Digger." Although gold is found in every section of the country, almost three-quarters of the total gold production is from a single district in Western Australia.

Silver, lead, and **zinc** are all produced from one of the greatest ore bodies of the world at Broken Hill, on the Darling River in northwestern New South Wales. It has produced nearly $1 billion worth of metals since it was discovered in 1883. A second great producer of these metals, as well as **copper,** is at Mount Isa in western Queensland. Owing chiefly to the output of these two mines Australia is among the first three producers of lead and zinc in the world and is one of the leading exporters of the two metals.

Fig. 13.9—Riverina Country of the Murray Basin, Australia. Two-year-old merino stud rams. (Courtesy, Australian News and Information Bureau.)

Other minerals from the desert and steppe-lands include **tungsten** and **tin,** the output of which is significant but not large.

Transportation. The railroad system of Australia reflects the distribution of population and human activity on the continent. Those lines within the arid and semiarid lands were with two exceptions primarily built to transport their products to the coast. This has been especially beneficial to the grazing industries by providing rail outlets they could not themselves support.

One of the exceptions is the Trans-Australian Railroad, built in 1917 across the south coast of the continent between the settled southeast and the southwest. It was the political answer to uninformed popular demand. The freight and passenger revenues cannot pay for the route's construction costs because of the hundreds of miles of wasteland it traverses in South Australia in the Nullarbor region.

The second exception is a similar development that was never completed. It extends from the Lake Eyre region north to a remote hamlet in the center of the desert—**Alice Springs.** The original intention was to connect it with the short line that extends south from Darwin (see Chapter 11, p. 200), but since the folly of the earlier east-west transcontinental line has become apparent it is doubtful whether the north-south, equally extravagant, line will ever be finished.

CITIES OF THE AUSTRALIAN DESERT AND STEPPE

Name	State	Type	Population (1954)
Broken Hill	New South Wales	Mining	31,000
Kalgoorlie	Western Australia	Mining	10,000

Cities. **Broken Hill** is located in the Darling River Basin in northern New South Wales about 35 miles from the South Australia border. It is exclusively a mining town. Smelters were once in operation adjacent to the mines, but these were shifted to a coastal site because of the shortage of water.

Kalgoorlie lies in the desert in the center of the most important gold field of Australia. Its water problem is even more pressing than that of Broken Hill, as its supply must be obtained from great distances. Kalgoorlie is the only town of any size between the two terminals of the Trans-Australian Railroad.

F. THE ATACAMA-PERUVIAN DESERT

General Aspects. The west coast of South America between 5° and 30° south latitude is the site of the Atacama-Peruvian Desert (Fig. 13.10). This stretch of some 2000 miles comprises the northern two-fifths of Chile and the entire coastal region of Peru. It is the product of the towering **Andes**, which form an all-too-perfect rain barrier to the southeast trades, and of the cold, north-flowing **Humboldt Current** (also known as the Peru Current). The Atacama is a trade wind desert caused, rather singularly, by mountains on the west coast rather than the east coast of a continent. As the trade winds here first cross almost the width of a continent and then surmount lofty mountains, the aridity of the west coast in the lee of the ranges is extreme. Moreover, it is intensified by the offshore cold current and the locally prevailing west, i.e. onshore, winds. These winds, accordingly, blow from over the cool ocean water to warmer lands and so are evaporating, not precipitating.

This combination of circumstances gives rise to the driest region on earth, one which approaches nearest to the popular conception of deserts as absolutely dry, absolutely barren areas. Many places in the Atacama province of Chile have no rain whatsoever for 5- to 10-year periods. At one recording station less than one-half inch of rain fell in a 19-year period!

Not all of even the Atacama Desert is that dry, however. The center of aridity is about 100 miles south of the Chile-Peru border. Rainfall increases slightly both north and south of this section. (With a starting figure of about zero an increase to two inches a year is large!) The focal region, as might be expected, is quite devoid of plant life. Bare rock and gravel surfaces extend for miles on end. For a distance of 500 miles from north to south only one stream maintains its flow from the mountains all the way to the sea, and then only in years of heavy snowfall in the mountains.

Because of the cold Humboldt Current the average temperature is cooler than that of most trade wind deserts. In fact, most if not all of the west coast of South America has lower temperatures than equivalent latitudes on the east coast of this continent. West-coast winters are damp and even cloudy; fog often occurs some miles inland.

Because the Andes are close to the sea along all western South America, the desert is not very broad. In the Atacama region there is an abrupt rise from sea level to a small coastal range of 4000 to 6000 feet elevation. Inland from this is a region of terraces and basins, comparatively level, which ends in the foothills of the Andes. The great mountains themselves here average 13,000 feet in altitude. The desert in general ranges be-

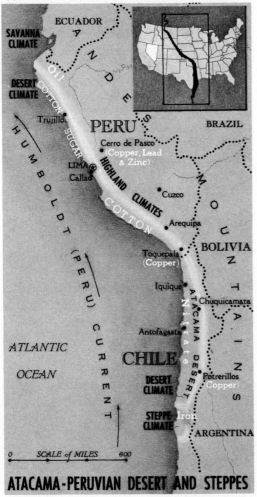

Fig. 13.10—Atacama-Peruvian Desert and Steppes. The inset compares the area of the region with the approximately equal area of the state of Nevada.

tween 3000 and 5000 feet above sea level.

The oases of this desert are few in number and of minor importance compared to those of the other warm deserts. There are three types: the irrigated valleys on the northern border of the Atacama proper, a rather large irrigated district on the south border of the desert region (which produces much of the food for the desert inhabitants), and oases developed on the alluvial fans along the foot of the mountains (through well borings or by irrigation ditches bringing water from wells higher up in the mountains).

Countries of the Atacama-Peruvian Desert Region

1. NORTHERN CHILE (THE ATACAMA DESERT)

Climatically, the Chilean (Atacama) section of the desert is far more unpleasant than the Peruvian, yet the very climatic defect that has made this region the world's driest desert has also brought about its endowment with valuable mineral wealth. A part of the Atacama between 5 and 50 miles wide, 450 miles long, and between 4000 and 7500 feet in altitude is the site of the world's only commercially significant deposits of **nitrate.** One of the most important of all plant fertilizers, nitrate "ore" is extremely soluble in water. The Atacama deposits owe their existence to the great aridity of the desert. Nowhere else on earth are conditions sufficiently dry for such accumulation.

The nitrate occurs as a salt surface-crust known as *caliche* which ranges from a few inches to more than 10 feet thick. The *caliche* is blasted loose and taken to the *oficina,* or plant, where the nitrate is leached out and reprecipitated in collecting tanks. The mining and processing are simple enough, but to carry out the operations in such a region requires fantastic effort. Every item, from food and water to fuel and construction materials, must be imported. To supply meat, cattle are driven over the summits of the Andes from Argentina!

For many years Chile had a complete monopoly on this commodity for which there was a world-wide demand. To a much greater degree nitrate was to Chile what coffee is to Brazil and wool is to Australia at present. As much as 80 percent of the total Chilean government revenue was derived annually from an export tax on nitrate. This comfortable state of affairs was rudely upset, however, by the invention and world-wide utilization in the 1920's of cheap processes for the manufacture of "synthetic" nitrogen, i.e., fixation of nitrogen from the air. The Great Depression of the 1930's brought about a complete collapse of the Chilean nitrate industry, and with it political chaos and instability. At present less than 10 percent of the world's nitrate needs are being supplied by Chile, yet hundreds of millions of tons of rich nitrate *caliche* are still in the Atacama.

A valuable by-product of the nitrate industry is **iodine,** 90 percent of the supply of which formerly came from Chile. But this near monopoly, too, has been lost; the American market now gets its iodine as a by-product of the domestic oil industry.

Although the history of those Atacama mineral industries with deposits resulting from climatic factors has been unfortunate, the decline of nitrate was offset by the rise in the importance of **copper** deposits unrelated to the desert conditions. Chile is the world's second producer and leading exporter of this valuable metal. A large portion of the world's known reserves is within its borders. Almost everything about Chile's copper industry may be described in superlatives. Thus, the world's greatest single copper deposit is located at **Chuquicamata** (Fig. 13.11), on the western slope of the Andes at an altitude of almost 10,000 feet. Here a body of copper ore two miles by one-half mile in area and of unknown depth is being mined on a gigantic scale by an American corporation. A second important copper development is at **Potrerillos,** 300 miles south of Chuquicamata and 90 miles inland.

The third major mineral exploitation of the arid region of Chile is a large **iron** mine near the southern border of the desert, also developed by American capital. At one time it was the largest iron mine in South America. Sizable tonnages are shipped annually to blast furnaces in northeastern United States.

Besides nitrate there is an unusual non-metallic resource, fossil guano (deposits of bird droppings since turned to rock rich in phosphorus).

Because of this great mineral wealth and the activity connected with its exploitation, the Atacama Desert is comparatively well

2. COASTAL PERU

General Aspects. The Peruvian portion of the Atacama-Peruvian desert comprises less than a quarter of the area of the country but is economically the dominant region. Although Peru is not a desert country in the same sense as Saudi Arabia and Egypt, geographically it is as a whole appropriately considered to be within the warm arid climates.

Fig. 13.11—Chuquicamata Copper Mine, in the Atacama Desert, Chile. The dimensions of the mine, an open pit, indicate the vastness of the deposit. (Courtesy, the Anaconda Company.)

populated. The coast is dotted with minor seaports, all maintained as export points for the mineral products of the land behind them and as the landing places for the imports necessary to support the mining populations and the supplies for the mines themselves.

The coastal desert region is a strip 1400 miles long varying between 50 and 100 miles in width. Except for a minute area on the extreme north it can be said to extend the entire length of the Peruvian coast. Across this desert strip 52 small streams flow from the highlands immediately behind. The valley floor of each of these is, in effect, an oasis. The desert lands are the western slopes of the low coastal range. The coastline is practically straight, with only one or two good ports in all its 1400 miles. As in the Atacama region, however, numerous small harbors dot its entire length.

Like the Atacama region the Peruvian desert, also, is cool and often damp near the coast. The Humboldt Current is the major climatic factor. The meteorological balance is so delicate here that a minor variation in the velocity or position of the current can produce torrential rains.

Inland from the coastal desert is the "Sierra" or mountain region, the country of the Andes. This is a region of plateaus, deep valleys, and lofty cordilleras but contains two-thirds of the population. The climate, both in temperature and in precipitation, varies greatly, according to altitude and local wind conditions.

Agricultural Products. Approximately 80 percent of the Peruvian population is dependent on agriculture, but only some 10 to 15 percent of the total arable land is cultivated. The leading cash crop is **cotton,** grown in the irrigated valleys of the coast. The most valuable variety, a long-fibered, crinkly type, is indigenous to Peru. It is grown on large estates (*haciendas*), giving high yields at low cost, so that Peru ranks second to Brazil as a cotton producer in South America. The special qualities of Peruvian cotton, which make it highly prized in the manufacture of certain textiles, give it a special significance in the world market.

The second cash crop is **sugar cane,** also grown under irrigation on large estates in the coastal valleys. Production is concentrated in a few valleys in the north. The yield per acre is higher than that in Cuba (see Chapter 10, p. 175), but this advantage is offset by the longer growing season of 18 to 22 months needed to produce a crop in Peru.

The subsistence crop of the coast is **rice,** grown in only two of the irrigated valleys. **Corn,** on the other hand, is the staple crop of the country as a whole, grown everywhere from the coastal valleys to the high slopes of the Sierra. **Potatoes,** the second subsistence crop, are grown in the cooler climates. Both plants are considered to be indigenous to Peru (i.e., Peru is one of the regions of the New World in which they grew wild before they were cultivated). Barley and wheat are grown at high altitudes.

Grazing is the principal occupation in the Sierra. Not only sheep but such indigenous animals as the domesticated *alpaca* and *llama* and the wild *vicuña* (Fig. 13.12) produce the **wool** which ranks as the third "agricultural" product. That of the vicuña is world famous for its high quality and is

Fig. 13.12—A Vicuña. (Courtesy, The Peruvian Embassy.)

the most expensive of all textile materials.

Mineral Products. The leading mineral product in value is **petroleum.** The oil fields occur in the northwest corner of the country; they are an important domestic fuel source but account for only an infinitesimal portion of world production. The area has not, however, been either fully explored or developed as yet.

Second in value and the most important of the metallic mineral products is **copper.** The center of mining is at **Cerro de Pasco,** in the

Sierra about midway between the northern and southern borders of the country, some 100 miles inland. Mining activity has been in progress at this site for three centuries. The altitude at Cerro de Pasco is over 14,000 feet, so high that only Indians can endure work in the mines. The foreign technicians and the managerial staff must come down to the coast for periodic rests to recover from the ill effects of the rarefied air. A second large copper development was begun in 1955 at **Toquepala,** in the southern corner of the country.

After copper in terms of the value of the annual production are **gold, silver,** and **lead.** At the time of the Spanish conquest gold and silver were the great products of the country. Peru is today second only to the United States as a producer of **vanadium.** Still other minerals recovered are **zinc, tungsten,** and **bismuth,** produced, along with the previously mentioned mineral products except vanadium, in the Cerro de Pasco district.

Iron occurs in considerable deposits not yet developed. Coal, mostly anthracite, is also found in several places. Lastly, Peru is a source of guano, collected from small islands off the coast that are the nesting places of great numbers of sea birds.

CITIES OF NORTHERN CHILE AND PERU

Name	Country	Type	Population
Antofagasta	Chile	Seaport	62,000 (1952)
Iquique	Chile	Seaport	40,000 (1952)
Lima	Peru	Governmental	835,000 (1950)
Arequipa	Peru	Commercial	97,000 (1950)
Callao	Peru	Seaport	88,000 (1950)
Cuzco	Peru	Commercial	56,000 (1950)
Trujillo	Peru	Commercial	48,000 (1950)

Cities. **Antofagasta** is the largest port of the Atacama region and the chief center of the nitrate and copper export trade. This large community, in the middle of the desert coastline, is supplied with water by a pipe line 230 miles long. In 1948, after 27 years of spasmodic construction work, the city was linked with northern Argentina by a railroad across the Andes that crosses the Continental Divide at an altitude of 15,760 feet.

Iquique, a center of nitrate export halfway between Antofagasta and the Peru border, is at the center of the most arid part of the Atacama Desert.

Fig. 13.13—Spanish Colonial Architecture. Front of church in Lima, Peru. (Courtesy, The Peruvian Embassy.)

Lima is the capital and largest city of Peru, situated eight miles inland on the desert midway between the north and south borders of the country. The city is thoroughly Spanish in tradition and aspect for unlike most of the South American capitals dating from the Spanish conquest it was not founded on the site of an older native city. The metropolis of Lima has a very pleasant look owing to the preservation of so many specimens of Spanish colonial architecture (Fig. 13.13). Its suburbs are the site of the only industrial concentration in Peru, chiefly light industries. Its University of San Marcos claims to be the oldest in the Western Hemisphere.

Arequipa is located in the southern part of Peru about 50 miles inland. It is an unusually beautiful city in a very scenic setting—a valley at an altitude of 7500 feet surrounded by volcanic peaks. Extensive use in building construction is made of a local pink and white volcanic stone, so that Arequipa is often called "the White City." An invigorating climate and exceptionally clear air greatly enhance the attractiveness of life

Fig. 13.14—Peruvian Indian Mother and Baby. (Courtesy, The Peruvian Embassy.)

there. The city is the center of the wool trade of southern Peru and has a few light industries.

Callao, the port of Lima and the major port of Peru, has one of the few good harbors on the west coast of South America. It is also part of the light industrial complex around Lima, eight miles to the northwest.

Cuzco, some 200 miles north of Arequipa, is situated at an altitude of over 11,000 feet in a valley in the high Andes. It was the ancient capital of the Inca Empire, and is a fascinating city, dominated by great Inca ruins. Thus it retains the atmosphere of the old Indian city despite the presence of many Spanish buildings. Its population is chiefly Indian and mestizo. Cuzco is the commercial center of a large region of southern Peru, but trade is handicapped by lack of adequate transportation.

Trujillo, 300 miles north of Lima, is located four miles inland from the Pacific. Like Lima, it is a Spanish-founded city. It is the commercial center of the chief sugar-producing region and is served by a port eight miles distant.

Peru as a Whole. The Republic of Peru comprises some 500,000 square miles, about the same area as that of the seven west-north-central states (Minnesota, Iowa, Missouri, Kansas, Nebraska, and the Dakotas). The population of Peru is 9 million, of which about half are white or mestizo, half Indian (Fig. 13.14). There is a great social and economic gulf between the Indians, whose lot, formerly miserable, has been considerably improved by recent law, and the few whites of Spanish origin, who constitute the ruling class and who live mostly in the coastal cities.

For an understanding of present-day conditions and problems in Peru it is necessary to take a brief look at the country's history. In the tenth century the Inca civilization began its development, centered in Peru and later including much of the area now included in Ecuador, Bolivia, and Chile. This civilization was one of the greatest in the Western Hemisphere. It was restricted to the forbidding environment of the plateaus and uplands of the Andes (Fig. 13.15) but, by dint of prodigious efforts, a tight social organization, and the construction of irrigation and other public works, maintained a population far greater than that now living in the same territories.

This great civilization was completely overthrown within a period of five years by a Spanish army of about 400 in the first half of the sixteenth century. The empire crumbled like a house of cards and the Spaniards

Fig. 13.15—Inca Ruins, Machupicchu, Peru. (Courtesy, The Peruvian Embassy.)

proceeded to loot the country of its stores of precious metals and to enslave the population for work in the mines. As a consequence the irrigation works and agriculture were neglected and the country was impoverished.

Under Spanish rule Peru was a viceroyalty, the highest-ranking colonial adminstration in the Spanish New World. The descendants of the local Spanish nobility have never forgotten this position of eminence of their ancestors and remain unusually proud and haughty. The Indians still cling to the Inca culture in their daily life.

Independence from Spanish rule was gained in 1824. Fifty years later Peru experienced another disaster when, in the War of the Pacific, fought by Peru and Bolivia against Chile, it lost control of the nitrate provinces. The defeat by the superior military and naval forces of Chile was crushing; the country lost one of its most valuable resources and collapsed into a state of economic ruin until the turn of the century.

In the twentieth century, however, there has been a recovery due to the investment of foreign capital in the mineral industries. Boundary disputes with Ecuador, Colombia, Bolivia, and Chile continued nevertheless to plague the country. The Chile dispute was not finally settled until 1929, after 46 years of bickering.

Despite the handicaps imposed by lack of transportation facilities and the hardships of life in the Sierra and Amazon Basin sections of the country, the initial stimulus provided by the mineral developments under foreign capital since World War I has finally led to developments locally initiated and supported. Typical of this encouraging turn of events is the hydroelectric project completed in 1949 on one of the small coastal streams in central Peru. Here exceedingly cheap electric power is being supplied for industrial enterprises of various kinds.

With coal, hydropower, and oil in addition to the great mineral wealth of the Sierra, Peru has the resource potential to raise the standard of living of its inhabitants and to use its great natural endowment for their benefit. For the first time this is at least possible.

QUESTIONS. Explain the climatic basis of the Thar desert and steppe region. Why has it been possible to develop irrigation so extensively in West Pakistan? What are the leading crops? What is the racial composition of the people of Pakistan? Why is Pakistan a "geographic anomaly"? Explain why the commercial location of Karachi is favorable.

Describe the general topography of the Great Australian Desert. Describe its vegetation and climate. Compare the significance of the native population of Australia with that of the natives of southern Africa. What is the major industry of the dry regions of Australia? Explain why this industry is so well fitted to the Australian environment. What are the major products of this industry? What is the major crop of the region? What mineral is found throughout the region? Where is the major center of its production? Name two important lead-zinc districts of the region. Discuss the development and significance of the railroad system in the arid and semiarid sections of Australia.

Give the reasons for the existence of the Atacama-Peruvian desert-steppe region. Describe the topography. Why is the Atacama unusually valuable for a desert? What is *caliche*? What metal is produced in very large quantities at Chuquicamata?

Describe the climatic and topographic pattern in Peru. Why is Peruvian cotton signifi-

cant in the world market despite the modest size of the crop? Where is the cotton grown? What other crops are grown in the same localities? What are the two major subsistence crops? Name three animals in addition to the sheep that are important sources of wool in Peru. What are the two major mineral products? What was the name of the great civilization that existed in this part of South America at the time of the Spanish conquest? What are the major handicaps to Peruvian development? What is the major activity of Antofagasta? Contrast the setting, tradition, and population of Lima and Cuzco.

G. THE SONORA-CHIHUAHUAN AND SOUTHWESTERN UNITED STATES DESERT

Extent and Climate. Of all the warm desert-steppe regions that of northern Mexico and

Fig. 13.16—Sonora-Chihuahuan and U.S. Desert and Steppe Region. The inset compares the area of the region with an equivalent area of the United States (states in white).

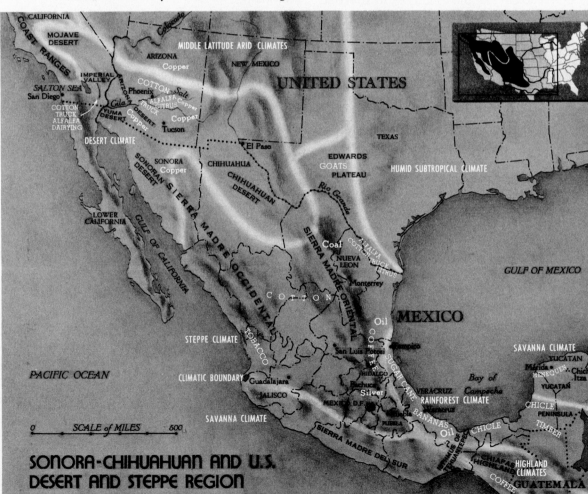

SONORA-CHIHUAHUAN AND U.S. DESERT AND STEPPE REGION

southwestern United States is the most difficult to describe concisely yet informingly. Although it is as much a geographic unit as the deserts discussed above it has never been known by a single, inclusive name.

The heart of this desert is in the state of **Sonora,** in northwestern Mexico (Fig. 13.16). The entire peninsula of **Lower California,** across the Gulf of California from the **Sonoran Desert,** is almost as arid but has never been known by a desert name. In north central Mexico another portion of the desert in the state of **Chihuahua** is called the **Chihuahuan Desert.**

The United States portion of the desert is a small part of a large region formerly known as "The Great American Desert." The term at one time referred to almost all the United States west of the Mississippi, for the land was either semiarid or arid, and unproductive (hence "desert"). The "Great American Desert" gradually shrank, however, as new agricultural techniques pushed farming and grazing activity farther south and west. The true desert area actually comprises only southeastern California, southern Arizona and New Mexico, and southwestern Texas. Different portions of it are known as the "Arizona Desert," the "San Bernardino Desert," the "Colorado Desert," and the "Gila Desert."

The warm steppe border of this desert region is entirely within Mexico except for a small area in south central Texas. The northern border is every where a cold, dry climatic region.

The Sonora proper is a true trade wind desert, situated in the rain shadow of the Sierra Madre Occidental, on the west coast of the continent. The United States portion is mostly the product of the subtropical high-pressure belt (see Chapter 6, p. 95), in which it remains throughout the year. The **Sierra Nevada** and **Coast Ranges** to the west also serve to keep any stray moisture-laden winds from bringing precipitation to the region from the Pacific.

Topography. The Sonora occupies a west-sloping plain between the Sierra Madre Occidental and the Gulf of California and extends about 1000 miles southeast from the United States border. The Chihuahuan portion is situated on the central plateau of Mexico between the two Sierra Madre ranges. The United States portion is in the southern part of the **Basin and Range province,** a topographic division of the western United States characterized by short mountain ranges that rise above the flat floors of both wide and narrow basins between them.

In the entire arid region there are only two streams of consequence, the **Colorado** and the **Rio Grande.** South from the Colorado River for 500 miles along the west coast of Mexico only two permanent streams cross the Sonora, and in the 700 miles between the Pacific Ocean and the source of the Rio Grande only five permanent streams of any size cross the international boundary.

Economic Activity. Human activity in this region is limited to the three occupations of stock raising, irrigation agriculture, and mining, all carried on in separate, isolated localities. The difference north and south of the border is merely in the level of technology, a circumstance indicating the dominance of geographic factors. In the United States, for example, great irrigation projects permit the cultivation of cotton and vegetables on a large scale, with highly developed, expensive techniques. In Mexico small irrigated patches are cultivated less efficiently yet for the same market, the United States.

The aridity has also been a determining factor in the system of landholding. The value of land for grazing purposes depends on accessibility to water, but the water holes and springs are far apart. The landholdings have thus tended to be large—ranches and *haciendas* in Mexico are as much as 500,000 to one million acres in extent.

Countries of the Sonora-Chihuahuan-United States Desert Region

1. SOUTHWESTERN UNITED STATES

Agriculture. As in all warm arid and semi-arid regions, agriculture in the southwestern United States is completely dependent on irrigation. But unlike Pakistan or Egypt, where irrigation is general over wide continuous areas, Arabia and the Sahara, where irrigation is carried on in oases, or Peru, where irrigation is limited to narrow strips along small streams, this region has irrigation based on huge, widely separated projects that involve the damming of great rivers and the distribution of the water through large, elaborate canal systems. There are many such projects in the Southwest of varying size and importance.

The **Imperial Valley** is just north of the international boundary in south central California. Much of it is below sea level. It is a portion of the Gulf of California that was cut off by the delta of the Colorado River as it grew across the Gulf. In a desert climate, the trapped portion of the Gulf evaporated, leaving an arid valley with a floor of highly fertile deltaic deposits.

The valley was transformed into an oasis of almost unbelievable productivity by the construction of an irrigation canal from the Colorado River through the desert south of the international boundary and up into the valley. This was later superseded by the "All-American Canal," wholly within the United States.

An unusual feature of the valley is the **Salton Sea,** an accidental product of irrigation activity. During a particularly great flood of the Colorado the river broke into the main irrigation canal and flooded the valley, forming a temporary large lake. The lowest portion of the lake has persisted, fed by the surplus irrigation water from the surrounding farms. The danger of floods has since been largely eliminated through the construction of numerous dams along the Colorado.

The Imperial Valley has been called the "American Egypt." Its climate, except for the burning hot summers, is excellent, with long, mild winters that allow year-round production. It has the most sunshine during the year of any place in the United States. Like Egypt, it is a producer of **long-staple cotton,** an important crop of the valley. It is also known for its high yield of **alfalfa,** a very nutritious cattle feed that is the basis of

a **dairy** industry. As the plant grows here the year round, Imperial Valley farmers harvest five or six crops of alfalfa a year compared with the two or three harvested elsewhere in the United States.

The valley is also famous as a "truck farming" area, producing garden **vegetables** (especially **lettuce**) and **melons** (it is the greatest melon-producing area of the world). Grapes (Fig. 13.17), figs, and some citrus fruits are also grown.

Almost equal to the Imperial Valley in fame and productivity is the **Salt River** irrigation project in south central Arizona. Here also **cotton** and **alfalfa** are produced prolifically, as are **vegetables** and **citrus fruits.**

A third large irrigation area is the **Lower Rio Grande Valley** in southwest Texas. More than 50 different crops are grown, including the ubiquitous **cotton, alfalfa,** and **vegetables.** The vegetables are shipped to the populous Northeast and Middle West during the winter and spring, when there are no local supplies in those regions. The lower Rio Grande Valley is also the largest center of **grapefruit** production in the United States. A particular climate and soil combination there is ideal for the production of pink grapefruit.

Other irrigation projects of large size are located on the **Gila River** (a tributary of the Colorado) in Arizona and on the **Upper Rio Grande** in New Mexico.

The grazing industry is represented by a scattering of **beef cattle** over all the south and west of Texas and all of southern Arizona and New Mexico. This is a relatively minor area in relation to the total production of beef cattle in the United States. Moreover, there is chronic overgrazing of the range, which kills off the grass and results in a progressive reduction in the amount of pasturage.

The **Edwards Plateau,** in southwest Texas on the border of the steppe country, is the greatest center of the **goat** industry of the United States. **Mohair** is the chief product. Sheep and cattle also graze on this upland.

Mining. The Arizona-New Mexico portion

Fig. 13.17—Imperial Valley, California. Vineyard of Tokay grapes grown under irrigation. (Courtesy, U.S. Bureau of Reclamation.)

of the warm arid land is the site of great **copper** deposits. Although singly they are not in the same class as the Chuquicamata deposit, together they make Arizona the leading copper state in the United States, the major copper producer of the world.

Other mineral products of Arizona and New Mexico include gold, silver, iron, molybdenum, uranium, vanadium, lead, zinc, and potash.

2. Mexico

Although Mexico, the southern neighbor of the United States, is here discussed as a whole with the countries of warm dry climates, it is like Peru in not fitting neatly into the category. In Mexico the arid climates of the northern portion give way southward to typical Central American rainforest regions on the east coast, savanna on the west coast, and complex vertical zoning in the central highlands. But since the more populous areas and the centers of economic activity are in the north and central portions of the country Mexico is best considered as a country of the warm desert-steppe climates.

Topography. Mexico's 764,000 square miles (it is almost three times the size of Texas) encompass a variety of topographic forms. The major unit of relief is the large central plateau (see Chapter 2, p. 25), a rather level intermontane surface that rises from an altitude of 4000 feet at the northern boundary to more than 7500 feet at its southern end. Two-thirds of the cities and two-thirds of the total population are located on this plateau. Its soil is rich, a mixture of volcanic debris (Fig. 13.18) and sediments washed down from the bordering mountains.

Much of the plateau has a steppe climate, with characteristic undependable rainfall

Fig. 13.18—Paricutin Volcano in Eruption, 1943. A volcanic vent on the western border of the Mexican plateau that built up a cone over 1000 feet high in 10 weeks. All the area where the men stand is deeply covered with volcanic debris. (Otto Brehme, from Three Lions.)

which comes, however, during the summer growing season, when it is most needed. The climate in general is delightful. May, the hottest month, has an average temperature of 65° F.; the coolest month, January, averages 54° F. Although it gets hot in the sun during the summer it is always cool in the shade because of the altitude.

The plateau is bordered on the east and west by the two Sierra Madre ranges, which rise some 2500 feet above the plateau and descend an average of 9000 feet to the sea on their coastal sides. The eastern range is somewhat lower and less rugged than that on the west. The vertical climatic zoning which these ranges exhibit has been recognized by the Mexicans in popular terms that

Fig. 13.19—Market Scene in Tierra Caliente, Mexico. Papaya for sale, peon customers. *Photo., Otto Brehme.*

divide the vertical range into three zones: the **Tierra Caliente** (hot land) from sea level to 3000 feet (Fig. 13.19); the **Tierra Templada** (temperate land) between 3000 and 7000 feet; and the **Tierra Fria** (cold land) over 7000 feet. This zoning is especially well developed on the east side at the southern end of the Sierra Madre Oriental.

South of the central plateau is a mountain range known as the **Sierra Madre del Sur** (south), whose peaks are lower than the mighty volcanic cones which mark the southern border of the plateau.

East of this range the lowlands of the **Isthmus of Tehuantepec** and the **Yucatan Peninsula** are encountered. The latter is a low plain almost completely lacking a soil cover and divided between a rainforest southern part and a savanna northern part. Lowlands continue as a border belt northward along both coasts. Those on the west are of little value; their climate is too dry and the land too rough.

The **Chiapas Highlands** in the extreme southeast of the country comprise the remaining topographic division of Mexico. This is an isolated region inhabited by Indians who preserve almost unmodified the customs and traditions of their pre-Spanish ancestors.

The People. About one-third of Mexico's population of 26 million people are pure-blooded Indians. Mestizos constitute approximately 60 per cent of the total; white descendants of the Spanish conquerors are a small minority. The pure Indians are descended from two ancient peoples, the *Aztecs* and the *Mayas.* The Aztecs developed a civilization on the central plateau that was in its flower when Cortez and his little company of soldiers abruptly terminated its existence. The Mayas built a civilization in Yucatan and the neighboring foothills of the Chiapas that antedates the Aztecs. Dating from the fourth century A.D., it had practically disappeared at the time of the Spanish conquest for reasons not yet fully understood.

The old cultures are still evident in the present-day customs and traditions of the Indians. The Spanish influence, on the other hand, is dominant among the upper-class Mexican whites (Fig. 13.20).

The great mass of the population is engaged in subsistence agriculture. The Mexi-

Fig. 13.20—Upper-Class, Spanish Mexican in Charro Costume. *Photo., Otto Brehme.*

Fig. 13.21—Mexican Peon, Carrying Native Pottery to Market. *Photo., P. Yadez.*

can peasant, or *peon*, is economically self-sufficient (Fig. 13.21). The industrial and commercial activities of the country do not affect his life to any great extent. Stubborn adherence to the ancient customs perpetuates ignorance, illiteracy (almost one-half the Mexican population cannot read or write), and poverty, greatly handicapping the government's efforts to build a modern nation.

Agriculture. Mexico is an agricultural country, as some three-quarters of the population are engaged in subsistence farming. Agriculture is still dominated, moreover, by the feudal system initiated by the Spanish. Large estates, or *haciendas,* many of them originally granted by the Spanish crown, are owned by rich landlords and farmed by peons either through sharecropping or through virtual bondage.

As part of the social reforms of the 1930's millions of acres were confiscated from absentee landholders and distributed to the peons. The land was not given outright to the individual farmer but was apportioned as communal holdings to the rural villages. Under this system each peon must keep his land under cultivation in order to retain the right to use it. The system has had only mixed success: over one-half of the arable land is in communal farms, but only a few of the establishments are self-sustaining.

Under the *hacienda* system millions of acres are left idle; vast tracts of potentially productive land still remain unused both in the tropical lowlands and on the plateau. Deep-well irrigation must be introduced, however, to bring the plateau lands under cultivation.

The great staple product of the country, grown entirely for domestic consumption and mostly by subsistence farming, is **corn,** the staff of life of the peon. About one-quarter of all the cultivated land is in corn. Although cool nights and poor practices result in low yields, the crop supports the population.

Beans are the second great staple crop, grown everywhere with corn. **Wheat** and **barley** are grown in the north, where **cattle** are also raised.

A product of the outer slopes of the central plateau, especially on the east and also in the Chiapas Highlands, is **coffee.** Mexico is one of the ten ranking producers of coffee, but the volume of the crop is not important in the world market as most of it is consumed domestically.

Similarly, some two-thirds of the **cotton** output, centered in the north central part of Mexico, is for domestic use.

Typical tropical products are grown on the lowlands of the east coast around an embayment of the Gulf of Mexico known as the **Bay of Campeche. Sugar cane** and **bananas** are the two important crops, the former for domestic use, the latter for export to the United States (with the advantage over the other Central American countries of a shorter haul). Mexico is one of the five ranking producers of bananas. **Rice** and **tobacco** are grown in scattered areas in the same general region.

A special product of Mexico is **henequen fiber,** grown on the Yucatan Peninsula. Approximately one-half the world's supply of the raw material for binder twine and small ropes formerly came from Yucatan before the rise of Tanganyika as a producer of sisal, a competing fiber (see Chapter 9, p. 147). In the near absence of soil the plants are grown in holes dug in the rock. This practice and the necessity of constantly keeping down the wild plant growths require much hand labor, which is supplied by the poverty-stricken descendants of the once mighty Mayas.

Many products are obtained from the Mexican forests, which cover about one-seventh of the country's area. The leading product is **chicle.** Mexico is the major producer of chicle, which is obtained from wild trees in the Yucatan and on the southern coast of the Gulf of Mexico. **Vanilla** is produced in the Gulf of Campeche region. **Timber** products include tropical hardwoods from the rainforests of western Yucatan and middle-latitude woods—spruce, pine, and cedar—

from the cooler climatic upland regions.

Mineral Products. Although Mexico is predominantly an agricultural country, its chief industry is mining. This paradox stems from the subsistence nature of the agriculture, which places mining first in value of commercial output. The mineral resources, of large size and wide variety, are concentrated almost entirely within the plateau and its bordering Sierra regions. The mines are over 90 percent foreign-owned, mostly by United States companies.

For many years Mexico has been the world's leading producer of **silver,** between 30 and 40 percent of the total output coming from Mexican mines. It is the only country in which most of the silver output is obtained from silver ore rather than as a by-product of the recovery of other metals. Even in Mexico almost every other type of mine yields silver as a paying by-product. The largest silver mines, as such, are at **Pachuca,** an ancient source of the metal in the state of Hidalgo in the central part of the country. Other leading sources are in the northern part of the central plateau.

Lead and **zinc** are obtained chiefly from mines at **San Luis Potosi,** in the center of the plateau, and from the state of Chihuahua to the north. Mexico is one of the three leading producers of both metals.

Mexico is second to Bolivia in the production of **antimony,** a by-product of the lead and silver mines. This metal is used extensively in lead alloys.

Copper production is mostly from the northwest border states of Chihuahua and Sonora, where there is a continuation of the great copper belt of the southwestern United States. Output is a minor fraction of the world total.

Iron ore occurs in moderate amounts in northeast Mexico, just south of the Rio Grande. **Coal** of medium quality is mined close by.

At one time in the early 1920's **petroleum** was Mexico's leading product and export item. Mexico was then second to the United States as a world producer. The fields along the northern section of the east coast were discovered early in the century and astounded the world with their prodigious "gushers." Oil under natural pressure spurted from the wells to heights of 600 feet. When capped, the wells gave the largest volume of flow in the history of the world oil industry. This spectacular yield resulted from the occurrence of the oil not in the interstices of porous rock, as is usually true, but in actual pools or underground reservoirs, the popular fancy for all oil occurrence. Under these circumstances the wells could have only a short life. Since the peak years there has been a great decline in Mexican oil production.

Manufacturing. Mexico is the fourth-ranking "industrial" country in Latin America. Despite the lack of good coal resources there is a small **iron and steel** industry located near the coal and iron ore deposits in the northeast. The bulk of the manufacturing enterprises is, however, classified as light industries, of which the two most important are **food processing** and **textiles.** Industry in general is protected by tariffs and produces almost exclusively for the domestic market. **Handicraft** industries flourish on the tourist trade from the United States.

Transportation. Mexico possesses a fairly good road and railroad system in view of the great construction difficulties imposed by the plateau and mountain rim topography. Nevertheless, transportation in general is inadequate relative to the further development of the agricultural and forest industries.

Both roads and railroads connect with the United States networks, thus greatly facilitating international trade between the two countries and aiding the American tourist trade with Mexico. Mexico constitutes an important link in the *Pan American Highway,* which will eventually provide a motor route throughout the entire north-south length of the two Americas. Mexican railroads are almost completely state owned and operated. Yucatan has a separate system of railroads for the collection of the henequen crop.

CITIES OF THE SOUTHWESTERN UNITED STATES AND MEXICO

Name	State	Country	Type	Population (1950)
San Diego	California	U.S.	Seaport	335,000
El Paso	Texas	U.S.	Commercial	130,000
Phoenix	Arizona	U.S.	Governmental and commercial	105,000
Tucson	Arizona	U.S.	Commercial and resort	45,000
Mexico City	Federal District	Mexico	Governmental, commercial, and industrial	3,000,000 (1955)
Guadalajara	Jalisco	Mexico	Commercial and governmental	378,000
Monterrey	Nuevo Leon	Mexico	Industrial, commercial, and governmental	333,000
Puebla	Puebla	Mexico	Hydropower and governmental	211,000
Mérida	Yucatan	Mexico	Commercial and governmental	143,000
Veracruz	Veracruz	Mexico	Seaport and governmental	102,000
Tampico	Veracruz	Mexico	Seaport	94,000

Cities. **San Diego** is the largest city of the desert-steppe region of the southwestern United States. It has the best harbor of the California coast south of San Francisco and is an important naval base. The climate of San Diego is about as ideal as can be found within the United States. The average daily temperature is 70° F. and the nights are slightly cooler. The city is surrounded by a citrus-growing district that specializes in lemons.

El Paso is located on the Rio Grande at the junction of Texas, New Mexico, and Mexico. It is a railroad junction of east-west and north-south routes and thus a port of entry to the United States from Mexico.

Phoenix is the capital and largest city of Arizona. It is located in the rich Salt River irrigation district. **Tucson** is approximately 100 miles to the southeast. Both cities are noted as winter health resorts because of their dry, invigorating air and mild winter climate.

Mexico City, the capital of Mexico, is known to Mexicans as Mexico, D.F. (Federal District). The city is thought to be named for an Aztec chieftain and is situated on the site of the former Aztec capital, in a saucer-shaped valley in the south central portion of the plateau at an altitude of 7350 feet—the highest metropolis in the world. Mexico, D.F., is an unusually pleasant place to live for a large city because of its scenic locale, its many wide thoroughfares and parkways, and the abundance of palatial residences, churches, government buildings, and other large edifices. It is the cultural, commercial, and industrial center of the country and is a sophisticated, cosmopolitan center quite unlike other Mexican cities.

Guadalajara, Mexico's second city, is some 250 miles northwest of the capital, at an altitude of one mile. It is a beautiful city; almost all the houses have open patios to take advantage of the ideal climate. It advertises: "Guadalajara has the climate California boasts about." The city is on the western edge of the plateau, where it receives the agricultural products of both upland and lowland environments. Guadalajara is known also for its pottery.

Monterrey (King's Mountain) is the third largest city of Mexico. It is the capital of its state and the center of the Mexican steel industry.

Puebla, another of the Mexican state capitals, lies on the eastern edge of the plateau at an altitude of over 7000 feet 100 miles southeast of Mexico, D.F. It is the center of a textile industry whose mills use the hydropower developed by falls on the plateau's edge.

Mérida, the capital of Yucatan, is 21 miles inland from the northern coast of the peninsula. It is the commercial city of Yucatan and the center of trade in henequen and the products manufactured from it. The city also attracts a considerable tourist trade by reason of its proximity to the great Mayan ruins such as **Chichen Itza.**

Veracruz is the major port of Mexico, on the Gulf coast 200 miles southeast of the capital. The site of the landing of Cortez in his conquest of the country, it was the first Spanish town in Mexico. In addition to handling the foreign trade of the country it is the center of the tobacco industry as well as of other light industries.

Tampico is another Mexican port, on a small river seven miles inland from the Gulf of Mexico and about 200 miles northeast of the capital. Tampico is the center of the country's oil-refining industry; the oil fields are situated within 100 miles of the city. It is a modern urban center because it was built up during the oil boom in the early part of the twentieth century. Because of this Tampico is unlike the typical old Mexican city.

Mexico as a Whole. Although Mexico has made great advances during the present century it cannot be considered to have achieved the status of a well-developed country. There has been much progress in the adoption of modern agricultural practices and machinery, but crop yields in general remain low because of the relatively limited application of the new techniques. The great need is to convert agriculture in general from subsistence farming to the production of surpluses that can be sold, either domestically or abroad. Similarly, millions of acres of new land have been brought under cultivation through irrigation projects, yet millions more could be added through further projects of no greater difficulty and expense than those already completed. Again, much effort has been spent on the development of hydroelectric capacity as a base for the expansion of industry, yet less than 10 percent of the hydro potential has been utilized. Improvement of transportation facilities has already been mentioned as a prime need.

Having achieved political stability and begun the work of development, Mexico faces a challenging future. Its resources are large and diversified. Further progress, though it will continue to be beset with problems, will be immeasurably easier than that already made from the slight start at the beginning of the century.

QUESTIONS. Explain the changing significance of the term "Great American Desert." What is the area of true desert (in terms of states or portions of states)? What is the cause of the Sonora Desert? Describe the topography of the Mexican-American desert-steppe region. What are the three major occupations of the region? Contrast the difference between these occupations as they are carried on in Mexico and in the United States.

Contrast the way in which irrigation is practiced in the southwestern United States with that in other desert-steppe areas of the world. Describe the Imperial Valley. What are its major products? Name two other irrigation districts of the Southwest and their products. Why is the area as a whole relatively unimportant in United States beef production? What products are associated with the Edwards Plateau? What is the major mineral product of the Southwest?

Describe the general topography of Mexico. What two ancient peoples are the forebears of the present-day Indian population of Mexico? Describe the general type of agriculture in the country. What are the major staple crops? What are the major products of the east coast and eastern highlands? What is the special product of the Yucatan Peninsula? What is the leading mineral product of Mexico? In what way does its production differ from that of other countries? Compare the present with the previous state of the petroleum industry in Mexico. What are the chief industries of the country? What is the major handicap to the development of adequate transportation facilities? Compare the progress already achieved in the development of the Mexican economy with its future opportunities.

What special use is made of the harbor of San Diego? Why are Phoenix and Tucson resort cities? Why is Mexico, D.F., of unusual importance?

Medium-Temperature Humid Climates: The Mediterranean Climate

CHAPTER 14

The Type Region—The Mediterranean Basin

■ DEFINITION AND CAUSES OF THE MEDITERRANEAN CLIMATE

The Mediterranean climate is characterized by cool, rainy winters and hot, dry summers. Though the winters are cool the temperatures are well above the frost level and allow a winter growing season. The summers are so dry that irrigation is regularly an adjunct to agricultural operations in the warm months. Characteristic features of agriculture in the regions of Mediterranean climate are, accordingly, year-round cultivation, two harvest seasons, and production of a great variety of crops.

The Mediterranean climate results from the winter movement of the westerlies far enough toward the equator to bring their low-latitude border belts in both hemispheres into the paths of the westerlies cyclonic storms and their precipitation. In summer, contrariwise, the trades move poleward to a similar extent so that Mediterranean climatic regions then experience what amounts to warm desert or steppe climatic conditions. With dry, tropical summers and humid, middle-latitude winters, the Mediterranean climate is thus transitional between the significantly hot and the medium-temperature climatic belts of the earth.

The regions that experience this trades-westerlies alternation occur in the belt between 30° and 40° latitude. As the trades are commonly dry winds on the western coasts of continents, these areas are the typical locations of Mediterranean climatic regions in the Northern Hemisphere. In the Southern Hemisphere the continents taper off in this latitude belt; hence the Mediterranean climate there affects southern rather than western coasts. The Mediterranean regions are thus found on the borders of continents. They are commonly backed by a mountain chain, the other side of which exhibits either an extremely wet or extremely dry climatic environment.

■ REGIONAL ASPECTS

Living conditions in regions of Mediterranean climate are particularly mild and agreeable. The regions are famous for their sunny days and blue skies, which recur characteristically even during the winter rainy season. Violent temperature fluctuations are unusual. Winter days range between 40° and 50° F., summer days between 70° and 80° F. The summer heat is not unpleasant because the relative humidity is moderate—not too dry but, on the other hand, not sultry. Because the summer is "tropical" the diurnal temperature range is large—up to 30°.

Seasonal changes are not accompanied by erratic temperature fluctuations and changeable weather, as they commonly are, for example, in the westerlies interior regions of the United States. Summer approaches imperceptibly. The days gradually grow warmer and the rains come less frequently and as thunderstorms. The approach of winter, also, is almost unnoticeable. The short spring period between the cool winter and the dry summer is exceptionally pleasant because there is a lavish display of native flowers during this time. In many places the ground then appears to be carpeted with colorful blooms.

The total rainfall is not large—between 15 and 25 inches annually, almost all of which falls in winter. And, in keeping with the low quantity, it is highly variable and undependable (see Chapter 6, p. 98). As the Mediterranean climate is transitional, total rainfall and the length of the rainy season both increase poleward across such regions. The drought period ranges from five or six months' duration on the low-latitude margins to one month on the high-latitude margins.

The characteristic vegetative aspect of a Mediterranean region is a landscape of low trees and shrubs. The predominant climatic influence is the summer drought, which the plant life combats in a number of ways. The trunks of the trees are covered by thick, gnarled bark; the leaves, characteristically, are few and small, thick and stiff, and have leathery or waxen surfaces—features that reduce evaporation to a minimum. Thus the leaves can be retained through the dry period. The shrubs possess abundant thorns or spines and are, in consequence, predominantly woody rather than leafy. All the plants have deep, wide-ranging roots to insure their access to adequate supplies of ground water.

The uncultivated trees are mostly scrub oaks, chestnuts, laurels, and myrtles. Their drought-resisting characteristics make them gnarled and knotty, and hence unfit for lumber. The leaves and bark of the shrubs afford food for goats, the only animals able to browse on such forage. Burrowing mammals constitute a large part of the wild life.

The plant life has two regional aspects. There are "forests" that consist of widely spaced trees interspersed with a shrubby undergrowth. (True middle-latitude forests, however, are often present on higher ground owing to heavier, year-round precipitation and lower temperatures there.) Each tree thus has a large area from which to draw water during the dry period. Where trees

are absent shrubs form the entire plant cover, a type of growth difficult to penetrate known as *maquis* (a name made famous through its adoption to designate French resistance forces during World War II) in southern France and as chaparral[1] in California.

Such a landscape changes its appearance radically between one season and the next. During the rainy winter everything is lush and green, and the countryside resembles a summer landscape in the westerlies belt. But the Meriterranean summer drought fades out the green; the shrubs become dust-covered and the vegetation then presents a uniformly gray aspect.

■ UTILIZATION OF MEDITERRANEAN REGIONS

Agriculture is the notably predominant economic activity of all the Mediterranean climatic regions. It comprises a unique combination of (1) tree crops—citrus fruits, olives, figs, almonds, plums, peaches, and apricots—(2) grapes, and (3) the cereals wheat and barley. In addition, local climatic variations permit the commercial cultivation of a variety of flowers and of almost the entire gamut of vegetables for home consumption and local markets. As the low annual rainfall comes chiefly in months other than the growing season of most of the crops, dry-farming, irrigation, and intensive agriculture are regular practices.

It is possible to distinguish between four types of farming practice in the Mediterranean climatic regions: (1) the growth of cereals and vegetables with dependence on the natural precipitation only, (2) cultivation of olives, figs, dates, and grapes, which ripen in the fall and need no irrigation (but which yield better if irrigated), (3) irrigated cultivation of summer crops of fruits, vegetables, and forage plants, and (4) cattle grazing and livestock farming. Two or more of these systems used conjointly result in a far greater and more varied yield than

[1] From the Spanish name for a type of scrub evergreen oak common in California.

could be had from an agricultural routine relying merely on seasonal succession.

Except in one region, **wheat** is the major crop in all Mediterranean climatic areas. Wheat requires a cool, moist growing season and a warm, dry ripening season, conditions well fulfilled by the Mediterranean seasonal pattern. **Barley** is important in the more arid portions of Mediterranean climatic regions because its short growing season results in a better yield than wheat under these circumstances. These two grains are the major winter crops, sown in late fall, reaped in early summer.

Although not the most important in terms of acreage, value, or volume, the most characteristic, truly Mediterranean crop is the **olive.** The tree thrives on steep slopes under semiarid conditions. It is thus ideally suited for land in the Mediterranean climatic regions which, because of topography and rainfall, is unfit for any other crop. The olive tree yields more under irrigation but is generally grown by default on lands where irrigation is impractical.

The most important nut crops are the **almond** and **walnut,** both well suited for the hot, dry conditions, with no need for irrigation.

In the Mediterranean climatic regions **grapes** find their ideal requirements of well-drained land (hill slopes), a definitely warm season, and not too much rain.

To sum up, the agriculture of the Mediterranean climatic region is at the same time diversified and specialized. An extraordinarily wide range of crops and animals can be raised. The defects of the climate for productive agriculture have been overcome by resort to many artful adjustments and adaptations, learned through centuries-long experience.

■ REGIONS AND COUNTRIES OF MEDITERRANEAN CLIMATE

As its name indicates, the Mediterranean climate has its most typical and extensive expression in the area known as the **Mediterranean Basin,** that is, the lands bordering on the Mediterranean Sea (Fig. 14.1). Other Mediterranean regions are much smaller and more localized. Because of the pleasant environment and the marked and peculiar agricultural possibilities they are, however, all centers of population. These other regions are: a tract around the **Cape of Good Hope** at the southern tip of Africa, two areas on the **south coast of Australia, central Chile,** and a large portion of **California.**

A. THE MEDITERRANEAN BASIN

The extensive development of the Mediterranean climate around the sea that is its namesake is largely a consequence of four circumstances:

First, there is no topographic barrier at the west end of the basin to prevent the winter cyclonic storms from moving eastward past the Strait of Gibraltar.

Second, the sea itself is a warm-water body. Although there is a continual great influx of water from the Atlantic to balance a large loss through evaporation over the Mediterranean, the inflow consists of relatively warm surface water from the Atlantic.

Third, since the Mediterranean waters are strongly warmed by the sun during the summer, the air over the Mediterranean in winter is abnormally heated by contact with this warm water and becomes a low-pressure area because of its lightness.

Fourth, the ring of mountains and highlands that rims the Mediterranean on the north prevents the cold air masses of the westerlies that originate in high latitudes from moving into the area. The inflowing winds toward the center of the Mediterranean winter low accordingly come from the south and west, and those from the west are high in moisture content.

This persistent winter low-pressure condition is capable of generating very strong inflowing winds. These, brought in from over the Sahara, are anticipated with dread because of their harsh effect on both man and his crops. The law in Sicily and southern Italy is likely to be lenient with a man who

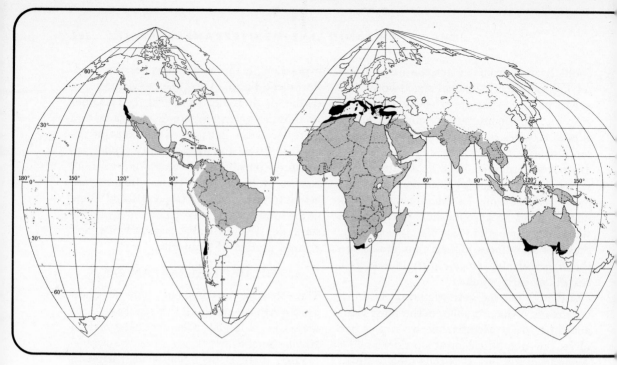

Fig. 14.1—World Distribution of Mediterranean Climatic Regions.

commits a crime while the *sirocco* is blowing. The *khamsin*[2] of Egypt, which blows in late spring, is another of these desert winds. In the west the southeast coast of Spain suffers from the *leveche*, also a hot, dust-laden wind from the Sahara.

In spite of the northern mountain barrier there is a constant tendency for the winds along the northern Mediterranean coast to be from the north in response to the Mediterranean low. Occasionally an unusually large cold air mass generates violent winds through the gaps in this barrier. The Rhone Valley in France is thus plagued by the *mistral*, a blast of cold, dry air so strong that the trees there grow inclined to the southeast. A similar wind is the *bora*[3] of the northern Adriatic coast. The violence of these winds is due to the weight of the colder air in the highlands. The extreme original cold of the air from these sources is not entirely mitigated by the usual heating effect of compression on descending winds (see Chapter 6, p. 98).

[2] From the Arabic for "fifty," referring to the superstition that this wind blows for 50 consecutive days.
[3] From the Latin *Boreas,* the personification of the North Wind.

Because the winter rains are a product of such cyclonic storms as wander to the far south of the westerlies belt they are likely to come in concentrated downpours. The "rainy season" of the Mediterranean Basin thus resembles the rainy season of the savanna climate. Most of the days are clear; the comparatively few that are rainy have notably heavy precipitation.

The Mediterranean climate at the western end of the Mediterranean Basin has a wider latitudinal extent than at the eastern end because of the influence of the adjacent Atlantic Ocean. Also, the more southerly location of the eastern Mediterranean places it out of reach of some of the winter cyclonic storms, so that the climatic zone is restricted to a narrow belt along the coasts, or else is entirely absent. The Anatolian peninsula (also known as Asia Minor) just to the north is, on the other hand, in the direct path of the westerlies' storms and has a much wider coastal belt of Mediterranean climate. Innumerable local variations from the typical Mediterranean climate also exist throughout the region because of protecting mountains, desert influence, and other factors.

Although the name "Mediterranean Basin" is applied to the region, there are no extensive, continuous lowlands along the shores of the Mediterranean Sea. Instead there are certain major coastal plains, the flood plains of the larger rivers, and many minor valley plains between projecting highland ridges. If it is remembered that the typical Mediterranean climate is restricted to the lowlands, then it will be realized from the preceding statement that the true areas of that climate comprise a series of restricted, discontinuous, and rather isolated tracts strung around the Mediterranean shores, reaching varying distances inland.

Historical Significance. The Mediterranean Basin has had immense significance in the origin and development of Western civilization. It was the site of the ancient civilizations of Crete, Phoenicia, Greece, Carthage, Rome, Byzantium, and, by extension, of Egyptian culture—all of which have contributed in varying degree to Western civilization.

The tangled and fragmentary trails of the prehistoric migrations and movements into the Mediterranean Basin available to historians are not sufficient to give a definite picture of the first developments of civilization along the shores of the sea. It is probable, however, that the climatic resemblances between this region and Egypt and Mesopotamia were important factors in the beginnings of Mediterranean social and cultural organization and development. As in the two older centers of civilization, Egypt and Mesopotamia, the necessity for irrigation and for seasonal accumulation and storage of crops was profoundly stimulating to such development. The absence of a heavy forest cover such as existed in northern Europe was also an important factor; the agricultural techniques developed in the steppe and desert oasis environments could not have been applied in a region of continuous forests.

Another favorable factor was the Mediterranean Sea itself, which, by fostering the development of overseas transport, facilitated commercial and cultural intercourse between the various portions of its shores, with consequent stimulation of intellectual and technical advances as against the tendency toward stagnation engendered by isolation.

Lastly, but no less important, the region was favorable for developing civilization because of the northern mountain barriers with their dense forest cover, which helped keep out both the pastoral nomads inhabiting the lands to the east and the "barbarians" occupying the lands to the northeast, groups which throughout early Old World history were notorious for their fondness for aggressive war and invasion.

Present-Day Agriculture. The Mediterranean climate, in general, and the type of natural vegetative cover that develops in response to it are not conducive to the development of good soils. The rough topography that prevails along the Mediterranean shores is a further deterrent to the natural formation of soil in the region.[4] Areas of good soil are therefore comparatively rare and localized, and are highly prized by their fortunate possessors. The average mediocre soil necessitates intensive farming methods involving much hand labor, which in turn tends to give rise to dense populations.

Cereals are grown along the coast, more or less in the same areas in which some two-thirds of the population is situated (Fig. 14.2). As the cereal lands are limited, the basic food needs of the large population are supplemented by cultivation and consumption of various kinds of beans (which also supply protein in a meat-poor diet).

The lack of good pasture and forage for domestic animals forces the Mediterranean farmer to raise sheep and goats rather than cattle, and mules and donkeys rather than horses. A smaller supply of meat[5] or motive power per animal is tolerated in return for more efficient utilization of the means of sustenance at hand. The seasonality of the food supply for the animals is met by the practice of *transhumance.* When the lowland grass

[4] The drought during the summer heat keeps chemical activity in the soil to a minimum, and the lack of frost in winter tends to prevent the soil-building processes of mechanical disintegration of the rock from acting. The heavy rains on the steep slopes consequently tend to remove soil faster than it is formed.

[5] The sheep are "wool sheep," which are more suited to sparse forage of low nutritive value than are "mutton sheep," raised primarily for their meat value.

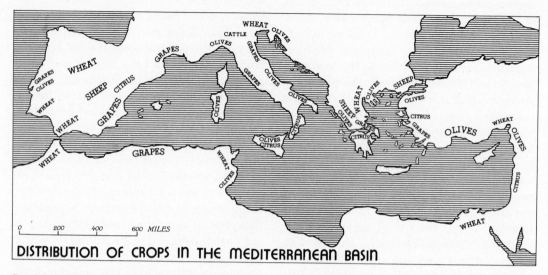

DISTRIBUTION OF CROPS IN THE MEDITERRANEAN BASIN

Fig. 14.2—Distribution of Crops in the Mediterranean Basin. A few products are characteristic of the entire region, despite the many countries concerned.

that does grow withers during the summer drought, the Mediterranean herdsman, accompanied by his family, takes his animals up to highland pastures. In winter the snow-covered pastures are forsaken in favor of the lowland grass, in this season lush and green.

The olive, previously mentioned as the characteristic product of the Mediterranean climate, is even more closely identified with the Mediterranean Basin. Over 90 percent of the world's olive acreage is in this region, and is concentrated in those parts of the basin where the yearly rainfall is 20 inches or more. The olive is valued primarily not as a fruit but for the oil it contains. The better grades of olive oil are highly important as a source of fats in a diet low in meat. The poorer-grade oils are an important raw material for the soap and chemical industries.

Grapes, less exclusively a Mediterranean product but nevertheless highly important there, are grown in those parts of the basin where the yearly rainfall is 14 inches or more. The trellises familiarly associated with vine culture in the United States are used in the Mediterranean region only in the cooler, rainier areas. Elsewhere the vines grow on the ground to keep evaporation to a minimum during the hot, dry summer.

Vine culture is eminently suited to the large supply of agricultural labor available in the Mediterranean countries. Cultivation, pruning, spraying, irrigation where practical, and the harvesting and preparation of the crop all require a great amount of hand labor.

Of the three uses of grapes—as fruit, wine, and raisins—wine is by far the most important in the Mediterranean Basin. Its use as the main liquid in the diet is not merely a matter of preference. In many places the supply of water for all uses is low during the summer drought; everywhere use of water for drinking is dangerous, because it is a source of infections such as typhoid fever and dysentery. The bottle of cheap wine that regularly accompanies the Mediterranean meal is not a sign of widespread dissoluteness but indicates only that it is the best available substitute for water where safe, potable water is not easily had.

Countries of the Type Mediterranean Region

1. PORTUGAL

General Aspects. The Republic of Portugal is a rectangle of 34,000 square miles (slightly larger than Maine) comprising most of the western coast of the Iberian Peninsula (Fig. 14.3). Located outside the Mediterranean Basin, the country is nevertheless almost entirely within the Mediterranean climatic region. It is far enough south to get the effects of the wind-belt alternation, and, as the slope of the country is predominantly toward the west, winter brings orographic rains over the entire country. Further, the open exposure to the Atlantic moderates the summer heat.

Historical Factors. The establishment of Portugal as an independent nation occurred between the eleventh and thirteenth centuries. Its frontiers have remained unchanged from that time to this. The original partition and the continued existence of Portugal were due in large measure to the topographic isolation of the country from the rest of the peninsula. This also was the background for the development of a slight difference in language and nationality between the Portuguese and the Spaniards.

The pioneer role played by Portugal in the age of discoveries is well known. In their zeal to conquer the Moors after their expulsion from the country in the thirteenth century, the Portuguese carried the fight into the North African Moorish homeland. But what began as the military pursuit of a defeated foe became by degrees part of the historic search for an ocean trade route to the East.

Portugal's small size and the paucity of its resources compared with those of Spain and England were ultimately responsible for the lapse into the comparative obscurity of the country today. In a minor way, however, Portugal's position as the westernmost extension of continental Europe has given it an importance as a transatlantic air terminal.

The People. Portugal's population is ap-

Fig. 14.3—Iberian Peninsula. The inset compares the area of the region with that of Wyoming and Colorado, which is approximately equal.

IBERIAN PENINSULA

proximately 8.5 million. The people are racially very similar to the Spaniards, but a Moorish admixture is traceable throughout the southern half of the country. The religion is predominantly Roman Catholic. Approximately one-half the population is literate.

Topography. Portugal is situated between the western edge of the Spanish Meseta (see Chapter 2, p. 24) and the Atlantic coast. Its topography comprises the dissected, rugged slope which is the descent from the high western edge of the Spanish Meseta to sea level. The hindrance to internal and inland communication which the steepness of the slope introduces is intensified by the numerous canyons which furrow it deeply.

The northern part of the country is mountainous, with peaks averaging 3000 to 4000 feet in altitude. This region, which receives more rain because of its altitude, also gets heavier precipitation because it borders immediately on a humid middle-latitude climate. The forest cover is thus much heavier than in the typical Mediterranean country. The composition of the forest—oak, pine, and chestnut—is also a departure from the type Mediterranean growths.

Specifically, three large rivers and their valleys are the most significant physical features of Portugal. Of these the two northern ones, together with their tributaries and minor intervening streams, convert the northern and central part of the country to a grid of east-west valleys opening onto a coastal lowland. All three streams rise in the interior of the Meseta, and all three form, for parts of their courses, portions of Portugal's boundaries.

The northernmost river, the **Douro,** flows almost due west across Portugal some 50 miles below the northern boundary. The central river, the **Tagus,** runs from northeast to southwest across the center of the country. The **Guadiana** flows practically due south in the extreme southeast corner of the country.

Though formerly they were much used, the three rivers today have little importance as navigable routes. Overland transportation facilities are also poor. Such roads and railroads as do exist have in recent decades been al-

lowed to deteriorate to a sad state of disrepair.

Products. The predominance of agriculture in Portugal is manifested in the fact that more than half the working population consists of farm laborers. The pattern of agriculture is representative of the Mediterranean Basin. **Wheat** is the major crop in both acreage and production, followed by **corn, oats, rye,** and **barley,** in that order. Potatoes and beans are the important vegetables.

Despite the large acreage in wheat the total crop is not very great, and this cereal is one of the major imports. Wheat production is concentrated in the southeast; corn replaces it as the chief food in the more humid parts of the north. Barley, grown mainly for stock feed, is cultivated in the drier portions of the country. Rye and oats thrive on the more humid uplands.

Wine, one of the outstanding exports of the country, is made from grapes grown principally on the terraced sides of the major river valleys. The world-famous variety known as *port* comes from the upper Douro Valley. It was developed to please the English taste as a result of a commercial treaty between the two countries in 1703 that gave special trade preference to Portuguese wine.

Another important export product (of which Portugal is the leading producer) is **cork,** procured by stripping the outer bark from the cork-oak tree (Fig. 14.4). Most of the cork-oak groves in Portugal are wild, as it is difficult to establish a grove by forestry techniques. The tree at maturity is some four feet in diameter and about 40 feet high. It yields its first harvest of cork when approximately 20 years old and can be cut thereafter on the average once every ten years. The stripping does not hurt the tree in any way. Most of the cork-oaks are in central and northern Portugal, especially along the valley of the Guadiana.

The cork bark is not the only useful product of the tree. Wood is obtained when the groves are thinned as the trees grow large. **Goats** browse beneath the oaks to keep down the brush and large herds of **hogs** feed on the acorns. Between one-half and two-thirds of the hog population of Portugal is acorn fed.

Fig. 14.4—Stripping Bark From a Cork-Oak Tree, Alentejo, Portugal. (Courtesy, Portuguese Embassy.)

Portugal stands about midway among the Mediterranean countries in output of **olive oil**. The centers of production are along the Tagus River and on the lowland south of its valley.

The fishing industry of the Douro and other points along the west coast is a source of much income from the well-known canned **sardine**. Sardines are the leading item in the food exports of Portugal, and the country is one of the major canners of this food item.

The mineral wealth of Portugal is considerable, but its exploitation is handicapped by lack of power. The major product and leading export is **tungsten**. Portugal is an important producer of this alloy metal.

The chief industrial products of the country are **textiles**, manufactured for domestic use from imported raw materials, and a particular variety of **porcelain tile**, production of which is based on knowledge inherited from the Moors.

CITIES OF PORTUGAL

Name	Type	Population (1950)
Lisbon	Governmental and seaport	790,000
Oporto	Seaport	285,000

Fig. 14.5—Lisbon, Portugal. The public square at the harbor, and the downtown area. (Courtesy, Portuguese Embassy.)

Cities. **Lisbon** (Fig. 14.5), the capital and principal port of Portugal, is at the mouth of the Tagus River. It rose to prominence during World War II as the sole transatlantic air terminal in a neutral country. Lisbon is considered one of the most beautiful ports of Europe. Its climate is very pleasant—the temperature averages 70° F. in summer, 50° in winter.

Oporto, the second of the only two major cities of Portugal, is on the Douro River three miles from its mouth. As the export center for the trade in port wine it gave its name to the variety. The city is a center of the textile industry and the chief harbor of northern Portugal. A bar at the Douro's mouth limits Oporto's trade to vessels of comparatively shallow draft.

Portugal as a Whole. The natural resources and the standard of living in Portugal are high in comparison with those of some of the other countries of the Mediterranean Basin. Portugal is very small, however, and any further development of agriculture or of its unexploited mineral resources will not suffice to effect a major change in the fortunes of the Portuguese people. On the other hand, the intelligent, enlightened development of Portugal's little utilized empire (the major units of which have already been discussed under tropical climates) has great possibilities.

QUESTIONS. Describe briefly the Mediterranean climate. Explain its origin. What factors govern its distribution and how? Describe the natural vegetation of the Mediterranean climatic regions. What unusual type of crop is important? Describe the four types of agricultural activity. What is the major crop? What replaces it in more arid districts, and why? What is the most characteristic crop? Why? What "vine crop" is important? Why?

What are the three major factors responsible for the type region? Separate the following winds into two contrasting classes: *leveche, sirocco, bora, khamsin, mistral.* What is the cause of each of these two types? Why is the Mediterranean climatic region wider at the western end of the Mediterranean Basin than at the eastern end?

Discuss the circumstances responsible for the importance of the Mediterranean Basin in the development of civilization in that part of the world.

Why is good soil a rarity in the Mediterranean Basin? Where are the cereals grown? Why are sheep, goats, mules, and donkeys, rather than cattle and horses, the domestic animals of the Mediterranean farmer? What is "transhumance"? Why is it important in the Mediterranean region? What is the major importance of olives as a crop? Are grapes grown in the drier or wetter portions of the Mediterranean region? Why are grapes not grown everywhere on trellises? Why is the raising of grapes well suited to the Mediterranean Basin? What is the most important local use of grapes? Why?

What geographic factor has been largely responsible for the development and continued existence of Portugal apart from Spain? Why was Portugal unable to retain the position as a major world power that it enjoyed during the age of discoveries? Describe the major topographic features of Portugal. What is the major crop? The leading export products? Name the chief mineral product. The chief industry.

2. SPAIN

Topography. Spain, 190,000 square miles in area (about the size of Utah and Nevada together), occupies the major portion of the Iberian Peninsula (Fig. 14.3). The dominant topographic feature of the country is the large central plateau, the **Meseta.** East-west across the center of this plateau runs a block of the earth's crust that has been lifted higher than the general level of the plateau, the **Guadarrama Mountains.** These mountains divide the Meseta into northern and southern portions known as **Old Castile** ("Castle") and **New Castile,** respectively. Other mountain ranges, higher but less important, also traverse the Meseta. Between the mountains, however, the surface of the plateau is remarkably flat and even, and stands at an average of 2700 feet in altitude in the north, 2600 feet in the south.

Spain is ringed more or less completely by mountains. On the north coast are the **Cantabrian Mountains,** which reach over 8000 feet, on the south coast the **Sierra Nevada** range rises to well over 11,000 feet, and on the northeast the **Pyrenees** are equally high. The western portion of the southern rim of the plateau is known as the **Sierra Morena;** between these mountains and the Sierra Nevada is a large depression, the plain of **Andalusia,** over which the **Guadalquivir River** flows southwest to its mouth west of Gibraltar. In the northeast, between the Pyrenees and the Meseta, there is another large depression in which the **Ebro River** flows to the Mediterranean. The Mediterranean coast along the south and east is bordered by narrow, discontinuous coastal plains.

Climate. Although Spain is considered here as a country with Mediterranean climate, only half or less of its area is actually within such an environment. The entire northern third of the country is in the westerlies belt; hence the wind-belt alternation of the Mediterranean climate does not occur there. The plateau is climatically transitional between the northern climate and the Mediterranean climate. (The central portion is so much in the rain shadow of the mountains to the north and west that it has a steppe climate, with a yearly rainfall of 15 inches or less. The vegetation is the typical steppe grass cover.)

Historical Factors. From prehistoric times Spain has been the scene of repeated invasions from both Europe and Africa, although comparatively isolated from both continents. The result has been a highly complex racial history that has had an invigorating effect on the inhabitants but, because of the diverse topography and climate of the peninsula, has also brought about political disunity.

It has been said that the true Spaniards live on the Meseta. They are surrounded by Spanish-like, yet different, peoples with different customs and traditions. Because of such alien characteristics Portugal gained a separate existence. Also, for 700 years before they were united under Ferdinand and Isabella, the separate kingdoms of Castile, on the plateau, and Aragon, in the Ebro Valley, existed side by side. The northeastern portion of Spain, known as **Catalonia,** is even now inhabited by people who speak a language that is not true Spanish, who have such different customs and traditions that they prefer to be known as Catalonians, and who have tried repeatedly to set up an independent nation.

The lasting influence of the Moors on southern Spain also contributed to the diversity of the peoples in the various regions of the Iberian Peninsula.

As in the case of the Portuguese the stimulus provided by victory over the Moors in 1492 enabled the Spaniards to reach the height of their glory during the colonial period in the New World. But social and economic deterioration at home was by then already in progress: the short-sighted Spanish colonial policy was an external evidence of this decay. The decline of Spain was due in no small measure to the failure of the Spaniards to appreciate the basic agricultural achievements on which the Moorish civilization of Iberia had rested.

In modern times the devastating civil war of the 1930's reduced the country to a new low from which recovery has been slow.

The People. The "border peoples" referred to above form large, dissident minorities within Spain's 28 million population. The Catalonians of the northeast, for example, are an energetic, ambitious, and progressive group who are irked at being tied down by the arrogant, quixotic, unambitious Spaniards of the central and southern regions.

The social cleavage is even greater. The agricultural and industrial workers are poverty-stricken. A great preponderance of all the wealth of the country is possessed by a few large landholders and an unusually strong and temporal clergy who share political power with the military. Extreme poverty and extreme wealth exist side by side without any appreciable middle class between. As a consequence the country's economic life is virtually stagnant.

Transportation. The plateaus and mountains that comprise so much of Spain are a basic handicap to development of a transportation system. The Pyrenees on the northeast, for example, are so effective a barrier to overland movement that until the twentieth century rail communication with France was restricted to coastal routes.

Another difficulty with rail transportation is the utilization of various widths of track, though approximately 80 percent of the mileage is standard gauge. Connections with France have been deliberately kept different from the French gauge for strategic reasons. Spain has, however, constructed a system of good, modern trunk highways that serves the convenience both of the few who possess automobiles and of the buses which are a major utility for internal transportation. Secondary roads, on the other hand, are almost impassable for cars.

The Spanish rivers are of little significance for internal transportation. Most of them are shallow and have shifting courses. Since they flow at the bottom of valleys eroded to depths far below the upland surface they cannot, in general, be interconnected or improved by canal construction. The one really navigable river is the Guadalquivir, which barges can utilize. The Ebro is less useful, but navigation along its middle section is facilitated by one of the oldest canals in Europe, the **Imperial Canal,** part of which dates back to the sixteenth century.

Agriculture. Although Spain is a country with over half the population engaged in agriculture and a considerable additional fraction directly dependent on crop production for employment, less than one-half its land area is under cultivation.[6] The typical Mediterranean disadvantage of poor soils is, over much of Spain, aggravated by even less than the average, undependable rainfall of a Mediterranean climate. Crop yields are thus exceptionally low save in certain restricted areas where irrigation is practiced, such as the numerous small plains along the Mediterranean coast.

Because of their high productivity these coastal tracts are known to the Spaniards as *huertas,* or "gardens." The irrigation works were originally constructed by the Moors, whose civilization was based on such intensive agriculture and its high productivity. There are only two interior irrigation districts, one of which utilizes the Imperial Canal.

Agricultural development within this unfavorable natural environment is further handicapped by the Spanish system of landholding. Such large tracts of good land as do exist are held in enormous estates whose pro-

---

[6] The ratio of cultivated land per person in Spain has been calculated as 2.6 acres, compared with 8 acres in the United States.

prietors either do not utilize them fully or have them worked by poorly paid peasant labor with highly inefficient methods. These workers, in typical Mediterranean fashion, live in large towns and cities.

Agricultural Products. In keeping with the typical Mediterranean pattern, the largest agricultural acreage of Spain is devoted to the production of cereals, of which the most important is **wheat.** The wheat district is centered on the plains of Old Castile in the drier, steppelike climatic region of the Meseta upland. Wheat is also grown under olive trees in Andalusia and in the Ebro Valley.

Barley is important along the headwaters of the Tagus River. Oats, rye, and rice are produced in smaller quantities and are grown under conditions similar to those in Portugal.

Spain is by far the leading **olive oil** producer; it averages about one-third of the total world output. There are some 300 million olive trees in the country. The great olive center is Andalusia, where much of the landscape is one huge olive grove. The Ebro Valley is a second producing center. Upper Andalusia is the source of the best pickling olives.

Spain also ranks as the world's third **orange** producer and is the leading exporter of that fruit. (The orange was introduced into Spain by the Moors.) This eminence has been gained not only through natural advantages but by intensive irrigation and fertilizing along with what is probably the most highly commercialized food production in Europe. Approximately 80 percent of the total Spanish production comes from the large *huerta* that is the **Valencia** district (which has given its name to a leading variety of orange). A district along the lower Guadalquivir is the source of large exports of the bitter-flavored variety used in making English marmalade.

The production of grapes is also important in Spain. The main centers are the Mediterranean *huertas;* secondary concentrations are present in the major valleys. All three uses of the fruit are important in Spain. The most famous **wine** is *sherry,* which receives its name from the town of **Jerez de la Frontera,** near the southern coast northwest of Gibraltar. **Raisins** are produced from a district on the southern Mediterranean coast, and fresh grapes along the coast farther east.

Spain follows Portugal as an important producer of **cork** from groves along the Guadiana on the Portuguese border, and in northeastern Catalonia.

Less important in total value are almonds and dates. Sugar cane is grown under government subsidy, making Spain the only European country with that crop.

The most important animal product of Spain is **wool** of high quality, obtained from the world-famous *merino* breed of sheep developed on the southern and eastern Meseta. The sheep population is one of the largest in Europe. The Meseta is also the home of a large **mule** population. The **asses** from which they are bred are considered the finest stock in the world, and there is an important export trade in breeding animals.

Fishing is a sizable industry in Spain, the third largest in Europe in size of catch. Sardines, horse mackerel, and cod are caught in the Atlantic and Mediterranean.

Mineral Products. Spain is rich in mineral resources. Until the discovery of the New World it was one of the major mineral centers of the world. The products mentioned below include only those from the Mediterranean climatic portion of Spain.

The country is the world's leading producer of **mercury,** obtained at **Almaden,** on the north side of the Sierra Morena. **Copper** and **sulfur** come from the great **Rio Tinto** mine in the southern Sierra Morena. Lead and silver are produced in the upper Guadalquivir Valley; iron and coal are mined at many places throughout the country. Potash, an important fertilizer constituent, is found in a large, high-grade deposit in Catalonia. Production in almost all instances is far below potential output because of inefficiency, lack of enterprise, and persistence in the use of obsolete methods and machinery.

Manufacturing. Catalonia is the principal manufacturing center of Spain. **Textiles** made chiefly from imported material are the most important item; **glass, machinery, paper, electrical equipment,** and even **automobiles** are also produced. In addition to being the home of the energetic Catalonians the district has the advantages of hydropower from the Pyrenees and good transport connections with European markets.

A **silk** industry, established by the Moors, flourishes at two centers on the eastern coast.

CITIES OF SPAIN

Name	Type	Population (1952)
Madrid	Governmental	1,640,000
Barcelona	Seaport and industrial	1,290,000
Valencia	Seaport and industrial	516,000
Sevilla	Seaport	384,000
Malaga	Seaport	279,000
Zaragoza	Commercial	268,000
Granada	Commercial and industrial	156,000

Cities. **Madrid,** the capital of Spain, is the largest city of the country. It is located in the northern part of New Castile at almost the geographical center of the Iberian Peninsula. The reasons for its existence are chiefly political, but it is also the financial and cultural capital. Its climate is wretched: cold winters with piercing winds, hot, blazing summers, and large diurnal temperature variations. The climate has been disparagingly likened to that of Siberia.

Barcelona, on the Mediterranean coast about 75 miles south of the French border and some 300 miles northeast of Madrid, is the second city, principal port, and greatest industrial center of Spain. It is an unusual combination of a modern, bustling, industrial, and commercial city that is also a garden city. Textiles and machinery are its main industries; there are also many small "workshop industries."

Valencia is another port on the Mediterranean coast about midway between Barcelona and Gibraltar and 300 miles southeast of Madrid. It is located two miles inland on the plain of a small river. Like Barcelona it is an industrial center and, like all of Spain's largest cities, is the capital of its province of the same name. It is very picturesque, full of Moorish architecture and in the center of the largest and most beautiful *huerta* in Spain. Its chief industry is silk manufacture.

Sevilla, situated 50 miles inland on the Guadalquivir, not only is a present-day provincial capital but was for centuries the capital of the Moorish civilization. It is also a major church administrative center; its cathedral is one of the world's largest churches, and it is celebrated for its religious festivals, in which the entire population takes part. These fetes attract tourists from all over Europe and the Americas.

Malaga is the second seaport after Barcelona and is located on the Mediterranean coast about 75 miles northeast of Gibraltar. Its hinterland is the southern slopes of the Sierra Nevada. It is also a center of light industries, such as food processing.

Zaragoza is a commercial and rail center 175 miles northeast of Madrid, on the middle Ebro River at an intersection of trade routes. It is in one of the drier regions of Spain and is the center of an oasis of sorts—the rich, irrigated district watered by the Imperial Canal.

Granada lies 135 miles southeast of Sevilla in the foothills of the Sierra Nevada. It was the former capital of the Kingdom of Granada. Today it is far less important than it was under the Moors. Although a commercial and "industrial" center for the sugar industry, it is actually more a tourist city, for it is the site of the *Alhambra,* a palace famous as the supreme architectural accomplishment of the Moors, and one of the great masterpieces of the World.

Spain as a Whole. Although Spain does not possess the potentialities for renewed greatness as a world power, neither is it a pauper country; nevertheless it is grossly overpopulated for its present level of productivity. The near feudal conditions under which the country continues to exist have been cited as both the cause and the result of Spain's troubles.

The dry Meseta, which comprises over 50 percent of the country, is undoubtedly a great deterrent to high productivity in relation to size. (Its topographic dominance makes Spain the second highest country in

Europe, with an average elevation of over 2000 feet.) Yet some writers maintain that Spain at one time supported by domestic production a far larger population than it has today, and that the heavy emigration of the past few centuries has actually deprived the country of those elements of the population that could have furthered its advancement.

Whatever the significance of past events has been in contributing to the present state of affairs, a better future for Spain will depend on an increase in basic productivity of all kinds. Only thus can the country pay its way internationally. Such an increase in turn can come about only through a drastic change in the social and political structure.

3. THE SOUTHERN COAST OF FRANCE

General Aspects. The southern coast of France is, to paraphrase Caesar, divided into three parts (Fig. 19.2). On the west it is a continuous lowland behind which rise the **Cevennes Mountains,** the dissected escarpment of an interior highland. This western portion is known as the **Languedoc.**[7] In the

center is the delta and lower valley of the **Rhone River,** the single great stream of the southern coast. Farther east the lowland becomes narrower and more discontinuous until it disappears where the Alps come down to the sea as the **Maritime Alps,** in the region known as the **French Riviera** (Fig. 14.6). The Riviera and the Rhone lowland together form the region known as **Provence.**[8] Both Provence and Languedoc are regional names today and have no reference to the present political subdivisions of France.

A truly mild Mediterranean climate prevails in the Languedoc and Riviera, both of which are rather well shielded on the north by mountains. In the Rhone Valley, however, the winters are not so mild because of the easy avenue this wide depression affords for the cold *mistral* from the north.

Agriculture and Products. The most important product of the region as a whole is **wine,** known not so much for quality as for

---

[7] *Languedoc* ("language of *oc*") refers to the fact that in medieval times the local inhabitants used *oc* instead of *oil* (*oui*) for "yes."

[8] From *Provincia Romana* (Roman Province). The region was one of the early Roman colonies.

Fig. 14.6—French Riviera Scene Along the Coast Near Nice. The Mediterranean Riviera has for northwest Europeans the same resort significance as Florida has for people of the northeastern United States. (Courtesy, French Government Tourist Office.)

quantity. The Languedoc, the greatest single wine-producing district in the world, is responsible for one-third of all French wine production and is the only large single-crop region of France. So great is the output that the *vin ordinaire* (ordinary wine, with no distinguishing name) produced there is shipped about in tank cars.

Vegetables are grown throughout the region in the frost-free winter to supply the large markets of the north during their cold season. **Wheat** fields and **olive** groves, though present, are not so extensive as in the average Mediterranean region.

The Riviera is the site of an uncommon regional occupation—**floriculture.** It is a highly commercialized industry; during the winter nightly express trains carry cut flowers to the large cities of central and western Europe. Associated with it is a **perfume** industry, which prepares perfume ingredients from flowers. During the "harvest" haywagon loads of beautiful, fragrant blossoms such as jasmine move along the country roads to the perfume factories or shipping points.

On the Rhone delta, which is plentifully watered by the large river, cattle are raised on pastures better than the average Mediterranean grassland.

Bauxite is the only significant mineral product. It occurs in large deposits east of the Rhone delta. The mineral's name is derived from *Les Baux,* an ancient castle of the region.

CITIES OF THE SOUTHERN COAST OF
FRANCE

Name	Type	Population (1954)
Marseille	Seaport and industrial	662,000
Nice	Resort	245,000
Cannes	Resort	50,000
Monte Carlo (Monaco)	Resort	20,000 (1951)
Toulon	Seaport	141,000
Nimes	Industrial and commercial	89,000
Avignon	Industrial and commercial	63,000

Cities. The leading city of the region, the second city of all France, and one of the great ports of the world is **Marseille.** It is some 30 miles east of the mouth of the Rhone River (see Chapter 1, p. 16, for explanation of why it is not located on the Rhone proper), protected from the cold winds of the Rhone Valley by local highlands immediately to the north. Several canals provide connections with the internal water transport system of France. The city is more an import than an export center. It is the funnel through which France receives the products of its tropical and subtropical colonies, and through which the products of the Far East are often transshipped to Britain to avoid the long voyage around the Iberian Peninsula. A considerable portion of the import trade of Marseille is based on the needs of the city's own diverse industries. This is typified by the soap and margarine industries, which originally were developed on the basis of local olive oil but now depend almost wholly on imported copra, palm oil, and peanut oil. Similarly, an important metal smelting industry processes foreign ores, and there is a nearby center of petroleum refining (developed since World War II) based on Middle East crude oil.

Nice, the fifth city of France and the largest city of the Riviera, is situated on the coast not far from the Italian border. It is one of the great resort cities of the world, deriving in full the benefit that the sunny, mild winters afford in attracting tourists. The Maritime Alps provide scenery as well as protection from the cold north winds. Rarely is there any frost, and just as rarely does the temperature go above 90° F. The city is also a center of light industries, chief among which is the making of perfumes.

Cannes, 20 miles to the southwest of Nice, is another famous resort spot, traditionally patronized by the very wealthy. Most famous of all, however, is the town of **Monte Carlo,** the fabulous gambling center that constitutes the tiny, semiautonomous **Principality of Monaco.** Monte Carlo is only a few miles from the Italian border.

Toulon, on the coast about 35 miles east of Marseille, is a port city with a modest scale of commercial and fishing activity. Its significance, however, is entirely related to the fact that it is the site of the major French naval base and arsenal, together with their supporting works.

Nimes and **Avignon** are two inland cities of the Rhone Valley, northwest of Marseille. Both were important provincial centers in this part of the Roman Empire. Nimes has many well-preserved Roman ruins. The cities are local commercial centers and have a few light industries.

4. CENTRAL AND SOUTHERN ITALY

Topography. The resemblance in map outline of the long Italian peninsula to a boot, complete with heel, toe, and spur, projecting southeastward from Europe and seemingly in the act of kicking Sicily, is familiar to everyone. Throughout its 600-mile length the peninsula has a central mountain chain, the **Apennines**, a rugged range, highest in the central portion of their length, where they

rise to altitudes of over 9000 feet (Fig. 14.7). They continue into Sicily and neighboring small islands, where they contain active volcanoes. There is also an active volcanic district west of the central Apennines. (In an unusual application of such earth energy the underground heat in these districts is employed to heat homes and to provide local power on a rather large scale.)

Along the coasts of both sides of this central ridge are a series of more or less continuous plains, narrower and less important on the east than on the west. In order from north to south, the western plains are: the plain of **Tuscany**, over which flows the small but historically famous **Arno River**; the plain of **Latium**, with the equally small and even more famous **Tiber River**; the Naples plain

Fig. 14.7—Italy. The inset compares the area of the region with an equivalent area of the United States (states in white).

ITALY

around the bay of that name; and the **Sa-lerno** plain, famous in World War II as a beachhead in the Italian campaign.

In the extreme south of Italy (the "ball of the foot") in the district known as **Calabria** the mountains are heaved up in huge blocks. The lowlands between them are the best lands of the district, but because they are the breeding grounds of malaria mosquitoes the local population has preferred to live on the hill slopes away from the lowland farms. In-deed, all the lowlands of Italy, although the basis of the country's agriculture, are poorly drained and have been malaria infested. In modern times considerable attention has been given to their drainage and the elimina-tion of the malaria scourge.

The island of Sicily is densely populated and is an important agricultural district of Italy. Sardinia, to the northwest, is much more rugged and undeveloped.

Climate. The summers of central and southern Italy are typical of the Mediter-ranean climatic region. The highlands, how-ever, experience severe winter cold. Frigid winds from these central highlands also cause the coastal plains to have a winter that is colder than the typical Mediterranean win-ter. The rainfall distribution pattern is char-acteristically Mediterranean in that it is higher in the north than in the south. The eastern side of the peninsula is also drier than the west because of the rain shadow of the Apennines. On the other hand, the moun-tains and the west coast get the benefit of orographic rainfall. On the whole, the rain-fall of Italy is somewhat higher than average for the Mediterranean climate.

Agriculture and Products. The bulk of the land in southern Italy and Sicily is cultivated by tenant farmers, with irrigation practiced wherever possible. The good drainage sys-tems of Roman construction by which much coastal marshland was reclaimed in ancient times, but which were later allowed to de-teriorate completely, are now in the process of being slowly rehabilitated. The crop yields from such areas are therefore still gen-erally low. Wherever feasible the lower slopes of the Apennines are used in terrace

agriculture. The higher slopes serve as pas-ture or support what little forest remains in Italy.

Again the typical Mediterranean agricul-tural pattern of production prevails. The dominant crop, **wheat,** is raised on almost one-half the total cultivated area. It is an important crop everywhere, but there is a heavy concentration of production in Sicily. The wheat is used both in bread and in spaghetti, the staple Italian food.

Italy is second to Spain as an **olive** country but is the leading producer of **olive oil.** Cen-ters of production are along the east central coast on the "heel of the boot."

Italy is the second-ranking **wine** producer of the world. The vineyards mostly occupy terraced hillsides as part of a "mixed" agri-cultural practice (other crops are grown be-tween the vines). There is a large export business to France, where the wines are blended with French brands for export. The vineyard centers are distributed along nearly all the west coast and the northern east coast within the Mediterranean climatic portion of Italy.

Italy also ranks high as a **citrus fruit** pro-ducer, especially **lemons.** It is, after Spain, the leading European exporter of these fruits. Sicily is the chief producing area (it has al-most a monopoly on the European lemon market); other centers are on the west coast of the peninsula in the "toe of the boot."

Early spring **vegetables** wherever possible, **flowers** in the Riviera, **chestnuts** on the higher slopes and **almonds** on the southeast lowlands, and a minor production of figs and cork complete the Mediterranean pattern of agriculture in Italy.

Sheep (10 million) and **goats** (2 million) are pastured in the Apennines during the summer and the central western lowlands in winter.

Mineral Products. Although Italy in gen-eral is woefully deficient in mineral re-sources, production of a certain few materials in the Mediterranean climatic portion of the country is of some importance. The country is the second producer of **mercury;** about two-thirds of the Italian output comes from the northwestern section of the peninsula. Sulfur production from Sicily makes Italy an important source of that commodity. A major European lead-zinc district is located on the island of Sardinia. And the Carrara marble of the northern central part of the peninsula is in world-wide demand as the highest-quality marble quarried anywhere, especially prized by sculptors.

CITIES OF CENTRAL AND SOUTHERN ITALY

Name	Type	Population (1951)
Rome	Governmental and religious	1,700,000
Naples	Seaport	1,000,000
Genoa	Seaport	683,000
Florence	Commercial	391,000
Bari	Seaport	273,000
Palermo	Seaport	501,000
Catania	Seaport	300,000
Messina	Seaport	221,000

Cities. The capital city of Italy is **Rome** (Fig. 14.8), one of the great cultural centers of Western civilization. Known as the "Eternal City," it merits the name as the former capital of the Roman civilization and as the site of the *Vatican,* the residence of the Pope and the capital of Roman Catholicism. The ruins of ancient Rome stand today in the midst of the modern city and give the metropolis a flavor of antiquity unique among the world's large cities. Present-day Rome is neither industrial nor commercial; it is a political, cultural, and religious center.

Naples, Italy's third city and one of its major ports, is located 135 miles south of Rome on the Bay of Naples. Its scenic set-

Fig. 14.8—Rome, Italy. In the right foreground the modern Victor Emmanuel II monument; in the middle distance, far right, the ruins of the Roman Forum; in the center background the Colosseum. (Courtesy, Italian State Tourist Office.)

caption
Fig. 14.9—Genoa, Italy. View from the city over the harbor. (Courtesy, Italian State Tourist Office.)

ting is one of the most beautiful in Europe. Ten miles to the southeast is the volcano **Vesuvius,** at the base of which are the ruins of the Roman cities of **Pompeii** and **Herculaneum.** With such attractions Naples is one of the outstanding tourist cities of the world. Its university, museums, and other similar institutions make it in addition the cultural center of southern Italy. The romantic and enchanting island of **Capri** just outside the Bay of Naples, a famous resort even in the days of the Roman emperors, continues to exercise its lure for those in search of the beautiful in nature.

Genoa (Fig. 14.9), the chief port of Italy, is located on the northwestern coast at the base of the Italian peninsula. It serves not only the northern part of Italy outside the Mediterranean climatic region but also Switzerland and southern Germany. The city is unusually picturesque, as it is built mostly on the slopes of hills that extend to the shoreline and afford almost no flat land for a city site. Streets are in consequence a maze of narrow alleys, stairways, and tunnels. In addition to handling a busy traffic in goods Genoa also serves as a center of large merchant, shipping, and trading establishments and is a major industrial city, with heavy industry such as foundries and shipyards in addition to the usual light industries. Even without these features Genoa would be assured of permanent fame as the birthplace of Christopher Columbus.

Florence (Fig. 14.10) is about 60 miles inland from the west coast of Italy on the Arno River, which flows through a wide valley in the Apennines. It is the commercial center of a fertile agricultural district and the site of industries manufacturing all kinds of artistic and semi-artistic products. Its chief fame, however, stems from its role as one of the most vigorous and productive centers of the Renaissance. The city is virtually one great museum of architectural, literary, and art treasures of that era and for that reason is a major tourist center.

Bari, on the east coast of the peninsula just above the "heel," is the leading port of southeast Italy. It is the port for trade with the Balkans and the eastern Mediterranean countries and the site of several food-processing industries.

Palermo, the capital of Sicily, is located on the northern coast of the island, the port for

Fig. 14.10—Florence, Italy. View from Piazza Michelangelo across the Arno River, showing the famous architectural monuments of the city. (Courtesy, Italian State Tourist Office.)

the region of the island with such high agricultural productivity that it has been called the *Conca d'Ora* (Horn of Gold). The city was founded as a Phoenician colony and is rich in the architectural remains and monuments of many successive Mediterranean civilizations.

Catania, the second of the large Sicilian cities, is on the east coast of the island 100 miles southeast of Palermo. It is located in the shadow of the volcano **Mount Etna,** which periodically menaces the city with lava flows. Catania is an export center for fruits and sulfur.

Messina, a port 60 miles north of Catania, is on the northeast tip of Sicily at a point where the **Strait of Messina** separates it from Italy by only some three miles. It is a "modern" city by Mediterranean standards, having been almost completely destroyed in 1902 by one of the most disastrous earthquakes in history.

5. Albania

General Aspects. Albania is a small country on the east shore of the Adriatic Sea between Yugoslavia on the north and east and Greece on the south (Fig. 15.2). Its area of 10,000 square miles is about that of Maryland.

The land surface is rugged; most of the country is mountainous, with peaks of over 9000-foot altitude. Short, swift streams flow down deep valleys to the restricted coastal lowlands. Most of the coastlands are marshy, and no good harbor site exists.

On the coastal plains the Mediterranean climate of Albania is much like that of southern Italy, across the Adriatic. The highlands receive considerable orographic precipitation, even in summer. Winter is, of course, colder in the mountains than is typical of the Mediterranean climate.

The People. Albania's population is estimated to be somewhat over one million. The racial ancestry is uniform, but the mountains, the isolation of most of the country, and the natural belligerency of the inhabitants (see Chapter 2, p. 27) have preserved a tribal or feudal order of society despite the postwar establishment of Communist rule. The absence of social unity is manifested by the lack of a common language and by the religious diversity. Almost 70 percent of the population is Moslem, some 20 percent is in the Albanian (Greek Orthodox) Church, and the remaining 10 percent is Roman Catholic.

Economic Activities. Albanian farming is a primitive, subsistence agriculture. **Corn** is the chief crop on the fertile coastal lowlands. As in Italy, malaria interferes with the full use of this better land.

The raising of domestic animals is the most important activity in terms of exportable products. Over 1.5 million **sheep,** 900,000 **goats,** and 400,000 **cattle** are pastured under the practice of transhumance.

Albania as a Whole. Albania is at present the most backward country of Europe, but such was not always the case. The lowlands in former times supported a sizeable, energetic population. Whether malaria or something else was responsible for the decline is disputed. It is significant, however, that not all the natural geographic factors are deterrents to progress in Albania. There are mineral deposits within its borders that could be profitably exploited. The dense forest cover on the mountains, which extends over one-third of the entire area of the country, is also of potential use. But lack of transportation and the unstable political history of the region have precluded any intensive development of these resources.

QUESTIONS. Describe the general topography of Spain and name the major features. How has the topography and climate of the country influenced its history? Describe the social conditions of Spain. What are the handicaps to transportation in Spain? What are *huertas?* What factors retard the full development of the agricultural resources of the country? Name the major agricultural product. Spain is the leading producer of what characteristic Mediterranean agricultural product? Discuss the importance of oranges and grapes in Spanish agriculture. Spain is the leading producer of what mineral product? What is the chief manufactured product? Discuss the problems that must be solved if Spain is to overcome its handicaps of geography and history.

What are the general topographic features of the southern coast of France? What is the outstanding product? What are the two major "industries" of the Riviera? Why is Marseille mainly an import center?

Give a brief description of the general topography of central and southern Italy. Name the major agricultural products of this part of the country. The major mineral products.

What serious geographical disadvantages have contributed to the backwardness of Albania?

CHAPTER 15

The Mediterranean Basin

(CONTINUED)

6. GREECE

Topography. Greece is a country of mountains, peninsulas, and islands (Fig. 15.1). The total extent of Greek territory is 50,000 square miles, about the same area as that of Alabama, but islands constitute 9000 square miles of the Greek lands. The peculiar topography of Greece results from the fact that it is a mountainous region partly sunk beneath the sea. Extension of the mountains of Albania continues southeast into Greece, where they run out into the Mediterranean as long, narrow promontories, and along the floor of the sea where, almost completely submerged, their peaks form the countless islands bordering the mainland.

The different parts of Greece can be best described by using the classical regional names. The **Pindus Mountains** dominate the northern, mainland portion of the country (Fig. 15.2). This rugged highland area, with peaks of over 6000 feet, is even today crossed only by primitive trails. The western side of these mountains, facing the **Ionian Sea,** is the region of **Epirus.** Small plains, alternating with projecting spurs from the main Pindus range, constitute the coastline here. Most of this part of Greece is rough, infertile, and sparsely populated.

On the eastern side of the Pindus range

Fig. 15.1—Kepkypa, Greece. "Greece is a country of mountains, peninsulas and islands." (Courtesy, Royal Greek Embassy.)

subsidiary spurs also run out to the coastline, but the plains between them are larger and rather well populated. The northernmost spur is surmounted by **Mount Olympus,** a peak of over 9500 feet elevation famed as the legendary home of the Greek gods. South of this spur is the large, fertile plain of **Thessaly.**

Still farther south, beyond another spur and a small valley, a large subsidiary range of the Pindus forms the southeastward peninsular projection of Greece which ends in **Attica,** site of the highest development of the ancient Greek civilization. This range contains **Mount Parnassus** (elevation 8000 feet),

Fig. 15.2—Greece and Albania. The inset compares the areas of Albania and Greece with Maryland and Alabama, which have, respectively, approximately equivalent areas.

the home of the Muses of Greek mythology.

The mainland portion of Greece continues eastward along the north shore of the Aegean Sea as **Macedonia** and **Thrace** in the typical pattern of alternating ridges and valleys opening on the sea. These valleys are the most fertile and prosperous areas in the country. The most westerly one contains the lower reaches and delta of the **Vardar River,** the largest stream of Greece. East of this valley the peninsula of **Khalkidike** projects southward, ending in three long, narrow sub-peninsulas. The most easterly of these, **Mount Athos,** is a geographic curiosity—a politically independent, self-governing area inhabited solely by the monks of 20 monasteries of several nationalities.

South of the main Greek peninsula is another peninsula, a continuation of the main

GREECE AND ALBANIA

Pindus range, the **Peloponnesus.** It is separated from the mainland by the **Gulf of Corinth** and is connected to Attica by an isthmus only four miles wide. This isthmus has been cut through by a sea-level canal (Fig. 15.3), making the Peloponnesus technically an island. The topography of the Peloponnesus repeats that of the mainland on a small scale—isolated plains facing the sea and separated by intervening ridges which project as finger-like promontories into the sea.

Of the Grecian islands the southernmost, **Crete,**[1] is the largest (3200 square miles). It was the site of the ancient, pre-Greek Minoan civilization. Second largest of the islands is **Euboea,** which parallels Attica on the northeast. Northeast of Crete are the **Dodecanese Islands** and north from these, parallel to the coast of Anatolia, are the **Sporades,** rough and almost uninhabited. The **Cyclades,** scattered over the sea to the southeast of Attica, are also poor and barren. In earlier times, however, they provided a safe retreat for those who wished to flee the perennial internecine wars waged on the Greek mainland. As a consequence the Cyclades have a relatively dense population that cultivates the hillsides on minute terraces. On the northeast, off the coast of Epirus, are the **Ionian Islands,** also densely populated in comparison with the mainland facing them.

Climate. Greece is a much more arid country than either Italy or Spain. The summers are drier and hotter; the rainfall is generally lower throughout the year. As a consequence the short, lush spring of the Mediterranean is an especially characteristic feature here. In Greece all plants must bloom before the summer drought.

These general climatic conditions are considerably modified locally by the topography. Thus the main mountain range in the west receives twice as much rainfall on the average as does the country to the east, which is in its rain shadow. Again, the south-

Fig. 15.3—Corinth Canal, Greece, Cutting Off the Peloponnesus From the Mainland.

ern shore of Crete is warm enough for tropical plants to thrive.

Greece is subject to the vicissitudes of both the *bora* and *sirocco* winds (see Chapter 14, p. 262); the former blows over the western and the latter over most of the central and southern parts of the country.

Historical Aspects. Geographical factors have from its beginning been important in the course of Greek history. The country is adjacent to the place where Europe and Asia meet, a circumstance that has had significance both in the strategy of wars and in the growth and spread of culture and civilization.

The civilization of ancient Greece and the city-states on which it was centered are directly related to the geography of the region. Civilized practices appear to have come into Greece from the southeast, through the is-

[1] Crete is a British possession; most of its inhabitants are Greek. It is here considered as Greek geographically rather than politically.

lands. When, therefore, the first stirrings of cultural progress occurred on the mainland, the form of its organization was molded by the natural environment of basin and mountain.

The result was the Greek political unit—the city-state—that of a miniature nation occupying and developing a small geographic unit. Each such independent division comprised a mountain-rimmed plain. The fields of the plain provided the agricultural base, the mountains the protection from invasion. The city itself was commonly situated on or at the base of a high point, within the plain itself. If such a site was not available a location in the center of the plain afforded a measure of protection by allowing early detection of an approaching invader.

But the very geographical factors that helped mold the Greek civilization were also largely responsible for its downfall. Isolation and separation bred suspicion, jealousy, and hate between the states. Only in times of great common peril was it possible for the Greeks to unite in a common defense and make the most of their geographic defensive factors. Eventually, however, internal warfare exacted too great a toll, and Greek civilization declined.

In modern times Greece has been an independent nation only since 1829, when the country won its freedom from Turkish rule. The political organization of Greece has long been unstable, with constant alternation between monarchy and republic. At present, as the result of a confused series of events after World War II, Greece is a kingdom once more.

The People. The inhabitants of Greece, looking out on the sea from their otherwise mountain-girt plains, have from the first been subject to a geographical prompting to venture over the Mediterranean. It was, accordingly, almost inevitable that they should become pioneers in navigation and be among the leading seafaring peoples of ancient times.

The modern Greek (Fig. 15.4), as an individual in a population of 8 million attempting to gain a livelihood from a land that

Fig. 15.4—Greek Shepherd and Part of His Flock. (Courtesy, Royal Greek Embassy.)

would probably support only half that number comfortably, views life as a grim struggle for survival. The social structure exhibits the same sharp division between rich and poor that is found in Spain, with no middle class between. The prevailing sociological atmosphere is one of cynical opportunism.

Transportation. There are fewer than 2000 miles of railroads in Greece, a significant indication of the status of commerce and industry in the country. Even the best highways are in a state of chronic neglect. The Corinth Canal has not the importance as a navigational facility that its location would suggest because of its narrowness and the menace to shipping of the swift currents that course through it.

Agriculture and Products. The Greeks are confronted with an appalling agricultural situation: Whereas over half the working population is supported by farming, only 20 percent of the area of the country is arable land, and Greece is far from able to meet its food needs. The rainfall deficiency is a further handicap to agricultural production. Greece is also the worst example among the larger countries of Europe of the harm to the land wrought through several thousands of years of human occupancy. The forests that once covered the mountains were cut away many centuries ago (Fig. 15.5); since then torrential Mediterranean rains have been stripping away the soil. Age-long destructive grazing by sheep and goats on the hillsides has aggravated this deterioration of the soil cover. The result is a landscape in which all too commonly the Mediterranean scrub growth is the only vegetation that can maintain itself—if, indeed, any plant cover exists.

Wherever there is enough water and soil the mountain slopes are terraced for agriculture, but in the main cultivation is restricted to the lowlands, which amount to less than 5 percent of the total area of Greece. As a consequence of all these unfavorable agricultural conditions the Greeks have been prompted to the sea, and many have been led to gain a livelihood from shipping and fisheries.

The dominance of cereals in Mediterranean agriculture definitely applies to Greece. Grains occupy three-quarters of all cultivated land. **Wheat** and **barley** alone cover half of such land. The chief producing regions of the two grains are the plains of Thessaly and Macedonia, and the western Peloponnesus. Corn, oats, and rice are also grown.

Fig. 15.5—Barren Hillside of an Island Near Piraeus, Greece. Communication is by caiques, the type of craft seen here, a design unchanged for centuries. (Courtesy, Royal Greek Embassy.)

Much of Greek agriculture is also devoted to fertility-robbing "money crops" that will sell abroad. One such crop, not entirely characteristic of Mediterranean agriculture, is **tobacco,** grown in Thessaly. Greek tobacco is a mild variety, one of the "Turkish" tobaccos of commerce. Tobacco shipments to Egypt and the United States for cigarette manufacture account for almost one-half the total value of Greek exports.

Another important export product, of which Greece is the source of 90 percent of the world supply, is **currants.** These are dried grapes of a small, seedless variety that flourishes only on a special combination of soil and climate found around the Gulf of Corinth.[2] There is a large export to France, where currants are used in the fermentation of high-grade wine, itself an export item.

Other **grapes** are grown wherever possible to produce the very resinous Greek wines. On the terraced mountainsides wheat and figs are planted between the vines.

Greece is the third in rank among the producers of **olive oil.** The country is so dry

[2] "Currant" is a corruption of the word "Corinth." This currant is not the same as the currant used for jelly in the United States.

that even the olive tree survives only with difficulty, and the yield per tree is small. Nevertheless the dependence of the Greeks on the olive and olive oil for fat foods is as high as anywhere in the Mediterranean Basin. The chief districts of olive growth are the Khalkidike peninsula, on the Isthmus of Corinth, the western Peloponnesus, and the north shore of Crete.

Oranges and **lemons** are produced on the north and west sides of the Peloponnesus. Cotton is grown in eastern Macedonia.

Sheep (8 million) and **goats** (4.3 million) are the chief domestic animals, found mostly in the mountains where the land is good for little else but pasture. Transhumance is practiced between the Pindus Mountains and the plains of Thessaly.

Mineral Products and Resources. The mineral resources of Greece are significant but not large. Almost the entire mineral production of the country is exported. **Iron ore** has first place in value. It is produced in the Cyclades and in several places on the mainland. Output is minor relative to the world total.

Fig. 15.6—Acropolis, Athens, Greece, Seen From the Ruins of the Temple of Zeus. (Courtesy, Royal Greek Embassy.)

Several mineral products of Greece are used in the manufacture of steel products. **Magnesite** (for lining furnaces) is mined in Euboea. **Manganese** comes from the southwest Peloponnesus. **Chromite** comes mostly from Thessaly, and **nickel** from the mainland opposite Euboea.

CITIES OF GREECE

Name	Type	Population (1951)
Athens	Governmental, commercial, industrial	561,000
Piraeus	Seaport, industrial	185,000
Thessaloniki	Seaport	217,000
Patras	Seaport	88,000

Cities. **Athens,** the largest city of Greece, is one of those cities that typify the character of the countries of which they are the capitals. Like Rome, Athens is the site of some of the world's most magnificient ruins, remains of ancient edifices which even in their dilapidation dominate the locale. The *Acropolis* (Fig. 15.6), the ancient citadel of Athens, rises 500 feet above the city spread over the plain at its base. Its summit is studded with the ruins of beautiful temples, including the *Parthenon*, greatest of them all.

The present city of Athens is a modern phenomenon. In 1833 it was chosen because of sentiment to be the capital of the new, independent Kingdom of Greece. At that time it was a village of a few thousand inhabitants. In a little more than a century it has experienced so tremendous an expansion that it has become one of the important cities of the eastern Mediterranean.

Four miles southwest of Athens is its harbor city, **Piraeus.** Both cities have expanded so much since 1833 as to constitute now a continuous great seaport. The success of Athens-Pireaus is due to its central position at the crossing of the chief trade routes of the country. The two cities are also an industrial concentration, the chief industries being textiles, food processing, other light industries, and metallurgical plants.

The second port of Greece and one of the leading ports of southeastern Europe is **Thessaloniki** (more often known as **Salonika** in the English-speaking world). The city is located in central Macedonia at the base of the main peninsula of Greece. Although itself not on the river, Salonika is the port for the **Vardar River** and its valley, one of the major gateways to the interior of the Balkan countries from the Mediterranean. The fact that Yugoslavia maintains a "free port" in Salonika is indicative of the importance of the Vardar trade route for that country. In normal times the city is a trade center for almost all the Balkan countries. It has a variety of industries ranging from textiles and tanning to brickmaking and iron foundries.

Patras, on the north coast of the Peloponnesus at the western end of the Gulf of Corinth, is the chief port of western Greece, is a traditional emigration port for Greeks leaving their homeland, and is the major export point for the currant crop.

Greece as a Whole. The future of Greece is not bright. There is here a clear, unqualified case of overpopulation. Handicapped by the devastation of war and enemy occupation, wracked by civil strife following World War II, and lacking the initiative to attempt the limited improvement that is feasible, the Greeks are in the unfavorable position of an agricultural people who must import foodstuffs to satisfy their needs. Payment for these imports is based in part on the services of the large merchant marine, in part on exports, but the international economic position of the country is not very sound.

The large influx of repatriated refugees from Turkey in the early 1920's led to all the development and expansion (chiefly in Macedonia) that was possible in agriculture. Opportunities for exploitation still exist in the mineral fields, but for these domestic capital is lacking and it is difficult to attract foreign capital. In the absence of demand for farm labor the growing population of Greece gravitates to the cities, where the large numbers of unemployed constitute a difficult problem.

A satisfactory and lasting solution to the dismal overall economic plight of Greece has not as yet been suggested.

7. TURKEY

Topography. The Republic of Turkey is a country 296,000 square miles in area (somewhat larger than Texas). Of this territory only some 9000 square miles (about the size of New Hampshire) is in Europe (Fig. 15.7). This section is known as **Thrace.** Most of the Asiatic portion of the country is included in the peninsula of **Anatolia** (also known as Asia Minor), which is bordered by the Black Sea on the north, the Mediterranean Sea on the south.

Like Spain, Turkey in Asia is chiefly a plateau country. Its eastern portion is composed of high mountains and narrow valleys running east-west. **Mount Ararat** (elevation about 17,000 feet) in the extreme east is the highest point in the country. The mountains dwindle in height westward where they skirt a plateau to the south known as **Kurdistan,** the headwater country of the Tigris and Euphrates rivers. The **Taurus Mountains,** a southwest trending range on the southern side of the Anatolian peninsula, attain 12,000-foot altitudes and are the highest mountains on the peninsula proper. They continue westward to connect with the

Fig. 15.7—Turkey. The Inset Compares the Area of Turkey With That of Texas, Which Is Approximately Equal.

sunken mountains beneath the Aegean Sea.

Most of the peninsula is about 3000 feet in elevation. Surrounding it are coastal lowlands, narrow but continuous along the Black Sea, larger but separate along the Mediterranean coast. The more important of these lowlands are: **Cilicia,** a mountainrimmed coastal basin at the extreme eastern tip of the Mediterranean; **Antalya,** a smaller lowland farther west; the wide valleys of three rivers on the west coast of the peninsula; and the lowlands surrounding the Bosporus and Dardanelles. These are the fertile agricultural regions of Asiatic Turkey. Less important fertile districts are in Turkish Thrace.

Climate. Except for the easternmost portion along the Black Sea, the entire coast of Anatolia and all of Turkish Thrace have typical Mediterranean climate. As in all the Mediterranean countries of Europe, the rainfall within this climatic region increases to the north. In Anatolia the rise to the interior plateau induces orographic rains on the windward slopes, but, in consequence, the uplands become progressively drier with distance inland. The rainfall decreases, for example, from 25 inches a year on the west coast to 13 inches in the center of the plateau. Still farther east the mountains cast their rain shadows over the Kurdistan plateau region.

This generalization as to the plateau climate is of course subject to qualifications because of local topographic influences. The plateau as a whole is considered to have a steppe climate, but both areas of actual desert and well-watered tracts occur. In the basins with interior drainage salt lakes are present: a large one, **Lake Van** (about the size of Great Salt Lake in Utah) in the extreme east and elsewhere four other rather large ones and several smaller ones.

The People. The old Turkish Empire prior to World War I contained many diverse nationalities and racial groups. The Turkish Republic of today is, however, inhabited almost exclusively by Turks (Fig. 15.8). The west coast of Anatolia was dominated by Greeks (some of the area was Greek territory) until the Greek-Turkish War subsequent to World War I. As a result of the Greek defeat, over one million Greeks were deported to Greece in exchange for thousands of Turks repatriated from that country. The present population of Turkey is 21 million. Although Turkey is 98 percent Moslem, there is no state religion. Various Christian sects comprise the bulk of the religious minorities.

The modern Turk is far different from the generations of his forebears prior to World War I. While retaining the courage and stamina that have always made him one of the world's best fighting men, the Turk has acquired the ambition and determination to do the work involved in building up his country to the status of a modern Western nation. In his willingness to adopt and accept any change that will better his life he is much like an American. Indeed, American aid programs in the postwar era in both the economic and military fields have been outstandingly successful because of the enthusiasm with which Americans and Turks have worked together to achieve their common purpose.

Transportation. The rivers of Turkey, like those of Spain, are of little use for navigation. The larger cities are all connected by railroad but the total mileage is less than 5000 miles. The main cities, villages, and centers of population are connected by some 30,000 miles of roads, about half of which are paved. Approximately one-third of the railroad mileage and three-quarters of the road mileage have been constructed since the establishment of the republic in 1923. A large road-building program as part of the American aid referred to above has given

Fig. 15.8—Street Scene in Ankara, Turkey. Turkish city population types. (Courtesy, Office of Turkish Press Attaché.)

Turkey additional miles of all-weather roads and has enabled isolated interior areas to produce for export rather than engage in subsistence agriculture.

Agriculture and Products. Turkey is an agricultural country, with three-quarters or more of the population engaged in cultivating some 20 percent of the land area. Traditional farming techniques are quite primitive; in many areas the plow is merely a stone-tipped crooked stick that does little more than scratch the surface of the ground. The Turkish government is engaged, however, in replacing such equipment and practices with modern implements and techniques as rapidly as possible.

The cereals **wheat, barley, corn, oats, rye,** and **rice** follow the typical Mediterranean pattern of importance. Wheat and barley predominate in the drier regions of the plateau but are grown to some extent everywhere. The heaviest concentrations of corn production are on the eastern portion of the Black Sea coast, although this cereal is also grown wherever conditions are not too dry. Under the postwar modernization program production has so much improved that whereas the country was formerly a wheat importer that cereal is now the leading export, and Turkey's sales are a significant fraction of the world market.

The second export and chief cash crop is **cotton,** grown in Cilicia. **Tobacco** is the third export crop; the best qualities come from the central Black Sea coast and central Aegean coast. Turkish leaf is in general a high-quality item in the world tobacco market.

Turkey is second to Greece in the export of **raisins.** Most of the crop comes from the same Aegean district as does the tobacco. **Grapes** for a special local product known as *pekme* (grape juice converted into a honey-like substance by boiling and beating) are cultivated along most of the coastland of the country. **Olives** are grown along the entire Mediterranean coast. The southernmost of the three river valleys on the Aegean coast is the most important center of production.

The Aegean tobacco-raisin district is also the center of citrus fruit and fig production.

Indeed, it is the world's leading fig district. Large quantities of the fruit are shipped in dried form to the United States.

Less important products are opium, produced from poppies at two centers on the plateau and sold abroad for medicinal use, sugar beets from Turkish Thrace and other sections in the north, and such fibers as silk, flax, and hemp. The Black Sea coast, with its heavier rainfall, is also the site of large groves of many kinds of nut trees.

Almost without exception the noncereal products mentioned above are productions of the coastal, Mediterranean climate lowlands. The aridity of the plateau is, of course, responsible for the lack of noncereal products. As one proceeds inland, wheat land gives way to pasture land almost exclusively. The animal population of Turkey is impressive: 27 million **sheep,** 17 million "ordinary" **goats** and 5 million **Angora goats,** 11 million **cattle,** over 1.5 million **asses,** 1.2 million **horses,** over a million **water buffalo,** 100,000 **camels,** and about the same number of **mules.** This large number and variety of domestic animals is not due to the richness of the pasture. On the contrary, the grass is so poor and sparse that nomadism is the rule, and on the plateau borders the use of the steppe land is possible only through transhumance. The abundance of animals is due rather to the large area involved—more than half of Turkey.

The goats and sheep are the source of the usual hair and wool products in addition to providing a meat supply. The Angora goats are the source of mohair, most of which is exported to the United States, the remainder utilized domestically in the manufacture of fine **rugs.**

Other nonmanufacturing industries include **fishing,** conducted in the narrow straits of the Dardanelles and Bosporus where the constricted waters are ideal for the purpose, and **lumbering,** in the extensive forests of the north and northeast.

Mineral Resources and Products. Turkey apparently possesses rich and varied mineral deposits, but they have as yet been little developed. The most important export product is **chromite.** The country is one of the three leading producers of this mineral, which is the source of the steel alloy metal chromium and is also used in lining steel-making furnaces.

Iron ore is produced in Anatolia, and high-grade **coal** is mined at a site on the western portion of the Black Sea coast. These materials supply an **iron and steel** works located 45 miles southeast of the coal deposits. Unfortunately, this apparent symbol of an industrially developing Turkey is not on a sound economic basis and could not be maintained without state subsidization.

Development of **copper, lead,** and **zinc** deposits has been rapid since World War II. Other mineral products include **emery,** an abrasive material of which Turkey is the leading producer; **meerschaum,** a material well known to pipe smokers, of which Turkey has a virtual monopoly; and **magnesite, antimony, sulfur,** and **lignite** (of which last there are large, scattered, locally used deposits).

Industries. In addition to iron and steel, other industries, under a plan inaugurated in 1934, have been established with state aid. The major developments of this program have been in **textiles, cement, paper, glass,** and **sugar.** Attention is also being given to the utilization of Turkey's large **hydropower** potential.

CITIES OF TURKEY

Name	Type	Population (1950)
Istanbul	Seaport	1,000,000
Izmir	Seaport	231,000
Ankara	Governmental	288,000
Adana	Commercial	118,000

Cities. The greatest city of Turkey is **Istanbul,** or **Constantinople,** as it was known for centuries. For thousands of years Istanbul has played an important role in the history of this part of the world because of its unsurpassed strategic and commercial position on the Bosporus, at the crossroads of the land route between Europe and Asia and the sea route between the Mediterranean and Black seas. For centuries after the fall of Rome it was the most important city in the Western world. Istanbul today is the educational capital of Turkey and one of the great cultural centers of Islam. The mosque of *St. Sophia* (originally a Christian church) is one of the largest churches in the world. The city has over 700 mosques and it is also the administrative capital of the Greek Orthodox Christian Church. Commerce is still the major activity of Istanbul, based on its excellent harbor known as the "Golden Horn" because of the rich fishing its waters afford.

Most famous of the ruins of ancient cities that abound throughout Anatolia is the site of ancient **Troy,** fabled city of the Iliad. Troy stood on the northwest coast of Anatolia just outside the entrance to the Dardanelles—a recognition even in those times of the strategic and commercial significance of the straits between two landlocked seas.

Ankara (or in its anglicized form, Angora), the capital of Turkey, is situated on a 500-foot hill in a broad plain in the center of the Anatolian plateau, some 200 miles southeast of Istanbul. It is located on the site of an ancient city, but the present city was built almost completely during the last few decades (Fig. 15.8). The leaders of the new Republic of Turkey chose this site for their capital with the idea that it should be a purely Turkish city, which Istanbul is not. With its broad boulevards and fine new government buildings it is a fitting representative of the modern nation.

The third city of Turkey is **Izmir** (formerly known as **Smyrna**), at the head of a bay which serves as a good harbor between two of the major coastal lowlands of western Anatolia. Izmir is the shipping center for the major part of the export trade in the products of Anatolia. It is the hub of the tobacco and fig industries of Turkey and is the "fig capital" of the world.

Adana, about 100 miles southeast of Ankara, is located on a small river about 30 miles from the Mediterranean in the Cilicia district. It is the commercial center of the surrounding fertile agricultural district.

Turkey as a Whole. Until World War I Turkey was the ruling state of the Ottoman Empire, a decadent, religious-political unit that embraced most of the country around the eastern Mediterranean. The Turkish defeat in that war caused the already shaky structure to fall apart. Those portions of the empire not established as mandates to Allied countries proclaimed their independence, and in 1923 the Republic of Turkey, with boundaries much like those of today, was proclaimed by a group of progressive leaders known as the "Young Turks."

The program of the new republic was to become a modern, Western democracy in the shortest possible time. Amazing progress was made along that difficult road. In 1928, for example, education in the Latin alphabet rather than Arabic script was made compulsory. By 1930 the new alphabet was in universal use! This was possible partly because of the low literacy rate and a simultaneous drive to raise it. Other changes included the adoption of Western legal codes in place of the old Moslem ones, the emancipation and enfranchisement of women, and the complete separation of church and state.

Progress in the economic and industrial sphere has been less rapid. This tardiness is due not so much to lack of resources and ability as to the fact that it takes time to achieve such programs. Economic changes can be encouraged but cannot be brought about at once merely by passing laws. The

Fig. 15.9—Syria, Lebanon, and Israel. The inset compares the area of the three countries with that of Minnesota, which is approximately equal.

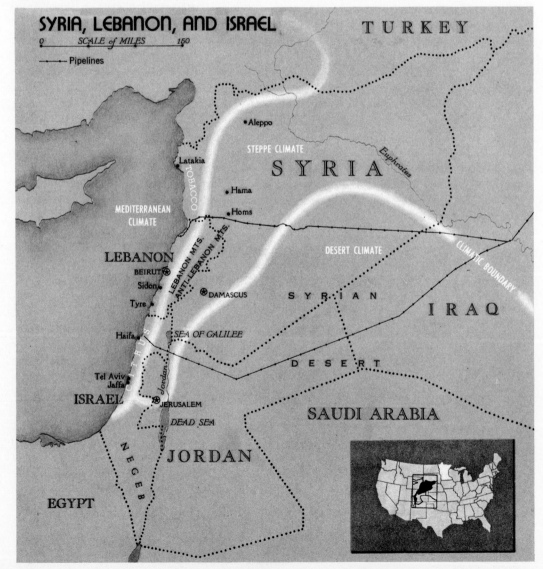

greatest need for further progress is the establishment of an adequate transportation system, (a) to provide the facilities necessary for economic movement to market of the agricultural and mineral products of the interior and (b) to enable new production techniques to be brought more easily to the isolated inhabitants of those parts of the country.

In contrast to the bleak outlook for Greece, the future of Turkey seems bright. The country has the advantages of a combination of important mineral resources, fertile agricultural tracts, an excellent commercial position, and an energetic people aware of their present deficiencies and imbued with a determination to remedy them.

8. SYRIA AND LEBANON

General Aspects. The Republics of Syria and Lebanon occupy the extreme eastern shore of the Mediterranean Sea (Fig. 15.9). Formerly part of the Ottoman Empire of the Turks, these areas became semiautonomous states under a French mandate after World War I. After World War II they attained full sovereignty. The total area of the two countries is roughly 70,000 square miles (about the size of Oklahoma). Of this, Lebanon occupies an area of 3400 square miles (three-quarters the size of Connecticut) on the southern half of the coast.

The topography near the coast is dominated by the northernmost development of the great system of rift valleys that runs from south of the Taurus Mountains to central Africa (see Chapter 9, p. 147). A highland parallels the coast a few miles inland, culminating in Lebanon in the **Lebanon Mountains** (Fig. 15.10), a range 100 miles long which rises to peaks of nearly 10,000 feet. The eastern side of this range drops off into the rift valley, on the other side of which is a smaller and lower range, the **Anti-Lebanon.** To the east the country merges into the plateau of the upper Euphrates River Basin; to the southeast the land is also high.

The Mediterranean climate is restricted to a narrow coastal belt in front of the Leb-

anon Mountains. The mountains themselves, because of the mild temperatures due to their altitude, are a popular resort district for all the eastern Mediterranean people able to afford such recreation. As in Anatolia, the climate becomes progressively more arid as the Mediterranean is left behind. To the east it becomes a warm steppe climate; to the southeast is the **Syrian Desert** (Fig. 15.11), where Syria, Jordan, Saudi Arabia, and Iraq meet.

The People. The total population of this area is nearly 4.7 million, of which about one-fourth is in Lebanon. The vast majority of this population lives near the coast, for which reason Syria is discussed as a country of Mediterranean climate although only a small fraction of its area actually has that climate.

This region, with its long history as a focal point of contact between the numerous peoples of the Middle East, contains a jumbled mixture of races and nationalities (Fig. 15.12). Besides Syrians there are Turks, Armenians, Jews, Persians, and many others. The chief language is Arabic but many dialects of this are spoken. Similarly, the principal religion is Islam, but there are numerous sects of that faith as well as of both Catholic churches. Some Protestants are also present.

Agriculture and Products. Both countries are agricultural, with about two-thirds of the population dependent on cultivation of the land. The best agricultural districts are the populous Lebanese coast and the rift valley. **Wheat** and **barley,** the Mediterranean staple cereals, are planted in the largest acreage. Wheat is exported from Syria to Lebanon.

In addition there is the usual Mediterranean assortment of olives, grapes, citrus fruits, figs, and apricots, plus cotton and tobacco, all produced on a small scale. The tobacco is an aromatic, mild variety named for the **Latakia** district in which it is grown, and used for blending purposes in smoking tobaccos throughout Europe and the United States.

Sheep, goats, camels, cattle, and asses are

Fig. 15.10—Lebanon Mountains, Parallel to the Mediterranean Coast in Lebanon. (Courtesy, Lebanon Embassy.)

the domestic animals in that order of importance. A small silk industry is centered in the northern and coastal cities, and oil refining is carried on at the coastal terminus in Lebanon of the pipe line from Iraq (see Chapter 12, p. 228).

Syria and Lebanon are not abundantly endowed with natural resources, although Lebanon does have pleasant scenery. A tourism industry developed on this basis in Lebanon is of considerable importance in the national income.

Cities. **Aleppo,** the largest city of the region and the commercial capital of northern Syria, is located in the northwest corner

CITIES OF SYRIA AND LEBANON

Name	Country	Type	Population
Aleppo	Syria	Commercial	381,000 (1952)
Damascus	Syria	Commercial and governmental	373,000 (1952)
Beirut	Lebanon	Seaport and governmental	400,000 (1953)
Homs	Syria	Commercial	262,000 (1952)
Hama	Syria	Commercial	156,000 (1952)

Fig. 15.11—Syrian Desert in Jordan. (Courtesy, A. H. Detweiler.)

of the country not far from the Turkish border. It was formerly an important intersection of trade routes on the overland route to the Far East, but the opening of the Suez Canal deprived Aleppo of all significance in that trade. It is still important commercially, however, by reason of its rail connections with the other large cities of Syria and Lebanon, and with the railroad systems of Turkey and Iraq.

modern buildings and broad avenues traversed by streetcars and buses.

Beirut, about 50 miles northwest of Damascus, is the capital of Lebanon and the chief port of both countries. It is located on a narrow coastal plain backed by the Lebanon Mountains. It is the legendary site of the slaying of the dragon by St. George, who became, through a very roundabout process, the patron saint of England. Beirut is a cos-

Fig. 15.12—Lebanese Peasant Couple Outside Their Home. (Courtesy, Lebanese Embassy.)

Damascus, the chief city of southern Syria and capital of the country, is located 50 miles from the Mediterranean east of Lebanon. Damascus is said to be the oldest city in the world inhabited from its founding to date. Its history goes back to the nineteenth century B.C. The city is built astride a small stream which flows along the edge of a large, fertile oasis. Thus it is a kind of port for the Syrian desert lands that extend beyond the city to the east. Despite its long history Damascus has a modern, Western look, with

mopolitan city with a large French section, a reminder of the days when it was the French administrative capital of the mandate. Beirut is also the site of the American University of Beirut, an American-supported and -administered institution of high repute and influence throughout the Middle East. As part of the astute cultivation of tourism the city boasts the most elaborate airport (Fig. 15.13) in the Middle East, and has become an important international stopover point.

Homs and **Hama** are two commercial centers on the railroad north from Damascus to Aleppo, 115 and 80 miles, respectively,

Fig. 15.13—International Airport at Beirut, Lebanon. (Courtesy, Lebanese Embassy.)

south of Aleppo in a fertile valley location. An unusual feature of Hama is the nine gigantic water wheels (Fig. 15.14), dating from the fourteenth century, used to raise water for irrigation from the nearby river.

Syria and Lebanon as a Whole. The present status of the Syria-Lebanon region is in sharp contrast to its great significance in ancient times. This was once one of the centers of civilization. Here the enterprising and powerful Phoenician state flourished, but its famous great cities of **Tyre** and **Sidon** are now sleepy, minor ports. A large population was then supported by the local agriculture, but the hillside terraces have been allowed to fall into neglect and the region now

Fig. 15.14—Ancient Water Wheel for Irrigation, Hama, Syria. (Courtesy, Embassy of Syria.)

sustains the present much smaller population only with difficulty. The famed "Cedars of Lebanon" of the Bible all but vanished centuries ago through over-exploitation of the forests.

As in Greece, the combination of removal of the forests, centuries of overgrazing by sheep and goats, and the Mediterranean climate has resulted in devastating erosion of the soil. Such arable land as is left cannot be made much more productive. Though reclamation projects are being undertaken, and though there can be some improvement in agricultural output, the fertility of former times cannot be restored.

QUESTIONS. Describe the general topography of Greece. Locate Epirus, Thessaly, Attica, Macedonia, Thrace, the Peloponnesus. Discuss briefly the influence of geographic factors on the development and character of the ancient Greek civilization. Describe the characteristics of the modern inhabitants of Greece. What are the handicaps with which agriculture in Greece is confronted? What are the major crops of Greece? The major mineral products? Explain why the outlook for Greece is rather discouraging. What is the basis of the commercial importance of the twin cities of Athens and Piraeus? Why is Salonika a significant port for other countries besides Greece?

Describe the general topographic features of Turkey. What portions of the country have a true Mediterranean climate? What is the climate of the other portions? In what ways do the modern Turks differ from their predecessors in character and attitude? What are the leading crops in Turkey in terms of acreage? What are two important cash crops? Why is there such an abundant and varied assemblage of domestic animals in Turkey? What are the important mineral products? Describe the progress made in the transformation of Turkey from a feudal Mohammedan country of the East to a modern Western nation. Explain the strategic and commercial significance of the site of Istanbul.

Describe the chief physical features of Syria and Lebanon. What is the climate of the greater part of this region? Which portion has a Mediterranean climate? Why is there such a mixture of races, nationalities, religions, and languages in this region? Why is it so backward in comparison with its flourishing condition during earlier times? What is an important, recently established "industry" in Lebanon?

9. ISRAEL (PALESTINE)

General Aspects. The country formerly known as Palestine occupied some 10,000 square miles at the southeastern corner of the Mediterranean Sea between Syria and Lebanon on the north, Asiatic Egypt on the south, and Jordan on the east (Fig. 15.9).

The Palestine region is unique because of its deep religious significance for three of the four major religious groups of the world. Of no other region on earth are the names of the districts, cities, and even small villages familiar to millions throughout the rest of the world. To the Jew it is the ancient homeland, the site of the glorious achievements of his people. To the Christian it is the Holy Land of the Bible and scene of the life of Jesus Christ. To the Moslem it is the site of many holy shrines, including the spot where Mohammed ascended to Heaven.

Accordingly, rivalry for the possession of this region has stirred up armed strife ever since the time of the Crusades, beginning in the twelfth century. After Roman days it became and remained part of the Ottoman Empire until World War I, when it was made a British mandate. After World War II the age-old hope of many Jews throughout the world, especially those of Europe, for the reëstablishment of Israel in the Promised Land of the Old Testament was realized. At that time Great Britain, no longer willing or able to maintain control over the country, gave up its mandate authority. On May 14, 1948, coincident with the British withdrawal, the independent sovereign state of Israel was proclaimed.

The birth of the new nation precipitated open warfare between Arab and Jew for possession of the country. This continued for about a year until, through the offices of the United Nations, an armistice was arranged. The boundaries of Israel were determined by the battle line as it existed at that time.

As a result, Israel consists of about 80 percent of the old Palestine, or an area of 8000 square miles (a little larger than New Jersey). The remainder of Palestine, except for a small coastal strip on the west held by Egypt, was incorporated into the Kingdom of Jordan (see Chapter 12, p. 224).

Topography and Climate. The topography

tion of 3000 feet, flows down (Fig. 15.15) to the **Sea of Galilee** (also known as Lake Tiberias), which, though it is almost 700 feet below sea level, is a fresh-water lake, and continues its descent south to the **Dead Sea,** whose shores are nearly 1300 feet below sea level—the lowest dry land on the surface of the earth. This tremendous descent of 4300

Fig. 15.15—Upper Reaches of Jordan River, Above the Sea of Galilee. (Courtesy, Israel Office of Information.)

of Palestine, as such, is in general rugged. The overall relief is dominated by the great rift valley that courses north-south through the country. From the coastal plain there is a gradual rise over rough terrain to a narrow plateau some miles inland. On the east the plateau drops off precipitously to the rift valley. Through this valley flows the **Jordan River** of Biblical fame. The Jordan rises in country to the north of Palestine at an eleva-

feet in 200 miles endows the Jordan with a large hydropower potential that Israel yearns to exploit in full measure, even though a large section of the central plateau and of the lower Jordan lies within the Kingdom of Jordan. Israel holds the Sea of Galilee and the southwest portion of the Dead Sea.

The Mediterranean climate prevails over only the northern portion of Israel. As is typical of the Mediterranean countries, the climate becomes drier away from the sea, and in the case of Israel deteriorates to desert in the south. The desert region, known as the **Negeb,** constitutes a large part of the country.

The People. The total population of Israel is approximately 1.7 million, of whom 1.5 million are Jews, the remainder Arabs. The state religion is Judaism.

Although there was a considerable Jewish population in Palestine before the creation of Israel, a large fraction of the present Jewish population is composed of immigrants from all over Europe, the Middle East, and even the United States. For the first few years of its existence it was the official policy of Israel to encourage and aid the unrestricted immigration of Jews from everywhere. The resulting influx of immigrants from diverse cultural environments has resulted in a polyglot population even though Hebrew is the official language.

The large-scale immigration also gave rise to serious social and economic problems. The Jews from Yemen, in southern Arabia, for example, have little but religion in common with those from Europe. The latter are preponderantly from the business, professional, and technically trained classes. In a country that began its existence with no industries and an imperative need to sustain itself as far as possible through its own agriculture, the development of a farming population from such an assemblage proved to be a fearfully difficult undertaking. Considerable success in the conversion of such workers into agriculturalists has been achieved, however, and is speeded by the superior intelligence they are able to apply to the problems of crop production.

The Israeli, in other words, because they are fiercely proud of their new nation, have attacked the development of the desert and the establishment of industries with a zeal and self-sacrifice that have yielded remarkable results in a land climatically and topographically harsh and difficult to subdue. Artisans, professional persons, and former businessmen are eagerly learning the techniques of farming and have created highly productive agricultural districts even in the barren Negeb.

Agriculture and Products. With between 10 and 15 percent of the total manpower engaged in agriculture, Israel manages to produce about one-half of its food requirements. The most fertile and productive land is the coastal plain, the Mediterranean climatic portion. A lowland area in the north and the upper Jordan Valley are also good farm land. Irrigation of the lowlands and terracing of the hillsides (where water is available) are the two special agricultural techniques.

The leading crop in value and the major export commodity is **citrus fruit,** especially **oranges.** Israel is one of the leading citrus exporters of the world. The groves are mainly on the coastal plain. Grapes and olives are also important, mostly in the highland areas. The largest acreage is in field crops, of which wheat and hay are the leading products in value. Vegetables of all kinds are grown for domestic consumption and, despite the shortage of pasture land, **dairy products** for domestic consumption are also important.

Industries and Mineral Resources. Because of the good supply of immigrant skilled labor available, Israel was quickly able to establish a considerable number of light manufacturing industries. Of these the leading one in value of output is **textiles,** followed by **food processing** and **diamond cutting and polishing.** Other industries include such diverse types as plastics, electric appliances, and automobile tires.

Israel is notably deficient in mineral wealth. The most important source of minerals is the Dead Sea. Its remarkably high content of dissolved salts can be economically extracted for fertilizer (potash) and chemical raw materials. As for metallic resources, an ancient copper mine in the Negeb has been reopened. Oil was discovered in the Negeb in 1955.

CITIES OF ISRAEL

Name	Type	Population (1950)
Tel Aviv-Jaffa	Industrial-seaport	400,000
Haifa	Seaport	200,000
Jerusalem (Israeli sector)	Religious and governmental	155,000

Fig. 15.16—Jaffa, Israel. A corner of the old city at the water front. (Courtesy, Israel Office of Information.)

Fig. 15.17—Tel Aviv, Israel. A modern city. (Courtesy, Israel Office of Information.)

Cities. **Tel Aviv-Jaffa,** near the center of the Mediterranean coast of Israel, until 1950 consisted of two separate cities. Jaffa, the original city, dates back to Phoenician times (Fig. 15.16). Tel Aviv was founded in 1909 as an all-Jewish suburb of Jaffa and rapidly eclipsed the "mother" city in size and importance. Since the establishment of Israel its growth through immigration has been phenomenal. Jaffa is a typical congested, Middle East city, whereas Tel Aviv (Fig. 15.17) is modern in every respect, so identified by its many up-to-date concrete apartment buildings and the general bustling air of the new nation. Tel Aviv was the first capital of Israel and remains the cultural and industrial capital of the country. Despite a poor harbor, it carries on considerable overseas trade.

Haifa, 50 miles northeast of Tel Aviv-Jaffa, is the major port of Israel, with large, modern harbor facilities. It is also an industrial center, with machine shops, cement, textiles, and metalworking plants. Haifa is also one of the two Mediterranean terminals of the pipe line from Iraq (see Chapter 12, p. 228). Like Tel Aviv-Jaffa, Haifa has had an ex-

ceedingly rapid growth during the present century, a growth that became almost explosive with the flood tide of immigration into Israel.

Jerusalem (Fig. 15.18) is probably known and revered by more people than any other city of the world. The Holy City epitomizes the religious importance of the Holy Land in which it is situated. It embodies the great traditions of Judaism; it is the third holy city, after Mecca and Medina, of Islam; and it is significant throughout Christendom as the scene of the most sublime events in the life of Jesus Christ. Jerusalem is located on a plateau 35 miles southeast of Tel Aviv-Jaffa at an elevation of 2500 feet. The site is far from level, however; Jerusalem has been termed a "city of hills." Despite its name, which means "City of Peace," Jerusalem has been the scene of much strife, of which the battles during the warfare attendant on the founding of Israel are a recent example. Since the boundaries of the new state were fixed by armistice rather than by treaty, the city is divided between Israel and Jordan. The latter country holds the Old City or "religious Jerusalem," the site of the great

Fig. 15.18—Mount Zion, Jerusalem, Israel. Jerusalem is referred to as the "City of Hills." (Courtesy, Israel Office of Information.)

religious shrines and monuments. Israel possesses the New City, dating from 1860, suburbs that lie mainly on the south and west. During 1952 and 1953 Israel moved its governmental offices from Tel Aviv-Jaffa to Jerusalem, so that technically, at least, the city is again "Zion," the ideological center of Jewish national life.

Israel as a Whole. To survive, Israel must solve a serious problem: the nation is greatly overpopulated in relation to its natural resources. It has not been able to manufacture sufficient marketable industrial products to compensate for this disadvantage. Despite the incredibly great results that have been obtained through the agricultural development of its desert regions and the piping of water from northern Israel to the Negeb, the fact remains that limitation of the water supply finally restricts the measure to which such development can be carried.

In consequence Israel has been able to maintain its solvency as a national state only through substantial gifts and loans from abroad, chiefly from individuals and institutions in the United States. On the face of it, Israel's ambition to establish itself on a self-sustaining basis appears impossible of realization. Yet the very fact that the nation came into existence at all was of itself refutation

of the impossible. With the absolute determination to succeed that pervades the life of the Israeli people it is likely that they will nevertheless be successful.

10. THE NORTH COAST OF AFRICA

General Aspects. The Mediterranean climate exists only where there is protection from the winds and temperature influences of the adjacent climatic zone. On the north shore of the Mediterranean Sea there is an almost continuous line of mountains to provide such protection, but continuous highlands are lacking on the south shore. Less than half the southern coastline is sheltered by a topographic barrier. Where the mountains are absent the African steppe or desert climate extends to the coast.

The sheltering **Atlas Mountains** extend across the northwest corner of Africa (Fig. 15.19). A narrow coastal lowland strip is backed by a range known as the **Tell Atlas.** In the west this range curves north as the **Rif,** opposite the end of the Sierra Nevada ranges of Spain where these terminate at the Strait of Gibraltar.

The Mediterranean climate is best developed along the narrow coastal strip and on the slopes of the Tell Atlas. Behind the Tell the rainfall diminishes rapidly inland, where the steppe climate of the plateau and the desert climate of the Sahara, farther south,

are encountered. As the rain-bearing winds are the westerlies, the westernmost portion of the coastal tract gets the most precipitation, but even the eastern end has a high enough rainfall to qualify in the Mediterranean category.

In general, the products are like those of Mediterranean France, but as the season is earlier on the African shore they may be sold to advantage in the north European winter markets.

The Countries. The three countries—Tunisia, Algeria, and Morocco—which comprise the northwest corner of Africa and across which the Mediterranean climatic region extends are often referred to as the "Barbary States." The name comes from the original inhabitants of the region, the *Berbers,*[3] whose origin is the same as that of the European races. All three countries were until 1956 subject to French political control.

a. **Tunisia,** the easternmost of the three countries, is situated where the shore of the Mediterranean makes an abrupt southward bend opposite Sicily, in the section known as as the "waist of the Mediterranean." The country is 48,000 square miles in area (the size of New York State) and has a population of 3.5 million, all Arab or Arabized Berbers save for some 250,000 Europeans. Islam is the prevailing religion.

Fig. 15.19—Barbary States. The inset compares the area of the region with an equivalent area of the United States (states in white).

[3] The name comes from the Roman *barbari,* the term applied by the Romans to all foreigners. The Berbers refer to themselves as *Imazighon,* or "free men."

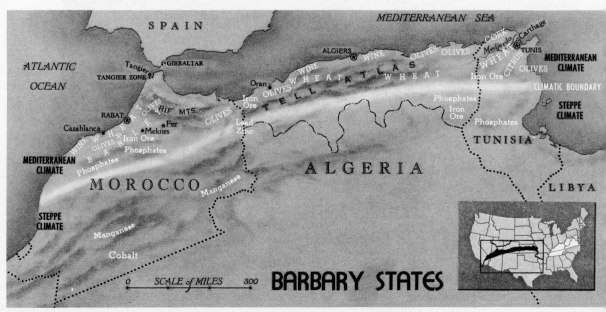

The country from 1881 to 1956 was a French protectorate, with French administration of most civil and legal affairs. In the latter year it became a fully independent country.

The Atlas ranges in this region make a northeasterly turn to form the northernmost capes of the south shore of the Mediterranean. Between two of these capes is the valley of the **Medjerda River,** the most fertile and populous part of Tunisia. South of this projection a wide lowland extends along the coast, behind which is the Plateau of Shotts (see Chapter 12, p. 218). Still farther south a large depression with its floor below the level of the Mediterranean is partially occupied by a large shott which acts as a barrier to transportation and trade between the Medjerda Valley and the desert oases.

Agriculture is the occupation of some two-thirds of the population of Tunisia but is handicapped by the inadequate water supply. **Wheat** is the major product, grown all along the coast; **barley** is the other important cereal. The olive production of the northeast and eastern coast, together with that of the southern portion of the country (see Chapter 12, p. 218), provides an output of **olive oil** well down in the ranks of world producers but far exceeding that of the other Barbary States. **Cork** is obtained from forests on the north side of the Medjerda Valley. The extreme northeast of the country is devoted to **citrus fruits.**

The mineral products include **iron ore,** mined in the northwest, a modest output of **zinc** and **lead** from deposits near the northeast coast, and important **phosphate** production from the southern portion of the country.

b. West of Tunisia is **Algeria;** its area of 847,500 square miles is divided into two general divisions, Northern and Southern Algeria. The latter, comprising by far the greater portion of the territory, was discussed in Chapter 12. Northern Algeria, although only 80,000 square miles in extent (about the size of Minnesota), is the important section of the country. It contains almost all the productive resources and some 8 million of the total

population of 9 million, and it is regarded by France as a political division of the mother country. Of the total population only one million are European; the rest are Berbers or Arabs.

Almost three-quarters of the Algerian population is engaged in agriculture, but the productive and profitable farms are mostly in the hands of French colonists. The cultivated land is concentrated in the lowlands and valleys of the Tell district along the coast, where good yields are secured with the aid of irrigation.

Wheat, barley, and **oats** occupy about half the land under cultivation. Algerian barley is in active demand in Europe for the manufacture of malt. The output of **wine,** derived from vineyards along the coast on the lower slopes of the Tell, is very large. It is nearly all exported to France. The French market for **oranges** is in large part also supplied from this district. **Olive oil, tobacco,** and **vegetables** are other important agricultural products from the Mediterranean region of Northern Algeria.

Back from the coast the lower hills are forested with cork-oak, pine, and cedar, supporting cork and lumber industries. On the higher lands, farther inland, sheep are raised.

The leading mineral product of Algeria is **iron ore,** far richer than any iron ore found in France and constituting an important source material for European industry. Deposits occur on the coast in the extreme west, a few miles inland in the center, and in the interior along the Tunisian border. Although Algerian **phosphate** production is the smallest of the three Barbary States it is still important, coming from mines on the Plateau of Shotts. A modest output of **lead** and **zinc** is obtained from many small mines throughout the country.

c. Occupying 172,000 square miles in the northwest corner of Africa, **Morocco** is under the rule of a sultan, but its political status prior to 1956 was rather complex. The country was formerly divided into three zones. The southernmost was "French Morocco," north of this was "Spanish Morocco," and on the extreme northwest corner of the coast was the "International Zone of Tangier." As indicated by their names, the three zones were under French, Spanish, and international control, respectively. In 1956 this control was lifted voluntarily by the countries concerned.

The population of Morocco is over 9 million. Again, the great bulk is composed of Berbers and Arabs.

The Atlas ranges occupy most of Morocco, but there are the usual coastal lowlands on which almost one-half of the population is settled. Agriculture is even more important in Morocco than in the other Barbary States, 85 percent of the population being dependent upon it. Cereals from the western plains are the chief crops, but the normal Mediterranean order is reversed. Here **barley** is the major product, grown over the largest area, **wheat** second, although it is nevertheless an export product. **Olive oil, citrus fruit, wine,** and **cork** are other leading products.

Morocco is by far the most important of the three Barbary States in value and variety of mineral output. **Phosphate,** the leading product, is mined near the west central coast in quantities greater than the combined output of the other two countries. Indeed, Morocco is second only to the United States as a world producer, and the Barbary States together dominate the export market. **Iron ore** is produced in both northern and southern Morocco. **Manganese** is another important product, mined from deposits in the south on the southern flank of the Atlas Mountains and in the east near the Algerian border. A major addition to the mineral production of Morocco occurred shortly after World War II, when one of the world's greatest **lead-zinc** deposits was discovered astride the Morocco-Algeria border. This provided an important new source of those metals close to Europe, and within a few years the output was contributing substantially to Europe's needs. **Cobalt** from a deposit in the southwestern Atlas is still another significant Moroccan mineral product.

Cities. The capital and only large city of Tunisia is **Tunis,** located near the northeastern corner of the country on an isthmus between two lakes. A six-mile canal through the eastern lake connects the city with the Mediterranean and enables it to function as a port. As a North African city, Tunis is unusual in that it is predominantly European rather than Arab in population. About 10 miles to the northeast, on the shore of the Gulf of Tunis, is the site of ancient **Carthage,** center of the great civilization utterly destroyed by the Romans.

Algiers, the capital and major port of Algeria, is located in the center of that country's coastline on the steep shore of the Bay of Algiers. It is the largest Mediterranean city of northwest Africa. Algiers is a picturesque city, and its native section, the *Casbah* (the name originally referred only to the palace of the former local rulers), has been given a romantic fame in motion pictures. Actually the Casbah is a dirty, malodorous slum.

Oran, some 200 miles to the west, is also located on the steep slopes of an indentation of the Mediterranean coast. It is the chief outlet for the products of western Algeria.

Casablanca, near the center of the Atlantic coast of Morocco, is the largest city of the country and handles more than three-quarters of the import-export trade. Like all the ports of this part of Africa its harbor is an engineering construction, but it is one of the largest and best artificial ports in the world. Its growth has been the most rapid of any of the Moroccan cities. Before World War I Casablanca was a sleepy fishing village; now it is a modern, bustling city with many fine buildings.

Fez is an interior city in north central Morocco 100 miles from the Atlantic and 85 miles from the Mediterranean. It is the site of many varied handicraft industries and is the center of the native commerce of the country, situated at the intersection of the east-west trade route between the coasts and the north-south route from Tangier to the Sahara. It is the Moslem cultural and religious capital of western North Africa (it contains the largest mosque in all Africa) and has been termed the "Mecca of the West." As a city untouched by the mod-

CITIES OF THE BARBARY STATES

Name	Country	Type	Population
Tunis	Tunisia	Seaport and governmental	500,000 (1952)
Algiers	Algeria	Seaport and governmental	315,000 (1948)
Oran	Algeria	Seaport	257,000 (1948)
Casablanca	Morocco	Seaport	682,000 (1955)
Fez	Morocco	Commercial	179,000 (1952)
Meknes	Morocco	Commercial	140,000 (1952)
Rabat	Morocco	Governmental	156,000 (1952)
Tangier	Morocco	Seaport	85,000 (1947)

ernization of urban Morocco, Fez retains a medieval appearance and atmosphere.

Meknes, 35 miles southwest of Fez, is one of the residences of the sultan, containing a palace four miles in circumference. It is of little importance in Moroccan commerce.

Rabat, 55 miles northeast of Casablanca, is similarly unimportant commercially, despite the fact that it is a seaport, being significant only as the chief residence of the sultan.

Tangier's advantage in possessing the only good natural harbor on the north coast of Morocco, not very large but well protected, is insignificant in comparison with the supreme importance of its strategic position, commanding the entrance to the Mediterranean on the African side as Gibraltar does for Europe. During the early part of the century each of the major European powers coveted its possession but would not consent to any other nation's control of it. The result was the International Zone, a rare example of the rational and amicable solution of an otherwise permanent sore spot in international relations. The zone was controlled jointly by representatives of the major world powers, including, after 1945, both the United States and the Soviet Union. Prior to its return to Moroccan control, Tangier was unique. As one of the few spots on earth where no passport visa was needed, it was a natural haven for offenders (political and criminal), spies, expatriates, and adventurers of all kinds. The minimal restrictions of law on personal conduct in Tangier gave it the name "The Crime Capital of the World." And as it was outside the common national rules and regulations of commerce and trade Tangier was a city of unusual businesses, chief among which was smuggling. Currency of all kinds changed hands, and there were virtually as many banks as bars.

The Barbary States as a Whole. In the last few decades the French worked hard to develop and improve the area of North Africa under their control. Health standards were raised considerably, public education was fostered, the general standard of living raised, and even French citizenship was offered the native peoples of Northern Algeria. In addition, great hydroelectric and irrigation projects made electricity plentiful and increased the area of arable land; a railroad and modern highway network was built; larger harbor facilities were constructed; and modern production techniques were introduced on a wide scale in both agriculture and mining. The greatest progress in general was in Algeria, with Morocco and Tunisia following in that order.

The social and economic level of the local native population nevertheless remained far below that of the European colonist farmer in all three countries. Despite the many improvements made by the French, the inhabitants continued to be more interested in political independence than in receiving any further material benefits under foreign rule.

Despite the achievement of independence by Tunisia and Morocco in 1956 the outlook for them is linked closely with that of Algeria. Given political stability, Tunisia and Morocco can remain economically healthy, although in Tunisia the combination of a runaway birth rate and a meager agricultural base poses a serious problem. But political stability in all of North Africa is unlikely so long as Algeria remains under French control. Until such stability is achieved the future progress of the Barbary States is clouded with uncertainty.

QUESTIONS. Explain the special religious significance of the Palestine region. Why is the area of Palestine divided between the states of Israel and Jordan? Describe the general topography of Palestine. Discuss the composition of the population of Israel and the problems this creates. Name the major agricultural products of Israel. What is the chief handicap to agriculture? What are the major industries? Discuss the most serious problem facing Israel in its attempt to become a self-sustaining economic unit. Compare Tel Aviv-Jaffa and Haifa as to their growth and development in recent times. Why was the capital of Israel moved to Jerusalem despite the fact that only a portion of the city is within that country's boundaries?

What is the configuration of the Mediterranean climatic region along the north coast of Africa? Describe the general topography of this region. What countries comprise the Barbary States? What nation or nations have or formerly had political control over each? What are the leading agricultural products of each? The mineral products? What social and economic progress was made under the French? What political issue is involved in the future progress of the Barbary States? Which of the Barbary States ports is the most important? Which of the Moroccan ports is the leading Mediterranean port? The chief Atlantic port? Describe the former unique aspects of Tangier.

CHAPTER 16

Other Regions of Mediterranean Climate

B. THE CAPE OF GOOD HOPE REGION
General Aspects. The second of the two regions of Mediterranean climate in Africa is the extreme southern tip of the continent, comprising a portion of the **Cape Province** of the Union of South Africa. The Mediterranean climate is restricted to a narrow coastal strip averaging some 50 miles in width and 400 miles long (Fig. 16.1).

The topography of this coastal strip is rugged, consisting of a series of mountain ranges known as the **Cape Ranges.** In general the ranges increase in altitude inland from the coast. The outermost range is some 1500 feet in elevation; the innermost contains peaks of over 7000 feet. Behind the Cape Ranges are the plateau uplands of the Little and Great Karroo (see Chapter 12, p. 221).

The highland barrier effectively protects the region from the effects of the steppe and desert climates to the north. On the other hand, the open ocean on the south permits inblowing cold winds in winter to bring temperatures well down below typical Mediterranean levels. The rainfall pattern is standard Mediterranean—winter rainfall and summer drought, with an advantage over the climate of the Mediterranean Basin in that here the precipitation is in drizzles rather than downpours; hence soil erosion is less a problem. The higher ground receives as much as 70 inches per year; more characteristically Mediterranean is the 25 inches of rainfall at the Cape of Good Hope itself.

Agriculture and Products. Owing to the rugged topography, agriculture is restricted to intensive farming of the valleys and lowlands. And because of the rather low rainfall, irrigation is practiced throughout the district.

In general the list of products is typically Mediterranean. **Wheat** and **barley** are not quite so dominant as in the Mediterranean Basin but are nevertheless important. Both are grown for domestic use, as is **tobacco** also.

Whereas the cereals are grown throughout most of the Union of South Africa, viniculture is synonymous with the region of Mediterranean climate. The Cape region is one of the best in the world for this purpose, and the introduction of American vines in the nineteenth century to replace the disease-susceptible plants brought from Europe by the first white settlers provided a sound basis for a large **wine** industry and a considerable export trade in wine.

Many kinds of fruits are also raised in quantity. **Oranges** are available for Europe, especially Great Britain, during the Northern Hemisphere summer, whereas those from the Mediterranean Basin are ready in winter. Still further advantage is derived from the hemispheric reversal of seasons in the production of "temperate" fruits such as **peaches, pears,** and **plums** for consumption in Great Britain. Large quantities of fruits are also exported in frozen, dried, or canned form, as well as in the preserves and jams so much relished by the British.

The olive tree is significantly unimportant. Like the other Mediterranean products

UNION OF SOUTH AFRICA

DESERT CLIMATE

CLIMATIC BOUNDARY

MEDITERRANEAN CLIMATE

STEPPE CLIMATE

GREAT KARROO

HUMID SUBTROPICAL CLIMATE

WHEAT FRUIT

CAPE RANGES

TOBACCO

LITTLE KARROO

FRUIT

GRAZING

CAPETOWN

CAPE OF GOOD HOPE

WHEAT

CAPE AGULHAS

0   SCALE of MILES   150

CAPE OF GOOD HOPE REGION

Fig. 16.1—Cape of Good Hope region. The inset compares the area of the region with an equivalent area of the United States (Massachusetts, Connecticut, and Rhode Island).

listed above, the olive was introduced into South Africa, but the plentiful meat supply from the neighboring regions precluded the development of a substantial local demand for olive oil.

The Mediterranean region of the Union of South Africa has the highest population density of the country, but aside from its agricultural aspects its contribution to the economic activities of the country is relatively unimportant compared to that of the neighboring regions of other climates.

City. **Cape Town,** the only large city of the Mediterranean region of the Union of

Fig. 16.2—Cape Town, South Africa. Table Mountain in the background. (Courtesy, Government Information Office, Union of South Africa.)

CITY OF THE CAPE REGION

Name	Type	Population (1951)
Cape Town	Seaport	578,000

South Africa, is the capital of the Cape Province and seat of the national parliament. It is situated on a lowland strip on the southwestern shore of **Table Bay** against the backdrop of **Table Mountain** (Fig. 16.2), a flat-topped, precipitous mass two miles long and 3300 feet at its highest point. The Cape of Good Hope projects due south from the city for 40 miles.[1] In the scenic beauty of its setting Cape Town rivals those of Rio de Janeiro and Naples.

As the original white settlement in South Africa, Cape Town is the oldest city in the southern part of the continent. It contains many monuments and buildings reflecting both the Dutch and English colonial periods and because of its scenic site and pleasant climate is a resort center for much of South Africa.

Cape Town is a major port of call for ves-

[1] The tip of the Cape of Good Hope is not, as is commonly thought, the most southerly point in Africa. The tip of the continent, Cape Agulhas, is 100 miles southeast of Cape Town.

sels rounding Africa and is the chief port of the Union. Its trade is, nevertheless, handicapped by distance from the bulk of the population and the major production centers of export goods in the Union.

C. SOUTHERN AUSTRALIA

General Aspects. The term "Southern Australia," like the term "North Coast of Africa" in the case of that continent, is somewhat of a misnomer in referring to Mediterranean Australia, as not all of the southern portion of the continent has such a climate. This discontinuity of the Mediterranean coastal strip has the same origin in both instances. Both coastlines curve toward the equator (away from the edge of the westerlies in the winter) in the central portion of their east-west extent. This central section, therefore, has a warm steppe climate, the border of the inland desert. The poleward projections of the coast on each side of the central arc are regions of Mediterranean climate because they extend into the winter westerlies and thus escape the desert regime.

The region of Mediterranean climate in

Fig. 16.3—Mediterranean Australia. The inset compares the area of the region with an equivalent area of the United States (states in white).

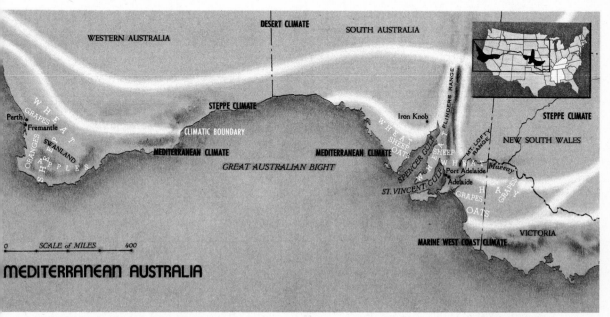

MEDITERRANEAN AUSTRALIA

Australia, accordingly, is a strip between 50 and 200 miles wide along two portions of the southern coast: (1) the extreme southwest part of the continent, a portion of a district of the state of Western Australia known as **Swanland**, and (2) the western side of the southeast projection of the continent, comprising the southeastern corner of the state of **South Australia** and most of the northwest portion of the state of **Victoria** (Fig. 16.3).

Topography. In Swanland the coastal lowlands are backed by a series of terraces that rise in steps to the level of the interior plateau. In South Australia the Mediterranean region consists of a district of gulfs and lakes occupying a part of the central north-south structural depression (see Chapter 13, p. 235). To the east of **Spencer Gulf** and the **Gulf of St. Vincent** a block of the earth's crust has been pushed up to form the **Flinders Range** in the north, the **Mount Lofty Range** in the south. To the southeast of the mountains is the **Murray River** basin, the southern portion of which is within the Mediterranean climatic region. The extreme southeast part of the region is somewhat higher and rougher, where the mountains of southeastern Australia die out at their western limit.

Climate. The climatic regime is in all major aspects like that of the Mediterranean Basin. The trades cause a summer drought, the westerlies bring cyclonic storms in the winter. On the equatorial margins it merges into the warm steppe climate, at the poleward margin (in the east) it borders on middle-latitude climatic regions.

Precipitation decreases inland except along the mountain ranges. In the more humid portions of Swanland, where the yearly rainfall is 30 inches or more, extensive eucalyptus forests exist. Smaller forest areas occur in the Flinders Range country. In the drier portions of both east and west a type of arid land vegetation known as the "mallee scrub" occurs. It is a plant assemblage composed of unique Australian species but is a response to climate similar to the maquis growth of the Mediterranean Basin.

Agriculture and Products. As in the Cape district of South Africa the products of the region, though typically Mediterranean, were all introduced by the European colonists. The leading position of **wheat**, although true to the Mediterranean pattern, is very largely a reflection of the place of Australia as a major world producer of the grain for export. The great wheatlands of the steppe regions of the continent (see Chapter 13, p. 237) merge with those of the drier margins of the Mediterranean regions. Partly because of this and partly also because the great extent of level land makes possible the use of large-scale mechanized farming methods, the wheat of Mediterranean Australia is not a subsistence crop for domestic consumption but a money crop, as it is characteristically in steppe regions.

The distribution of the wheatlands in the Mediterranean climatic regions includes: (1) a belt in Swanland where the rainfall ranges between 10 and 20 inches yearly and (2) the peninsula between the two gulfs of South Australia, and most of the southern half of the Murray River basin.

Barley and oats are less important than in the Mediterranean Basin. In contrast to the overpopulated Mediterranean countries, Australia is actually underpopulated, so that these less desirable grains are not needed locally for human food.

Similarly, hay (which occupies some 10 percent of all cultivated land) is an important crop in Mediterranean Australia, in contrast with land utilization in the countries of the Mediterranean Basin, which in view of their food needs cannot afford hayfields. The size of the yearly hay production in Australia bears a close relationship to the rainfall of a given year. If there is a good rainfall not only is the wheat yield good but there is also good pasturage for the domestic animals. In years of low rainfall pasturage is scant and it is more profitable to cut the wheat as hay and feed it to the animals than to harvest the grain crop.

Grape culture in southern Australia is almost as important as in the Mediterranean Basin. Both **wine** and **raisins** are produced in quantity, the latter a new but growing industry. The best land for grapes is on the slopes of the Flinders Range, where the vines can be grown without irrigation. Important centers of irrigated production of grapes have been developed along the Murray River in both Victoria and South Australia. In addition, viniculture pushed into the semiarid lands after it was discovered that with application of appropriate dry-farming methods grapes could be made to withstand droughts wheat cannot endure. Australia is also increasing its production of **currants** to such volume as to become a serious rival of Greece in the world market.

In the same general districts fruits of all kinds are grown, including **oranges, peaches, pears,** and **apricots.**

Like wheat growing, the **sheep** industry of Australia spills over into the Mediterranean region from the steppe region where it is dominant (see Chapter 13, p. 236). Sheep are plentifully distributed throughout the Mediterranean regions, although there are no major concentrations. **Beef cattle** are also numerous.

An unusual product from a Mediterranean region is **lumber,** obtained in Australia from certain eucalyptus species in the dense forests along the southwestern highlands. They provide logs used for pilings and railroad ties.

Mineral Products. The major mineral resource and product of Mediterranean Australia is **iron ore,** found in the peninsula just west of Spencer Gulf. In the percentage of iron present the deposit at **Iron Knob** is the richest in the world, exceeding even the ore of Minas Geraes, Brazil (see Chapter 10, p. 160). Production is sufficient to maintain a small iron and steel industry on the southeast coast of the continent. Reserves, although not large, are adequate for Australia's moderate requirements in the foreseeable future.

Cities. **Adelaide,** the capital of South Australia and the fourth largest city of the continent, is seven miles inland from the eastern shore of St. Vincent Gulf, with the Mount Lofty Range behind it. It is a very pleasant city, with many gardens and public parks within its limits. In addition to serving as the major commercial center of South Australia, Adelaide is also the trade center for the Murray River basin, as there is no port at the mouth of the river itself. A suburb of the city known as Port Adelaide serves as the actual port.

Perth (Fig. 16.4), like Adelaide, is the capital and chief commercial city of its state and also has an inland position with a suburb—**Fremantle**—serving as a port. As the

Fig. 16.4—Perth, Australia. (Courtesy, Australian News and Information Bureau.)

CITIES OF MEDITERRANEAN AUSTRALIA

Name	State	Type	Population (1954)
Adelaide	South Australia	Commercial and governmental	484,000
Perth	Western Australia	Commercial and governmental	301,000
Fremantle	Western Australia	Seaport	47,000

western terminus of the Australian transcontinental railroad, Perth is the major commercial center of the entire western half of the continent and through Fremantle handles the products involved in overseas commerce.

D. CENTRAL CHILE

Chile is usually thought of in terms of a desert environment, for the great export products of the country come from its arid portion. The heart of Chile is nevertheless in its central region of Mediterranean climate. For more than 300 years this region constituted all there was to Chile. Only in the second half of the nineteenth century did human occupancy and activity on a significant scale spread north and south from the central core. The great bulk of the population is still concentrated in this region, along with the chief agricultural activity as well as the manufacturing, political, commercial, and cultural centers of the nation.

Topography. The topography of central Chile consists of three major elements: (1) coastal highlands, (2) a central valley, and (3) the Andes on the east (Fig. 16.5).

The coastal highlands average under 1000 feet, although they rise inland in places to 7000 feet. They are pierced at intervals by the valleys of streams that have their sources in the Andes.

The central valley ranges from 300 to 1000 feet in altitude and is 30 to 60 miles wide and some 900 miles long from north to south. Only the northern 400 miles is within the Mediterranean climatic zone. The valley is cut off on the north by lateral spurs from the Andes that reach across the coastal hills. Small streams from the Andes cross the valley, separated by low Andean spurs, so that the valley is actually a series of basins.

Climate. In general the region receives

somewhat less rain than the typical Mediterranean region. The coastal hills, despite their

Fig. 16.5—Central Chile. The inset compares the area of the region with that of Florida, which is approximately equal.

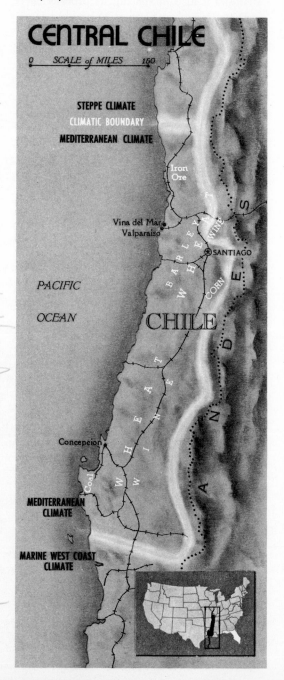

low elevation, cast a slight rain shadow over the central valley. The northern part of the valley, bordering on a very narrow steppe belt south of the desert, receives only 10 inches of rain annually. Southward the rainfall increases to 40 inches or more.

Summer temperatures average below 70° F., which is somewhat lower than in the typical Mediterranean region. Winter temperatures, on the other hand, do not get below 50° F. on the average.

Agriculture and Products. The dominant position of the central valley in agriculture is evident from the fact that it contains some two-thirds of all the cultivated land in the country and is the home of 90 percent of the total population. The central valley of Chile is the richest and most populous agricultural district in all South America west of the Andes. The Mediterranean section of the valley accounts for 18 percent of the total area of the country and contains about two-thirds of the total population.

The productivity of the valley and the energy displayed by its inhabitants are both unusually high for the Mediterranean climate. The bright, sunny days are exceptionally pleasant and stimulating, owing to the lower average temperature. A deep, fertile soil (300 feet thick in places), accumulated through the washing down of material from the Andean slopes, provides a superior basis for agriculture. The rainfall deficiency characteristic of the Mediterranean climate is not a handicap, for the snow-capped Andes provide a constant, adequate supply of irrigation water, and dependable high productivity is assured. On the other hand, only 12 percent of the land is under cultivation, the rest being used for pasture.

The agricultural pattern and list of products are similar to those of the Mediterranean Basin. The small population and distance of Chile from large markets have, however, precluded the development of specialized cash-crop farming. Instead, each farm raises most of the products listed below.

Wheat occupies almost one-half the cultivated land. The bulk of the crop is consumed in Chile but there is always a surplus for export. **Barley** is important in the northern (more arid) end of the valley and supports a considerable Chilean brewing industry. **Corn** does not thrive especially but some is raised for stock feed. **Alfalfa** and **clover** are also grown for feed purposes. In addition, **oats, beans, peas,** and **potatoes** are produced for human consumption.

This list accounts for the employment of almost three-quarters of the cultivated land. Crops such as **potatoes** and **truck vegetables** occupy only a small acreage, but with irrigation the yields are high and under the balmy skies three or four such crops are possible annually. Oats and potatoes are rather extensively grown in the more humid southern part of the region.

As in the other Mediterranean regions **grapes** are important. Over 10 percent of the cropland is planted to vines and approximately one-third of the vineyards are irrigated. Most of the grapes are used for wine which is consumed in Chile, but there is also a considerable export trade to Ecuador, and Chilean wines are winning favor in the world market.

Other fruits include both the **citrus** varieties common to the Mediterranean regions and all sorts of "temperate" fruits such as **apples, pears, peaches, plums,** and **cherries.** Much of this production is consumed domestically both in fresh and in processed form. In part the temperate fruits are exported to the Northern Hemisphere to take advantage of the reversed seasons. When apple trees are blooming in the orchards of upper New York State the autumn harvest of Chilean apples is being unloaded at the docks of New York City.

Cattle and sheep are of secondary importance on Chilean farms. The animal industry is maintained by both pasturage and fodder crops under the practice of transhumance so characteristic of the Mediterranean regions. The herds move to the highland pastures during the summer and back to the valleys for the period of the winter rains. There are no large cattle ranches as such; instead each farm keeps herds as a

Fig. 16.6—Chilean Cowboys, Called "Huasos," on an Estate Near Santiago Devoted Chiefly to Vineyards. (Courtesy, Panagra.)

subordinate activity (Fig. 16.6). The cattle supply both **dairy** and **beef** products, but additional beef is imported to meet the Chilean demand.

Mineral Products. The Andes of central Chile appear to have mineral resources quite as great as those in the same mountains farther north in desert Chile. Only one large development is as yet operative in the central region, however. This exploits a large **copper** deposit about midway along the north-south extent of the Mediterranean region. **Iron ore** is mined not far inland at the northern edge of the region, the output going to a steel mill on the eastern coast of the United States.

The other large mineral development is the **coal** mines on the coast at the southern limit of the region. Unfortunately there are formidable production difficulties, as the mines extend far out under the ocean.

CITIES OF CENTRAL CHILE

Name	Type	Population (1952)
Santiago	Commercial, industrial, and governmental	1,350,000
Valparaiso	Seaport and industrial	219,000
Vina del Mar	Resort	85,000
Concepcion	Commercial and industrial	120,000

Cities. **Santiago** (Fig. 16.7), the capital and largest city of Chile, is also the largest city on the west side of South America. It is at the north end of the central valley at an elevation of 1800 feet. It is a handsome, open city with wide avenues and fine public buildings, as well as skyscraper office buildings and apartments—despite the frequent strong earthquakes. The city was founded by the Spanish and contains many examples of Spanish ecclesiastical architecture. It is not only the political and cultural center of the country but also a commercial center and the site of half of Chile's industry.

Valparaiso is the chief port of Chile and the largest on the west coast of the continent. It is 75 miles northwest of Santiago, on the low hills that line a semicircular bay. Since the bay is exposed to the north, the harbor is artificial. Valparaiso is a modern-looking city because of its many rebuildings as a result of periodic earthquakes. As the incoming port for raw materials, Valparaiso has developed an industrial concentration for their processing and manufacture. A few miles to the north is the resort city of **Vina del Mar** (Fig. 16.8), which offers the attractions of a bathing beach, race track, and casino for the relaxation of the inhabitants of both Valparaiso and Santiago.

Concepcion is at the southern end of the Mediterranean climatic region seven miles inland on a small river. Concepcion was originally founded by the Spanish at a site on the coast but was moved inland in the eighteenth century after a series of destructive earthquakes. The city is the commercial center for the middle section of the central valley and also has an industrial concentration.

Chile as a Whole. The virtual identification of Chile with its Mediterranean region makes discussion of Chile as a country appropriate at this point. The Republic of Chile has the most unusual configuration of any country in the world. Its area of nearly 290,000 square miles (larger than Texas) is strung out ribbon-like along the west coast of South America for 2500 miles. At its widest the country is less than 200 miles across; its average width is slightly over 100 miles. Its topography includes impassable

Fig. 16.7—Santiago, Chile. Principal street of the city. (Courtesy, Panagra.)

Fig. 16.8—Vina del Mar, Chile. Beach of the resort city of the country. (Courtesy, Panagra.)

mountains and numberless islands. Its climate ranges from the world's most extreme desert to that of a region with a superabundance of rainfall. Despite these handicaps it is the leading country of the South American west coast, and as the third member of the "ABC powers" (Argentina, Brazil, and Chile) ranks third among the nations of the continent as a political power.

Historical Aspects. As the exploring and conquering Spaniards advanced down the west coast of South America in the fifteenth century they experienced a great joy when, in central Chile, they encountered a green land again after traversing the long stretch of desert coast to the north. Their satisfaction was greatly enhanced by the discovery that this new land much resembled the coastal regions of their own Spain. Their enthusiasm is reflected in the name they gave the first city they founded in the region —Valparaiso, or "Vale of Paradise."

When Chile was struggling for independence from Spain in the early nineteenth century its isolated, remote position was a factor of first importance in making the revolution successful. A Chilean navy came into being during that period. The long coastline made the expansion of naval power essential to national defense. The soundness of such enterprise was demonstrated in the "War of the Pacific" in the early 1880's when the Chilean navy was the prime factor in the victory over Peru and Bolivia (see Chapter 13, p. 245). Since then Chile has been the major sea power in the South Pacific.

Chile's population of 6 million includes about 30 percent of persons with pure European ancestry. The rest of the people are *mestizos* with varying degrees of European-Indian mixture. Here intermarriage of European immigrants with the natives has produced an unusually energetic population.

The indigenous stock basic to this successful combination of two races is that of the *Araucanians,* who inhabit the valleys and slopes of the west side of the Andes. The Araucanians are a fierce, proud Indian group which was not politically conquered until 1882. Araucanian traditions and racial characteristics are preserved as important traits of the major part of the Chilean population. In the north another, less virile Indian group, the *Changos,* has been enlisted to supply the the manual labor necessary to operate the desert mineral industries.

Almost all Chileans are Roman Catholic in religion. Until it was disestablished in 1925, the Roman Catholic Church was supported as the state religion.

The *roto,* or peasant, constitutes some 60 percent of the total population. He lives on one of the great estates (*estancias*) which average thousands of acres in extent, and works for a token wage in return for the use of a small plot of land and possession of a few domestic animals. He and his family are under virtually feudal obligations to the master, or *patron,* in return for which the *patron* sees to it that they do not starve. The dominant position of the *patron* in the rural economy is evident from the fact that one percent of the population owns almost two-thirds of the good agricultural land.

Transportation. Because of the shape of the country and the topographic extremes it exhibits, Chilean transportation and communication problems are unusually difficult of solution. Most of the small transverse streams are of no use for navigation. The major transportation facility is the Longitudinal Railway, a line 2000 miles long from the southern end of the central valley to the Peruvian border on the north. This line was constructed despite its great cost to promote unification of the commercial life of the country. It has never paid expenses, for such north-south trade as has developed is almost wholly maintained by coastal shipping. The short, east-west spurs from the main line connecting the central valley with points along the coast are more important rail carriers than the trunk route itself.

The two major cities of Chile are connected with Argentina by a trans-Andean railroad, the construction of which involved overcoming fantastic engineering difficulties. The tunnel through which it passes under the crest of the Andes is over 10,000 feet above sea level. The high freight rates that must be charged sharply limit the volume of goods that can be profitably transported over this route. Thus, despite the existence of extensive railway and road networks (the Pan American Highway runs the length of the northern two-thirds of the country), there has been an intensive development of air transport in both external and internal traffic.

Manufacturing. With iron ore and coal both available, a domestic **steel** industry was established in 1950 utilizing some of the excellent hydropower potential of the country. The major development, however, has been in the field of "light" industries. Chile is practically self-sufficient in the products of such industries.

Food, beverage, and **tobacco** processing leads these industries, followed by textiles, **metals and metal products,** and **chemicals.** In general, Chile can boast of a well-diversified light industrial establishment, in which one-fifth of the population is engaged.

Further Development of the Country. Chile is a country with great possibilities and serious limitations. On the favorable side are the climate (at least in the well-populated section), the fertile agricultural land, the immense mineral resources (both developed and potential), and the character of the people. To these should be added the tremendous power potentialities—as yet relatively unexploited—of the many streams that make the steep descent from the Andes to the Pacific.

The handicap imposed by Chile's configuration and location has been largely overcome. Despite its length and environmental diversity the country is strongly unified both by the concentration of population in the central valley and by the concerted national effort during wars with the Indians and neighboring states. The disadvantage of the remote location was removed by the opening of the Panama Canal in 1914. The severe blow suffered by Chile when it lost its monopoly in nitrate has been offset by the development of other mineral resources. A persisting handicap is the feudal character of rural society, an anachronism dating from the Spanish conquest.

The great mineral deposits of the north have yielded enough tax revenue to bear the major burden of governmental costs, so that landholdings have been taxed lightly if at all. The feudal system has also been responsible for the continued use of backward, inefficient techniques, and the uneconomic utilization of rich farm land for pasture.

Chile is nevertheless making determined efforts to develop its own resources and to strengthen the economic foundation of the country. A government corporation is financing electrification, agricultural modernization, petroleum exploration, housing developments, and industries of all kinds. Although plagued by a shortage of capital, as are all underdeveloped countries, Chile has been aided by international loans.

QUESTIONS. Describe the general topography of the Mediterranean region of the Cape of Good Hope. What are the chief products of the region? What unusual advantage does the region possess in marketing its products in Europe? What major handicap applies to Cape Town as a port of the Union of South Africa?

What are the common features in the occurrence of the Mediterranean climate on the southern coast of Australia and the northern coast of Africa? What is the topography of the Mediterranean climatic region of Australia? Compare the position of wheat as the chief crop of Mediterranean Australia and of the countries of the Mediterranean Basin. Why is hay an important crop in Australia but not in the Mediterranean Basin? What is the major mineral resource and product of Mediterranean Australia?

Why is central Chile virtually synonymous with Chile as a nation? Describe its general topography. Why is Mediterranean Chile a more productive agricultural region than the Mediterranean Basin? Why is farming in the region diversified rather than specialized? Name the major agricultural products. The chief mineral products. Describe the racial and social composition of the Chilean population. Discuss the significance of Chile's unusual shape in the construction and utilization of its internal transportation system. Describe the position of manufacturing in the country and name the major industries. Discuss the advantages and handicaps of Chile in the achievement of further progress. What natural phenomenon presents a constant serious threat in Chile?

E. CALIFORNIA

Topography. The topography of California is very similar to that of the Chilean Mediterranean region. On the west are the **Coast Ranges,** north-south mountain ridges interrupted in the center of their length by **San Francisco Bay** and furrowed by parallel valleys of coastal streams (Fig. 16.9). In the center is the **Great Valley of California,** 500 miles long and from 40 to 50 miles wide, along the central axis of which the **Sacramento River** flows from the north and the **San Joaquin River** from the south to meet in the center, where both streams empty into San Francisco Bay. On the east the **Sierra Nevada** range, the highest mountain mass in the United States, bounds the full length of the valley. To the north of the valley lie the **Klamath Mountains,** and at its southern end

Fig. 16.9.—California.

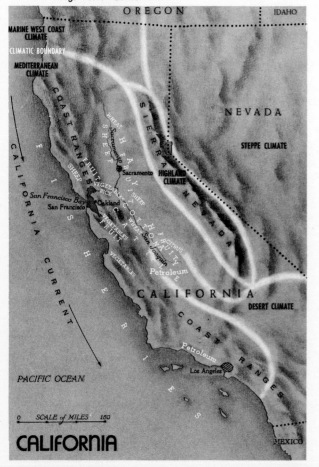

it is terminated by the Sierra Nevada range as it bends southwest to meet the Coast Ranges. South of this there is a rather broad coastal plain with east-west valleys which penetrate the Coast Ranges.

Climate. Although most of California possesses a Mediterranean climate, topographic factors result in a very irregular configuration of the climatic zone within the state. As in Chile, the slight rain shadow of the Coast Ranges reduces precipitation in the central valley. A good part of the southern half of the valley has five inches or less, so that technically it is desert. The average for all agricultural districts in the valley is 18 inches, which is more typically Mediterranean. The higher slopes on the west side of the Sierra are also outside the Mediterranean region, as their precipitation is over 100 inches a year. The eastern border of the southern half of the state is part of the desert-steppe region in the rain shadow of the Sierras (see Chapter 13, p. 248).

Summer temperatures in the coastlands are moderated by the cool **California Current** that flows down from the north close to the shore. In California the average summer temperature is only a little over 70° F., about 10° colder than the average on the east coast of the Mediterranean Sea at the same latitude. The current also produces thick offshore fogs that often roll inland on ocean breezes.

In the central valley daytime summer temperatures exceed 100° F., but as the air is dry and the nights cool owing to rapid radiation the climate is not enervating. "Freezes" are, however, a winter hazard to agriculture. These frost periods have on occasion done tens of millions of dollars' worth of damage to crops. At times the *Santa Ana,* a hot, dry wind, blows in from the southern deserts. This is the Californian counterpart of the Mediterranean *sirocco* and its variations.

Historical Aspects. California has not always been the richly productive state it is today. When it was first seen by Europeans the land was barren, affording for the local Indians so little sustenance that they were among the most poverty-stricken and least advanced of the North American aborigines.

The turning point in California's economic history came with the discovery of gold in 1848 and the famous Gold Rush of '49. The great increase in population and the isolated position of California, far removed from sources of supply in eastern North America, necessitated the local production of foodstuffs. As a consequence wheat and barley, the grains best suited to the climate, were planted and harvested over a rapidly expanded acreage.

In 1869 the transcontinental rail connection between California and the East was completed. Further improvement in transportation and the development of intensive irrigation methods changed Californian agriculture from the earlier bonanza wheat farms to the mass-production, highly specialized agricultural industry of today.

Agriculture in General. In a discussion of the agriculture of Mediterranean California it is difficult to avoid the use of superlatives in every sentence. A combination of factors —a variation from the type Mediterranean climate that is highly beneficial to agriculture, a water supply unusually large for a Mediterranean region, and a resident population possessed of exceptional industrious-ness and enthusiasm—has led to the development of a pattern of agriculture quite unlike that of any other Mediterranean region.

The Californian pattern differs first of all in the tremendous variety of its products, made possible by the large range of both latitude and altitude within the region. Second, the cash-crop farming that is fairly well developed in certain parts of the Mediterranean Basin is here brought to near perfection in efficiency in order to realize and profit from the maximal possibilities of intensive agriculture.

There are three reasons why such intensive agriculture is possible: (1) The physical setting for irrigation is well-nigh ideal. The large alluvial deposits from the Sierra Nevada are composed of porous soil admirably suited to irrigation, and the slope of the land is gentle—just about right for the grade of irrigation ditches (Fig. 16.10). (2) There are large areas of such land (about 6 million acres in all) so that it pays to engage in large, coöperative improvement projects.

Fig. 16.10—Nearly Level Alluvial Lands, Ideal for Irrigation, at Base of Sierra Nevada. View westward from Exeter, California. (Courtesy, U.S. Bureau of Reclamation.)

(3) There is a huge market in the eastern United States for the products of this region. Over 90 percent of the agricultural produce of California is sold to consumers outside the state.

Full advantage is taken of these favorable environmental circumstances. The land is worked right up to the road's edge—there are no ragged fence rows such as are so commonly seen in the East between cultivated fields. The unusually plentiful water supply is fully utilized; irrigation canals are covered to prevent loss of water by evaporation. Water from the streams is supplemented by more from wells and from horizontal tunnels into the alluvial deposits.

In themselves these circumstances would not sufficiently account for the great development that has taken place. The metamorphosis from a cereal-producing region to that of specialized production which occurred around the turn of the century is an outcome of two things: (1) the great improvements that were made in the technique and efficiency of transcontinental rail transportation and (2) the growth and development of producing and selling organizations to handle the marketing of the crops all the way from producer to ultimate consumer.

The introduction of refrigerated freight cars made it possible for each California farmer to devote all his effort to the production of those crops for which his land (or portion of that land) was best suited, secure in the knowledge that there would be a market for such high-priced products. Efficiency in transportation was matched by efficiency in processing and marketing. Growers' associations standardized their products to a high degree, and great advertising campaigns made such names as "Sun-Maid" and "Sunkist" household words throughout the country.

Despite the efficiency in selling and transportation, however, the distance from the markets is so great that only the very best fraction of many of the crops can be shipped fresh or packaged fresh-frozen. Accordingly, an enormous volume of produce is canned and dried. In many instances the intensive

agriculture is highly mechanized, which is economical only when done on a large scale. Less than 5 percent of the total number of farms comprise well over half the farm land. These large-scale operations employ most of the migratory labor used in the harvest seasons.

Agricultural Products. A comparison of Californian agriculture with that of the United States as a whole yields a crop of superlatives. The value of Californian output per acre is as great as, if not greater than, that of any other area of the country. California is the leading fruit, vegetable, and nut producer; it is responsible for one-third of the United States production of canned and dried fruit; it grows more than one-third of the winter vegetables consumed in the country and is the major producer of many of them; it is a leading citrus fruit district and is practically the sole source of many other fruits in the continental United States. In the variety and quantity of its food production California is, more than any other region of comparable size on earth, the proverbial horn of plenty.

The agricultural product for which California is best known is probably **citrus fruit,** especially **oranges.** Much of the coastal lowland district around Los Angeles was formerly one gigantic orange grove, but most of the trees have disappeared since World War II as the land was converted to housing developments. The leading center is now the San Joaquin Valley.

Among other typical Mediterranean fruits **grapes** are second to oranges. They are grown for all three uses: as fresh fruit, for **wine,** and for **raisins.** In the southeast section of the San Joaquin Valley conditions for raisin making are ideal. With grapes rich in sugar, bright days, high sun temperatures, and low humidity, perfect drying is assured.

Although olives are grown in California, they are a crop of minor importance, intensively cultivated to yield high-quality fruit for canning.

Practically every temperate fruit known is grown in California. **Prunes** (dried plums of a special variety) come from the valley south of San Francisco Bay, which grows one-quarter of the world's supply. California **peaches** account for more than 40 percent of the United States crop. Most of the California output is canned, as the fruit when grown under irrigation is of such uniform size as to be ideal for the purpose. **Apricots, plums, pears,** and **cherries** are grown in the upper Sacramento Valley, **apples** in the Coast Ranges around San Francisco—all of these, significantly, in the cooler portions of the Mediterranean region. **Strawberries** come from the coastlands north of San Francisco and in the lower San Joaquin and Sacramento valleys.

There is also large-scale production of many varieties of vegetables. Although harvests may be obtained at any season, plantings are chiefly scheduled so that crops will be ready in winter, when eastern producers cannot supply the large city markets. The great truck farm area is located on the San Joaquin-Sacramento delta. Two thirds of the **lettuce** in the United States is grown there; the crop ranks high in value among the state's products. This district is important also for **asparagus, peas, carrots, cauliflower, tomatoes,** and **cantaloupes** and other **melons. Tomatoes** are also produced in quantity around Los Angeles. **Sugar beets,** of which California grows more than any other state, are produced in the same districts as tomatoes. About 40 percent of the **dried beans** (mostly limas) of the United States come from California. **Almonds** and **walnuts** are grown on the drier margins of the fruit lands and on the borders of the cultivated land along the roads. Still another intensive use of the land is in the production of fruit, vegetable, and flower **seeds,** an industry in which only the highest-quality product can find a market.

Completing the list of the major crop types is cereals. Grains are not now the dominant crop, but **wheat** still occupies a good many acres scattered throughout the central valley. **Barley,** the ubiquitous companion of wheat in the Mediterranean regions, is also important in California. It yields a greater money return per acre than does wheat and may profitably be fed to animals.

An unusual bulk crop for a Mediterranean region is **rice,** grown on the lowest parts of the Sacramento-San Joaquin delta, where the alkali soil is unsuitable for other crops. With irrigation and highly mechanized techniques this area can compete successfully in Asia with the monsoon rice producers (see Chapter 11, p. 198) because of the high yields obtained.

Despite the great quantities of valuable food crops produced in California, the lowly field crop **hay** exceeds all other agricultural products in value. This paradox stems from the fact that, with sufficient water, hay from alfalfa and similar feed crops can be cut every six to ten weeks throughout the year.

An important crop not within the previous categories is **cotton,** grown throughout the San Joaquin Valley. California ranks third in the country among cotton-producing states.

The unusual occurrence of grass in a Mediterranean region coupled with the large production of irrigated feed crops makes possible a large domestic animal population in Mediterranean California. There is a notable annual **wool** clip from almost 2 million **sheep** and **mohair** from several thousand **Angora goats.** The **cattle** population is over 2.5 million, including almost a million **dairy cows.**

In addition to the highly productive agriculture of California there is a large **fishing** industry, centered around Los Angeles and San Francisco.

Mineral Products. Although the value of the mineral output of California is somewhat less than the output of its farms, the region is nevertheless extraordinary in the richness and variety of its mineral products. California is one of the three ranking states in total value of mineral output.

The mineral product traditionally associated with California is **gold.** Production has declined since the bonanza days of the Gold Rush, but the state is still the third-ranking producer. Production comes from the enormous gravel deposits in the central valley derived from the Sierra Nevada, as well as from the vein and lode deposits in the mountains themselves. Silver is found with the gold in many places.

In present-day California **petroleum** and **natural gas** far outrank gold in value of output. The state is the second producer of the country, with large fields in the southern half of the central valley and in the coastal region of Los Angeles.

Manufacturing. Rich as it is in both agricultural and mineral resources, California is best known for its **motion-picture** industry. No other industry can boast a greater market for its product in every country of the world. Important factors in determining the location of the industry in southern California were the sunny climate (350 days of sunshine a year) and the great variety of environments (mountain, sea, desert, forest, and glacier) available within a comparatively short radius.

Petroleum refining and the manufacture of **petrochemicals** (chemicals from petroleum) is the leading standard industry, followed by **food processing**. The largest center of **aircraft** manufacturing in the world is in the Los Angeles area, attracted, like the motion-picture industry, by the climate that permits year-round outdoor activities. Other sizable industries include **electronics, tires, automobile assembly, clothing,** and a small, war-born **steel** industry. In total industrial employment the Los Angeles area alone ranks third in the nation.

Mediterranean California has been called "the most fully developed region on the North American continent" and, it might be added, in the world. Yet the region continues to grow in population and in bulk and diversity of output at a much faster rate than the United States as a whole. No one can tell what the limits to future growth may be, but certain warning signals are apparent.

One such limitation is the water supply. The great climatic advantage of sunny skies is a serious handicap in satisfying the ravenous thirst of population, agriculture, and industry for ever larger quantities of water. Each succeeding project to provide water involves greater expense and the tapping of water resources farther away from the area in which it is needed.

Another limitation is the supply of fuel and power. Even though Mediterranean California contains one of the great oil and gas districts of the world, a gas pipe line from Texas was required after World War I to aid in satisfying the demand, and electricity is obtained from Hoover Dam, on the Arizona-Nevada border.

Whether these and similar limitations will curtail further expansion in the near future depends on the ingenuity brought to bear in overcoming them. If the successes to date can be repeated, the Californian horn of plenty, already fabulously productive, can increase in yield indefinitely.

CITIES OF CALIFORNIA

Name	Type	Population (1950)
Los Angeles	Commercial and industrial	2,000,000
San Francisco	Seaport	775,000
Oakland	Seaport and industrial	385,000
Sacramento	Commercial and governmental	138,000

Cities. The fantastic qualities of Mediterranean California are epitomized in **Los Angeles**[2] (Fig. 16.11), largest city of the region and one of the four largest in the United States. The city limits extend such long distances in such an irregular fashion as to make it one of the largest cities in the world in terms of area. Actually, metropolitan Los Angeles is one great city that includes scores of communities ranging in size from villages to large cities. On this basis it is not only a commercial and industrial city but also a seaport, a resort, and an educational city. The growth of this metropolis has been even more spectacular than that of Mediterranean California as a whole; in the era since World War II it has had the most rapid growth in the nation. There is a constant immigration of new inhabitants from all over the country, especially the Midwest,

[2] The last two words of the original flowery Spanish name meaning "Our Lady Queen of the Angels."

Fig. 16.11—Downtown Los Angeles, California. The large tower at left is the city hall. (Courtesy, Los Angeles Chamber of Commerce.)

attracted by the famous climate and the ever expanding opportunities. With a way of life different from that of the rest of the United States, and unique in the world, Los Angeles is truly the fabulous city of a fabulous region.

San Francisco (Fig. 16.12), the second city of California and leading port of the West Coast, is one of the major ports of the United States by virture of its magnificent harbor in San Francisco Bay. The city is located on the end of a peninsula which forms the southern shore of the *Golden Gate*, the mile-wide entrance to the bay. The natural setting of the city is spectacular; from the hills of the peninsula one can look west over the Pacific, east to the densely populated highlands across the bay, and north to the comparatively unsettled, wild peninsula across the Golden Gate. Man has recently added two major features to the land-

scape—the Golden Gate and San Francisco Bay bridges—both outstanding engineering achievements. A city of hills, San Francisco has romantically preserved an exotic relic of its past in the archaic cable cars that travel a major thoroughfare.

Oakland, the third city of California, is located on the eastern shore of San Francisco Bay opposite San Francisco. The city is the western terminus of three transcontinental railroads and shares in the harbor and port trade with San Francisco. As a whole, the "bay area" is the marketing and financial headquarters of the western United States.

The business section of Oakland is located on the lowlands along the bay shore, with the residential districts climbing the 1500-foot hills to the east that provide scenic views of the bay and the larger city on its western side. A large tidal lake in the heart of the city is utilized as an unusual park site. Oakland is also the site of a large industrial concentration, especially automobile assembly plants.

Fig. 16.12—San Francisco, California. Water front (Embarcadero) and Market Street centering on the tower of the Ferry Building. In the background is the hilltop residential district. (Courtesy, San Francisco Chamber of Commerce.)

Sacramento, the capital of California, is located 75 miles northeast of San Francisco on the east bank of the Sacramento River. It is the commercial center of the northern half of the central valley and the site of large food-processing plants for the varied products of the surrounding rich agricultural district. The original gold discovery that initiated the Gold Rush of 1849 was made in this vicinity.

QUESTIONS. Name the major topographic features of California and compare them with those of Chile. What effects has the topography had on the distribution of the various climates in California? Explain the factors responsible for the transformation of California from a barren, unproductive region to a region of grain production, and in turn to the kind of agricultural region it is today. In what way does the agriculture of Mediterranean California differ from that of the Mediterranean Basin? Why? Summarize the position of California as an agricultural district in the United States. What is the leading crop by value, and why? Name the major mineral products. The chief industries. What limitations may handicap further expansion and progress for Mediterranean California? Why can Los Angeles be described as a commercial, industrial, seaport, resort, and educational city all in one?

Medium-Temperature Humid Climates: The Humid Subtropical Climate

CHAPTER 17

The Humid Subtropical Climate: Western Hemisphere

■ DEFINITION AND CAUSES OF THE HUMID SUBTROPICAL CLIMATE

The five types of climate discussed in the preceding chapters are distinguishable from each other principally by precipitation characteristics, i.e., amount, type of occurrence, seasonal distribution, and dependability. In the humid subtropical type a different basis for establishing climatic units is introduced. Precipitation remains important, but with two or three exceptions the distinction between the remaining climatic types is based on temperature differences, primarily on the duration of the frost-free season. Thus the major feature of the humid subtropical climate is the seasonal alternation between summer and winter.

The humid subtropical climate is a contrasting climatic development on the *southeast* borders of continents, in the belt between 25° and 40° latitude in both hemispheres, to the *west coast*, Mediterranean climate. The east coasts of these latitudes have warm rather than cold ocean currents flowing past them. As a consequence easterly winds that reach them are warm and moistureladen. Moreover, the monsoon and antimonsoon development on the eastern side of the larger continents tends to prevent the seasonal wind belt shift that is so pronounced in Mediterranean regions. The larger the continent the more effective this modification becomes, and hence the larger the humid subtropical region.

Although the humid subtropical regions are commonly bounded by steppe regions on their western sides there is no progressive aridity inland from the coast. Rather, precipitation begins to fall off only along the actual humid subtropical-steppe border. On the northern and southern borders precipitation remains high owing to the occurrence there of other rainy climates.

■ CHARACTERISTICS OF THE HUMID SUBTROPICAL CLIMATE

PRECIPITATION

In humid subtropical regions the annual rainfall ranges from 30 to 65 inches and is either nonseasonal (i.e., distributed evenly throughout the year) or concentrated in the summer. In no instance is the summer definitely dry. The summer monsoon winds bring in moist air (the stronger the monsoon development the greater the summer rainfall), which results in precipitation through convectional thundershowers, especially in the lower latitudes. Atmospheric conditions, accordingly, are then much like those in the rainforest regions—high humidity (both relative and absolute) plus convectional currents due to differential heating of the earth's surface. Because of this the summer precipitation at any one place is likely to be erratic and unreliable, depending on the chance occurrence of local thundershowers.

In winter the rainfall is derived from the "fronts" along air mass contacts, or the cyclonic storms of the westerlies. These storms draw in moist air from the east and south (in the Northern Hemisphere) by their great counterclockwise swirls. A single winter rainfall may continue much longer than a summer shower but be of less volume. Snow is infrequent; when it does fall the amount is not great and it is not likely to remain on the ground very long.

TEMPERATURE

The winter of the humid subtropical climate is mild, as is that of the Mediterranean climate, but has a much greater temperature range in both place and time. That is, the average winter temperature on the high-latitude margins of humid subtropical climatic regions is generally much lower than on the low-latitude margins, and the range between the warmest and coldest winters occurring at any one place is likely to be very great. The determining factor is the ease and frequency with which the great cold air masses of the westerlies belt reach any given place during the winter. When such a cold air mass arrives, freezing temperatures occur. This can happen at any time in the winter but generally occurs only infrequently during a single winter season. Obviously, the frequency increases with latitude.

The opposite condition of mild or even high winter temperatures under the influence of stray tropical warm air masses occurs oftener. Since freezing weather is the exception rather than the rule, people in the humid subtropical regions are not well equipped to combat it. Houses usually are not built to withstand freezing cold; heating facilities are likely to be primitive or lacking. As a consequence, living in the humid subtropics at such times becomes distinctly uncomfortable for most of the population.

Nor are the summers like the hot, dry, yet comfortable Mediterranean summers. Not only are humid subtropical summers hot, with day temperatures between 75° and 80° F. and not uncommonly around 100°, but because the humidity is high the sensible temperature is also high and difficult to endure. Night brings little relief; the humidity prevents the rapid radiation that makes the nights of the clear, dry Mediterranean climate so pleasant.

The humid subtropical regions of the Northern Hemisphere are the major sufferers from autumnal hurricanes (or typhoons) (see Chapter 6, p. 100). The northwesterly paths from their breeding grounds followed by these great storms almost invariably bring them into these regions.

■ REGIONAL ASPECTS

With higher rainfall, the plant cover is more abundant and varied than in the Mediterranean regions. In the low-latitude portion of the regions the predominant vegetation is that of broadleaf evergreen trees such as live oak and magnolia (trees that do not shed their leaves but are not conifers). In the middle-latitude portions deciduous forests (trees that shed their leaves in winter), chiefly ash and gum, are prevalent. On sandy soils conifers are characteristic throughout the regions, as are cypress and gum trees in swamp areas. On the less humid western margins areas with a thick grass cover may be present.[1]

■ UTILIZATION OF THE HUMID SUBTROPICAL REGIONS

The most significant difference between agriculture in the Mediterranean and humid subtropical climates is that the Mediterranean farmer *fears* an occasional frost, whereas the humid subtropical farmer *expects* frost during certain seasons. Thus the growing season (the time between the last killing frost of spring and the first of autumn) is restricted in the humid subtropical climate by tempera-

[1] This grass differs from the steppe-land grass. It is tall (3 to 6 feet) and deep rooted in its natural state, whereas the steppe grass is short and clumpy.

ture, not by a seasonal water supply. Year-round agriculture such as is practiced in the Mediterranean regions is not possible; accordingly the length of the growing season is the factor of fundamental importance. It varies from 11 months on the low-latitude margin to approximately 200 days on the middle-latitude margin. Nevertheless, because frost is infrequent and rain is plentiful, especially during the growing season, the humid subtropical climate is extremely favorable for agriculture. Certain areas with exceptional soils are exceedingly productive.

In contrast to the Mediterranean regions there is no "pattern" of agriculture common to all humid subtropical regions. Quite the opposite is true; each region has its own peculiar dominant crops or products, although it would be possible for all the regions to grow substantially the same things.

The problem of soil erosion is, however, as troublesome in certain humid subtropical regions as in the Mediterranean regions, although for different reasons. In winter there is no cover of snow to protect unused soil, nor does frost bind the soil particles together as it does in higher latitudes. Consequently, severe erosion under the winter rains results

if fallow fields are not planted with a "cover crop" to keep the soil in place.

The range of crops grown varies from tropical products to those of the middle latitude—from sugar cane and tea to corn and potatoes. But, as in every climatic region, the extremes are rarely if ever present in the same district.

In general the most important commodities, referred to the different continents, are: **rice, silk,** and **cotton** in Asia; **cotton, tobacco, citrus fruits,** and **vegetables** in North America; **citrus fruits** and **alfalfa** in South America. As for domestic animals, **cattle** and **hogs** are important in North America, **cattle** and **sheep** in South America. **Timber** is important in all humid subtropical regions, but not much of the original forest cover is left in the Orient.

Several of the regions contain important mineral deposits and some have a considerable development of manufacturing industries. But, except in North America, the humid subtropical climatic regions are not outstanding on either count. On the other hand, they have on the whole the highest population density of all the climatic subdivisions of the world. In addition they exhibit the greatest diversity in standards of living and in the economic and cultural status of the inhabitants.

Fig. 17.1—World Distribution of Humid Subtropical Climatic Regions.

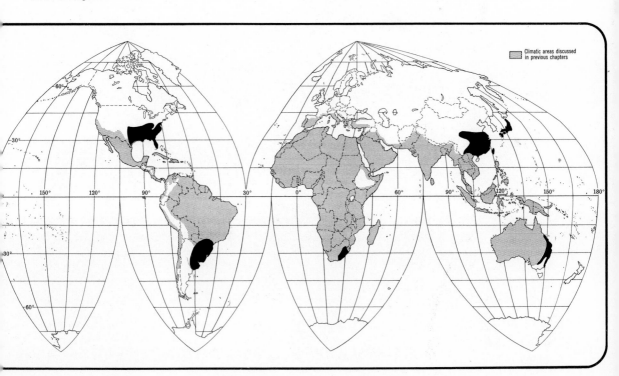

■ HUMID SUBTROPICAL REGIONS AND COUNTRIES

There is a single region of humid subtropical climate on each of the inhabited continents except Europe (which has no eastern coast) (Fig. 17.1) as follows: (1) **southeastern United States**, including all the Gulf Coast; (2) **southeastern South America**, including Uruguay and parts of Paraguay, Brazil, and Argentina; (3) **southeastern Asia**, including central and southern China and most of Japan; (4) the **southeast tip of Africa**, wholly within the Union of South Africa; and (5) the **east coast of Australia**, or, more specifically, a narrow strip along the east central and southeast coast.

A. SOUTHEASTERN UNITED STATES

The term "southeastern United States" for the North American region of humid subtropical climate is only an approximate designation. Actually, the region includes all the states south of the Ohio River and east of the Mississippi except West Virginia, in addition to an area west of the Mississippi comprising in part or as a whole Texas, Louisiana, Arkansas, Missouri, and Oklahoma (Fig. 17.2).

Topography. This large area is predominately lowland country. A wide belt along the entire south and east coast, including all of Florida (Fig. 17.3), is known as the **coastal plain**. Inland from this along the east coast is a belt of higher land, the **Piedmont**, which rises westward from the inner edge of the coastal plain at a 500-foot altitude to an elevation of 1000 feet along the eastern base of the **Appalachian Mountains** (Fig. 17.4). The Appalachians are not very high (although the southern portion has peaks of over 6000 feet) but have considerable relief over much of their extent. Because of their geologic structure they are in the form of parallel, northeast-southwest, alternating ridges and valleys. The higher parts of the Appalachians are not included

Fig. 17.2—The U.S. South and pertinent adjacent regions.

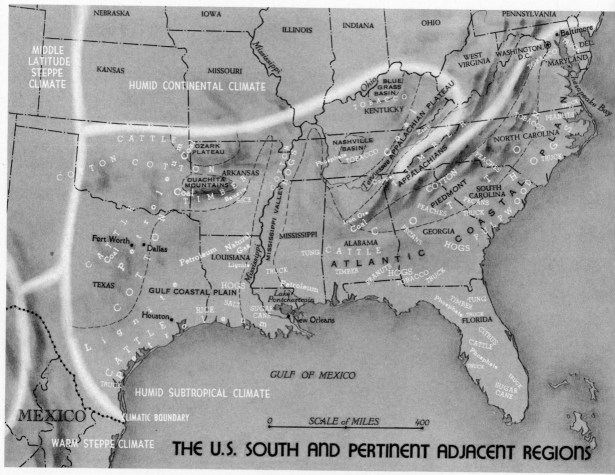

THE U.S. SOUTH AND PERTINENT ADJACENT REGIONS

Fig. 17.3—Coastal Plain, Florida, West of Fort Lauderdale. (O. D. von Engeln.)

in the humid subtropical region technically, as they experience lower temperatures and more rainfall than occur within that climate.

Behind the mountains the **Appalachian plateaus** extend down into Kentucky and Tennessee. The original plateau surfaces remain only as the tops of hills between the river valleys; consequently much of this area also has considerable relief. The **Blue Grass Basin** and **Nashville Basin,** in Kentucky and Tennessee, respectively, are lower areas within the plateau region.

The dominant feature in the western part of the humid subtropical region is the **Mississippi River** and its broad, low valley. West of the Mississippi are two highland areas, the **Ouachita Mountains** in Arkansas and Oklahoma and the **Ozark plateau** in Arkansas and southern Missouri.

Climate. Because of the open, unobstructed reaches of the central part of North America the southeastern United States is affected by more cyclonic storms than any of the other humid subtropical regions and

Fig. 17.4—Appalachian Mountains in the South. Blue Ridge near Afton, Virginia. (O. D. von Engeln.)

hence receives the highest rainfall in winter. Moreover, the rainfall is more dependable throughout the entire region than is typical in this kind of climate, as there is a moderate summer monsoon development in the Gulf coastal districts. (The convectional thundershowers of the summer and conditions of the fronts in the winter make thunderstorms more frequent in this region than anywhere else in the United States.)

The low relief of the central plains region permits cold winds and air masses from the north to penetrate unusually far south, and much of the region has more freezing weather than is typical of the climate. The lowest winter temperatures in the humid subtropical regions are recorded here.

The Florida peninsula, on the other hand, under the moderating temperature influences of its low latitude (the southernmost point in the United States, in Florida, is not far north of the Tropic of Cancer) and the warm waters of the Gulf of Mexico and the Gulf Stream, has almost the warmth of a savanna climate.

Almost any place in the region is likely to be visited by a hurricane from the equatorial Atlantic. Texas and Arkansas are also afflicted by tornadoes; several of these localized but highly destructive storms are experienced there annually.

Forests and Forest Resources. The natural plant cover of the region ranges from the palms of Florida to the middle-latitude hardwoods of the Appalachians and the grasses of Texas and Oklahoma. Where poor soils occur, coniferous forests are present, especially on the sandy parts of the coastal plain. The broadleaf trees such as oak, chestnut, gum, and black walnut grow on the better soils and in the mountain regions of the Carolinas. The Appalachians in general are covered with pines and oaks. Cypress and gum trees occur in large stands in the nu-

Fig. 17.5—Cypress Swamp, Ocala, Florida. (O. D. von Engeln.)

Fig. 17.6—Paper Mill Near Brevard, North Carolina. In the background the hardwood forest of the southern Appalachians. (Courtesy, North Carolina News Bureau.)

merous swamps (Fig. 17.5) of the coastal plain.

Altogether, about one-third of the forest resources of the United States are in this region. Timber is thus a major resource and **lumber** a major product. The large, open stands of pine on the flat coastal plain can be worked for lumber at low cost and represent the major part of the yield. In addition certain species of pine grow remarkably fast and can be cut for **pulpwood** (the raw material for paper) (Fig. 17.6) at from eight- to ten-year intervals. The pine yield is supplemented by hardwood lumber from the Carolina region and cypress, a good decay-resistant lumber, from the swamps.

Another group of forest products of the coastal plain is the commodities known as **naval stores**[2]—turpentine and its related products. Gashes cut in the trunks of the pines are kept open from March to November, during which time sap exudes more or less continually. It collects in cups underneath the gashes and is processed for various products.

The forest industries were formerly conducted as ruthless exploitations. They moved steadily southward from the Carolinas as the pine forests were depleted. Mod-

[2] The name comes from their former use for such purposes as caulking wooden ships.

ern conservation practices are increasingly followed, however, and the industries are nearing the time when they will be permanent and self-regenerative.

Agricultural Products. The crop traditionally associated with the South is **cotton.** Although cotton is grown in all the humid subtropical areas it is truly important in this type of climate only in North America. During much of the nineteenth century cotton was by far the leading United States export commodity. Because of its dominant position in the economy of the South and in American politics and policies in general the crop became known as "King Cotton." Its present position in southern agriculture is still vital. The United States, as the world's leading cotton producer, accounts for over one-half the world crop. For the country as a whole cotton ranks approximately fourth in value among agricultural products and fifth in acreage. The largest part of this production is from the humid subtropical region.

The cotton plant has certain definite climatic requirements. It needs a growing season of at least 185 days, a hot summer with rain of the thundershower type, and less than 10 inches of rain during the autumn maturing season. The North American humid subtropical region includes the largest area in the world that satisfies these requirements (although it is not ideally suited to cotton). The plant must also be intensively cultivated during the growing season. Thus the natural tendency of the region to suffer severely from soil erosion is heightened by such agricultural practice unless specific antierosion measures are taken. Cotton also makes heavy demands on the soil, which rapidly declines in fertility unless it is regularly fortified with commercial fertilizer.

Cotton as an important crop is restricted to a belt stretching from the Texas Panhandle east to North Carolina, and from southern Missouri almost to the Gulf Coast —a district known as the "cotton belt." Within this district itself cotton has varying significance. The cotton belt includes all sorts of terrain, from hill slopes to flat delta lands, and grades of soil ranging from the submarginal residual soil of the Piedmont to that of the highly fertile alluvial lowlands along the rivers.

The most productive cotton land is along the valley of the Mississippi, in the lowlands known as "river bottoms" adjacent to the great stream and its tributaries. This highly fertile soil produces excellent fiber.

The newest cotton district is in Texas and Oklahoma on the dry western margin of the humid subtropical region. The yearly rainfall here is low (30 inches or less) but enough falls during the growing season to make a cotton crop possible. The wide expanses of flatlands are divided into large, mechanized farms. The yield is lower than on the river bottoms but the costs are less. As all the bolls can be left on the plant until the last ones are ripe, mechanical cotton picking is highly profitable (Fig. 17.7). In the more humid districts to the east this is not feasible because the mature bolls will deteriorate if left unpicked. Hence picking must be done by hand throughout the final stages of maturation. Texas is the leading cotton state; the rank of the other states declines generally eastward.

The second great crop traditionally associated with the South is **tobacco**, a native American plant already used for smoking by the Indians when the first explorers arrived. United States tobacco production is preponderantly from the humid subtropical region.

Tobacco resembles cotton in many aspects of its growth requirements and in the regional history of the crop. It is favored by sandy soils and is extremely demanding in its plant food needs. A single crop can deplete the soil fertility of a field so thoroughly that, without treatment, two or three years must elapse before another crop can be grown on it. With generous application of commercial fertilizer, however, tobacco can be harvested perennially on the same soil. A great amount of hand labor for pruning and cultivation is required during the growing season.

Tobacco antedated even cotton as a cash

Fig. 17.7—Cotton Picking by Machine, Texas. The machine does the work of 30 to 40 hand pickers. (Courtesy, Houston Chamber of Commerce.)

crop of the South; it was important from the time of the very first colonies. But in the absence of heavy applications of fertilizer its excessive demands on the soil ruined many acres in Virginia and Maryland. The major center is now in southern Virginia and in the Carolinas on the Piedmont, where perennial planting and fertilizing are practiced. A second center is in Kentucky (the second producing state) and Tennessee, in the rich basin areas of those states. The United States is the leading tobacco producer and exporter.

A comparatively new crop, introduced into

this country from Brazil around the turn of the century, is the **peanut**. The commercial significance of peanuts is as a source of peanut oil, a raw material of the food processing and chemical industries.

The peanut is not a true nut. The plant is actually a "legume," one of the same family as peas and beans. It grows about 18 inches high; after it flowers the stalks turn down into the soil and peanuts form at the stalk ends. The peanut plant needs a growing season of five months with moderate temperatures and ample, even rainfall, requirements that are well satisfied on the inner coastal plain. It is a good soil enricher and is thus

steeply sloping that in many parts of the world it would be terraced if used at all is here planted to fields of corn. But the cultivation required by corn intensifies soil erosion on such lands, the great regional menace to agriculture almost everywhere, and here especially ruinous.

Vegetables of the truck-farm type are an important source of income from sandy soil areas of many sections of Florida and the Atlantic coastal plain, and on the lands of the lower Mississippi delta.[3] This industry provides an excellent illustration of the latitudinal progression of the growing season, and the profits to be derived from taking ad-

Fig. 17.8—Grapefruit, Foreground, Orange Grove in Distance, Lake Weir, South of Ocala, Florida. (O. D. von Engeln.)

useful in a crop rotation scheme.

Almost the entire United States peanut production is from the humid subtropical region. Peanuts for human consumption come from Virginia and North Carolina; those for oil and pig feed come from the region where Georgia, Alabama, and Florida meet.

Second in rank after cotton as a crop in the South is **corn** (known as *maize* outside the United States). Corn has an almost universal distribution throughout the cotton belt, where it is the basic food crop of man and important as an animal feed. It will yield on poor soils, and because of this, land so

vantage of this climatic phenomenon. Beginning in midwinter the truck farms of Florida send their products north to the great metropolitan markets, where the high off-season prices more than offset the high cost of transportation. As the season advances, the source of each particular vegetable moves north, its position dependent on the temperature requirements of each. Delaware and Maryland are covered with truck farms that become the source of supply for the New York–Philadelphia market area during the summer

[3] The amount of potential vegetable land on the coastal plain is sufficient to satisfy the demand of the United States many times over. There is a constant tendency toward overproduction under such circumstances.

months, at which time proximity to the market area is the surpassing advantage.

Oranges and **grapefruit** (Fig. 17.8) are important crops of the humid subtropical region because of the large production from Florida, the only part of the region where they can be grown commercially. After a single great freeze in the 1890's almost wiped out the industry in northern Florida, where it began, the lesson was learned that commercial production is possible only in the center and south of the state. Florida leads in the production of both oranges and grapefruit.

Another crop of rather restricted acreage within the region is **rice,** grown on plains land in Texas, Louisiana, and Arkansas. Some three-quarters of the United States production comes from this district. The land is level, and low enough to be flooded but high enough to be drained at will. It is farmed in large plots that enable the process to be entirely mechanized from planting to harvest. In this way, despite the relative scarcity of labor in the United States, rice can be successfully produced in competition with the Orient and tropics with their abundant labor. One man with machines can take care of 80 acres or more of rice in the United States compared with the one or two acres laboriously cultivated by the Oriental coolie.

Even more restricted than the distribution of rice is the acreage devoted to **sugar cane,** since this is almost entirely concentrated in Louisiana on the Mississippi delta and in the Everglades region of southern Florida. The Louisiana industry is an outstanding instance of reliance on a protective tariff, or tax on competing imports. Sugar cane is so little fitted to the Louisiana climate that it must be cultivated as an annual rather than as a perennial. Whereas the grower in Cuba can harvest cuttings year after year from a single planting, in Louisiana the cane must be planted anew each year after being killed by the winter's frost. Secondly, the cane must be harvested before the first frost, when it is still immature and the sugar content is still low (although immature cane is better suited for the production of molasses and syrup).

Thirdly, hurricanes and floods frequently do great damage to the crop. Finally, the sugar mills, which in other countries operate during a relatively long harvest season, are here idle except for a very short period each year.

The Florida sugar cane industry based on the reclaimed Everglades land is, however, on a much sounder economic basis.

Only a few of the many less important crops grown in the humid subtropical South can be mentioned. The upper Piedmont of Georgia and the Carolinas is an important **peach** and **pecan** district. Georgia and northern Florida follow California in the ranks of peach states. Pecans are also grown in the west on the coastal plain. In northern Florida a new development with great possibilities is the production of **tung oil** from the nuts of the tung tree. This oil has special qualities important in the paint and chemical industries.

Among the domestic animals the important kinds are **hogs** and **cattle.** Southern hogs (not quite one-fifth of all in the United States) are commonly semiwild animals that roam through fallow fields and uncleared land to feed on whatever they can find. They are, accordingly, lean and scrawny by comparison with the fat porkers raised on milk slops and corn on northern farms. Like so many of the food crops and animals in the South, hogs are raised for farm (subsistence) use, or for local sale.

In Texas and Oklahoma ranch production of beef cattle prevails. The herds are allowed to roam over large areas of grazing land. The largest cattle ranch in the United States is on the central Gulf Coast of Texas. Throughout most of the South, however, cattle raising has never been a large-scale industry. Although the shift away from cotton has been accompanied by an increase in beef cattle production, the output is still small compared with total production in the United States. Florida has made the most advances in such enterprise; the cattle graze on the "range" under pine trees and among palmetto,[4] and are also fed processed orange

[4] A dwarf variety of this kind of palm constitutes most of the scrub growth in Florida.

rinds from citrus fruit canneries and frozen juice plants.

Mineral Resources and Products. The humid subtropical region of North America far surpasses all other regions of that climate in the richness of its mineral resources and the degree to which they have been developed. It contains an estimated one-third of all the mineral resources of the United States.

The most spectacular occurrences and utilization have been those of **petroleum** and **natural gas.** For both these resources the greatest producing fields of the Western Hemisphere are located within this region or along its borders. Two-thirds of the natural gas and petroleum production of the United States comes from this region. The outstanding fields are scattered throughout Texas and Oklahoma. Another large area extends along the Gulf Coast of Texas and Louisiana, with production coming from wells in the Gulf itself, beyond sight of land in water 100 feet and more in depth. New discoveries have gradually extended the producing fields east into Mississippi, and oil shows have even been found in Florida. The gas fields of Louisiana are among the largest in the world. Since World War II a giant pipe-line network has been developed to carry this most desirable of all fuels to the great industrial and population centers of the Great Lakes and the Northeast.

Salt and **sulfur** occurrences are curiously associated geologically with the presence of oil along the Texas and Louisiana coasts. Almost pure sulfur is produced from wells under such low-cost conditions that the district has a virtual monopoly on world supply.

One of the world's unique mineral occurrences is that of the Birmingham, Alabama, district. Here an abundant supply of low-grade **iron ore** occurs along with the two essentials of iron smelting—**coking coal** and **limestone**—all within a radius of some 10 miles. In consequence an important **iron and steel** center has developed to supply the regional demand.

The **coal** resources of the region as a whole are enormous. Birmingham is at the southern end of an almost continuous coal field that parallels the Appalachians on their western side north into Pennsylvania. Large fields of lower-quality coal are also found in Alabama, Mississippi, Louisiana, Arkansas, Texas, and Oklahoma.

The region also contains important **phosphate** resources. Production from deposits in western Florida and Tennessee accounts for almost half the world total and over 95 percent of the United States output. There is a considerable export trade in the Florida phosphate.

Bauxite deposits in Arkansas are the source of about 90 percent of the United States production, although it satisfies only a relatively small portion of the domestic consumption of this aluminum ore.

Other significant mineral production includes **copper** from Tennessee, **zinc** from Tennessee and Virginia, and **marble** from Tennessee and Georgia.

Manufacturing. The outstanding manufacturing activity of the South (although not typical of the humid subtropical region as a whole) is the manufacture of **cotton textiles.** In the early history of the United States New England was the textile manufacturing center of the country. All during the present century, however, there has been a persistent migration southward of cotton manufacture. The industry is concentrated in the Piedmont of Alabama, Georgia, and the Carolinas, and this is now the undisputed cotton textile center of the United States (Fig. 17.9).

As finished cotton goods are practically as bulky and heavy as the raw cotton, freight savings are of little consequence to the location of the industry if the goods are marketed outside the South. The chief reason, accordingly, for the migration of the industry to the region has been the availability of a suitable labor supply and the lower wage rates prevailing in the South, although the disparity between northern and southern conditions is tending to narrow. This advantage is enhanced by the existence of good local supplies of hydroelectric power and the lower tax rates of the South. The industry has thus been able to specialize in the mass pro-

Fig. 17.9—Modern Textile Plant at Johnston, South Carolina. (Courtesy, State Development Board, South Carolina.)

duction of the cheaper fabrics.

Since World War II there has been a marked expansion of all kinds of industries in the humid subtropical region. Many of the new industries process or manufacture raw materials brought in from outside the region, as the abundant labor supply and other advantages outweigh the extra freight costs. In general, however, the region's manufacturing has been directed toward the processing of local raw materials. Thus, despite the growth of large **aircraft** and **automobile** assembly plants in Texas, the development of the **petrochemical** industry has been even greater. The list of important industries includes **refining** (oil and turpentine), **cigarettes, fertilizer, paper, plastics, furniture, rayon, sugar,** and **frozen citrus concentrating.** These are only a few of the more significant items.

Development of the Region. A discussion of the humid subtropical region of North America involves consideration of a very extensive portion of the United States, both areally and population-wise (over one-quarter of the nation's population is within the region), that is economically important as well. Yet as recently as 1938 the President of the United States proclaimed the South, which comprises almost all of the region, as the "number one economic problem" of the country.

At that time it was unfortunately true that the South had lagged behind in the general growth and progress of the United States.

The lag was due to many factors: the destructive exploitation of the soil, the severe wounds of the Civil War and the chaos of the Reconstruction, the economic discrimination of tariff laws and freight rates, and the persistence of a race problem at the base of the social structure.

Fortunately, this background of untoward influences is being rapidly eliminated. Crop diversification has been adopted in many districts and is spreading throughout the region, as are soil conservation practices. Economic discrimination is less important, and the race problem, although still significant, is already a lesser handicap and gives promise of fading into obscurity with time.

Perhaps the most important is the new spirit of industry in the South. With the very rapid growth and diversification of industry the economy is climbing to a parity with that of the northern states. There is a new awareness that the former role of the southern region was not dictated by any lack of resources or other environmental handicaps. With this realization of its potentialities such problems as remain can be adequately dealt with.

No discussion of the renaissance of the South would be complete without mention of the *Tennessee Valley Authority.* This agency of the federal government began work in 1933 to develop the resources of the entire watershed or drainage basin of the Tennessee River as a unit[5] (Fig. 17.10). Although the exigencies of World War II

[5] The watershed includes portions of Mississippi, Alabama, North Carolina, Virginia, and Kentucky, as well as most of Tennessee itself.

Fig. 17.10—Tennessee River at Knoxville, Tennessee. Companion pictures show conditions before and after river improvement. Before, navigation out of the question; after, channel 627 miles long. (Courtesy, Tennessee Valley Authority.)

and the momentum of the postwar national growth have been of immense benefit in aiding the development of the South, it can be said that the TVA provided the original spark, the beneficial effects of which will continue to be evident as the South achieves still greater economic health and prosperity.

CITIES OF HUMID SUBTROPICAL UNITED STATES

Name	State	Type	Population (1950)
Baltimore	Maryland	Seaport and industrial	950,000
Washington	District of Columbia	Governmental	802,000
Houston	Texas	Seaport and industrial	596,000
New Orleans	Louisiana	Seaport	570,000
Dallas	Texas	Commercial	434,000
Fort Worth	Texas	Commercial	279,000

Cities. **Baltimore,** the sixth largest city of the United States and the largest of the humid subtropical region, is located on the northwestern side of **Chesapeake Bay.** It is the second-ranking seaport of the country in point of overseas tonnage handled. Its industries include iron and steel, shipbuilding, aircraft, sugar refining, and many others.

Baltimore presents a singular aspect because of the local custom of building red-brick houses in solid rows up to the edge of the sidewalks, with white marble steps leading up to the front door.

Washington, D.C., the capital of the United States, is preëminent among the purely governmental cities of the world. The city's imposing collection of public buildings and monuments and its unique street plan are known to all Americans. Although Washington is on the northern border of the humid subtropical region, its climate is definitely subtropical.[6]

Houston is located in southeast Texas nearly 50 miles inland from **Galveston Bay,** a projection of the Gulf of Mexico. By the construction of the Houston Ship Channel (Fig. 17.11) along the course of what was originally a small stream connecting the

[6] Washington's muggy, uncomfortable summers are notorious. Indeed, the British Foreign Office is said to advise its diplomats that Washington is a tropical city during the summer!

Fig. 17.11—Houston, Texas. Ship channel at the city terminal. The "turning basin" in left foreground permits ships to turn around for the outward passage. Note industrial facilities along the canal in the distance. (Courtesy, Houston Chamber of Commerce.)

city with the sea, Houston has been transformed into a major port, specializing in the export of such local raw materials as wheat, salt, sulfur, and petroleum. It is also a manufacturing center. The growth of Houston since World War II has been of the same explosive nature as that of Sao Paulo, Medellin, and Los Angeles.

New Orleans is located on the Mississippi River some 100 miles upstream from its mouth. It occupies the space between a bend in the river and a landlocked arm of the Gulf of Mexico, **Lake Ponchartrain.** Like Houston, it is one of the leading export centers of the country and is also the chief receiving port for the products of Latin America. New Orleans is proud of its picturesque aspects and quaint customs dating from its earlier French history.

Dallas and **Fort Worth** are cities about 30 miles apart on the plains of eastern Texas, in the western portion of the cotton belt and of the great oil fields of that part of the country. With excellent railroad and air-line connections—Dallas is served by 10 railroads—they are important commercial centers for a large region. Dallas is the major inland commercial center of the Southwest, with a heavy concentration of banks and insurance and wholesale firms. It also boasts a well-diversified list of manufactures. Fort Worth is an aviation center, with aircraft plants and military installations, and is the leading meat-packing center of the South. There is intense rivalry between the two cities as each attempts to obtain the greater gains from the general "booming" development of the region.

QUESTIONS. In distinguishing the humid subtropical climate from other climates, what climatic factor is introduced that was unimportant in the climates previously discussed? What is the general region of the earth's surface within which the humid subtropical climate occurs? What is the relation between the size of a humid subtropical region and the size of the continent on which it occurs? Describe the typical precipitation conditions of the humid subtropical climate. Why is the temperature range between different regions of the humid subtropical climate, and the annual variation within a given region, so much greater than in the Mediterranean climate? Why are humid subtropical summers usually more uncomfortable than Mediterranean summers? Describe the general vegetative aspect of the humid subtropical regions. What difference between the humid subtropical and Mediterranean climates is of most importance for agriculture? What is the "growing season"?

Describe the extent of the humid subtropical region in North America. Outline the general topography of this region. In what respects does the climate of the region vary from the typical, or "normal," humid subtropical region? What three types of product are obtained from the forest resources of the region? What is the traditional crop of the South? In what section of the region is it an important crop today? Which is the most productive region of the crop? Name the major tobacco districts of the North American humid subtropical region. What adverse effects do tobacco and the traditional southern crop both have on the soil in which they are grown? What is the major use of the peanut? Why is its cultivation good for the soil? Explain what is meant by "latitudinal progression" in the growing of vegetables on truck farms along the Atlantic seaboard. What is the major citrus fruit district of the region? The rice district? Why does the growing of sugar cane in the United States require a subsidy in the form of a tariff?

What is the outstanding mineral resource of humid subtropical United States? What unusual combination of mineral resources occurs in the vicinity of Birmingham, Alabama? What states of the humid subtropical region are important for phosphate? For bauxite? What is the outstanding manufacturing industry of the South? Why has this industry tended to concentrate in the South in recent decades?

What major handicaps formerly held back the development of the South? How have these handicaps been erased or overcome? What is the significance of the Tennessee Valley Authority in the renaissance of the South?

In what respect is Houston an unusual seaport?

Fig. 17.12—Humid Subtropical South America. The inset compares the area of the region with an equivalent area of the United States (states in white).

B. SOUTHEASTERN SOUTH AMERICA

The South American region of humid subtropical climate is the largest such region in the Southern Hemisphere. It includes the southern third of **Paraguay**, southernmost **Brazil**, all of **Uruguay**, and northeastern **Argentina** (Fig. 17.12).

General Aspects. The single feature dominating the entire region is the estuary of the **Rio de la Plata** and the stream system that drains into it, comprising the **Uruguay** and **Parana-Paraguay rivers** (see Chapter 2, p. 36). Most of the region consists of the flood plains of these rivers.

In almost every respect the South American humid subtropical region exhibits lesser climatic extremes than does its North American counterpart, owing to the smaller continental mass on the west and poleward of the region. The climate is thus freer from continental influences. Temperature ranges are smaller; precipitation, because of the lesser monsoonal development, is less seasonal and descends more uniformly throughout the year. The rainfall decreases toward the west and south as the neighboring steppe region is approached.

The South American humid subtropical region does not suffer from the hurricanes and tornadoes that plague the Gulf region of the United States. On the other hand, some parts of the region are occasionally afflicted by unpleasant winds from neighboring climatic regions. In the summer the *zonda,* a hot, drying wind that scorches crops, blows from the north. In the winter a cold, dry wind from the south, the *pampero,* causes low temperatures and great human discomfort.

Agriculture and Products. The soils of the region are much like those of the United States South. They are better in the drier portions, where they have been less subject to leaching. The leading position of cotton in the agricultural economy of the South is here occupied by **cattle** and **sheep.** Important as these animals are in many other parts of South America, their significance in those areas is minor compared to the immense domestic animal population and the large output of animal products from the South American humid subtropical region. It is one of the major stock districts of the world, all climatic regions considered.

Lumbering is second in importance, based on the extensive forests in parts of the region. The major crops are **wheat, corn,** and **alfalfa.** Cotton, rice, and citrus fruits are also grown, but large areas suited to their production are undeveloped because of the general low density of the population and lack of commercial outlets.

The composition of the population of much of the region is not typical of most of South America. The difference is a far higher proportion of whites, many of whom are of non-Spanish descent.

Countries of Humid Subtropical South America

1. SOUTHERN PARAGUAY

The Paraguay River bisects Paraguay, flowing south through the center of the country. The shape of Paraguay is roughly that of an ellipse whose outline has been interrupted along the line of the Paraguay River so that the eastern half has moved south relative to the western half. The two halves are known as the "Occidental" (western) and "Oriental" (eastern) sections of Paraguay. All of the Occidental and the northern half of the Oriental section are within the savanna climatic region (see Chapter 10, p. 172).

Topography. The portion of Paraguay within the humid subtropical climatic region lies between the Paraguay River on the west (the Argentine boundary) and the upper Parana River on the south and east (the boundary with both Brazil and Argentina). The western half of this district is lowland, swampy near the river and inundated during floods. It is, however, the agricultural district of the country.

The eastern half is an outlier of the Brazilian Highlands still farther east and is covered with a dense tropical forest. Its highest points are not much more than 2000 feet in elevation.

Agriculture and Products. Paraguayan agriculture is conducted by tenant farmers who provide their own implements, food, and housing, but who pay rent with a share of their crops. The tenant's surplus product above the needs of the family is also small, but it provides sufficient income to supply the minimum comforts of life. Farming is mostly confined to the triangle bounded by the two rivers and Paraguay's only railroad, which connects two port cities, one on each of the streams.

Corn, cassava, and **rice** are the subsistence crops, the first two grown throughout the region, the latter along the rivers and in the swampy areas.

Humid subtropical Paraguay has the best climate in the world for the **orange** tree. Orange groves are everywhere present and wild trees abound. Almost no care is given to the groves (in contrast to the intensive cultivation of citrus trees in all other citrus regions) yet excellent, juicy fruit is produced. This ideal environment for citrus fruit production is almost wholly unexploited. Poor handling and lack of transportation facilities, great distance from any large market, and competition from less-favored districts in neighboring countries have precluded development.

Tobacco is grown in a district near the Paraguay River. The crop is second only to corn in total acreage. Much of the product is made into cigars for an incredibly large local consumption—seven cigars per person per day! There remains nevertheless a considerable quantity for export to Argentina.

Cotton is also an important export product. Production is limited by lack of labor and equipment, and by the general handicaps of the country: poor transportation and distance from market.

The **cattle** industry of Paraguay has been referred to in connection with the Gran Chaco region of the northwest (see Chapter 10, p. 172). The original site of the industry in the country was, however, in the southern agricultural triangle, where lush grassland provides year-round pasturage. This area is still important.

The products of the eastern highlands are all derived from the dense forest cover of the district. **Lumber** production is small in comparison with possibilities but is a significant item in the export trade with the treeless lands to the south.

Another important product of the forested highlands is **yerba maté**, or "Paraguay tea," a product made from the leaves of a bush evergreen tree 12 to 25 feet high that grows throughout the district. The drink made from this product is consumed in very large quantities throughout South America south of the Amazon Basin and east of the Andes. It occupies a place in the life of the people similar to that of tea in England and wine in the Mediterranean Basin. It is very similar in taste to ordinary tea but somewhat stronger. Production in Paraguay is from both wild and cultivated trees, mostly the latter. Over one-half the Paraguayan production is exported to Argentina, but the country is a poor competitor among the other South American suppliers of the tea to Argentina.

CITY OF HUMID SUBTROPICAL PARAGUAY

Name	Type	Population (1950)
Asuncion	River port and governmental	205,000

City. **Asuncion**, the capital, is the only large city of Paraguay. It is located on the east bank of the Paraguay River at the head of regular steamer service, 950 miles from the sea, on a widening of the river known as the "Bay of Asuncion." With its cobbled streets and mostly one-story buildings, Asuncion reflects its remoteness despite the presence of streetcars and some of the other amenities of civilization.

Paraguay as a Whole. The area of Paraguay—150,000 square miles—is slightly larger than that of Montana. More than half of it consists of the Occidental section. This, plus the tropical character of the eastern forests, makes Paraguay more a tropical than a subtropical country, although the agriculture is typically subtropical.

Paraguay's population of 1.5 million is largely *mestizo,* the result of early large-scale intermarriage between the Spanish colonists and the local *Guarani* Indians. Both Spanish and an Indian dialect are spoken.

Paraguay is one of the poorest and least developed of the South American countries, the result of two factors: its history and its location. Although an independent republic since 1811, the country was never able to develop because of the losses it experienced in two devastating wars. In the first, between 1865 and 1870, Paraguay fought Argentina, Brazil, and Uruguay simultaneously, going down to a crushing defeat, the while losing much of its territory and most of its male population over 15. In the 1930's another war, this time with Bolivia over the Gran Chaco, resulted in a Pyrrhic victory which cost still more of its male population and much of the basis of its cattle industry.

Paraguay suffers from its location through being landlocked. Although the Parana River does afford direct access to the sea via a 900-mile route, the freight costs are so high that its imports are unduly expensive and its exports are at a competitive disadvantage.

The country is devoid of significant mineral deposits. The means by which Paraguay can lift itself out of the backward state in which it has remained so long would seem to be through the development of its agriculture and of light industries based on its agricultural and forest resources. The following quotation outlines such possibilities:

> If her hardwoods were properly worked and pieces correctly designed, Paraguay could make furniture that would sell all over the continent. You buy Argentine furniture throughout South America. But as Paraguayan woods are better and labor in that country is cheaper, she is surely in a position to meet this competition. Paraguay has any amount of good pigskin, which she makes into suitcases that sell for six or seven dollars apiece . . . they are mostly lined with wallpaper and mounted with cheap locks. But with the right design and workmanship . . . a tremendous trade could be developed.[7]

The beginnings of a development of Paraguay's economic potential (such as improvement of the internal transportation situation) have been made since World War II. If political stability can be maintained, Paraguayans may look forward to a considerable improvement of their lot.

2. SOUTHERN BRAZIL

General Aspects. Humid subtropical Brazil is an area of approximately 225,000 square miles (equal to that of Colorado and New Mexico together) comprising the extreme southern section of the country. It includes the southern part of the state of **Parana** and all of **Santa Catharina** and **Rio Grande do Sul** (Fig. 17.12).

The physical setting is in the southern extremity of the **Brazilian Highlands,** a rolling plateau country some 2000 feet above sea level, bordered on the east by a narrow coastal plain and on the west by the Upper Parana and Uruguay River valleys. The highlands are less extensive in the extreme south and the coastal plain is correspondingly larger.

Although the region borders on savanna country in the north it has a pleasant, healthful climate owing to the altitude. In general it receives about 60 inches of rainfall uniformly distributed throughout the year. The population is not typically Brazilian, as the

region was first settled during the nineteenth century by immigrant Germans, Italians, and Poles. French, English, Swiss, and Swedish nationalities are also represented.

Agriculture and Products. The character of the settlers and the fact that farms had to be developed by clearing the forests have established the pattern of agriculture as one of small, individual farm holdings devoted to general farming in a frontier environment. Agricultural activities and products are very similar to those of Paraguay.

The forests of the highlands yield important products. Western Parana and Santa Catharina yield **lumber** from the "Parana pine," a tree between 80 and 120 feet tall and six feet in diameter. It provides excellent timber logs, and if well seasoned the wood furnishes a high-quality softwood lumber. Because of these characteristics it is the most important softwood lumber of the continent, and the enormous stands of Parana pine are the most outstanding softwood resource of South America. In Brazil the Parana pine forests extend over some 150,000 square miles, providing large exports to the timberless regions to the south. The industry has been aided in its development by lumbermen from the United States, but there is still room for a very large expansion.

The forests are also a source of **yerba maté,** known in this region as "Brazilian tea." There is a large export to Argentina.

The main food crops are grown almost exclusively for local consumption. Corn occupies by far the largest acreage, with beans and cassava following in importance. Rice, sugar cane, and potatoes are also grown. Yields of all crops are low because of primitive farming methods and lack of equipment. Although wheat is not suited to the climate, a considerable portion of the Brazilian demand for it is supplied from this region.

Coffee production extends into this area but the volume is insignificant compared to that from the main region farther north. Oranges and cotton are of minor importance, but great expansion is possible.

Pastoral industries become dominant in the south, especially in western Rio Grande

[7] Betty de Sherbinin, *The River Plate Republics,* Coward-McCann, Inc., 1947, p. 218.

do Sul, as altitude declines and the forests give way to grass that can be used for year-round pasturage. Other parts of Brazil have been described previously as cattle lands of great potentialities (see Chapter 10, pp. 157, 160). In this instance, however, the potentialities have been at least partially realized, with the result that the district raises between one-quarter and one-third of all the **cattle** of Brazil and is the major **beef** producer of the country. The phrase "partially realized" is used because the industry suffers from the handicaps common to most South American cattle industries—poor stock, diseases, and insect pests. Advances have, however, been made in recent years.

The same district raises between two-thirds and three-quarters of the **sheep** of Brazil. The climate is actually too warm for the production of high-grade wool, but with continual importation of good breed stock **wool** is the chief product rather than mutton.

The region as a whole supports a large **hog** population; Rio Grande do Sul is again the leading state. The animals are raised in the same manner as in the United States South and as a consequence are thin and of poor quality. But as a local food supply they are satisfactory.

Mineral Resources and Manufacturing. The major mineral resource of the region is **coal,** found in all three states. The largest producing field of Brazil is in Rio Grande do Sul, but the fields of Parana have the largest reserves. The coal is of poor quality and is used mostly as locomotive fuel.

Manufacturing in southern Brazil is not very diversified, yet there is enough such activity to make Rio Grande do Sul one of the leading industrial states of the country. Mills of various kinds process the agricultural and forest products, and these together with meat-packing plants are the chief industrial establishments.

The healthful climate, the larger forest resources, and the nature of the population are noteworthy assets of this part of Brazil. In addition, large hydroelectric potentialities along the western border promise a future supplement to the mediocre coal resources. All in all, this region is second only to the east central plateau region of Brazil (see Chapter 10, p. 159) in prospects for future development.

CITIES OF SOUTHERN BRAZIL

Name	State	Type	Population (1950)
Porto Alegre	Rio Grande do Sul	Seaport and governmental	375,000
Curitiba	Parana	Commercial and governmental	138,000

Cities. **Porto Alegre,** the capital of Rio Grande do Sul and largest city of the region, is located 10 miles upstream on a small river emptying into the northern end of a lagoon-like, fresh-water lake. The city contains a large German and Italian population. It is the major commercial center of the region although a bar at the entrance to the lake, 160 miles to the south, restricts its ocean-borne commerce to vessels of shallow draft. Porto Alegre also has a few light industries such as furniture and textiles.

The only important inland city of the region is **Curitiba,** the capital of Parana state. It is a clean, modern city with 30-story skyscrapers, situated 50 miles inland at an elevation of over 3000 feet on the northern border of the humid subtropical region. Like Porto Alegre, it has a large foreign population, chiefly German. The city is the center of the yerba maté export trade.

3. URUGUAY

General Aspects. The Republic of Uruguay occupies the land between the Uruguay River on the west, the Rio de la Plata on the south, and the Atlantic Ocean on the east (Fig. 17.12). Its only land boundary, with Brazil, is on the north. Its total area of 72,000 square miles (somewhat larger than North Dakota) makes it the smallest of the South American republics.

Uruguay in general is a rolling, grass-covered plain. The southernmost minor extensions of the Brazilian Highlands reach into the north of the country, but the relief is not very great. Nowhere are there heights over 2000 feet.

The climate is equable. The temperature averages 70° F. in summer, 50° F. in winter; the rainfall averages 35 inches over the country as a whole and is nonseasonal. Frequent passage of cyclonic storms gives a pleasant alternation to the weather. On the unpleasant side, the country is liable to both the *zonda* and the *pampero* winds, severe droughts, and the visitation of locust hordes from the Chaco (see Chapter 10, p. 172).

The country was established in 1828 as a buffer state between Argentina and Brazil. Although geographically contiguous to the latter, its Spanish heritage as well as its close economic ties with the Plata estuary region have made Uruguay more or less provincial to Argentina. Its official title, "Republic East of the Uruguay," reflects this traditional alignment as part of the estuary region.

The People. Uruguay's estimated population of almost 2.5 million (the last census was taken in 1908) is almost 90 percent European, the highest proportion in any South American country. Uruguay has had a traditional open immigration policy. Most of the European immigrants are Italian and Spanish, but immigration has also occurred from neighboring Brazil and Argentina.

The social pattern is also unusual for South America. Uruguay is a middle-class country, without the usual wealthy landed class at one extreme and wretched Indians or *mestizos* at the other. Freedom for the individual is the watchword. The liberal immigration policy and the general economic prosperity have contributed to this commendable state of affairs.

The social pattern and economic health have enabled Uruguay to become the most politically stable and progressive of the South American countries. Education up to and including the postgraduate college level is free to all citizens. Public health measures of long standing have given Uruguay the highest health standard in South America. The country has managed to evolve an unusual combination of state-owned and -operated enterprises with a firm national belief in private enterprise. The intensive interest in the affairs of the government displayed by the average citizen makes Uruguay the best example of working democracy on the continent. Indeed, the distrust of Uruguayans for centralized executive authority led them to abolish the presidency in 1953 and to replace it with an executive council.

Transportation. The small size of Uruguay means that no point in the country can be far from its borders. Most of the border length, moreover, can be served by ocean transport. Both circumstances greatly facilitate getting the country's products from the interior to market. But the Uruguayans have not been content to depend solely on these natural geographic advantages. There is an excellent railroad network that connects with the rail systems of Brazil and Argentina. A good highway system also contributes to the advanced state of transportation in this South American country.

Pastoral Activities. As an important **sheep** and **cattle** country, Uruguay's significance lies not in the number of animals (although 23 million sheep, 8 million cattle, 550,000 horses, and 275,000 hogs constitute a large animal population for any country of such size) but in the thoroughness with which the economy is directed to stock raising. Sixty percent of the total area of the country is used solely for such purposes; another 20 percent is in ranch-farms. Uruguay is the first-ranking country of the world in number of sheep per square mile and per inhabitant. It is the ranch country *par excellence.*

There are several reasons why this high degree of specialization has occurred: (a) The grass is nutritious and plentiful and is rarely harmed by frost, so that year-round grazing is possible; (b) the relatively low population density (about 20 per square mile outside the urban centers) and the large holdings accompany a ranching tradition and promote its continuance; and (c) a well-developed transportation system for ready marketing of ranch products contributes further to the profitability of such enterprise. The only significant unfavorable circumstance is the prevalence of ticks in the northern, hotter, and more humid districts.

The great sheep industry of the country concentrates on the production of **wool** because of the early start of the industry in that aspect of sheep raising, and the fact that wool is easily stored and shipped from remote areas. Although some mutton is produced the emphasis continues to be on wool, and breeders strive to improve the quality of the fleece. Wool is the major export.

The cattle industry, on the other hand, is important as a producer of both **beef** and **hides.** Uruguay ships over 10 percent of the world's beef exports. At one time the industry followed the typical South American pattern in the production of hides and cured and processed meat. During the present century the great development has been in the shipment of chilled and frozen beef. The most recent trend has been toward **dairy** products. During World War II the country became self-sufficient on that score.

Agriculture. Less than 10 percent of Uruguay's land is devoted to crop production. Most of this is in a narrow strip along the southern coast, where the land is more fertile and crops can compete successfully with the alternative grazing use. It is in this area that dairying is important.

Wheat and corn are the leading crops in acreage. Oats are raised as a supplement to the pasturing of the domestic animals. The export market for linseed (the source of linseed oil, an important paint base) makes flax a profitable crop. Wine is produced from grapes grown in the south and east; among other fruits oranges, peaches, and pears are significant.

Mineral Resources and Manufacturing. Uruguay is almost devoid of mineral resources, its products being confined to building materials such as sand, gravel, and marble. There is a moderate export trade in these items with the great metropolitan district of Argentina across the estuary.

With a general lack of power resources as well as raw materials, industry is relatively unimportant in the country except for meat packing and similar enterprises. Uruguay nevertheless manages to supply almost three-quarters of the domestic market for manufactured articles from its own factories. The resort "industry" is also important, ranking third among nonagricultural enterprises. Uruguay has exploited its 120 miles of coastline to the full by functioning as the major seashore resort for Argentina.

CITY OF URUGUAY

Name	Type	Population (1953)
Montevideo	Seaport, governmental, resort	831,000

City. **Montevideo,** the capital, major port, and only large city of Uruguay, contains one-third of the country's total population. It is located in the center of the southern coast of the country and shares in the large trade of the Plata estuary. Montevideo is known as one of the cleanest large cities in the world. It has extremely varied architecture, and many parks and plazas. A dominant landmark is the unusually broad, fine boulevard running from the central plaza to the suburbs on the east. The suburbs are the resort section of the city, the attraction for thousands of tourists from Argentina during the summer.

Uruguay as a Whole. Uruguay is one of the best examples of international specialization of production and is currently enjoying the benefits therefrom. With its grazing resources so intensively utilized, however, there is not much room for further expansion in that line. The trend at present is for improvement of the grazing facilities and the quality of stock; with fewer animals, of higher quality, the same income accrues with use of less land.

This can lead to the desirable result of exploitation of the little developed crop potentialities. Heretofore the people have preferred the free, open life of the ranch, but the gradual growth of crop production in the south is significant. The conversion of the country to farming would, incidentally, support with the same standard of living a much larger population than at present.

4. NORTHEASTERN ARGENTINA

Topography. Humid subtropical Argentina consists of two distinct regions: the *Pampa* (Spanish for "plain") and the Argentine *Mesopotamia* (Fig. 17.12). The Pampa is one of the world's great plain districts and the outstanding site of economic development in South America. Located south and west of the Parana and Rio de la Plata, the Pampa comprises about 250,000 square miles (somewhat smaller than Texas), or one-quarter of Argentina. Its southern and western boundaries are climatic, the line of 20 inches of yearly rainfall coinciding with the border of the humid subtropical region. Its northern limit is generally taken as a western tributary of the Parana River, the **Salado.**

In two respects the Pampa is very similar to the Hindustan plain of India (see Chapter 11, p. 178). It is as flat as the proverbial billiard table, with a general imperceptible westward rise of five feet per mile, and is devoid of pebbles and boulders. So level is the land that there are only three significant streams of more than a few miles in length. Rain water sinks into the soil or accumulates in swamps and pools in the slight surface depressions. Two restricted highland areas in the southern part are exceptions to these general conditions.

The soils of the Pampa are mostly very fertile; in certain districts they are similar to the rich prairie soils of Texas on the western margin of the North American region. In the western Pampa, however, the land is relatively infertile.

The identification of the Pampa with Argentina is as complete as the correlation of Chile with its central valley. The Pampa harbors three-quarters of the country's population and contains about the same proportion of the railroads, industry, and cultivated land.

The Mesopotamian region is so called because it lies between the Parana and Uruguay rivers for most of their courses. Its 74,000 square miles (a little less than the area of South Dakota) includes the Argentine provinces of **Entre Rios** ("Between Rivers") and **Corrientes** and the territory of **Misiones,** a small northeastern projection of Argentina between Paraguay and Brazil.

Most of the Mesopotamian region is low and level like the Pampa, with the exception of the Misiones portion, which enters the foothills of the Brazilian Highlands. Corrientes province contains great marsh areas; only Entre Rios is naturally suitable for agriculture.

Climate. The Argentine Mesopotamia has a climate like that of the previously described portions of the humid subtropical lands. The Pampa, on the other hand, is a marginal portion of the humid subtropical region; hence its climate is less typical. In general the precipitation is more seasonal and lower to the south and west. In the north it merges into the savanna climate of the Gran Chaco. Although the yearly rainfall is between 40 inches on the coast and 20 inches on the interior margin, the Pampa suffers from recurrent serious droughts. Immense hordes of locusts from the Chaco invade the northern Pampa almost yearly and cause great fluctuations in crop yields from year to year.

Transportation. Northeastern Argentina is the center of the greatest railroad net in South America, comprising over one-half of all the railroad mileage on the continent. Railroad construction on the Pampa flatland is ridiculously simple, and since the region is devoid of navigable streams railroads are indispensable for its development. The net is so complete that no place on the Pampa is more than 25 miles from a railway.

The system ties together all the large cities of the country and connects with the lines of all neighboring countries—Chile, Bolivia, Paraguay, Uruguay, and Brazil. The lines extending to Bolivia and Chile are uneconomic and are maintained for prestige purposes and good will.

The single defect of the railway net is the use of three different gauges in different regions. This hinders interregional communication.

Agriculture in General. The crop pattern of northeastern Argentina reflects the non-typical humid subtropical climate. It does not include rice, cotton, or citrus fruits, which are important in the humid subtropical region of North America. The agriculture is an export agriculture, devoted almost exclusively to stock raising and cereals. Because of its large trade in such products the region ranks as one of the outstanding agricultural areas of the world. The advantage of generally fertile soils is somewhat offset by the locust plagues and the unreliable rainfall in the west and north, but the low population density relative to the food production results perennially in a large surplus for export. In the eastern Pampa windmills driven by the westerlies are used to pump water from underground; hence drought is less a problem.

The social pattern of the agricultural development has aspects common to other South American regions, together with one of the United States South. As in all the former Spanish colonies, much of the land is held in huge estates or *estancias*. These are a holdover from the time the land was first taken from the Indians and awarded in large grants to influential Spaniards. In Argentina much of the farming on the *estancias* is done by the tenant share-crop system. The resultant combination of absentee landlords who are often not interested in the efficient use of their land, and tenants who farm small tracts intensively has been a deterrent to agriculture in general and to the sound assimilation of the large number of immigrants who have come to the country during the past few decades.

Agricultural Products. Over one-half the total Argentine exports by value consist of agricultural products, of which approximately one-half, in turn, are products of the livestock industries. The country devotes two-fifths of its total area to pasturage for 45 million **cattle,** 55 million **sheep,** 7 million **horses,** 5 million **goats,** and 4 million **hogs.**

The ranching tradition in the country has fostered a pride in the quality of product that is an exception to the general retarding influence of the *estancia* system. Through the constant introduction of purebred stock the quality of the **beef** produced in Argentina ranks with the best in the world.[8] Argentina is second to the United States as a beef-producing country, and per capita consumption is third highest in the world, 70 percent higher than that of the United States.

Sheep were first introduced into Argentina in the Pampa and at the turn of the century were the basis of a large wool export from this district. Competition from cattle and crops has forced a complete change from wool to **mutton.** Mutton sheep thrive best in the humid eastern Pampa and the Mesopotamian region.

The lack of knowledge and tradition in a **dairy** industry for a long time held back its development in Argentina, but World War I cut off the imports of dairy commodities and stimulated a domestic dairy industry along the south shore of the Plata. Subsequent development has led to a currently significant export trade in **butter** and **cheese.**

A vital factor in the great development of the cattle industry has been the introduction and spread of **alfalfa,** the second-ranking crop in acreage. It has largely replaced grass as pasturage, except in the more humid southeastern part of the Pampa. Its deep roots enable it to thrive during a drought. The plant supports from three to five times as many cattle per square mile as does grass, and at the same time enriches the soil. The cattle are fatter and mature a year earlier, and, in general, their meat is of much higher quality. With such striking advantages this fodder has come to occupy more than half the acreage of many *estancias*. It is Argentina's most significant crop.

The leading crop in acreage and one of the important exports is **wheat,** grown in a great arc 600 miles long from the southeastern corner of the humid subtropical region up across the Parana River and into Entre Rios. The wheat belt lies between the

---

[8] An exception is the product of the Mesopotamian district, where the quality of the cattle is still poor owing to the prevalence of disease-bearing ticks.

20-inch-rainfall line and the cattle district to the east, although with dry farming and irrigation wheat cultivation has been pushed to the 16-inch-rainfall line.

The wheat industry is beset by many handicaps. In the north is the locust menace; everywhere is the possibility of frost damage during the *pampero;* and the poor agricultural techniques employed result in low yields. But so fertile is the land that wheat is still produced at low cost, and the fact that most of the wheat is grown within 300 miles of an ocean port gives Argentina a strong competitive advantage in the world market. The country is one of the world's leading wheat exporters.

Much of the wheat is grown on relatively small tenant farms within the large *estancias.* Thus in many parts of the wheat district cattle and alfalfa are also important.

Corn is the third crop in acreage and another major export. The center of its production is a belt some 50 miles wide on the west bank of the lower Parana, with a more scattered production from Entre Rios. It is in a district of 30- to 40-inch rainfall that overlaps the wheat area to a considerable extent.

Like wheat, the corn crop in Argentina is subject to numerous adversities. Drought and locusts are greater threats to corn than to any other crop. Nevertheless, one-half the total acreage of the corn district is devoted to the cereal, and output is so great that Argentina is the third-ranking world producer of corn. Again, most of the product is exported. Argentine corn is preferred over the United States product in the European market because it makes a better animal feed.

In addition to the wheat and alfalfa grown in the corn district, **flax** is also important as one of the large acreage crops, especially in Entre Rios. Flax is a good crop for variable rainfall and temperature conditions but rapidly depletes the soil of its fertility. A common practice is to harvest linseed as a high-value cash crop for two or three years and then put the land to alfalfa.

Yerba maté production in Argentina is centered in the extreme northeast, in the foothills of the Brazilian Highlands in Corrientes and Misiones. The efforts of Argentina to become self-sufficient in the commodity have made it a leading producer, but a large share of its demand must still be satisfied by imports.

Manufacturing. Lacking the resources for the development of power on a large scale, Argentina is handicapped as an industrial nation. The processing of agricultural raw materials—**meat packing, flour milling, leather working,** and the like—comprises the major segment of Argentine industry. Similarly, there is a considerable development of the **textile, cigarette,** and **beer** industries.

During the 1940's, however, the government made a concerted effort to stimulate the industrialization of the country, going so far as to construct a small iron and steel mill. With subsidization of various sorts shipbuilding, the manufacture of machinery, and even automobile production was undertaken. This industrialization attempt was only partially successful, and the gains accomplished were at the expense of declines in agricultural production.

Cities. The capital and metropolis of Argentina and the largest city in South America is **Buenos Aires,** in every respect one of the great cities of the world. It is among the world's largest ports, is the greatest railroad center and leading manufacturing city of South America, is one of the two cities in the

CITIES OF NORTHEASTERN ARGENTINA

Name	Province	Type	Population
Buenos Aires	Federal Capital	Seaport, industrial, governmental	3,400,000 (1951)
Avellaneda	Buenos Aires	Industrial	100,000 (1951)
Rosario	Sante Fe	Seaport	761,000 (1947)
La Plata	Buenos Aires	Governmental, seaport, industrial	325,000 (1951)
Santa Fe	Santa Fe	River port and governmental	168,000 (1947)

Southern Hemisphere with a subway system, and is a leading cultural center of the South American continent, with a magnificent opera house and many educational institutions and museums. Buenos Aires is located on the southwest shore of the Rio de la Plata 170 miles from the Atlantic and only 24 miles across the estuary from the coast of Uruguay. Its great port facilities are entirely artificial, the harbor works and a long channel connecting with the open sea having been dredged in the tidal flats at great expense. With its cosmopolitan appearance and atmosphere of hustle and bustle it is quite untypical of Latin America and even of its own country. It is a city on a grand scale, with an unusual number of public parks and plazas and very broad boulevards. Buenos Aires is also the industrial capital of Argentina, with packing houses and refrigeration plants as the leading industries. Among its many suburbs a major industrial concentration is centered in **Avellaneda,** a large city in its own right.

Rosario, 175 miles northwest of Buenos Aires on the west bank of the Parana River, is the second city and port of Argentina. It is at the head of navigation for large ocean vessels and, as such, is the principal export center for wheat, corn, and linseed, the products of its hinterland. It is also a railroad hub and the site of food-processing industries. In many respects it is the Chicago of its country.

La Plata is the capital of Buenos Aires province, five miles inland from the south shore of the Plata estuary and 30 miles southeast of Buenos Aires. It was founded in 1882 to be the provincial capital after Buenos Aires was chosen as the seat of the national government. Because it has deeper port facilities than its great neighbor, it handles the largest vessels in Argentine export trade. It is also the chief site of the meat-packing industry.

Santa Fe, the capital of the province of the same name, is located 250 miles northwest of Buenos Aires on the Salado River near its confluence with the Parana. The railhead for northwestern Argentina, it is chiefly a river port, although it can accommodate smaller ocean-going vessels.

Argentina as a Whole. Argentina, the second largest country of South America, is 2000 miles long, with a maximum width of 800 miles at its northern end. Its total area is over one million square miles, about one-third that of the continental United States. Like Chile, it embraces a wide latitudinal range and includes diverse climates within its territory, although without the climatic extremes of Chile.

Argentina's population of 18 million is, like the populations of Uruguay and southern Brazil, predominantly European in background. Today the aboriginal Indians of the country are no more a significant element of the population than are the Indians of the United States. As a people, the Argentines are the most energetic and industrious in South America. Although Latin in character and temperament, they have evolved a spirit of enterprise that is unmatched elsewhere in South America save in certain sections of Brazil and Colombia. The greatest fault of the Argentines is probably their pride, which at times leads them to disregard unpleasant truths and ignore adverse circumstances.

A number of factors contributed to the success of the Argentinians in developing their country to the rank of a leading South American nation. Political independence was achieved in 1810, but in the chaos that followed no progress was made until the 1850's. Then political stability was suddenly attained, the Indians were systematically subdued or exterminated, transportation across the Pampa was improved, and great numbers of European immigrants were attracted to the country.

After the initial establishment of large-scale ranching on the Pampa, alfalfa replaced grass and refrigerated ships came into use in the 1870's for transportation of meat to distant markets. The great population increase in Europe during the following period provided Argentina with an expanding market for its products. With the great advantages of rich soil, short hauls to seaports, and the natural trade funnel of the Plata estuary,

Argentina was embarked on a long period of growth and prosperity through the export of agricultural commodities.

Although Argentina thus became one of the great food producers of the world it has by no means achieved full utilization of its agricultural possibilities. Some 10 percent of the land is at present utilized for cereal crops, but about 30 percent could be profitably sown to grain.

Unfortunately, this favorable potential was considerably offset during the period immediately following World War II by a totalitarian approach that chose to ignore the geographic facts of life and attempted to convert the country into an industrial nation by rigid control over the direction of its economy. The meager results so obtained were achieved only at the great cost of the thorough demoralization of agriculture. The output of farms and ranches declined drastically in the face of governmental economic discrimination. With the dwindling of exports and appearance of food shortages even for domestic consumption, the program was abruptly halted in 1950 and emphasis was placed on aid to agriculture.

Such tampering with the basic workings of an economy is not easily offset, however. Not only had progress in rural development been checked, but Argentina's wealth is agricultural, and its limited population and supply of fuels are insuperable handicaps to the conversion of the country to the status of a great industrial power. Nevertheless, the fall of the totalitarian regime in 1955 again provided the Argentinians with the opportunity to carry on properly their country's development.

QUESTIONS. What countries lie partially or wholly within the South American humid subtropical region? How does the climate of the region differ from that in the North American region? What are the major products?

Describe the agricultural system of Paraguay. What are the chief products? What is yerba maté? Explain briefly the reasons for Paraguay's poverty and backwardness. What are the more encouraging lines of development open to Paraguay?

Describe the general topography, climate, and population of southern Brazil. Why is the Parana pine such an excellent forest resource? Why is southern Brazil one of the two potentially most significant districts in the future development of Brazil?

Describe the general topography and climate of Uruguay. Give a brief description of its people and social structure. Why is the social pattern unusual for South America? In what respects and why is Uruguay the outstanding ranch country of the world? Name the major products of the country. The chief "industries." Why is an increase in farming at the expense of ranching desirable for the further development of Uruguay?

What is the meaning of the term *pampa*? In what respects is the Pampa like the Hindustan plain of India? How is the Pampa like the central valley of Chile? What is the Mesopotamian district of Argentina and why is it known by that name? Discuss the railroad system of Argentina, pointing out the reasons for its measure of development. Why is northeastern Argentina one of the outstanding agricultural regions of the world? What are *estancias* and what is their significance in Argentine agriculture? Explain the great development of the beef-cattle industry in Argentina. What are the leading crops? Explain the significance of flax as one of those crops. What are the major industries of the country? Describe the people of Argentina as to character and outlook. Discuss briefly the factors that enabled Argentina to become so well developed. Describe the effect of totalitarianism on the Argentine economy in the period after World War II. Why is Argentina basically an agricultural country?

CHAPTER 18

The Humid Subtropical Climate: Eastern Hemisphere

C. THE SOUTHEAST TIP OF AFRICA

General Aspects. The humid subtropical region of Africa is mainly a coastal region which includes the western portion of the **Cape Province** of the Union of South Africa, the southern two-thirds of the province of **Natal,** a native territory known as **Basutoland,** and the southeastern half of another province of the Union, the **Orange Free State** (Fig. 18.1).

Topographically this region is very similar to the region of Mediterranean climate on the southwest. There is the same narrow coastal plain, although this widens to 50 miles on the east. Behind it terraces rise to the inner plateau but are less distinct than those to the west. The main escarpment of the interior African plateau, prominent for 1200 miles along its southern edge, is here the major feature of the topography. Facing east along the border between Natal and Basutoland, it is known as the **Drakensberg** (Dragon Mountain). Much of the crest there rises above 10,000 feet, so that eastern Basutoland is the most mountainous and scenic region of all South Africa.

Like its South American counterpart, the African region of humid subtropical climate enjoys, on the average, milder temperatures than do the Northern Hemisphere occurrences of the climate. This mitigating effect is chiefly due to the **Mozambique Currrent,** which brings warm waters from the Indian Ocean past the coast.

Fig. 18.1—Humid Subtropical South Africa. The inset compares the area of the region with that of Minnesota, which is approximately equal.

354

The high mountains behind the coast induce heavy orographic rainfall during the summer visitation of the southeast trades. The precipitation is thus markedly seasonal; in certain parts of the region as much as 90 percent of the yearly rainfall is in the summer. As might be expected, there is a rain shadow behind the Drakensberg on the plateau known as the **High Veld** (see Chapter 9, p. 140). The eastern portion of the High Veld gets fair rainfall, but the total yearly precipitation decreases toward the west and northwest.

In the strict sense only the coastal lowlands have a humid subtropical climate. The altitude influence on climate makes all the interior portions of the region liable to frosts —on the highest lands even during the summer. The northern and western portions, like those of the South American region, are plagued by droughts and by locusts from the adjoining savanna regions.

The People. Along the southeast coast, especially in Natal, an odd assemblage of races and modes of life exists. In addition to the native black population (denser here than elsewhere in the Union) and the European whites there is a large element of "Asiatics," as they are known, from India. Seven-eighths of the Indian population of South Africa is in Natal, where they earn their living either as coolies or as merchants. Primitive native tribal life and the customs of the East exist side by side with a European culture. Natal is predominantly British in traditions and associations, in contrast to the Dutch (Boer) predominance elsewhere in South Africa.

The Negroes of this region are mostly Zulus (on the north part of the coast) and Bantus (inland). The Bantus are one of the most energetic and advanced of the native black peoples of Africa. Unlike the majority of the Negro tribes on the continent subjected to similar circumstances the Bantus have preserved their identity and have not become wholly subordinate to the white civilization. Thus about 600,000 Basutos (a Bantu people) enjoy self-government directly under the British Crown within an area of some 12,000 square miles on the High

Veld. The entry of whites into this country is severely restricted.

Agriculture and Products. Much of the agriculture in the African humid subtropical region is the subsistence type, carried on by natives. **Corn** is the main cereal crop; other cereals, vegetables, and citrus fruits are also grown. There is no outstanding export crop such as cotton in North America or wheat and flax in South America. The nearest approach to this is **sugar,** from extensive plantations of cane on the coastal lowland of Natal. Tea and tobacco are also raised, as well as cotton inland on the higher ground. On the High Veld, in the more humid portions of the Orange Free State, corn is again the major crop, in this instance grown by Europeans as a cash crop.

Cattle and sheep are kept everywhere by the natives, the former especially in the more humid parts. Basutoland carries on a thriving export trade in **wool.**

The higher land between the Drakensberg and the east coast is the site of good forests which supply **lumber** for use as props in the gold mines of the Transvaal and for building construction in the treeless regions to the west. Another forest product is the bark of the **wattle** tree, a good tanning agent. Native to Australia, the tree is cultivated in Africa by European farmers at altitudes of 2000 to 4000 feet.

Mineral Products. The outstanding mineral product of the region is **coal,** from deposits located in Natal along the base of the Drakensberg escarpment at its northern end. About one-third of the coal production of South Africa is from these deposits, which rank in importance along with the gold and diamonds among the mineral resources of the Union of South Africa. The coal is used for electric power generation in mining, and is also suitable for coking purposes. This quality, together with the presence of **iron ore** deposits, has made possible the steel industry of Natal, which is, however, handicapped by lack of skilled labor and poor transportation facilities.

Cities. **Durban,** the leading port and third city of the Union of South Africa, is on the

CITIES OF THE SOUTHEAST TIP OF AFRICA

Name	Province	Type	Population (1951)
Durban	Natal	Seaport	480,000
Port Elizabeth	Cape Province	Seaport	190,000

northeastern edge of the humid subtropical region. It is the export center for the products of Natal and owes its development as a port to its good landlocked harbor and its proximity to the coal fields and the interior gold fields. Its industries are leather, food processing, and machinery. Durban's streets exemplify the racial conglomeration of this part of Africa. Zulus in tribal dress, Indians in saris, as well as Europeans in standard attire all throng its streets. Durban during the winter is also something of a resort city for the population of the interior because of its beach and recreation facilities—a sort of "South African Miami Beach."

Port Elizabeth ranks as the third port of the Union. It is located in the eastern end of Cape Province roughly halfway between Durban and the Cape of Good Hope. Its harbor is artificial, as it is on an open bay. It is the site of automobile assembly plants as well as several light industries.

The Union of South Africa as a Whole. The destiny of the Union of South Africa is, for better or worse, related to three things: nationality, race, and mining. The history of the country, its present situation, and its future prospects can all be characterized in terms of these factors.

Nationality is a factor in the course of events because of the particular tensions that resulted from colonization by the Dutch and British in turn. The Dutch were true pioneers who settled down on homesteads to carry on farming and ranching. The British, who subsequently obtained control of the country, busied themselves in founding cities and exploiting the mineral wealth that was discovered.

The conflict that shortly developed between the two interests has continued to this day. The Boers (Dutch) were intent on maintaining their political and cultural identity based on a farming and pastoral existence, a program which necessitated the ousting of the native blacks from their homeland. The British, on the other hand, were interested in developing a prosperous colony on the same basis as those of the rest of their empire, and hence sought to maintain the native culture wherever possible as a background for the local administration.

The victory of the British in the Boer War in the late nineteenth century was followed by a magnanimous adherence of the losers to a political union composed of all the European colonists. Unfortunately, this did not end the conflict of interests, and the Union has remained a nation divided against itself despite the maintenance of political stability. English and Afrikaans (a perverted form of Dutch) are both official languages, but the desire of the English to retain strong ties with the British Commonwealth is bitterly opposed by the Boer aspiration to make the nation completely independent and governed by the dour Boer political philosophy.

Boer-British friction is nevertheless quite submerged in a common attitude among the Europeans concerning the more basic and dangerous race problem. Racial conflict affects every aspect of life in the country and is the great issue confronting every inhabitant. The problem in brief is this: Of a total population of 12.5 million some 10 million are non-European, yet the political, economic, and social structure of the country is based on the complete and uncompromising dominance of the Europeans. The Union of South Africa is maintained as a "white" country although the whites are outnumbered four to one.

No acceptable solution to the race problem has as yet been proposed. The unbalance in the white-nonwhite ratio could be at least partially corrected by European immigration, which has been encouraged in a limited way. Although the choicer farmland is almost all in the possession of the whites, South Africa is agriculturally not yet fully utilized. Estimates as to the ultimate European population it could support range from 5 million

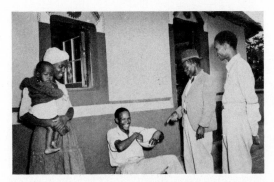

Fig. 18.2—Members of the Tswana Tribe, Western Transvaal, Gossip Outside a Better-Class Native Home. (Courtesy, Government Information Office, Union of South Africa.)

to 25 million. Although immigration would not alter the basic aspects of the race problem, it is nevertheless opposed by the more fanatical Boers because it would reduce their own percentage among the white population.

Meanwhile the black population is increasing more rapidly than the white because of improved sanitation and the elimination of intertribal wars (Fig. 18.2). With better education the non-European elements of the population are becoming increasingly restive and resentful of subjugation. They have become aware of and collectively object to segregation in appallingly neglected slums, regulations such as the requirement that they carry a pass if out after dark, and restriction of nonwhites to only menial labor.

With regard to its mining activities the Union of South Africa is in a paradoxical position. The country comprises a large portion of one of the great metallic ore regions of the world. It has a world monopoly on diamonds and is the dominant gold producer and a major source of at least 10 other minerals. Despite the diversified list of products, the national economy is built upon gold. Without the gold mines the industrialization that has been attained could never have occurred, and the relatively high standard of living enjoyed by the European inhabitants would not have been possible, for the country earns its way internationally by the sale of gold abroad.

The significance of this dependence on

gold is not so much that the ore reserves are becoming exhausted. The repeated extensions of the gold fields to date, plus the development of the highly important uranium by-product industry, insure that there will be a gold-mining industry indefinitely. Rather, it is the fact that the country's prosperity depends so completely on a single industry, a dangerous situation no matter what the attendant circumstances.

D. THE EAST CENTRAL COAST OF AUSTRALIA

General Aspects. The humid subtropical region of Australia includes portions of three states of the country: (1) the southeast coast of **Queensland,** (2) the entire coast of **New South Wales,** and (3) a small interior portion of **Victoria** (Fig. 18.3).

The topography somewhat resembles that of the African region of the same climate. A

Fig. 18.3—Humid Subtropical Australia. The inset compares the area of the region with that of California, which is approximately equal.

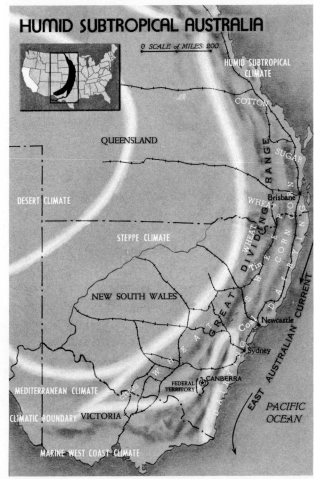

HUMID SUBTROPICAL AUSTRALIA

narrow coastal lowland strip is backed by mountains constituting the western escarpment of an interior plateau which slopes to the west.

The coastal lowlands are local and isolated. The mountains, part of the **Great Dividing Range** that borders the entire east coast of Australia, rise to approximately the same elevations as do the Appalachians in the United States. Actually the "mountains" are a series of more or less continuous plateaus containing numerous peaks of higher elevation (Fig. 18.4).

Fig. 18.4—Plateau Aspect of the Blue Mountains, New South Wales, Australia. (Courtesy, Australian News and Information Bureau.)

Some degree of unreliability of rainfall has been mentioned as ordinarily a minor feature of the humid subtropical climate. Since undependable rainfall is the great curse of Australia in general it could be expected that in the Australian humid subtropical region this defect would prove to be the critical climatic characteristic. The rainfall here is indeed more erratic than in any humid region in the world.

This is due to the fact that monsoon development in Australia is restricted to the northwest coast, the southeast receiving no such precipitation. Moreover, except for the northern portion of the region, which is under the trades-westerlies alternation, most of the east coast is within the westerlies belt and hence dependent on cyclonic storms for precipitation the year round. Rainfall therefore varies according to the fluctuating incidence of such storms.

The average annual rainfall for the coastal stretch as a whole is between 35 and 50 inches. In the north there is a pronounced winter dry season, and the figure varies from one inch to more than 30 inches. South of the Queensland border the rainfall is more uniform throughout the year and the total ranges between 20 and 80 inches. As in Africa the high, east-facing escarpment creates a rain shadow on the western slope of the interior plateau, with increasing aridity inland. Thus, while the eastern portion of the plateau immediately behind the escarpment receives sufficient rainfall to include it in the humid subtropical region, precipitation declines westward to steppe conditions.

The temperatures are very moderate, like those of the South American region. In the south the summer average is 70° F., the winter 50° F.; in the north the equivalent figures are 80° F. and 60° F. The lowest sea-level winter temperature ever recorded was 32° F. The ocean current responsible for much of the moderate temperature range is the **East Australian Current**. This is a 40-mile-wide current that flows south along the coast some 20 miles offshore and taps the warm waters of the Coral Sea to the north.

Invading winds from neighboring climatic regions are of two kinds. In the summer a cooling wind from the antarctic regions known as the *burster* brings relief from high temperatures. On the unpleasant side are the 13 hurricanes that on the average visit the region every year.

Transportation. A major part of the total railroad mileage of Australia is associated with the concentration of population in the humid subtropical region. There is rail communication between the larger centers all along the coast. In the north only a few spur lines run inland to mineral districts. In the south there is a fairly well-developed transportation net inland on the eastern portion of the plateau. Integration of the Australian rail system is handicapped by the existence of different gauges in the north and south.

Agriculture and Products. Although humid subtropical Australia is important in the economy of the continent as the major source of certain products, it resembles its counterpart in Africa in that there is no single predominant crop or group of crops. In general little arable land exists; most of what there is occurs in the valleys between the ridges and peaks.

The nearest approach to a dominant crop is **corn,** which is grown especially in the central coast region. The farming is mostly diversified; on the coastal lowlands fruits and vegetables are raised as cash crops, hay and oats for use on the farms. In the north on the coast sugar cane is important as a southern extension of the Queensland cane district of the savanna region (see Chapter 11, p. 199). Tropical fruits such as bananas are products of lesser significance. There is also a cotton district in the north and an orange center in the south. The plateau portion of the region is sparsely inhabited. It is, however, one of the ranking **sheep** and **wheat** districts of Australia.

The leading agricultural activity of the region is the **dairy** industry. Most of the cattle of Australia are pastured within this region and 75 percent of the herds are dairy cattle, concentrated along the coastal lowlands. The focal district is along the northern coast of New South Wales. When the rains are adequate there is plenty of grass for pasturage, but because of the frequent droughts the output of the main export product, **butter,** fluctuates greatly from year to year.

Lumber is obtained from the forests of eucalyptus hardwoods in the southern highlands (Fig. 18.5). At one time, before so much of the land was cleared for dairy farms, such forests were very extensive. The Australian Alps district is the only important lumber area now.

Mineral Products and Manufacturing. The outstanding mineral product and resource is **coal.** The region contains the most important deposits on the Australian continent and is responsible for 80 to 90 percent of the total output. Production is insignificant compared to that of a large industrial country but is sufficient for the needs of Australia and the South Pacific.

Tin is found in moderate amounts in the highlands in the Queensland–New South Wales border district.

As in South Africa the moderate supplies

Fig. 18.5—Eucalyptus Forest, Tree Ferns in Foreground, in the Southern Highlands of Australia. Dairy farms on valley floor. (Courtesy, Australian News and Information Bureau.)

of iron ore and coking coal support a small but flourishing **iron and steel** industry. The iron ore is brought from Iron Knob in South Australia (see Chapter 16, p. 311). The largest cities of coastal New South Wales, in particular, are centers of both light and heavy industry. Manufactures include textiles, leather, food processing, furniture, paper, chemicals, bricks and glass, machinery, and metal products. New South Wales is by far the leading state of Australia in diversity of industry and value of output.

CITIES OF HUMID SUBTROPICAL
AUSTRALIA

Name	State	Type	Population (1954)
Sydney	New South Wales	Seaport, industrial	1,860,000
Brisbane	Queensland	Seaport, industrial, and governmental	502,000
Newcastle	New South Wales	Seaport, industrial	178,000
Canberra	Federal District	Governmental	31,000

Fig. 18.6. Sydney, Australia. View of the city from over its harbor, one of the world's few perfect ports. The arch bridge is one of the largest of its type in the world. (Courtesy, Australian News and Information Bureau.)

Cities. The city of **Sydney** (Fig. 18.6), with one of the world's best harbors, is in the center of the New South Wales coastline on a coastal plain rimmed by rather precipitous highlands so that it is more or less cut off from the interior. Sydney is the site of the original colonization of Australia.

It would be difficult to overstate the importance of Sydney within its country. The largest city on the continent, it contains with its suburbs almost one-half of the population of its state and one-fifth of the total population of the country. Like Buenos Aires in Argentina (see Chapter 17, p. 351), Sydney dominates Australia. It is the commercial, industrial, financial, social, and cultural capital of the country and rates as one of the great cities of the world. (It is the other of the two cities in the Southern Hemisphere with a subway system.) Sydney was the Australian national capital until 1927.

Brisbane, capital of Queensland, is the second city of the east coast. It is 500 miles north of Sydney and not far north of the New South Wales border. It is on the Brisbane River 15 miles from its mouth and, like Sydney, is an industrial center as well as a major port.

Newcastle, the third-ranking port of Australia and second city of New South Wales, is about 60 miles north of Sydney. It rivals Sydney as an industrial center, chiefly because of its location near important coal fields. It is the site of a large steel mill and many associated heavy industries.

Canberra (Fig. 3.6) is some 80 miles inland, about 150 miles northwest of Sydney, in a mountain-rimmed basin at an altitude of 2000 feet. It is one of the few purely governmental cities among the world's national capitals, having been chosen as the governmental site because Australia's major cities could not agree which among them should have the honor. Canberra is a very beautiful city, based on a plan which won a world-wide contest. It became the functioning national capital of Australia in 1927.

E. CENTRAL AND SOUTHERN CHINA; JAPAN

As a whole, the area of the humid subtropical development in Asia is about the same as that of the North American occurrence. Of China it embraces that part bounded roughly by the 105th meridian on the west and the 33rd parallel on the north—approximately one-fourth of the country, plus the island of **Taiwan** (Formosa) off the southeast coast. It includes also a small area of southern Korea and all the important islands of Japan except the northernmost one. Collectively considered, this region is by far the most populous of the humid subtropical regions and has the longest history of human occupance.

Climate. The region is often referred to as "Monsoon East Asia," in recognition of the preponderant influence of the monsoon phenomenon in the climate and its wholly determinant effect on life within the region. Although the south and southeast monsoon wind is not so strong as that of the southwest monsoon of India, it is fully as important. The seasonal wind alternation here is not between the trades and the westerlies, as in the other humid subtropical regions, but between the monsoon and the antimonsoon. All temperature and precipitation phenomena of the continental portion of this region are derived from the two winds.

Precipitation over Monsoon East Asia ranges between 40 and 60 inches a year, lower in the north than in the south. The summer monsoon is normally accompanied by rains. But the usual winter parade of cyclonic storms and accompanying precipitation of the westerlies belt across a humid subtropical region is so much disrupted in Asia by the strong, dry antimonsoon from the interior of the continent that precipitation from such storms is not very great. More than 80 percent of the total yearly precipitation comes in the summer—the most pronounced seasonal rainfall of any humid subtropical region. As in Australia and North America, summer thunderstorms are frequent and severe. Drought years are not so numerous or of such extreme intensity as in Australia but are, unfortunately, not infrequent.

Temperatures range from a summer average of 80° F. to a winter average of 40° F. The summers are not unusually hot, but the winters are in general colder than is typical of the climate. An important difference from the North American occurrence is that the steady influence of the antimonsoon (which blows almost constantly at a 15-mile-an-hour rate from October to April) brings cold air from the continental interior to the region throughout the winter and results in low *average* temperatures in China. The United States South, on the other hand, is open to invasion by large cold air masses which produce low *minimum* temperatures. The two regions are alike in that frost affects almost their entire extent several times each winter.

So strong is the antimonsoon influence that frost and even snow occur at sea level in China at the lowest latitude in the world, i.e., actually south of the Tropic of Cancer. (Were it not for this the savanna climate in eastern Asia would extend east into China.)

The adjacent ocean current is also responsible for an unusual extension of the limits of the region. A warm current of small volume flows north from between Borneo and Sumatra past the China coast and on through the **Sea of Japan.** And, more importantly, the **Japan Current** flows north from the Philippine Islands past the east side of the Japanese Islands. Japan is thus bathed on both east and west coasts by warm currents, and the humid subtropical region, accordingly, here extends beyond 40° latitude, its northernmost limit at sea level. Thus the Asiatic development has the distinction of embracing the widest latitudinal spread, uninfluenced by altitude, of all the humid subtropical regions.

The typhoons that originate over the ocean to the southeast of the region are much more formidable than the hurricanes of the Western Hemisphere. Most of the tremendous population is concentrated on extensive lowlands that are recurrently the scene of great devastation by the vast floods that result from the torrential rains accompanying these storms. Tens of thousands of persons have perished by drowning in the floods caused by a single typhoon.

A final noteworthy climatic feature is the absence of a steppe climatic region to the west. The western border consists of mountains and plateaus which are so high they have no climate of a conventional category.

Agriculture. The paramount importance of cotton in the agriculture of the United States South is in southeast Asia exceeded by **rice**. **Tea, cotton,** and **silk** are the other agricultural products of first significance. The forest resources are small in comparison with those of the other humid subtropical regions. Originally they were extensive but as the result of long human occupancy were removed thousands of years ago, and their former existence is in many districts now only a legend.

QUESTIONS. Describe the general topography of the humid subtropical region of Africa. What political divisions or portions of divisions does it encompass? Why does it have a generally milder climate than the humid subtropical regions in the Northern Hemisphere? Discuss the composition of the population of the region. What is the major crop of the natives? Of the coastal plantations? What is wattle bark and why is it a significant export? Name the outstanding mineral product.

Discuss the three major factors in the development of the Union of South Africa to its present status. How do these factors affect the future prospects of the country?

Describe the extent of the humid subtropical region of Australia. Outline the major topographical features of the region. In what respect and why is the climate characteristically Australian despite its basic difference from the other climatic regions of the continent? What is the leading agricultural activity of the region as a whole? What are the major products of the plateau portion of the region? Name the major mineral resources. What industry do they support? In what ways is Sydney like Buenos Aires? Canberra like Washington, D.C.?

Why is the region of central and southern China, and Japan known as "Monsoon East Asia"? Why does humid subtropical China have lower average winter temperatures than the equivalent region in the United States, whereas the latter has lower minimum temperatures? Explain the fact that this region has the widest latitudinal extent of all the humid subtropical regions. Why is there no steppe climate on the western border of the region? What is the dominant crop?

1. CENTRAL AND SOUTHERN CHINA

Topography. The topography of humid subtropical China consists of five general features (Fig. 18.7):

a. Across central China, almost on the northern border of the region, the great **Yangtze Kiang** flows from west to east. Its large delta on the coast and the wide flood plains of the river and its larger tributaries along its middle reaches form a vast plain of fertile, productive land 600 miles in east-west extent and between 20 and 200 miles wide. Because of slight depressions in their surface the lowlands are dotted with large shallow lakes that fluctuate in size with the seasonal flooding of the river.

b. In the west, on the upper Yangtze, is the **Red Basin** of **Szechwan Province**, a region of approximately 75,000 square miles between 500 and 1000 feet in elevation surrounded on all sides by mountains. Szechwan means "Four Rivers," referring to the Yangtze and its tributaries which traverse the basin. In leaving the basin the Yangtze has cut a remarkable gorge rivaling those of the western United States in size, impressiveness, and wild rapids. The mountain borders serve as an effective climatic shelter from the continental cold winter air of the north and west. The **Chengtu Plain** in the western part of the basin, which measures 70 by 40 miles, is the only large level area. Most of the surface has considerable relief because of stream dissection.

c. South of the Yangtze and its tributary valleys and basins is an extensive upland mass, the mountains of South China, which is a less productive and less densely inhabited area.

d. Running slightly south of east not far north of the Indochina border, the **Si Kiang** has cut a valley in these mountains, building up a flood plain on the valley floor and a delta on the coast. In all respects the Si Kiang developments are small, however, compared to those of the Yangtze.

e. The southeast coast of China between the deltas of the Si Kiang and the Yangtze Kiang is rocky and bold. The subordinate highlands of the mountains come down to

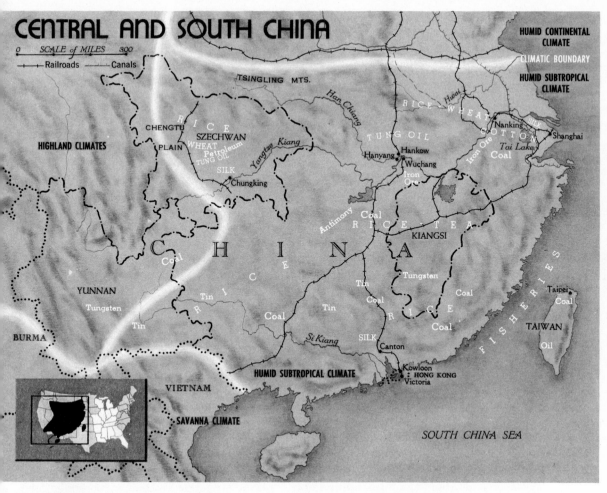

Fig. 18.7—Central and South China. The inset compares the area of the region with an equivalent area of the United States (states in white).

the water's edge, and sinking of the land in recent geologic times has made a coastline full of sheltered coves and harbors, and small offshore islands. Minor rivers have made small deltas and flood plains between the projecting headlands.

Offshore some 100 miles, midway between the two large deltas, is the island of **Taiwan** (Formosa), 14,000 square miles in area (slightly less than half the size of North Carolina). This is the domain of the Nationalist government which until 1949 exercised dominion over most of China. Much of Taiwan is mountainous.

On the west the region is bordered by the very high Tibetan plateau and the lower (5000 to 7000 feet) plateau of **Yunnan**, the latter a part of China. Yunnan is not typically Chinese in either climate or people. The indigenous population is composed mainly of aborigines with Thai characteristics.

Population. There is no doubting the fact that for sheer bulk of population the country has no rival. It is commonly agreed that the Chinese population is somewhere between 500 and 600 million. Although almost 90 percent of the population lives on farms or in small villages, in humid subtropical China alone there are 4 cities of over a million population, 6 cities over a half-million, and 11 over 100,000 on the basis of conservative estimates.

The population is unusual in density as well as numbers. The density reaches several thousand per square mile in certain rural areas. There are five such areas of high population concentration, which coincide significantly with the most productive agricultural areas. These are: (a) The **Yangtze delta** and (b) the **Si Kiang delta,** both of which have average population densities of well over 1000 per square mile; (c) the **Szechwan Basin,** with a density between 400 and 500; (d) the **central Yangtze basin;** and (e) the **southeast coast,** where the concentration is not so uniform but is scattered on the small deltas along the coast.

Agriculture in General. Agriculture in China is a wondrous activity. The enormous population directly dependent upon its own agricultural effort for its food imposes two dominant characteristics: (a) the most intensive agriculture practiced by man and (b) a mystic attitude of the farmer toward the soil as his sole source of sustenance.

The phrase "intensive agriculture" as used in previous chapters cannot begin to convey a sense of the incredible toil and care bestowed upon the arable land of China. Agriculture in China is closer akin to gardening than to farming. There appears to be a vicious circle in the relationship between the amount of labor and the size of the individual farm plots: the smaller the plot a family owns the greater the amount of labor it must expend on its cultivation in order to feed itself. (This generalization, of course, applies only to those regions of China where the dense populations reside.)

Even if the whole area of China is taken into account the population is so huge that there is available, roughly, only half an acre of farm land per person. Moreover, because of the Chinese custom of dividing the farm lands between all the male heirs of each generation the average farm has through the years been reduced to about three acres in extent, with over one-half the farms less than one and a half acres in size. Even this small area is commonly comprised of several individual, noncontiguous plots. Although such division permits the individual farmer to cultivate different kinds of land for different crops, it entails a waste of precious working time in moving from one plot to another.

Arable land is so precious that it is cultivated almost to the last square inch. The tremendous input of work per acre is mostly human effort, with the hoe as the chief implement. Use of a draft animal with a plow is ruled out because the individual plots are too small to make it feasible or worth while. Indeed, the keep of the animal would require more fodder than could be produced on the entire farm! Human toil is thus actually cheaper than animal labor.

Intensive farming in China includes the use of the best possible land, as thorough cultivation as is humanly possible, and the use of as much fertilizer as can be obtained. The chief fertilizer is human excrement, or "night soil,"[1] as it is called when disposed of in this fashion. The use of untreated sewage makes all uncooked food potential poison because of the great likelihood of disease contamination and gives the air a characteristic redolence offensive to Occidental noses.

Another feature of Chinese intensive agriculture is meticulous crop rotation, a practice developed in ancient times. Wherever possible both a summer and a winter crop are raised on the same land; and in the far south, where the growing season is longer, four crops in succession are raised during the year. Rice farming requires the painfully laborious transplantation of the young rice plants, irrigation by human porterage, and constant care of the terraces in hillside districts.

The pressure of population upon resources pervades all aspects of daily life. The stalks of food plants, stray twigs, and grass cuttings are collected either for compost to fertilize the land or for fuel, the ashes from which are returned to the land. Every farmer keeps one or more kinds of fowl (it is estimated that there are in China roughly 195 million **chickens,** 56 million **ducks,** and 7 million **geese**) and **pigs** (60 million) —all the kinds of animals which can feed on what little garbage the humans discard and which do not compete with man in their food requirements. No animal could be afforded that would require labor to be expended in its care and feeding.

[1] It is collected every morning in the cities and sold to the farmers in the surrounding districts.

The large number of fowl results in a considerable production of poor-quality **eggs.** The pigs yield **bristles,** an unusual product (collectible only in China because of the cheapness of human labor there) used in brushes in which China has traditionally dominated the world market.

Each farmer with more than the minimal acreage also has a few fruit trees in odd corners of his land, keeps some silkworms to feed on the leaves of the mulberry trees grown in other odd corners, and raises some tea, cotton, or sugar cane. In so far as the yields from these are in excess of family needs they serve as cash crops, and with so many farms a small excess product from each amounts to a large commercial supply.

The population pressure is so severe that any failure in output, whether due to flood, drought, or war, raises the specter of famine. These conditions have been part of Chinese peasant existence for thousands of years. As a consequence the peasant has a religious veneration for the land that is difficult for the Westerner to apprehend. Although this devotion is slightly less in evidence today because of the great modifications in Chinese life that have resulted from contacts with Occidental civilization it is still a major phenomenon. The only exception to this attitude and to the intensive use of all arable land is the reservation of certain plots for cemeteries, regardless of their agricultural value. This immemorial custom reflects the Chinese reverence for family continuity (commonly known as "ancestor worship"), and is the only sentiment strong enough to overrule the pressing need to use all the land for food production.

Agricultural and Allied Products. **Rice** is the major crop of humid subtropical China; it totals almost one-third of the world production. No other staple can support so many humans per acre as does rice; by weight the yield may be fifty-fold. The low, flat lands of the major river valleys and of the coastal deltas are ideally suited for rice paddies, and the rainfall distribution is perfect for the grain's growth. Rice is also grown on terraced hillsides in the southern mountains and in the Szechwan Basin. The mid-Yangtze basin district normally produces a surplus, an amazing feat in view of the population density of the district. In the Si Kiang region it has proved possible to produce two rice crops annually. **Wheat** and **barley** are important only as subordinate crops in the Yangtze and Szechwan basins and are practically unknown south of the Yangtze. They are grown in winter on the dry rice paddies.

Vegetables include the familiar Western varieties, but in small quantities compared to rice. On the fertile Yangtze flood plain they are grown during the interim between the dry, cold winter and the hot, wet summer, after wheat and before rice.

White and **sweet potatoes** were introduced into China from overseas. The sweet potato, although it is easily grown and from necessity is widely used, has encountered resistance owing to ancient food habits. The white potato is favored where rice cannot be grown.

Tea is widely grown, but production is centered chiefly in the Yangtze Valley, in the hills of the southeast coast between the two large delta regions, in adjacent Taiwan, and in the Szechwan Basin. As a Chinese social custom tea drinking is on a par with the consumption of yerba maté in humid subtropical South America. Its function, on the other hand, is the equivalent of wine in the Mediterranean Basin. The boiling of water for tea insures a germ-free drink.

At one time China was the largest tea exporter in the world, but its unstandardized product could not compete successfully with that of plantation agriculture in Ceylon and Assam (see Chapter 8, p. 122). The high reputation achieved by the "oolong" variety developed on Taiwan by the Japanese shows what might be done in China proper. As it is a secondary crop, Chinese tea does not come onto the market when prices are low; nevertheless China probably ranks first in the world as a tea producer. The bulk of the yield is for domestic use.

Cotton is widely grown as a cash crop. As much as one-quarter of the production is raised in the Yangtze delta area as an exception to the usual food farming. Cotton (quilted to provide warmth in winter) is the standard textile in China. Even in normal times production barely satisfied domestic demand despite the rank of China as the world's third producer. Cotton is planted late in the season after a food crop has been harvested. Because the soil is then depleted of fertility the quality of the crop is poor.

Silk is the other important fiber produced in this part of China. China was the original source of silk and the chief supplier of the world market until the present century, when it lost its premier position to Japan. Nevertheless it is probable that China is still the major silk producer of the world. There are three centers of production: one around **Tai Lake,** a large body of water on the Yangtze delta; another on the Si Kiang, where the warmer climate makes possible year-round production; and the third the Szechwan Basin. The customs and methods of sericulture are so old that, like many other aspects of Chinese life, they have an almost ritualistic formalism.

Ramie, a less important fiber, is derived from a nettle-like plant that grows from three to eight feet high and can be cut every six months during its life of 10 to 20 years. Ramie requires heavy fertilizing but yields a ton of fiber to the acre (compared to a few hundred pounds for cotton). It is grown chiefly in the Yangtze Valley and Taiwan. Because the fiber is extracted by a series of laborious hand operations it can be economically produced only with the extremely cheap Chinese labor and hence has never become a fiber of major importance elsewhere in the world.

Opium is a drug manufactured from the seed of the Oriental poppy. Its production has traditionally been illegal, but during the Japanese occupation poppy growing was actively encouraged.

Tobacco was introduced, like the two varieties of potatoes, from the Western Hemisphere. It is grown as a winter crop.

The **tung** tree is native to China, and a considerable quantity of **tung oil** is produced from trees in the Szechwan and central Yangtze basins.

The forest resources of humid subtropical China are now restricted to the mountains of South China, where virgin timber still exists. The lack of transportation facilities prevents development; consequently the lumber needs of China were, until China became Communist, largely met by imports from the west coast of North America! **Bamboo** grown in the valleys is used extensively as a lumber substitute. **Camphor** (distilled from the wood of a species of laurel tree) is produced in sufficient quantity in Taiwan to supply the bulk of the world's needs.

In China **fish** are a significant part of a diet generally low in protein. The southeast coast with its narrow lowlands and many sheltered coves and harbors has from very early times prompted the Chinese of that region to look to the sea for food. Consequently they have not been bound to the soil as have their compatriots inland and to the north. They became not only fishermen but, as well, the cosmopolitan overseas traders of the Orient. Fish are also available in the flat lowlands, for these are everywhere dotted with small ponds used for "fish farming." The aquatic plants flourishing in such ponds also provide food for human and animal consumption, and supply fertilizer as well.

Mineral Resources and Manufacturing. Humid subtropical China is the site of important producing mineral districts and of large undeveloped resources in addition. China formerly furnished some two-thirds of the world supply of **tungsten** and has by far the largest reserves. Tungsten deposits occur throughout the southern mountains and on the Yunnan plateau. Most of the production, however, is from the mountains of Kiangsi Province.

Antimony, a metal of considerable importance as a lead alloy, is another important mineral product. Roughly 95 percent of Chinese antimony is recovered in Hunan Province. Since the beginning of the Sino-Japanese War in 1937 various circumstances have, however, kept the Chinese production more or less out of the world market.

The Chinese **tin** region is a northern extension of the great Malay-Burma tin district that reaches into Hunan. In volume, on the other hand, China does not rank very high as a tin producer.

In terms of potential usefulness to the country China's greatest mineral resources are large deposits of **coal** and **iron ore,** the essentials of modern industrial development. Coal reserves include all grades and types. Anthracite is found in the mountains of the southeast coast; good coking coal occurs in the central and lower Yangtze Basin and in Szechwan Province. The third largest iron ore district of China is south of the lower Yangtze.

China's petroleum and natural gas resources are small in terms of proved resources but potentially great. There is now a small production on Taiwan; but the Szechwan Basin has the greatest promise.

Other mineral resources, both developed and undeveloped, include moderate-sized deposits of molybdenum, lead, zinc, bauxite, mercury, copper, and sulfur. The **hydropower** resources are large, especially in the southern mountains. It has been proposed that the enormous potentialities of the Yangtze Gorge be developed. If fully carried out, such development would dwarf the largest projects elsewhere in the world.

All the large cities are centers of manufacturing. The major industry is **textiles,** with mills for silk, cotton, and wool. **Iron and steel** works of modest size exist at various places. The relative inaccessibility of coking coal deposits and the previous political instability of the country have retarded the de-

velopment of a large-scale industry. Other industries include **electrical appliances** and **machinery, metal works, chemicals, tobacco,** and **food processing.**

Cities. The large cities of China, especially those on the coast, are unique among the major cities of a great country in the degree to which they represent foreign rather than native culture. When European nations were developing trade with China in the eighteenth and nineteenth centuries the Chinese imperial government restricted foreign trade to certain cities designated as "treaty ports" in order to prevent foreign influences from corrupting the Chinese way of life. The result was a concentration of Occidental influence in a few large cities, so that the commercial districts of these cities developed in the Occidental pattern, with Occidental architecture, technology, and customs.

The city of **Shanghai** is located at the mouth of the Yangtze 14 miles upstream on a small tributary, the **Whangpoo,** as the mouth of the Yangtze is too wide to provide a harbor. The greatest of the "treaty ports," Shanghai developed in less than a hundred years into one of the five greatest cities of the world, and second largest in the Far East. It grew to this size because of its unparalleled commercial location. Its enormous hinterland includes not only the entire drainage basin of the Yangtze but so much of the remaining parts of central and south China that the city actually serves as the trade center of about one-half of the whole country. As the major "treaty port" it became the center of European commercial and financial activity for most of the Orient and

CITIES OF HUMID SUBTROPICAL CHINA

Name	Province	Type	Population
Shanghai	Kiangsu	Seaport, industrial	6,200,000 (1953)
Nanking	Anhwei	Seaport	1,100,000 (1950)
Hankow	Hupeh	Seaport-River port, industrial	750,000 (1947)
Wuchang	Hupeh	River port, industrial	205,000 (1948)
Hanyang	Hupeh	River port, industrial	69,000 (1947)
Chungking	Szechwan	River port	1,600,000 (1953)
Hong Kong		Seaport	2,250,000 (1953)
Canton	Kwangtung	River port	1,500,000 (1950)
Taipei	Taiwan	Commercial, governmental	450,000 (1950)

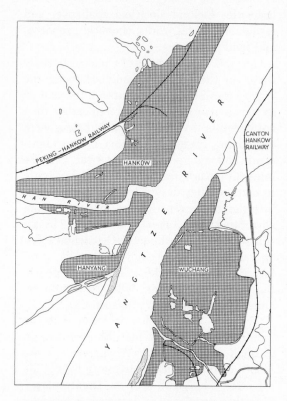

Fig. 18.8—The Triple City of Wuhan. The terminals of both railways are just off the map. The location of the new bridge across the Yangtze which links the two railways is not known.

supported a considerable industrial concentration based on its raw material imports. After the capture of the city by the Communists in 1949, however, Shanghai's international commercial position declined sharply, since its foreign commerce dwindled away owing to the Cold War conditions. Nevertheless, it remains China's greatest city.

Nanking ("Southern Capital") is located on the south bank of the Yangtze 200 miles northwest of Shanghai. Its name refers to the fact that it has been the seat of government at various times in Chinese history, the most recent being during the years of the Chinese Republic, 1928–37 and 1946–49.

Still farther up the Yangtze, 600 miles from the China Sea, is the triple city of **Wuhan** (1950 combined population, 1,200,000) (Fig. 18.8). The relation of its three component cities to one another resembles the Khar-

toum agglomeration on the Nile (see Chapter 12, p. 216). The major city is **Hankow,** with **Wuchang** across the main river and **Hanyang** on the other side of the Han River, an entering tributary. Wuhan's commercial position is very similar to that of St. Louis in the United States. It is located at the point where the great east-west trade artery that is the Yangtze is intersected by a major north-south route over which both rail and water transport moves. Its importance has been further enhanced by a railroad bridge over the Yangtze, the construction of which was begun in 1954. It is the largest bridge in the Eastern Hemisphere and the only bridge of any kind over the Yangtze in its entire 3100-mile length! In addition to its unrivaled commercial position Wuhan also boasts an industrial concentration, including an iron and steel industry (in Hanyang) based on nearby coal and iron ore deposits.

Still farther upstream on the Yangtze, 1400 miles from its mouth, is **Chungking,** the largest city of the Szechwan Basin. The city is on a hilly peninsula between the Yangtze and a large tributary. Chungking has always been the main gateway for trade between the Szechwan region and the populous eastern plains. From 1937 to 1946 it was in addition one of the world's famous cities as the capital of Free China. In the postwar period it has again become a provincial city but has retained a substantial portion of its added population and industry.

Hong Kong (Fig. 18.9), although geographically within China, is politically a British crown colony, the original commercial concession from China to a foreign power and one of the two surviving remnants of foreign territory in China. Hong Kong consists of a group of islands and a small peninsula on the south China coast just east of a large estuary, the **Pearl River,** the main entrance to a compound delta formed by the Si Kiang and two smaller streams.[2] The total area of the colony is just under 400 square miles. **Victoria,** the colony's capital, is on

[2] Si Kiang means "West River." The Si is the westernmost of the three streams.

Hong Kong island facing the **Kowloon** peninsula that constitutes the other portion of the city. As a free port, with the best harbor of the south coast, the colony has flourished by serving as the transshipment center for the exports and imports of all south China. Even the commercial stringencies of the Cold War have served merely to diminish, but not obliterate, its role. Victoria exhibits almost perfectly the characteristics of a British colonial settlement. It provides all the amenities and diversions considered essential to make life endurable for an Englishman in an "outpost of civilization." Kowloon, on the other hand, is Chinese in every respect save its political control.

Ninety miles to the east of Hong Kong at the head of the delta is **Canton,** the original trade center of the region. The great amount of sediment brought down to the Si delta by the three streams reduces Canton's connection with the sea to only a six-foot channel. This handicap was the chief factor in promoting the growth of Hong Kong to be the major port of the region at the expense of Canton. Nevertheless Canton functions as the seaward terminus of the 1000-mile east-west transportation route along the Si Kiang as well as of the major route to the north, and in this capacity has domestic commercial importance in its own right. The floating houseboat population characteristic of all Chinese ports is unusually large in Canton because of the great number of waterways, canals, and distributaries traversing the delta. The city is, accordingly, sometimes called the "Venice of China." Because of its early history of foreign trade Canton developed a population with a dialect and customs quite different from those of the rest of China. It has traditionally been the main port for the emigration of Chinese throughout the world.

Taipei, on the island of Taiwan, is at the northern end of the island 13 miles upstream from the sea on a small river. It is the largest city of Taiwan, but in no way compares with the preceding cities of China in general sig-

Fig. 18.9. Hong Kong, China. View, from Victoria, overlooks the harbor and illustrates the mountainous topography of the site. (Courtesy, British Information Services.)

nificance. It is mentioned here only because of its present function as the site of the Nationalist government of the Republic of China.

Fig. 18.10—Japan. The inset compares the area of Japan with that of Montana, which is approximately equal.

2. JAPAN

Topography. Japan, since World War II, consists of four large islands surrounded by more than a thousand lesser ones draped in a pendant arc off the east coast of Asia (Fig. 18.10). The islands are part of the great com-

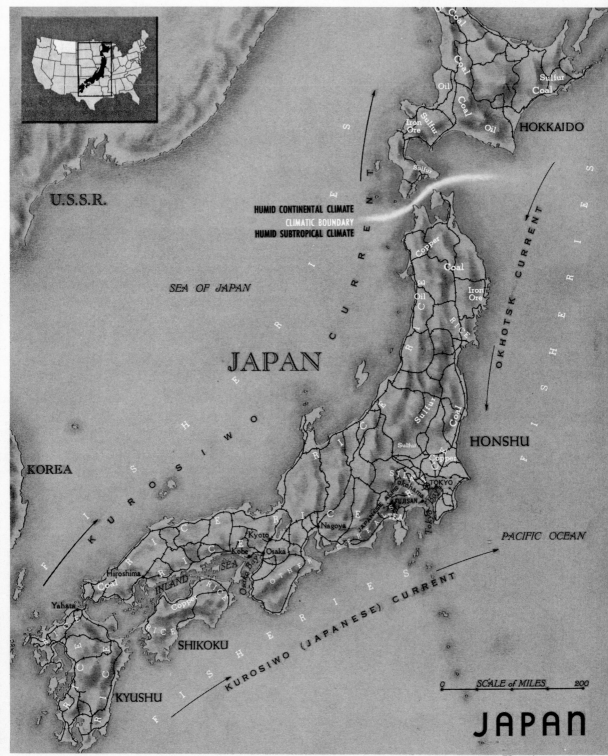

plex of circumpacific mountain chains (see Chapter 2, p. 28). A characteristic of these chains is the formidable number of volcanoes —Japan has more than 500, of which 60 have erupted in historical times. There are also some 1500 earthquakes a year, mostly minor, but occasionally, as in 1923 and 1948, severe enough to destroy entire cities.

Japan is a country of high relief. Viewed from the air the landscape is made up of high peaks, steep slopes, and narrow valleys. In some places the mountains or their foothills extend unbroken to the sea, but more commonly narrow coastal plains and deltas make up the shoreline. Where large blocks of the underlying rock have dropped below the general surface, major valleys extend far back into the interior. The general pattern of the mountains is that of two ranges, one on the east, one on the west, which jointly curve through the arc of the Japanese Islands. In many places, however, this arrangement is only obscurely in evidence.

The total area of Japan is 147,000 square miles (slightly larger than Montana), almost all of it in the four large islands—**Honshu, Hokkaido, Kyushu,** and **Shikoku**—in that order of size.

Kyushu, the westernmost, has a north-south elongation and is about half the size of the state of Maine. The coastline on the north, south, and especially west is highly indented, with many islands, bays, and good harbors. The interior mountains reach an altitude of 6500 feet and are rugged even for Japan. Most of the island is agriculturally unproductive, and its development is further handicapped by remoteness from the economic heart of the country.

Honshu, the main island, curves from east to north beginning at the north end of Kyushu. It is roughly 800 miles long and 175 miles in width at its widest, midway along its length. Its total area is somewhat larger than the state of Idaho. Western Honshu has very little lowland area; its north coast is steep and rugged. On the south, however, it faces the island of Shikoku (about the size of New Jersey). Between them, in the most extreme development of the valley between the two main mountain ranges, an irregular block of the earth's crust has dropped down to form the **Inland Sea.** This is a beautiful, island-studded body of water, the locale of the typical Japanese landscapes familiar from pictures to most Westerners. It is the heart of Western Japan. The constricted and easily guarded entrances to this sea, of which there are only three, made it an impregnable home base for the Japanese Navy until the arrival of American airpower in World War II.

East of the Inland Sea is the central portion of Honshu, where most of the Japanese people live. This is the center of Japanese economic activity; here are the highest mountains and largest plains. The southern coast of this region is deeply indented with wide bays. The largest and most important plain is at the southeast "corner" of the island. West of this plain, in the "Japanese Alps," are the highest peaks of Japan, including the volcanic cone **Fujisan** (Fujiyama, elevation almost 12,500 feet), a sacred mountain occupying the same place in Japanese mythology and religion as does Mount Olympus in the lore of ancient Greece (Fig. 18.11).

Northern Honshu has fewer lowland areas, is less densely populated, and is climatically transitional between southern Japan and Hokkaido. The latter island, somewhat smaller than Indiana in area, is north of Honshu. With cold and snowy winters it is not in the humid subtropical climate. It is sparsely populated and is in other respects unlike the rest of Japan.

Climate. The greater equability of the Japanese climate compared with that of the adjacent continental area has already been noted. Precipitation results from the orographic rise of both monsoon and antimonsoon winds over the mountains of the country. The southern coasts get summer, the northern coasts winter precipitation (much of it in the form of snow).

There is, in general, along the island chain of Japan a south-to-north transition from the humid subtropical climate to a cold climate. But this transition is greatly modified locally by altitudinal differences and the surrounding complex of ocean currents. The warm

Fig. 18.11—Fujisan, Also Known as Fujiyama, the Sacred Mountain of Japan. (Courtesy, Information Service, Embassy of Japan.)

Kurosiwo divides south of Japan; so also does a cold current from the north, the **Okhotsk Current,** when it reaches Japan. Owing to rotational deflection (see Chapter 6, p. 95) the western branch of the Kurosiwo hugs the western coast of Japan while the other branch turns east off central Honshu. Similarly, the eastern branch of the Okhotsk Current is thrust against the eastern coast of northern Japan, while the other branch is forced to the far side of the Sea of Japan along the Asiatic mainland. Thus the southern portion of the east coast is, in accord with latitude, warmer than its northern portion, but the west coast is warm throughout its length. As a consequence subtropical and freezing conditions regularly exist in winter within a score or so miles of each other.

All of Japan is within the typhoon area, but the southern coast, including most of Kyushu, all of Shikoku, and central Honshu, is especially subject to heavy damage from such storms. Most of the destruction is from floods caused by the typhoon winds in their orographic rise on the mountains. Wave damage, too, is often considerable.

The People. The origin of the Japanese is obscure, but it appears that Malayan, Indonesian, and Mongoloid stocks all contributed to their evolution. The invading peoples easily displaced the **Ainus,** the native aborigines, driving them steadily northward until they reached the northernmost islands, where their descendants live today.

The long isolation of Japan, especially from contact with the West, is well known. The sudden forced termination of this isolation by American intervention in 1853 prompted the Japanese to adopt the technology of the West and to resolve to make their nation one of the world's great powers. This deliberate acceptance of Western methods gave rise to a general belief in the rest of the world that the Japanese are merely imitators. True, they had in their earlier history adopted many Chinese customs in addition to Chinese religion and written language, but such borrowing has merely reflected an awareness of what is desirable and useful in other cultures. Yet along with their borrowings the Japanese have developed a culture all their own, and their contributions to art (and more recently to science and technology) have been very significant.

Nevertheless, the fact that the machine age in Japan arrived all at once, from abroad, has resulted in a certain amount of cultural indigestion (intensified by the occupation after World War II). The larger cities became very Westernized, with skyscrapers and all the complex facilities of a modern Western city. The business and commercial communities in such cities adopted Western dress and many Western customs. In the smaller cities of the hinterland, however, the ancient Japanese ways of life have persisted almost unchanged. At a deeper level the nation retained a heritage of feudalism and reliance on regimentation as a means of national accomplishment, and coupled these with employment of the technology of the West in furthering a vast program of aggrandizement.

The attempt to build a greater Japanese Empire derived partly from unbounded ambition, partly from a delusion concerning the national destiny from analogy with the British Isles and British history. But it had in addition an all too real physical basis—overpopulation—that has only been augmented by World War II and its aftermath.

Like China, Japan is an intensively cultivated agricultural country. Its total population of more than 86 million computes to an average density of nearly 600 per square mile, but with only 17 percent of the total area arable the real density is nearly 4500 persons per square mile of cultivated land.

By far the majority of the people are concentrated on the plains and lowlands around the Inland Sea and on the south coast of central Honshu. There the climate is regarded by the Japanese as ideal, there Japanese agriculture can be practiced under optimum conditions, and there, also, are almost all of the great cities of Japan. The number of large cities in a small area and the concentration of population they represent are astounding. There are four cities of over one million and 30 cities of more than 100,000 in Japan; all of the former and all but five of the latter are in the southern half of the country.

The greatest concentration is on the **Kwanto Plain,** at the southeast "corner" of Honshu, where dwell some 14 million people. A second concentration is at the eastern end of the Inland Sea on the **Kinai Plain.** A third concentration lies between them.

Transportation. Japan is justly proud of the best transportation system in the Far East, which fortunately came through World War II almost unscathed. The first railroad was built in 1872, and within 50 years there were 10,000 miles of railroads, of which 30 percent was electrified. This rapid and thorough development of a transportation network had much to do with the equally rapid industrialization of the country.

The difficulty of railroad construction in a mountainous terrain was offset by the highly centralized and integrated geographical situation of Japan. The size of the railroad system is nevertheless remarkable considering its necessary subordination to coastal shipping in a country that is completely maritime.

Agriculture in General. Although Japan was one of the major industrial nations in the period between the two World Wars the economy of the country has always been basically agricultural. Almost one-half the population was during this time dependent on farming as a livelihood.

In most respects Japanese agriculture resembles that of the Chinese. Since there is so little level land, terracing is carried up every hill slope as far as is humanly possible. Again, agriculture is more like gardening than farming. The farm plots are even smaller than in China; with the acreage of a single farmer scattered among several plots, the average total holding of an individual is two and one-half acres, and more than half of the total holdings are only one and a quarter acres or less. A plot this size is the equivalent of a large lot in a first-class residential district in the United States.

Draft animals, however, especially horses and oxen, are used more extensively than in China, often under common village ownership.

Tenant farming is another distinctive feature of Japanese agriculture. Only a third of the farmers own all the land they work. One-quarter cultivate only rented land. Moreover, one-third of the income of the average farm family must come from sources other than food crops. If cash crops cannot fill the gap, the farmer and his family must become part-time workers in some other line of endeavor.

Agricultural and Allied Products. The overwhelming importance of **rice** (Fig. 18.12) in the economy is as great as in humid subtropical China. Over half of all the cultivated land is in rice. Rice is grown as far up the hillsides as the necessary amount of water can be collected, and special varieties are grown even in cold Hokkaido. Total output ranks Japan among the four leading rice producers. Despite such intensive cultivation Japan is, however, chronically unable to satisfy its rice needs.

The importance of **wheat** has increased in

recent decades with the adoption of bread as a basic food item. Together with barley, rye, and oats it supplements rice and is more characteristic of the upland districts.

Beans, peas, millet, corn, and white and sweet potatoes are other supplementary home-grown items of the Japanese diet. They are grown on land not suitable for rice, except around the large cities where

Fig. 18.12—Threshing Rice by Machine Power in a Japanese Country Farmyard. (Courtesy, Information Service, Embassy of Japan.)

varieties, are more generally distributed.

In one respect Japan's mountainous topography in comparison to China's extensive plains has proved to be a national asset. The forests that occupy the higher and steeper slopes were never removed, so that approximately one-half of Japan is still tree-covered. Broadleaf trees comprise about one-half of the forest area (mostly in the south); conifer stands constitute most of the remainder. These forests were early considered to be of such importance that the government took

the Japanese equivalents of the truck farms of the Atlantic coast in the United States are located. By taking advantage of almost every hour of the growing season the Japanese truck farmer harvests four crops of vegetables annually.

Southern Japan, especially central Honshu and the districts around the Inland Sea, is also the source of those products typical of humid subtropical regions elsewhere in the world. Tea is produced chiefly in a district around a bay on the south coast of Honshu. Fruits, both the citrus and temperate

over their ownership and supervised their exploitation. Scientific forestry is here applied on the most comprehensive scale in the world.

One-half the standing timber is of scrub size and is good only for fuel, for which there is a large demand. Cooking in Japan is done over charcoal fires, and the acrid smell of burning charcoal tempers the somewhat stronger effluvium of night soil that is always in the air in the rural areas. In addition to fuel the forests supply building and industrial materials, food, and medicine.

Lacquer and camphor, from certain trees in the warmer parts of Japan, are also important products.

Despite the large forest resources Japan is unable to satisfy its domestic lumber demands, as the forests are conserved to increase the still more important resource, hydropower. The Japanese would rather import lumber than strip their hillsides bare.

Bamboo is grown in Japan as a field crop and, although its acreage is minor in comparison with the extent of forest land, it is the universal material for house construction and household utensils. In the form of bamboo shoots it also provides food.

The fisheries of Japan are more important, both to the nation and in world commerce, than those of any country or region yet discussed. The Japanese fish catch is almost half the world total.

As a wholly insular country Japan easily surpasses China in maritime fisheries. The Japanese, like the Chinese, practice fish farming in landlocked ponds, but this is only a minor development. Their islands are fortunately surrounded by one of the few great marine fishing grounds of the world. Not content with the rich hauls made close at home, the Japanese have sent out modern, efficient "floating canneries" and "whale factories" to range the Pacific from Alaska to the Antarctic and catch, process, and can on the spot.

Fish are also of greater importance in the national diet than in China. There is no supply of meat from livestock in Japan; moreover, the Buddhist religion forbids its use. The Japanese per capita consumption of fish consequently ranges from 50 to 100 pounds a year (compared with the United States figure of 13 pounds). As the second staple after rice in the Japanese diet fish is consumed raw, cooked, dried, salted, and canned. And lastly, the fishing industry yields large quantities of essential oils and fertilizer.

Mineral Resources and Products. Some 17 different important ores and mineral fuels are recovered within the Japanese Islands, but Japan is self-sufficient only in coal, the most important mineral resource, and in sulfur. More than one-half the output is from northern Kyushu; the largest reserves are on Hokkaido; less important fields are on the east coast of Honshu. The Japan of the future may very well be self-sufficient in total tonnage of coal produced, but coking coal, which is completely lacking, must always be imported.

Japan's home resources of iron ore consist of inadequate, low-grade deposits. The largest mine is in northern Honshu, but most production is from Hokkaido.

The mineral in most abundant supply is sulfur, of which there has consistently been an exportable surplus. Total production makes Japan the third-ranking country in output of this mineral. Northern Honshu is the most important source region.

Copper occurs on all three of the southern islands, but production is insufficient for Japan's normal needs.

There are very limited occurrences of petroleum on northern Honshu and Hokkaido, which Japan has developed with characteristic thoroughness to the point where they supplied 10 percent of annual needs before World War II.

Japan's hydropower resources are important and have been exploited to a degree exceeded in few other countries. Individual power plants are of modest size owing to the small streams in the country, but their output is very dependable and relatively great because of the more or less continual orographic rainfall and high heads. Hydroelectric developments furnish most of the power for industry and transportation.

Manufacturing. Despite the fact that Japan is basically an agricultural country it is also a truly industrialized nation. Japanese industry comprises a complete, integrated system which processes, refines, and fabricates all manner of raw materials into consumers' or industrial goods. In short, Japan possesses an industrial complex similar to that of the United States and the other industrialized nations. There was scarcely a major industrial item that Japan did not produce before World War II. At that time it was able to satisfy fully the domestic demand for manufactured consumers' goods.

Japanese industry differs, however, from that of the Western nations in one major respect. Japanese factories tend to be small. Indeed, a significant portion of the total production comes from family workshops within the home. Seventy-five percent of industrial employment is in establishments with 10 or fewer workers.

The leading industry by value of output is **chemicals**, followed by **metals**. Japan ranks seventh among world producers of **pig iron** and **ferroalloys**, and fifth in **steel** output. **Lumber** and **wooden articles** are the nation's third-ranking industry, followed by **textiles**. Japan is an important world producer of cotton, woolen, and rayon materials, manufacturing its own rayon from imported wood pulp in sufficient volume to rank third in the production of that synthetic fiber.

The Japanese combination of highly or-ganized factory production with home work-shops attained its highest development in the silk industry. Before World War II 90 percent of the world supply of silk came from Japan, so that for many years silk was the greatest single export item in the country's trade. Although the industry is still important in Japan, silk has been permanently supplanted as a textile fiber in the world market by the synthetics, and the country's advantage of a large supply of cheap, skilled labor in silk production is no longer a factor of much importance in the Japanese textile industry.

CITIES OF JAPAN

Name	Type	Population (1950)
Tokyo	Governmental, commercial, and industrial	7,000,000 (1954)
Osaka	Industrial, seaport	1,950,000
Kyoto	Religious	1,100,000
Nagoya	Industrial, seaport	1,000,000
Yokohama	Seaport, industrial	951,000
Kobe	Seaport, industrial	765,000
Hiroshima	Commercial	259,000
Yahata	Industrial	210,000

Fig. 18.13—Tokyo, Japan. Air view of the business section of the city. (Courtesy, Information Service, Embassy of Japan.)

Cities. **Tokyo** ("Eastern Capital"), the capital and largest city of Japan, is the third greatest city of the world in terms of population numbers. It is in the center of the coast of southern Honshu at the head of a long indentation, **Tokyo Bay.** Technically it is a seaport, but as it is a short distance upstream on a small river too shallow for ocean vessels, its overseas trade is limited. Although Tokyo is the financial and business capital of Japan it is not a great world city in the sense that it epitomizes national culture and character. The city is dominated by the Imperial Palace in its center and has many shrines and public parks. The business section (Fig. 18.13) is characterized by modern buildings of reinforced concrete, many of which survived the World War II bombings relatively undamaged. The central section has been generally rebuilt in the postwar period. The outer sections of the city are the site of numerous workshop factories.

Osaka is located on the south shore of Honshu at the northeast corner of the Inland Sea. It was originally a port but during the rise of Japan as an industrial power was transformed into the major industrial city of the nation. Modern port facilities, completed just prior to World War II, have made it Japan's third-ranking port. It is a center of heavy industry and is one of the few Japanese cities whose skyline consists of the smokestacks commonly associated with the large industrial centers of the United States.

Twenty-five miles inland, northeast from Osaka, is the city of **Kyoto** ("Capital City"), whose name stems from the fact that it was the capital of Japan until 1868. Today the city is the religious and cultural capital of the country, with dozens of important shrines and temples and the greatest concentration of Japan's art treasures. It also manufactures artistic handicraft objects. Because of its cultural significance it was spared the World War II bombings.

Nagoya, Japan's fourth largest city, lies almost 100 miles east of Kyoto at the head of another of the large bays on the southern coast of Honshu. Like Tokyo and Osaka, it is technically a seaport, but access to it is limited to smaller ships and it is more an industrial city. Its manufactures are pottery, textiles, and machinery.

Yokohama is the port of Tokyo, 15 miles south of the capital on the west shore of Tokyo Bay. At one time Japan's leading seaport, it lost that position as the result of its complete destruction by an earthquake in 1923. Although entirely rebuilt since then, it never regained its earlier preëminence.

Kobe, Japan's leading port city, lies 20 miles west of Osaka across Osaka Bay. It was this city that took over first rank from Yokohama among Japanese seaports. It shares in the concentration of metallurgical and chemical industries around Osaka.

Hiroshima, a local commercial center at the head of a bay near the western end of the Inland Sea, achieved eternal if tragic fame as the first victim of an atomic bomb. It is the largest city of Japan west of Kobe, evidence of the extraordinary concentration of population mentioned in the discussion of the Japanese population above.

Yahata is a few miles inland on the north coast of Kyushu and is one of a cluster of large cities around the narrow strait at the western end of the Inland Sea. It is the major center of heavy industry, with the largest iron and steel works. It is noteworthy that Yahata is the only major city of Japan not situated on southern Honshu.

Japan as a Whole. Although the menace of Japanese aggression in the Far East was removed by World War II, Japan remains the greatest economic problem of the entire region. In a remarkably short time after the war, the country was restored to temporary economic health under American occupation and with American support, but this status cannot, unfortunately, be maintained indefinitely on a self-sustaining basis.

Japan is confronted by two paramount problems. The first is the fate of the country's international trade. The great industrial machine of Japan was geared to supply (in addition to the armaments for its program of conquest) world markets based on commercial domination of East Asia. These markets have now disappeared and those of the rest of the world are also to a large degree lost. Moreover, Japan can no longer count on a ready supply of raw materials from the other countries of Asia, as they are all intent on developing and processing such materials themselves.

The second problem is that of overpopulation, the significance of which is greatly enlarged by the associated problem of foreign trade. Japan already depends on imports for one-fifth of its food supply, but meanwhile the population has been increasing by a million a year and is expected to increase by 6 million every ten years in the future. The solution of this dilemma was postponed after World War II, first by American support during the occupation, then by the country's earnings in supplying the United Nations forces in the Korean War. Until a solution to these major problems of trade and overpopulation is found Japan's future must remain uncertain.

QUESTIONS. Describe the five major features of the topography of central and southern China. What is the special political significance of Taiwan? What is the most noteworthy aspect of the population of China? Name the five regions of greatest concentration of population. What is the significance of the exceedingly small size of the Chinese farms? What relation does the character of the domestic animal population of China have to the type of agriculture and the size of the human population? Why are famines so frequent in China? Explain the paradox that China is the world's leading producer of many crops yet has never been noted as an exporter of these crops. Why was China forced to import lumber from the United States although there are still unexploited timber stands in the country? Why is the Chinese per capita consumption of fish so high? What mineral resources of China are of greatest potential value? What is the major industry of the country? What unique characteristic is possessed by the large coastal cities of China? Why did Shanghai achieve the status of a major world port? Explain the commercial significance of the location of Hankow. Of Hong Kong. Why are the Cantonese different in many respects from most Chinese in their customs and outlook?

Name the four major islands of Japan and describe their general topography. Explain how warm and freezing temperatures can occur within close proximity of each other during the Japanese winter. Describe the national character of the Japanese people. What is the relation between the population density of Japan and the history of Japanese aggression? Locate the three major sites of population concentration in Japan. Why was Japan able to develop a large railroad network? Compare agriculture in Japan with that in China, noting similarities and differences. What uses are made of the forest resources in Japan? Why is the Japanese fishing industry unusually significant in the economy of the country? Describe the general position of Japan with respect to mineral resources. In what respect is Japan fortunate in the character of its hydropower resources? Describe the general structure of Japanese industry and compare it with that of Argentina. Of the United States. Name the major Japanese industries. What is the unusual and significant feature of the distribution of the major Japanese cities? Why are the cities of Tokyo, Osaka, and Nagoya "technical" rather than true seaports? Why is the city of Hiroshima famous throughout the world?

Discuss briefly the two major problems facing Japan.

Medium-Temperature Humid Climates: The Marine West Coast Climate

CHAPTER 19

The Marine West Coast Climate in Europe

■ DEFINITION AND CAUSES OF THE MARINE WEST COAST CLIMATE

The regions of the two moderate-temperature humid climates discussed in the preceding chapters partially extend into the prevailing westerlies wind belt and were, accordingly, characterized as transitional climates. The marine west coast climate lies wholly within the westerlies and is, therefore, a typical climate of that wind belt. The climates wholly within the westerlies are often referred to as the "cyclone climates," as the phenomenon common to all of them is that they exhibit a continual progression of cyclones and anticyclones moving from west to east around the world with the general drift of the westerlies.

The two fundamental features of the marine west coast climate are indicated by its name. It is a climate developed on the west coast of continents, extending poleward from about 40° latitude until the polar climatic influences become dominant. Because it is a windward coast climate the temperature, precipitation, and humidity are almost wholly conditioned by the presence of the adjacent ocean. It is thus marked by "marine" as opposed to "continental" characteristics.

The longitudinal extent of a particular marine west coast climatic region depends on the topography. Where there is no mountain barrier to interfere with the westerlies this climate extends inland until continental influences prevail; but where there are mountain barriers the climate extends only over a narrow coastal strip between the mountains and the ocean. Toward the equator the marine west coast climate merges into the Mediterranean climate.

■ CHARACTERISTICS OF THE MARINE WEST COAST CLIMATE

PRECIPITATION

The marine west coast climate is the most humid of all climates outside the tropics. The annual precipitation exceeds 100 inches on the west slopes of mountains at places where the moist air from the sea is forced into an orographic rise within a short distance from the coast. The climate thus favors the development of mountain glaciers to a superlative degree in moderately high latitudes and at altitudes above the snow line. During the glacial epoch of recent geologic time a great expansion of the glaciers in such highland regions brought about the deep erosion of fiord valleys that extend far inland, bounded by almost vertical walls of rock (see Chapter 1, p. 15). Such fiord coasts of the marine west coast climatic regions constitute some of the most spectacular scenic areas of the world.

Seasonal variation in precipitation is slight, and such as there is results chiefly from the heightening of the warm water–cool land relationship that exists during the winter (see Chapter 6, p. 97). Rainfall occurs typically in mists and drizzles rather than in downpours; thunderstorms are infrequent. Rainy periods are likely to last for days or even weeks, but the total precipitation during such a period may not equal that of a heavy thundershower elsewhere.

The marine west coast climate also has the highest atmospheric humidity among the nontropical climates and could well be designated "the cloudy climate." Cloudy days, over and above those on which precipitation occurs, are so frequent that the sky is overcast 60 to 70 percent of the time. Most of the cloudy days occur in winter, but summer is also a distinctly cloudy season. In winter everything drips moisture. The long successions of dark, damp, raw days during which the sun is not seen have a depressing effect on the human spirit.

Dense fogs in winter, of which there may be 40 to 50 annually, are another unpleasant feature of the climate. At these times transportation, especially marine, is brought almost to a standstill in the absence of radar facilities. Equally disagreeable and disruptive are the winter storms or "gales" of great severity, which blow when the winds come in directly from the open sea.

TEMPERATURE

The marine west coast climate is noteworthy, considering the latitudes in which it occurs, for its mild winters and cool summers. The annual temperature range is very narrow—20° F. or less—and since this variation is around a mean temperature which coincides with the sensible temperature that human beings find most agreeable the climate is, thus, the only true "temperate" climate.

The average winter temperature ranges between 35°and 40° F., a good 20° higher than the winter temperatures of other land areas of the same latitudes. As this moderation of cold is the effect of the marine influence, average winter temperatures decline more markedly toward the inland border of the regions of this climate than in the poleward direction.

Freezing weather is generally infrequent; it occurs in cold spells resulting from the invasion of the regions by polar continental air masses (see Chapter 6, p. 99), during which times minimum temperatures may approach 0° F. Luckily for the inhabitants of the regions, however, such advances involve air movement from east to west against the prevailing winds and hence tend to be exceptional.

The summers are rather cool, but the high humidity results in very pleasant sensible temperatures. The average is 60° F., with a 20° diurnal range. It is a common custom in this climate to wear woolen clothes throughout the year. In summer the temperature increases inland, again owing to the decline in the moderating marine influence. Heat waves are rare, but during their occurrence temperatures as high as 100° F. have been recorded. In general, however, the pleasant temperature ranges offset the unpleasant precipitation aspects of the marine west coast climate.

■ UTILIZATION OF MARINE WEST COAST REGIONS

The marine west coast climate comes nearest of all the climates to the ideal circumstances for spurring human activity. Because excessive heat and cold are both uncommon, the climate is neither enervating nor numbing. At all seasons of the year, moreover, changes in the weather provide a stimulus to both physical and mental effort which appears to offset the depressing effect of cloud and rain.

Such stimulation, together with the historical circumstance that modern Western civilization developed in this climate, has prompted studies of the relationship between climate and the degree of human progress. Some geographers have come to the conclusion that human civilization can reach its peak only under such a climate. Although the validity of this thesis is vigorously disputed it is at least evident that the marine west coast climate has permitted the development of material civilization to its most advanced level. One of the three great industrial regions of the world is within this climate.

Whatever the relation between this climate and the status of civilization may be, it is quite clear that the climate is not ideal for many kinds of agricultural production. Some crops grow well enough but fail to mature owing to the moderate temperatures and lack of sunshine. Wheat and corn especially suffer on the latter score. **Rye** and **oats,** on the other hand, are much better suited to the climate and are widely grown. Certain **"temperate fruits"** and **berries** also do well. Root crops such as **sugar beets** and **potatoes** do best of all. On the side of advantages, the abnormally high winter temperatures so far north (or south) provide an exceptionally long growing season for such latitudes. In some places the growing season is actually longer than that of the humid subtropical climate in certain of its regions.

The combination of climatic features, suitable soil, and a great extent of sloping land in the marine west coast regions makes **grazing** the predominant agricultural and related activity in many of them. The humidity and rainfall that promote lush growth of grass also tend to reduce insect pests, so that conditions for **dairying** are almost ideal. Some of the world's leading dairy districts are within this climate. The pasture lands

Fig. 19.1—World Distribution of Marine West Coast Climatic Regions.

are also widely used for the raising of **sheep,** whose fleece is stimulated to heavy growth by the cool, damp conditions.

The high rainfall and moderate temperatures also favor heavy forest growth. Indeed, the term "rainforest" is applied to them by analogy with the equatorial rainforest. The **lumber** industry is, accordingly, important in many regions of the climate; logging is engaged in on a larger scale than in the forest regions of any other climate.

The **fishing** industry in the offshore waters of the marine west coast regions is also on a large scale. This is not directly due to climatic factors, but they are nevertheless operative to a degree.

■ MARINE WEST COAST REGIONS AND COUNTRIES

The marine west coast climate occurs on only four of the six inhabited continents— Europe, Australia, and the two Americas (Fig. 19.1). It is absent in Africa and Asia because the former does not extend into high enough latitudes and the latter has no western coast. Thus the four regions of marine west coast climate are: **northwestern and central Europe,** the **United States–Canadian Pacific coast,** from Northern California through the Alaskan Panhandle, **southern**

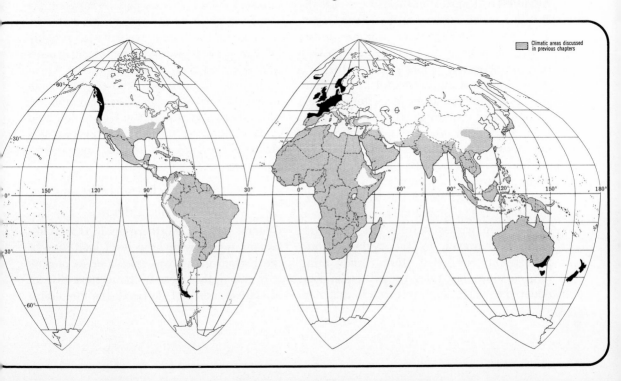

Chile, and New Zealand and the southeast coast of Australia.

A. NORTHWESTERN AND CENTRAL EUROPE

The European region of marine west coast climate, although comparatively small as climatic regions go, is the largest of the regions of this climate and embraces a great many countries because of the multitude of political divisions in Europe. Proceeding from southwest to northeast, it includes the following: the northern coast of **Spain,** all of **France** save its Mediterranean coast, the Low Countries (**Belgium** and the **Netherlands**) and **Luxembourg,** most of **Germany,** the **British Isles, Denmark,** and the southern and west coastal portions of Scandinavia, comprising southern **Sweden** and most of **Norway.** (It also includes southern Iceland, but that country is discussed in a later chapter.)

This largest development of the marine west coast climate is the result of two circumstances: (1) the **Gulf Stream** and (2) the fact that most of Northwestern Europe is plains area. The great mass of warm water composing the Gulf Stream spreads out widely as a surface layer and crosses the Atlantic at about 40° latitude as the **North Atlantic Drift.** The major part of the North Atlantic Drift moves northeastward past the British Isles all the way to the Arctic Ocean. Thus the westerlies over Europe during winter have been heated by their passage over warm waters before reaching the continent, and as there is (except in Scandinavia) no mountain barrier in western Europe to raise and cool them, their warming influence is felt far inland, and in fact extends over most of the continent.

Although the moderating marine influence keeps European summer temperatures down, it is the effect on the winter climate that is crucially important. The general trend of winds in winter is from the southwest, modified, however, by the cyclonic storm progression. Northwest storm winds bring rain or snow, but snow usually melts soon under the warm southwest winds that nor-

mally follow. The cold months of the region have been aptly described as "a series of small winters separated by thaws." Because of these circumstances northwestern Europe enjoys winters of only moderate severity at latitudes that suffer frigid winters with numbing cold elsewhere in the world. Indeed, outside the marine west coast regions the ground is in many places permanently frozen at the latitudes of their poleward borders.

Summer comes after a late spring, due to the retarding marine influence. The cyclonic storms during the summer are less frequent and less severe, owing to the smaller temperature differences; hence rainfall is lower than in winter. Precipitation, nevertheless, is rather uniformly distributed throughout the year.

The role of the European region of marine west coast climate in the development of modern Western society and its technology is familiar. Northwestern Europe is the second greatest industrial region on earth; it includes almost all the well-industrialized nations of the world. Agriculture, as always, is an important human activity, but this is one of the two climatic regions of the world in which agriculture is definitely subordinate to manufacturing in the region as a whole. The region's agricultural products are chiefly for its own use, and because of the emphasis given to the crops most suited to the climate the region accounts for roughly 50 percent of the world output of sugar beets and potatoes, and 20 percent of the wheat and barley. Moreover, because of the high proportion of total land area suitable for cultivation, a greater percentage of the land is actually used for agricultural purposes than in many of the leading agricultural countries.

Countries of Northwestern Europe

1. NORTHERN SPAIN

General Aspects. Northern Spain is a mountainous region with little level land save at the bottom of narrow valleys or in narrow strips along the coast. In the western district of **Galicia,** north of Portugal, the mountains run into the sea to form the type ria coast (see Chapter 1, p. 14). In the central portion the main **Cantabrian** ranges (see Chapter 14, p. 269) run parallel to the coast, which is steep and rocky. Farther east are the upper reaches of the **Ebro River** valley, bordered on the extreme east by the western half of the **Pyrenees** and their southern foothills (Fig. 14.3).

The humid climate of these districts is responsible for sharp contrasts between them and the arid scenery characteristic of the rest of Spain. Here, in the north, the higher mountains are mantled by unbroken pine forests, the lower slopes are grassy pasture lands, and the lowlands are the sites of small farms and orchards.

The people also differ from the majority of Spaniards. In particular the *Basques* of the northeast, descendants of a strange linguistic stock, are a progressive, ambitious people who in this respect resemble the Catalonians of the northeastern corner of Spain (see Chapter 14, p. 270). Northern Spain is the most densely populated section of the country.

Agriculture. The only agricultural product of any importance in the marine west coast portion of Spain is the **apple** crop from the orchard district extending along most of the northern coast. Mixed subsistence farming is the rule in these parts. Rye in most areas and corn in the southwest portion of Galicia are the chief field crops. Cattle are raised on the pasture lands.

The pine forests support a considerable **lumber** industry. The ria coast of Galicia shares in the **sardine** fishing industry of Portugal (see Chapter 14, p. 267).

Mineral Products and Manufacturing. The mineral resources of northern Spain are items of first importance in the economy of the country as a whole and are the basis of the only heavy industry it supports. **Coal,** both anthracite and bituminous, is produced from deposits in the **Asturias** district, east of Galicia, and in the Cantabrians to the south. The output of coal exceeds in value that of all other mineral products of Spain put together.

Iron ore is mined at many places, the largest deposits being on the east central portion of the coast. Although it is of rather low grade, its proximity to ocean transport and the low mining costs in Spain make it an important part of the supply for the iron and steel industries of England and Germany.

The national **iron and steel** industry referred to above is of modest size but is developed at two sites, one in the east, the other in the west. The western industry uses coke brought as return cargo by the ships carrying iron ore to Britain. Other industries of the region include metal manufactures and shipbuilding.

CITIES OF NORTHERN SPAIN

Name	Type	Population
Bilbao	Seaport, industrial	233,000 (1952)
Vigo	Seaport	118,000 (1950)

Cities. **Bilbao,** the leading city of northern Spain and one of the country's leading seaports, is seven miles upstream on a small river in the eastern third of the northern coast. It is a Basque city and, like Barcelona, the Catalonian city, is bustling and energetic. Its businessmen carry on the major part of the export trade in iron ore from nearby mines. Bilbao is the center of iron and steel manufacture based on the return coke trade. It is also the site of other supplementary heavy industries such as machinery and shipbuilding.

Vigo is at the other end of the region, on the western coast not far north of the Portuguese border. Its site is 12 miles inland, on the south shore of one of the largest bays of the ria coast. With its fine harbor it is a fishing center, a port of call for transatlantic commerce, and a major Spanish naval station.

2. FRANCE

Topography. The French Republic is a country of 210,000 square miles, or four-fifths the size of Texas. It is one of the few

FRANCE

SCALE of MILES
0   150

Fig. 19.2—France. The inset compares the area of France with that of Texas, which is approximately equal.

countries in the world whose political limits are almost entirely marked by natural geographic boundaries (Fig. 19.2). In addition it possesses geographical advantages of compact shape and good location—it and Spain are the only two European countries that have both Atlantic and Mediterranean coasts and hence share in the commerce of both seas. Still another geographic advantage of France is the small percentage of highland area and the general low relief of the country. Over one-half its extent is below 700 feet in elevation.

France has mountains for most of its land boundaries. In the south the **Pyrenees**, over

6000 feet in elevation along much of their length, are an almost unbroken barrier between France and Spain. In the east the **Western Alps**, very rugged mountains rising to almost 16,000 feet in **Mont Blanc** (Europe's highest peak), separate the country from Italy. North of the Alps the **Jura** highlands, a much lower range, form the border with Switzerland. Still farther north the **Vosges**, averaging 3000 feet in their southern portion, 1600 feet in their northern, parallel the **Rhine River** to the east, which is the actual boundary with Germany. Only the northern border is not parallel to a mountain range; however, its eastern portion, abutting on Germany, Luxembourg, and Belgium, is hilly.

Aside from these pronounced topographic features of the southern and eastern borders France is composed of five major geographic regions. The largest and most important is the **Paris Basin,** comprising the northern and north central third of the country. It is a basin geologically rather than topographically, for layered rocks underlie it like a set of nested saucers. In the northeast the etched-out edges of the "saucers" form a series of concentric curved ridges that figured prominently in the battles of the two World Wars. The Paris Basin comprises most of the drainage area of the **Seine** and the upper portion of that of the **Loire.** It is the site of the greatest concentrations of population and industry in France and is at the same time the chief agricultural region of the country.

West of the Paris Basin is the **Western Upland,** comprising the northwestern fifth of the country and containing the lower portion of the Loire Valley. Actually the region is generally below 1000 feet in elevation, but the relief is greater than in the Paris Basin. The Western Upland juts out into the Atlantic in two large, rocky peninsulas, **Brittany** and **Cotentin.**

The southwest fifth of France is the **Aquitaine Basin** region, another plains area that coincides with the drainage basin of the **Garonne River.** East of Aquitaine is the somewhat larger, interior highlands area of France, the **Central Massif,** a west-sloping plateau which drops off sharply on its eastern side.

The fifth region is a long, narrow structural depression, the **Rhone-Saone Valley,** which extends from north to south between the eastern edge of the Central Massif and the Alps and Juras. This valley is the line of flow of the lower **Rhone River** and of its tributary from the north, the **Saone.**

Climate. France experiences the marine west coast climate at its best, since its latitude is that of the southern border of the

westerlies belt, and the absence of a mountain barrier on the west coast permits the westerlies influence to be felt across the whole width of the country. There is, however, a moderate progressive decline in volume of precipitation inland from the Atlantic, so that the climate of eastern and southeastern portions of the country justifies the phrase "sunny France." The more typical marine west coast rainy spells that prevail throughout most of France were the cause of great disillusionment during the two World Wars for American soldiers, to whom the term "sunny France" was a grim joke.

Transportation. The exceptional advantage accruing to France by reason of the nature and disposition of its relief and the pattern of its water routes was noted earlier (see Chapter 2, pp. 18, 38). The courses of the major rivers form a radial drainage pattern, with the Central Massif as its hub. From this hub the main streams flow out to the four quarters of the compass. The widespread plains of their lower courses, moreover, have permitted their interconnection by canals; hence it is possible to reach almost any part of the country from any other part by water routes. To be sure, this river-canal system is chiefly used for local barge transportation of bulk goods. This, however, provides adequately for cheap movement of essential low-cost, large-volume commodities such as sand, hay, and coal.

Besides the river-canal routes there are dense railroad and highway networks serving all parts of the country for passenger and fast freight traffic. Few countries of the world have developed all means of internal transportation as completely and as well as has France.

The People. As one of the earliest countries of Europe to achieve geographic unity, France has a strong nationalistic tradition. At the same time, the Frenchman is an individualist. The reputation for low moral standards Americans tend to ascribe to the French stems from this emphasis on the right of the individual to act according to his personal convictions, without regard for adverse criticism by others. This individualism has enabled French artistic and cultural abilities to come to full flower, so that France has in modern times been the cradle of Western art and of some of the most creative political thinking on the international level. The emphasis on creativeness is carried over into industry, which is renowned for its ceramics, textiles of high craftsmanship, and the creation of leading styles in fashion, furniture, and other items requiring a sense of beauty and fine craftsmanship in their production.

On the other hand, individualism and the emphasis on artistry have been handicaps in employment of the mass production techniques of modern industry. In the political field the French have been notoriously poor colonial administrators and have suffered at home from a system of unstable government (yet on the basis of a fundamentally sound democracy) that is at once a source of wonder and despair to the other nations of the West. Agriculture has traditionally been characterized by the stubborn insistence of the French peasant (Fig. 19.3) on pursuing his accustomed ways, and his innate distrust of all things and ideas not French. This resulted in a technological backwardness that was remedied only through the compulsion to mechanization and modernization necessitated by the vast task of rebuilding imposed by the devastation of World War II.

Fig. 19.3—French Peasants in the Vineyards of the Champagne District in Eastern France. (Courtesy, French Government Tourist Office.)

The French, then, present something of a paradox. They are innovators, yet they put the brakes on progress. They have been responsible for some of the most important contributions to the philosophy, art, and science of Western society. On the other hand, their role as one of the leading nations of the West has been weakened by a lack of adeptness in applying modern technology to their own industries, and by the obstacles they themselves interpose to obtaining the full benefits of Western democracy in their government. Thus, made up of small towns, small factories, and small farms, France is a strong country but a weak nation.

The French population of 43 million has remained more or less static during the present century, one of the few such instances in the world. Although this stagnation has been due in no small measure to the severe population losses suffered in the two World Wars, the country has also had a long history of low birth rates. There has been an increase in the birth rate since World War II, but France remains a country with an aging population and a severe labor shortage.

Agriculture and Products. Among the countries of Europe France is especially well endowed with agricultural resources. Not only are the soils generally fertile, but there is more arable land per capita than in any other European country. Forty percent of the population is directly dependent on agriculture and 60 percent of the land is in use —two thirds of this in crops, the other third in grazing. Thus France is virtually self-sufficient in food. French soil feeds the French.

The technological backwardness of French agriculture mentioned above has been to some extent offset by generally excellent and intensive farming methods. Crop rotation and other care of soil fertility have resulted in high yields. Again, this has come about through the "social" rather than "technological" character of French agriculture. The peasant gives his land good care because he loves it, not because he is intent on high productivity.

The typical French farm is small—less

Fig. 19.4—Farm and Pasture Lot in Normandy. The architecture is typical of the region. (Courtesy, French Government Tourist Office.)

than 25 acres—and divided into several non-adjacent parcels. This uneconomic fractioning has resulted from the practice, .as in China and Japan, of dividing all land equally among the male heirs of each generation and is, as in those countries, a handicap to mechanization.

The major crop of France is **wheat**, an unusual circumstance in a marine west coast region. Wheat is grown in various sections of the country but especially in the northern part of the Paris Basin. This agricultural anomaly is due to the fact that the summers of France are drier than is normal for a marine west coast country. France is the fifth-ranking wheat country of the world, and its inhabitants eat more bread than any other people. **Oats, barley,** and **rye** are the other important cereals, in that order.

Viniculture is the agricultural activity of second importance (Fig. 19.3). The **wines** of France are world famous for quality and diversity, and France is, as noted previously,

the greatest producer and consumer of wine in the world. The great vineyard districts are in the eastern and southeastern portion of the Paris Basin, in the valley of the Loire, and in the lower Garonne and upper Rhone valleys. All of these are superior in quality but subordinate in quantity and value of output to the Mediterranean coastal district (see Chapter 14, p. 273).

Other leading crops are **sugar beets**, grown in a beneficial crop rotation with wheat, and **potatoes**, produced almost everywhere. Truck farming of **vegetables** is concentrated in the central Paris Basin and on the Brittany coast. **Fruit** orchards are also significant in the latter district.

The grazing industries are important in many areas of France. **Cattle** (17 million) are raised throughout the country, the leading sections being Brittany, the Central Massif, and the mountainous border regions. **Dairying** is a principal occupation in many sections, especially in Brittany and Normandy (Fig. 19.4) and along the Swiss border.

Forests cover about 20 percent of France, with hardwoods predominant. The country was originally heavily forested owing to favorable climate and topography, but millennia of human occupancy have reduced the forest lands to the present small extent. By giving preference in construction work, wherever possible, to any material other than **lumber,** and by good forestry practices, France has maintained a balance between cutting and regrowth of its existent forest resources.

With access to good fishing grounds in both the Atlantic and the Mediterranean, **fisheries** are important along all the coasts and especially in Brittany. The French catch of sea fishes ranks fifth in size among the countries of Europe.

Mineral Resources and Products. France is fortunate in possessing substantial resources of **coal** and **iron ore,** the basic industrial raw materials, but they are both of low grade and costly to mine, and present grave handicaps to French production. The major coal deposits are in the northern Paris Basin, part of a field that crosses into Belgium, and in the **Saar**[1] district on the German border in the northeast. The important French deposits of iron ore are also in the Paris Basin, in the **Lorraine** district on the northeast German border, and in the Vosges.

The coal deposits are difficult to mine because of unfavorable geological conditions, and some of the mines are 3000 feet deep. The iron ore, though very lean, can be mined in pits on the surface. Fundamentally the French coal and iron resources are of major significance because of their occurrence in a single *geographic* region. The fact that in this region they are divided and separated by political boundaries, however, has been a constant source of international friction in the past century and a serious handicap to their economical utilization. In their exploitation France ranks fourth in Europe as a coal producer and is one of the world's major producers of iron ore.

Petroleum production has been insignifi-

cant, but discoveries in southern France in 1955 indicate good future possibilities.

The **hydropower** potentialities of the southern and southeastern mountain borders have been well developed. France ranks second in Europe in the power supplied by these sources.

Manufacturing. The place of France as an industrialized nation is evidenced by the fact that it ranks fourth in Europe and fifth in the world in its output of **iron and steel,** the leading industry of the country. This rank has been achieved despite inadequate supplies of coal, especially of coking coal; hence France is the greatest coal importer of the world. On the other hand, it has a large surplus of iron ore, so that it has been able to trade its ore, almost on a measure-for-measure basis, for the surplus coal of its neighbors, especially that of Germany.

The major center of iron and steel production is in the northeast section of the Paris Basin. Other centers are near the coal fields of the Belgian border, in the Saar, and in the northern part of the Rhone-Saone Valley.

The second industry of France is the manufacture of **textiles,** centered in the northern Paris Basin, Lorraine, and northern Rhone-Saone districts. The first two districts produce **cotton** and **woolen** goods; the third specializes in **silk.** Most of the raw materials are imported.

None of the many other French manufacturing activities, including automobile manufacture, shipbuilding, and chemical production, compares in importance with the steel and textile industries. Because small size is an overall characteristic of French manufacturing enterprise, diverse types of activity are found in all the larger French cities.

[1] The Saar is one of the Franco-German border districts that have been fought over for two centuries. After World War II it was made economically a part of France, but in 1956 was returned to Germany.

CITIES OF FRANCE
(Other Than Mediterranean)

Name	Type	Population (1954)
Paris	Governmental, commercial, industrial	2,850,000
Lyon	Industrial	471,000
Bordeaux	Seaport	258,000
Strasbourg	Commercial	200,000
St. Etienne	Industrial	181,000
Le Havre	Seaport	140,000

Fig. 19.5—Paris and the Seine, France. The Eiffel Tower in the center of the picture. (Courtesy, French Government Tourist Office.)

Cities. There is really only one city in France—**Paris** (Fig. 19.5). With a population, including the suburbs, that numbers one-eighth the total population of the country, no other French city remotely approaches Paris in size or importance. Paris is the "universal city." Not only the French but all the world is said to want to see and be in Paris. Such a reputation cannot be undeserved. But, like Niagara Falls, Paris may be disillusioning on first sight; so much is expected that reality is disappointing. In both instances, however, the showpiece reacquires its virtues on better acquaintance. Paris charms by its intimacies rather than by its broad prospects. Though the overall views and long vistas the city affords are by no means disenchanting, it is the nooks and corners, the close-ups, the associations of place and history, the ebb and flow of life on the boulevards and sidewalk cafés, and the sophisticated bawdiness of its night life that give Paris allure. It is as the epitome of France, the cultural capital of Western civilization, that Paris stands as one of the truly great cities of the world.

Lyon, the third largest city of France, is situated astride the confluence of the Rhone and Saone at the intersection of an east-west trade route with the major channel of trade between northern and southern France. Originally commercial, it is now the center of a great industrial concentration. Its major industry is silk, but it is also the site of important chemical plants and an iron and steel works.

Bordeaux is the major Atlantic port of France and the outlet for the agricultural and forest products of the fertile Aquitaine Basin. It is on the west bank of the Garonne 60 miles upstream from the mouth of the Gironde estuary. Bordeaux possesses good harbor facilities and has several light industries.

Strasbourg is on the western edge of the Rhine Valley, on the German border. It owes its importance to its location at the intersection of the great Rhine trade route with the major east-west traffic flow between Germany and France. The city contains a node of canals, being the junction of the Rhine-Rhone canal with the canal that connects with the streams of the Paris Basin. It is also a river port, with extensive dockworks, for it serves as the head of the heavy-tonnage commerce of the Rhine. Strasbourg, however, functions most significantly as a general commercial city because of its excellent rail connections which tie in with the canal and river traffic. It is also the site of an automobile plant, flour mills, coking works, and food-processing establishments.

St. Etienne, 25 miles to the southwest of Lyon on the edge of the Central Massif, is the second city of the upper Rhone industrial region. Its textile and metallurgical industries are based on nearby coal fields, from which a large portion of French coke production also comes.

Le Havre, the port of Paris, is on the north side of the Seine estuary. It is one of the leading import centers of France but is best known as a major terminus of transatlantic passenger traffic. Here passengers disembark from the great liners to take the train to Paris. It also handles a good deal of the cross-Channel traffic with England.

France as a Whole. For centuries one of the dominant world powers, France must now be content with a secondary status. Moreover, the French are bitterly aware that they can do little to regain their former position. A major cause of this decline was the grievous loss of population and national assets suffered by the country in the Franco-Prussian and two World Wars. But it is also true that France lacks sufficient power resources to keep pace with the rate of industrial growth and expansion attained by the other major nations of the world.

It has also suffered from another handicap, this of its own making. The only way in which raw material imports can be paid for (and, in general, the country lacks the raw materials for its manufacturing industries) is through the export of the finished products of its industry. But France finds itself handicapped in meeting competition in the world market because of the high costs of its inefficient production.

Because home production of foodstuffs more than satisfies their needs, the French will never starve. It is true that the possibility of a higher standard of living is latent in the French industrial machine, but in agriculture more will be needed than mere mechanization. The inescapable conclusion is that greater productivity and consequent increase in economic strength can come only through a drastic revision of French social structure and customs.

QUESTIONS. Why is the marine west coast climate a "cyclone climate"? What are the two basic features of the marine west coast climate? How is the longitudinal extent of a marine west coast climatic region determined by local topographic conditions? What is the nature of the precipitation in this climate? Why does it favor the development of mountain glaciers? Why is this climate truly a "temperate" one? What effect does this climate have on human activity? How is it related to the development of Western civilization? What agricultural products and types of agricultural activity are favored by the marine west coast climate?

Name the countries and portions of countries included in the European region of marine west coast climate. What are the two major circumstances contributing to the occurrence of the European region of this climate? Why is agriculture important in these countries despite the fact that they are heavily industrialized?

Describe the main topographic features of northern Spain. In what respect are the Basques like the Catalonians? What are the major mineral products of the region?

What geographic advantages does France possess with respect to size, shape, topography, and boundaries? Name the mountainous border regions of France and the major geographic regions of the country proper. What advantages in transportation does France derive from its general topography? Describe the traits and outlook of the French people. In what respect are these characteristics disadvantages in an industrial nation? From what population handicaps does France suffer? Describe the major features of French agriculture. Name the chief crops. Name and locate France's major mineral resources. What handicaps pertain to the value

and use of these resources? What are the two major industries of France? What is characteristic of the size of most French manufacturing establishments? Explain the difference between the present and former position of France among the leading industrial nations of the world. Briefly characterize Paris and explain its position as one of the world's great cities. For what industry is Lyon famous?

3. THE LOW COUNTRIES AND LUXEMBOURG

General Aspects. The three countries of Belgium, the Netherlands (Holland), and Luxembourg are considered together because geographically and economically they are a unit. This fact was recognized by the countries themselves in 1948 by their organization of a customs union within which the commerce of all three can move freely. All three are small. The Kingdom of Belgium, just north of France, has an area of less than

Fig. 19.6—Belgium, Netherlands, and Luxembourg. The inset compares the area of the three countries with that of West Virginia, which is approximately equal.

12,000 square miles, only half that of West Virginia (Fig. 19.6). The Kingdom of the Netherlands, north of Belgium, consists of less than 16,000 square miles, about half the size of Maine. The Grand Duchy of Luxembourg, between France, Belgium, and Germany, is only 1000 square miles in area, slightly smaller than Rhode Island.

Topography and Climate. The designation of Belgium and the Netherlands as the Low Countries is, of course, a reference to their altitude. In the case of the Netherlands low really means low, for much of the land is old sea bottom dammed off from the North Sea by sand dunes and great dikes. Almost two-fifths of the country is artificially dry land, actually below sea level. Northwestern Belgium, known as Flanders, is not so low as this, but it too was sea bottom in the geological past and has only recently become dry land through natural uplift.

The coastlines of the two countries are quite different. Belgium's is smooth and unbroken, except for the point at which it touches the **Schelde** estuary. The Netherlands' coastline, on the other hand, is very discontinuous, much of it consisting of the delta of the **Rhine,** each of whose many mouths makes an indentation.

To the southeast both countries are higher. The extreme southeast point of the Netherlands attains an elevation of slightly more than 1000 feet. Southeastern Belgium consists of the **Ardennes Plateau,** which attains the altitude of 2000 feet on the east. Luxembourg is situated within this upland region.

Winter temperatures are lower and storms are harsher than in most of France, since the winds come primarily from off the cold North Sea.

The People. The Low Countries and Luxembourg are among the most densely populated nations on earth. Within their small areas Belgium has a population of almost 9 million, the Netherlands over 10 million, and Luxembourg about 300,000. In certain districts of Belgium the population density is over 1000 per square mile.

Belgium is a country of two distinct peoples. In the north and west are the *Flemings,* of Nordic stock and speaking Flemish (related to Dutch). The south and east is the home of the *Walloons,* a people with strong racial and cultural ties with France, who speak French. Belgium is thus a bilingual country. The boundary between the two languages runs east-west and divides the country in half (Fig. 19.6). Both Flemings and Walloons are Roman Catholics; thus there is no religious difficulty and the people are united as Belgians. Nevertheless there is constant cultural, political, and social friction. The Walloons, who comprise about 40 percent of the population, tend to dominate the situation.

The Dutch of the Netherlands, on the other hand, are a very coherent nation of Nordic stock, predominantly Protestant. Although great wealth exists in the Netherlands there is a large middle class and little or no abject poverty. It is a national ideal that every Dutch child shall have an opportunity, through education and consideration for employment, to utilize in full such talents as he may be endowed with. Birth control is sanctioned, is promoted by the government, and is generally practiced. In consequence, Dutch stature and general health were notably improved during the past century. The constant struggle against the sea has helped make the Dutch a highly industrious, resourceful people.

Luxembourg has been at various times part of Germany, Belgium, and France. Although it is, like Belgium, bilingual (French and German) there is in Luxembourg a strong sense of national unity fostered by the small size of the country and the desire of its inhabitants to remain independent.

Transportation. The development of excellent transportation systems in the Low Countries was a simple matter, not only because of their small size but also because of the many natural waterways that traverse them. The Dutch have supplemented these by constructing an extraordinarily dense network of canals. In part this was done from necessity, for the canals also serve to drain the lands that are below sea level. The Netherlands is thus the most canalized country in

Fig. 19.7—Zuider Zee, Netherlands. Ring dike under construction to dam off sea, at left, from lake, at right, which will then be pumped dry. (Aerofoto, "Nederland," Amsterdam.)

the world. In addition the three countries have excellent, dense rail nets.

Agriculture and Products. As one would expect, the Low Countries and Luxembourg are all countries of small farms. The average farm in Belgium is less than five acres in size. Although 58 percent of the area of Belgium, 73 percent of the Netherlands, and 55 percent of Luxembourg is arable land, the small total area, high population density, and large yields have prompted a remarkable development of intensive agriculture. In the Low Countries what is probably the most scientific intensive agriculture to be found anywhere is practiced.

Because of the high value of arable land the Dutch have expended great efforts and immense sums in draining and reclaiming large areas of shallow sea bottom for agri-

culture. In the thirteenth century a series of great storms caused the sea to break through the barrier coastal dunes and flood a vast area in the center of the country, forming the **Zuider Zee** (Fig. 19.7). In 1920 a huge reclamation project was begun which in 1929 succeeded in closing off the arm of the sea and converting it into a fresh-water body, **Ysel Lake.** Some of the submerged land was at the same time recovered. The project will take many years to complete, but as the Dutch since the thirteenth century have reclaimed in all some 2200 square miles of territory (almost 15 percent of the total area of the country) it may be assumed that they will carry on until it is done.

The typical Dutch farm in the reclaimed areas is the *polder,* a field surrounded by dikes and with pumps constantly at work to lift water into bordering drainage canals in order to keep the polder from being flooded (Fig. 19.8). The picturesque windmills that are a conspicuous element of the traditional

Fig. 19.8—Netherlands, Polder Landscape. In distance the polder fields. Windmills along the dikes, center, pump water from the drainage ditches into the canal. (Courtesy, Netherlands Information Service.)

landscape and formerly furnished the power for the pumps are now disappearing owing to their replacement by prosaic but more efficient motor-driven pumps. The polders generally serve as meadows, since the soil can be developed for crop raising only over a long period of time.

In the three countries agriculture is the leading activity only in the Netherlands. The cereals **rye, oats, barley,** and **wheat** are all important crops, in roughly that order. **Sugar beets, potatoes,** and **flax** are other leading field crops. A very unusual product is **flower bulbs** and **flowers,** Dutch tulips being internationally famous and a lucrative source of income for that country. The flowers are cultivated over wide acres on sandy land immediately behind the coastal dunes and present a brilliant carpet of color in spring. About one-half the agricultural land is used for pasture by the **dairy** industry; Dutch **butter** and **cheese** are also important export items.

The agricultural products of Belgium and Luxembourg are (with the exception of bulbs) the same as those of the Netherlands, and although the yields are larger and mostly consumed domestically, they are still insufficient in volume to satisfy completely the food needs of these nations.

Since both Belgium and the Netherlands border on the North Sea, **fisheries** are important in both countries; more so in the latter, however, as the Dutch have a strong maritime tradition.

Mineral Resources and Manufacturing. Belgium possesses important **coal** deposits in Flanders that are a continuation of those in northwestern France. The Netherlands has less significant deposits in the southeast and some minor oil fields in the northeast along the German border. Luxembourg contains a continuation of the Lorraine **iron ore** district of France.

Whereas the Netherlands is an agricultural country, Belgium and Luxembourg are highly industrialized. Both possess major **iron and steel** industries that are the leading industrial activity. Belgium has in addition a large copper, lead, and zinc (nonferrous) **smelting** industry founded on the basis of domestic deposits long since exhausted. In both countries the **textile** industry ranks high, Belgium being noted especially for its **linen** produced from Flanders flax. As fully industrialized countries, both Belgium and Luxembourg carry on industrial activities in fields too numerous to mention, among which the manufacture of **machinery** and **chemicals** are most important.

The Netherlands, with a much smaller industrial establishment, is noted more for specialized activities and quality products. High-quality **pottery** and **china,** and the **cutting and polishing of gem stones** illustrate this emphasis.

Cities. The capital and largest city of Belgium is **Brussels,** in the center of the country. Although north of the language boundary, it is more French than Flemish. It combines the charm of an old European city and the architecture of former centuries with the activities of a financial and business capital. The city carries on a variety of manufactures, notably the making of high-quality textiles and laces. Through a canal connection with the Schelde it is also a seaport of sorts.

Antwerp, on the Schelde a few miles upstream from the estuary, is one of the great

CITIES OF THE LOW COUNTRIES

Name	Country	Type	Population
Brussels	Belgium	Governmental, industrial	973,000 (1953)
Antwerp	Belgium	Seaport	258,000 (1953)
Ghent	Belgium	Industrial, seaport	165,000 (1953)
Amsterdam	Netherlands	Seaport, industrial	859,000 (1954)
Rotterdam	Netherlands	Seaport, industrial	705,000 (1954)
The Hague	Netherlands	Governmental	591,000 (1954)

Fig. 19.9—Amsterdam, Netherlands, Showing the Concentric Ring and Connecting Canals of the City. (Courtesy, Netherlands Information Service.)

ports of the world. It not only serves Belgium but is also the center of much commerce for Germany and Switzerland. The

city has many miles of dock works and other port facilities and is interlaced with canals that connect with the Rhine and the Dutch systems. Antwerp is the Flemish cultural capital.

Ghent, the second port of Belgium, is 30 miles west of Brussels and like that city connected with the Schelde by a canal. Most of its trade is to supply the city's large and varied textile industry. Ghent is also a center of flower raising (especially camellias and azaleas), so that certain sections of the city have pleasant aspects, in strong contrast with the ugly, crowded living quarters of the textile workers.

Amsterdam (Fig. 19.9), the largest city of the Netherlands, is its chief industrial center, second port, and legislative capital. It is located at the southwest corner of Ysel Lake 15 miles inland from the North Sea. Amsterdam suffered in competition with the other ports of the Low Countries because of its roundabout connection with the sea until a canal dug directly westward to the sea allowed it to accommodate large, ocean-going ships. Like most Dutch cities Amsterdam is thoroughly canalized, in this instance according to a very carefully planned series of concentric rings and radial connections. Amsterdam conducts a large import trade with the Dutch colonies.

Rotterdam is the Netherlands' chief port and the particular rival of Antwerp. Located 15 miles inland on the main mouth of the Rhine, it has the great advantage of the most direct connection with the river traffic of that stream. Like Antwerp, it handles a large share of Germany's import trade because large ocean vessels can ascend the Rhine.

The Hague,[2] some 10 miles northwest of Rotterdam just inland from the sea, is the site of the royal residence and the seat of government. As such it is the Netherlands' official capital. Because of the traditional role of the Netherlands as a neutral state it has been the scene of important interna-

tional treaty signings and meetings and was chosen as the home of the World Court.

The Low Countries as a Whole. The industry of all three countries is founded to an exceptional degree on international trade. Except for food processing and the Belgian linen industry, almost all the industrial activity consists of the processing and manufacture of imported raw materials for export as finished or semifinished goods. The small size (hence small home markets) of Belgium and Luxembourg makes it absolutely necessary that they find foreign markets for the output of their industrial plants.

Realization that their small size makes political separateness an economic handicap to each of the three countries led to the establishment of the customs union already referred to. It is the intention eventually to organize a full economic union, with a common currency and common trade policies. Although agricultural Netherlands to some extent complements the other two countries, the duplication of many manufacturing enterprises poses problems that make complete union a goal still far from attainment.

Of first significance, not only to the countries concerned but to Europe as a whole, is the similar common-sense, geographical approach to the organization of the coal and iron and steel industries of northwestern Europe, which was inaugurated in 1952. It is well understood by all that their coal and iron ore deposits are the basis of the industrialization of the countries concerned. Yet the irrationality of the political boundaries with respect to the coal and iron ore resources and the iron and steel industries of the region is obvious. France, Belgium, and Luxembourg all lack sufficient coking coal and so must rely on imports which come chiefly from West Germany. France has a surplus of iron ore, and Belgium and Luxembourg, which use the ore, must market almost their entire iron and steel output internationally.

The European Coal-Steel Community began functioning in 1953. All customs duties and restrictions on the movement of coal,

[2] The city's full Dutch name is *'s Graven hage* ("the Count's Hedge"), a reference to a count's garden that constituted its original site.

scrap iron, iron ore, and steel were abolished between France, Belgium, the Netherlands, Luxembourg, West Germany, and Italy, and a common market was established throughout these countries.

Although all the participating countries share in the benefits of this enlightened procedure, it is Belgium and Luxembourg that have the most at stake because of the greater dominance in their economies of the industries concerned. The prospects for these countries as well as for the Netherlands are good. With energetic populations and political and social stability, there is no reason why their peoples should not continue to enjoy higher than average standards of living among the European nations and maintain their positions in the forefront of European economic progress.

4. GERMANY

General Aspects. Germany is generally considered to be centrally situated in Europe, between the Low Countries and France on the west, Switzerland and Austria on the south, Czechoslovakia and Poland on the east, and Denmark on the north (Fig. 19.10). Its coastline, on either side of Den-

Fig. 19.10—Germany. The inset compares the area of Germany with that of Montana, which is approximately equal.

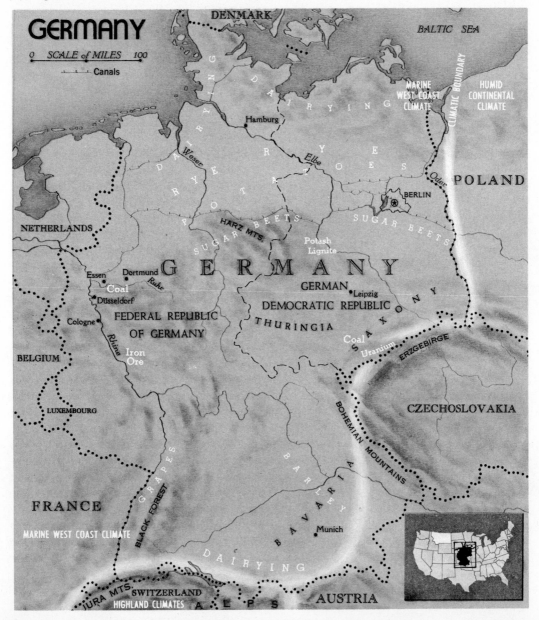

mark, is on the North Sea on the west, the Baltic Sea in the east. The total area of Germany is 143,000 square miles, almost equal to that of Montana.[3]

Topography and Climate. Like France, Germany is a country of moderate relief, although a good deal of its area is comprised of uplands of relatively high altitudes. The northern part of the country is a plains region dotted with lakes and swamps and covered with deposits, commonly sandy, left by the glaciers of the ice age (Fig. 19.11). Its soils are rather infertile. In general there is an increase of elevation and relief to the south. The central highlands or plateau region just south of the northern plains averages 1600 feet in altitude and contains a complex of old mountain ranges. The most important of these ranges are the **Harz Mountains** in the north central sector, the

Fig. 19.11—Luneburg Heath, a Wide Expanse of Level Sandy and Boggy Country (With Infertile Soil Overgrown With Sedges, Low Willows, Birches, and Conifers) in northern Germany. The largest of many such tracts. These are lonely, unoccupied areas. (Courtesy, German Embassy.)

[3] A geographical discussion of Germany is made difficult by the complex political circumstances of the country resulting from its defeat in World War II. The political elements of geography are, however, less fundamental than are physical and economic aspects. Germany, therefore, is here considered as a whole, within the *de facto* international boundaries established at the close of World War II. The division of the country under two separate governments is recognized only where relevant and necessary.

Erz and **Bohemian Mountains** along the Czechoslovak border, the **Juras** curving northeast from Switzerland, and the **Black Forest,** a highland area in the southwest. The mountainous areas are 2000 to 4000 feet in elevation and are separated by large basin areas of lower altitude.

Southern Germany consists of the northern foothills of the Alps and a small portion of the **Alps** themselves (Fig. 19.12). Western Germany throughout most of its extent is dominated by the **Rhine Valley,** a rift valley (see Chapter 9, p. 147) with steep sides whose floor is more than 1000 feet below the bordering regions. The southern portion of the Rhine Valley floor is often referred to as "the Garden of Germany," since its low altitude, lower latitude, and protected situation together insure mild winters. Middle Rhineland is bordered on the west by the uplands of extreme western Germany.

The climate of Germany is less typically marine west coast than is that of France and the Low Countries. It is really transitional between that climate and the continental climate that prevails farther east, since the country is so far inland from the west coast of Europe as to experience the gradual dwindling of the marine influence. Thus, the rainfall declines from 40 inches on the coasts and mountain slopes to 26 inches or less in the lowlands of the southeast. The extremes of continental conditions are not, however, felt even in the east.

Temperatures are rather uniform throughout the country, for the cooling effect of higher altitudes in the south is more or less offset by the opposite influence of lower latitudes. Indeed, in the sheltered valleys of the southern upland regions the combination of low elevation and lower latitude provides very agreeable climatic environments.

Transportation. Like France, Germany has an extraordinarily well-developed transportation network of highways, railroads, and waterways (both streams and canals). The river facilities especially are peculiarly suited to transportation requirements. This is most true of the Rhine, which is navigable

Fig. 19.12—Bavarian Alps and Loisach Valley in South Germany. (Courtesy, German Embassy.)

Fig. 19.13—Women of Nordic Stock Harvesting Vine Grapes in Pfalz Region of the Rhine Valley. (Courtesy, German Embassy.)

for vessels of considerable tonnage along virtually the entire western border of Germany. Its course, moreover, is directly in line with the major traffic movement of bulk commodities for the concentrations of heavy industry in western Germany.

Fig. 19.14—Bavarian Violin Maker, in Mittelwald on the Isar River—a Famous Locality for This Art. (Courtesy, German Embassy.)

Though not so serviceable as the Rhine, the other great rivers of Germany—the **Weser, Elbe,** and **Oder**—are also important arteries. They flow south to north, like the Rhine, and are fairly equally spaced west to east. The areas between them, furthermore, have continuous west-east depressions in thick soil deposits. Thus it was a simple matter to join the rivers with cross canals. Consequently a rectangular network of water routes is available over all the northern plains region.

The People. Germany's population of 69 million is the largest in Europe. Because of the diverse topography and history of the various sections of the country there is also a considerable diversity in religion and racial stocks. In the north the Nordic stock (Fig. 19.13) is dominant. The southern people are of Alpine stock, typified by those of the southeastern region known as **Bavaria** (Fig. 19.14). There is some admixture of Slavic stock in the central highlands and the northeast.

The Prussian tradition and characteristics have unfortunately predominated in recent German history. This is the tradition of militarism, of the ordered and regimented life, and of unquestioned obedience to higher authority. The northern people are industrious and efficient but are inclined to be stolid and serious minded. The religion of the north and center is Lutheran.

The Bavarian way of life is in direct contrast. Although also industrious, the southern German is more amiable and has a happier outlook on life. His part of Germany has produced many geniuses in the arts. His religion is generally Roman Catholic.

Despite these regional differences and the fact that Germany did not become a unified nation until 1871, the sense of national unity is strong throughout the country. The World War II defeat intensified this feeling.

Agriculture and Products. Germany has traditionally tried to be as agriculturally self-sufficient as possible. The result has been a very intensive use of the land and, in the German tradition, with scientific thoroughness. The high population density and

Fig. 19.15—German Farmhouse and Adjoining Sheds in Hesse. (Courtesy, Germany Embassy.)

lack of large areas of fertile soil have prevented the attainment of full self-sufficiency, but the deficiency is not too great. On an austerity basis the Germans could probably eke out an existence on black (rye) bread and potatoes as basic food staples. About two-thirds of the total area is arable; less than 30 percent of the population is engaged in agriculture.

Despite a large increase since World War II in the use of farm tractors in western Germany, German agricultural practices are distinctly backward compared to the highly developed techniques applied in industry. The average German farm is too small to be mechanized. The horse population—2.3 million—is nevertheless comparatively low; cows are often used as draft animals for reasons of economy. German farmers do not live on the farms but in small, centralized villages, where the domestic animals and equipment are kept in the houses or in adjoining sheds (Fig. 19.15). During the winter, especially in the south, the farmer augments his income with handicrafts.

Potatoes are Germany's major crop; the country leads the world in their production. The northern lowlands, particularly in the east, are the chief producing areas. **Sugar beets,** another root crop, are grown in the fertile soil belt that extends across the country at the southern border of the lowlands. Among the cereal crops **rye, oats, wheat,**

Fig. 19.16—Vineyards on the Steep Valley Sides of the Middle Rhine River. Castle Katz at the summit. (Courtesy, German Embassy.)

and **barley** are important, in that order. The predominance of the coarser grains is a reflection of the cool climate. Barley is important in the south, where it forms the basis of the malt used in making the very large output of **beer,** the national drink. The Rhine Valley is famous for its vineyards (Fig. 19.16) and the **wines** produced from their grapes.

The grasslands (about one-sixth of the total area) and fodder crops support a large **cattle** population (about 15 million), of which half are **dairy** cows. The dairy industry is concentrated along the northern coasts and in the Alpine regions. Pork is the major meat item in the diet. There are more than 21 million **hogs** in the country, fed on potatoes, turnips, sugar beet waste, and beer mash.

Roughly one-fourth of Germany is forest covered, two-thirds of the forests being coniferous. Scientific forestry is practiced on a high level to preserve the resource, so that only one-third of the **lumber** needs must be met through imports.

Mineral Products. For several hundred years before the eighteenth century Germany was the foremost mining country in the world. The art of mining may be said to have evolved in German mines and technical schools. In those years the metallic ores were of major importance, but depletion of these ores, combined with the rise in importance of mineral fuels as the industrial age developed, served to change the emphasis.

The major mineral product of Germany now is **coal,** in the output of which the country ranks fourth in the world. Both soft coal (bituminous) and brown coal (lignite) are mined at various places. The coal field of the lower Rhine and **Ruhr** (a Rhine tributary) valleys in the northwest accounts for some three-quarters of the output. Central Germany is responsible for half the lignite production.

Germany is, on the other hand, greatly deficient in iron ore resources. Small, low-grade deposits west of the Rhine produce only a fraction of the needs.

Germany's other major mineral resource is **potash,** occurring in the world's largest deposits in the southeast section of the northern plains. Germany accounts for almost half the world output of this basis of fertilizer and chemical products.

The older mining districts of the Harz and Erz mountains, formerly important for copper, lead, zinc, and silver, still produce moderate amounts of these metals. (*Erz* means "ore.") The Erz district acquired new importance after World War II as the only European source of **uranium** on a significant scale. Exploitation of this resource by the Soviet Union has been at a feverish pace and has shifted to the state of **Thuringia,** not far to the northwest.

Manufacturing. Germany in pre-World War II days was one of the three greatest industrial nations of the world, along with the United States and Great Britain. Emerging from the war in a state of industrial chaos, with virtually all manufacturing facilities in ruins, the Germans have made an astounding comeback in the western half of the country. West Germany alone is again one of the leading industrial countries of the world.

Fig. 19.17—Ruhr Steel Furnaces, Postwar, at Dortmund, Germany. (Courtesy, German Embassy.)

Saxony is the leader; and **chinaware** and **pottery**, also in Saxony. Manufacturing of all kinds is carried on in so many sections of the country that further enumeration here would become a catalogue list.

CITIES OF GERMANY

Name	Type	Population (1953)
Berlin	Governmental, industrial	3,480,000
Hamburg	Seaport, industrial	1,723,000
Munich	Commercial	906,000
Cologne	River port, industrial	670,000
Essen	Industrial	661,000
Leipzig	Industrial, commercial	608,000 (1946)
Düsseldorf	Industrial	595,000
Dortmund	Industrial	581,000

The range of manufactures in Germany embraces almost every conceivable field. This variety is a result of the traditional excellence of technical instruction and the generous support of research in pure science at the many technical schools and universities. Although mass production techniques are used, their employment is on a much smaller scale than in the United States. Emphasis is placed on high quality and precision. The fame of German cameras is an example of German superiority in this type of manufacture. German industry has also emphasized industrial experimentation. Using great imagination and boldness it has been responsible for the discovery and development of many processes and products, especially synthetics, in use throughout the world.

The major industry is, of course, **iron and steel.** The greatest concentration of the industry is in the Ruhr Valley (Fig. 19.17), which rivals Pittsburgh in the number and complexity of its plants. Germany's output of iron and steel places it fourth in the world—this despite the enormous handicaps under which the industry has operated since World War II.

Other leading industries include **chemicals,** concentrated in the Rhineland and in **Saxony,** the east central section; **textiles** of all kinds in various districts, among which

Fig. 19.18—Berlin, Germany. Kurfurstendamm, the "Fifth Avenue" of the former German capital, in 1954. (Courtesy, Germany Embassy.)

Cities. **Berlin** (Fig. 19.18) was formerly one of the world's great cities, having something of the same significance as Paris. At the close of World War II it was the outstanding example of how devastating city destruction by non-atomic weapons can be. Although Berlin is still large in terms of population, its national significance since the war has been chiefly symbolic, as the former capital of the country. The city is in the northeastern section of Germany in a district dotted by swamps and lakes, midway between the upper Elbe and the middle Oder. By developing to the maximum the excellent possibilities of the site for water, rail, and highway construction, Berlin became the transportation hub of Germany and the country's financial and commercial capital. It is not improbable that Berlin will eventually regain its former position as a great city, as part of a reunified Germany.

Hamburg, 175 miles northwest of Berlin, is 90 miles from the North Sea on the Elbe River. Prior to World War II it was the greatest port in Europe, tonnage-wise. By virtue of the almost unlimited area available for dock works along the Elbe, and extensive canal construction within the city, Hamburg has enormous port facilities (more than all the other ports of northern Europe combined). With excellent railroad connections in addition, it is Germany's greatest commercial city. As the most eastern port of Europe directly accessible to Atlantic commerce, Hamburg in normal times is the port for much of Europe situated farther to the east. Like Berlin, it suffered terrible damage during World War II but in contrast with Berlin was restored rapidly to effective functioning.

Munich, the old capital of Bavaria, is in the southeastern part of that province on a plateau of 1700-foot elevation. It is the outstanding cultural center of Germany, with many museums, galleries, theaters, and palaces. Its industries, including the manufacture of artistic objects, reflect this cultural atmosphere. Munich is probably best known, however, as the largest center of the brewing industry in Germany. It is the world's most renowned beer city. Its industries, nevertheless, are subordinate to its commercial activities, for it is on an intersection of old trade routes subsequently followed by railroads.

Leipzig, the largest city of Saxony and eastern Germany, also has a cultural tradition. Before World War II the best known among its great variety of industries were

publishing and musical instruments. With all the ancillary industries to these also at hand, it was the world's ranking book-publishing center.

Essen is the largest city of the urban-industrial agglomeration that constitutes the Ruhr and lower Rhineland. It is the site of the great Krupp works, the largest iron and steel plant in Europe. **Dortmund,** 20 miles to the east in the Ruhr Valley, is also an iron and steel center, with other heavy industries as well. **Düsseldorf,** another large industrial center about the same distance to the southwest, is astride the Rhine and hence is also important commercially.

Cologne (Fig. 19.19), the largest of the Rhine ports, is on the west bank of the river

Fig. 19.19—Cologne, Germany. The cathedral seen from the south. A Gothic structure begun in 1248, mostly finished by 1560, finally completed only in 1880. (Courtesy, German Embassy.)

20 miles south of Düsseldorf. An ancient city (its name stems from the fact that it was once a Roman colony), it is known for its medieval architecture, most of which was destroyed during World War II. Its prize treasure, the enormous Cologne cathedral, fortunately survived the bombings, however. The cathedral is one of the greatest examples of Gothic architecture in Europe. Cologne not only is a busy commercial city but has a variety of industries. Its perfume makers gave the world the famous *eau de Cologne* (Cologne water).

Germany as a Whole. Germany has demonstrated beyond question that it is the most important country of continental Europe. Three times in less than a century its enormous industrial vitality has been perverted for the purposes of war. Twice it has involved the entire world in the holocausts it began. At the close of World War II the victorious United Nations were determined that there should never be a third time. But the victors were confounded by a spontaneous resurgence that ironically achieved for the vanquished (at least in West Germany) a sounder economic status and better prospects than many of their conquerors had.

The fear of another misuse of this economic strength still perturbs Germany's neighbors, yet it is clear that an economically strong and healthy Germany is essential to the establishment of a strong, healthy western Europe. A major initial step has been the acceptance of the Germans as equal partners in the West European Community. Eventually, it is to be hoped, a unified, peaceable Germany will contribute to the progress and betterment of all Europe and will provide the German people with better living, and greater contentment, than they enjoyed at the height of their militant power.

QUESTIONS. What political commitment have the people of the Low Countries and Luxembourg undertaken in recognition of their geographic unity? Describe the general topography of the area. What is unusual about a large portion of the area of the Netherlands? In what respects is Belgium transitional between northern France and the Netherlands? Describe the unusual features of Dutch agriculture. Name the chief agricultural products of the three countries. What are their mineral resources? Their major industries? Why is international trade so vital to their economies? Describe the essential features of the European Coal-Steel Community and discuss its importance in the future of Europe as a whole. Why are Antwerp and Rotterdam of such great significance as European ports?

Name the major topographic features of Germany. In what respect does the climate of Germany differ from that of the previously discussed countries of the marine west coast region of Europe? Discuss the degree of development of the transportation system of Germany. What are the two major divisions of Germany in terms of the characteristics and attitudes of the people? Explain the paradox of scientific intensive agriculture that is at the same time unmechanized. What are the chief crops of Germany? The major mineral resources? Discuss the characteristics of the German manufacturing industries and name the leading ones. What circumstances tend to make Hamburg a port of the first rank? With what product is Munich associated? Why is Germany so important in the future of Europe?

CHAPTER 20

The Marine West Coast Climate in Europe

(CONTINUED)

5. GREAT BRITAIN

Great Britain, the largest of the British Isles, is 89,000 square miles in area (about that of South Carolina and Georgia combined), and constitutes almost three-quarters of the total area of that island group (Fig. 20.1). Together with a 5000-square-mile area of northeastern Ireland and a few minor islands of the British Isles it comprises the political entity known as the United Kingdom of Great Britain and Northern Ireland.

Topography. The island of Great Britain is roughly rectangular, extends 600 miles north to south, and is wider in the south (300 miles at the widest) than in the north. The coastline is interrupted throughout most of its length by deep bays, estuaries, and fiords, so that no point on the island is less than 75 miles from tidewater.

The north and west of southern Great Britain, **England** and **Wales**, is a country of old, low mountains, whereas the south and east is a region of lowland plains. **Scotland,** the northern third of the island, comprises three topographic districts: the **Scottish Highlands** (Fig. 20.2) in the north, the **Southern Uplands** on the southern border, and the **Central Lowlands** in between. The highlands area is a dissected plateau with considerable tracts of summit upland averaging 2000 to 3000 feet in elevation and attaining 4400 feet in one peak, the highest point in the British Isles. It is also the most rugged district of the islands, with little truly level land and long, deep fiords or "lochs" reaching far inland. The soil is thin and poor and the population sparse.

The Central Lowlands, which also have considerable relief, are the most important area of Scotland, containing the bulk of the population and industry. The Southern Uplands are lower than the Northern Highlands region but like it include large areas of swampy "moors." Indeed, most of the highland tracts of Great Britain consist of these soggy fields of heather and moss.

The **Pennines** extend south from the Southern Uplands about halfway down the rest of the island to form the "backbone of England." These old mountains, some 2000 feet in elevation, are much like the Southern Uplands in appearance. West of the Pennines, in the northwest corner of England, is the **Lake District,** a highland area known for its many scenic lakes and falls. West of the southern end of the Pennines is Wales, a highland region of much the same aspect as the Southern Uplands and Pennines but with greater relief. The remaining highland area is the peninsula of extreme southwest England, which comprises the districts known as **Devon** and **Cornwall.**

Lowland Britain is virtually all less than 1000 feet in elevation. However, the southeast is not flat but contains many low ridges and hills. In the northwest the **Midland Plain** wraps around the southern end of the Pennines. Most of the population and agriculture of Great Britain is located on the lowlands, so that they constitute the most important section of the country.

Climate. The British Isles derive exceptional benefit from the moderating influence of the North Atlantic Drift. The winters in consequence are remarkably mild for the

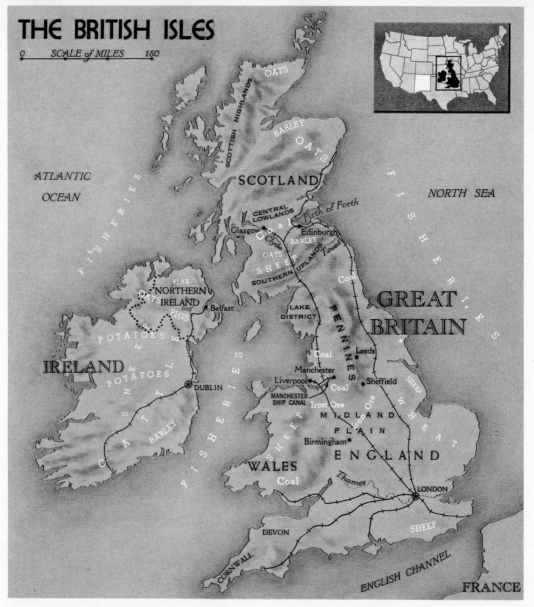

THE BRITISH ISLES

SCALE of MILES

0   150

ATLANTIC

OCEAN

NORTH SEA

SCOTLAND

SCOTTISH HIGHLANDS

OATS

BARLEY

OATS

FISHERIES

CENTRAL
LOWLANDS

Firth of Forth

Glasgow

Edinburgh

Clyde

Coal

BARLEY

OATS

SOUTHERN UPLANDS

Tweed

SHEEP

Coal

GREAT
BRITAIN

FLAX

NORTHERN
IRELAND

OATS

Belfast

PIGS

LAKE
DISTRICT

PENNINES

FISHERIES

POTATOES

SHEEP

IRELAND

Coal

Leeds

POTATOES

Manchester

Liverpool

Sheffield

Coal

DUBLIN

MANCHESTER
SHIP CANAL

Iron Ore

Iron Ore

SHEEP

FISHERIES

BARLEY

MIDLAND

PLAIN

SHEEP

WHEAT

CATTLE

Birmingham

ENGLAND

WALES

Coal

Thames

LONDON

DEVON

SHEEP

CORNWALL

ENGLISH CHANNEL

FRANCE

Fig. 20.1—The British Isles. The inset compares the area of the British Isles with that of New Mexico, which is approximately equal.

latitude, although even the small width of Great Britain suffices to make the east coast colder than the west. Even so, the winters of extreme northern Scotland are harsh and unpleasant because of the high latitude. In summer the general influence of the surrounding ocean keeps temperatures down (a summer "heat wave" in England brings temperatures into the 80's), and the north is distinctly colder than the south.

Due to the combination of prevailing west winds and the eastern highlands the eastern side of the island experiences moderate rain-shadow conditions. Precipitation may exceed 100 inches a year in the western highlands, as contrasted with less than 20 inches in certain east coast districts. No place in Great Britain can be called dry, however, and there has never been a year of serious drought in the country.

The People. The total population of the United Kingdom is over 50 million (including approximately 1.4 million in Northern Ireland), of which over 80 percent are in England, 10 percent in Scotland, and 5 percent in Wales. The average density of population is thus more than 500 per square mile, country-wise among the highest concentrations in the world.

The inhabitants of Great Britain are the

descendants of a long series of successive invading peoples that ended with the conquering Normans in the eleventh century. The three divisions of the country into England, Scotland, and Wales correspond to the three similar but distinct national types, each of which bespeaks the sequence of this invasion history.

Thus the English people contain strong admixtures of Teutonic stock introduced from northern Europe in post-Roman times. The driving force of the English was responsible for the unification of the island into a single nation and its rise to world dominance in the nineteenth century; and it was the development of English traditions of law

Fig. 20.2—Scottish Highlands. Ben Venue from the Trossachs. (Courtesy, British Information Services.)

and political stability that provided the national strength to acquire, colonize, and administer the greatest empire in the history of the world.

The great courage of the English, their capacity for hard work and self-discipline, and their other fine qualities of character were epitomized by their conduct during the crisis of World War II. Alone, and faced with what appeared to be certain eventual defeat, they refused to consider the slightest concession that would end the war, and with a morale that was only strengthened by adversity carried on until the tide turned.

The Scots are of Celtic origin, descendants of some of the pre-Roman peoples of Britain. For centuries, while England was evolving into a strong nation, the Scots carried on tribal feuds between their various clans. This so weakened Scottish ability to resist the English efforts to secure political domination of the island that despite great personal valor and fighting abilities the eventual incorporation of Scotland into the English state was achieved.

Today the description of the English character given above applies almost equally to the Scotsmen. The qualities of niggardliness and dourness attributed to the Scots in American humor are exaggerations of the Scottish character. Although the standard of living in modern Scotland is above the level of a grim struggle for existence, in former times making a living was, for the Scottish farmer (especially in the north), a precarious business. Because he could not afford to waste even a scrap of food or fuel, his circumstances did not evoke a happy, carefree outlook on life.

The Welsh are also of Celtic descent and owe the retention of their individuality to their highland isolation from the rest of Britain. Even now there persist communities in which are retained the racial characteristics of the pre-Roman peoples. The Welsh have laid great stress on their distinct traditions and customs, and to this day Welsh, a Gaelic (Celtic) language, tends to predominate over English.

Transportation. In contrast with the well-developed canal systems of France, Germany, and the Low Countries, the canals of Great Britain are of minor importance. In pre-railroad days British canals were more significant, but because even the lowland areas of the island are little suited for canal construction the invention of the railroad halted further development.

Great Britain is the home of the railway; the small size and generally low relief of the country made it a simple matter to provide a very complete railroad network. The highway net is similarly well developed and serves a truck and passenger car traffic second only to that of the United States.

Agriculture in General. Although agriculture is an important activity in Great Britain it suffers from several handicaps. The cooler and cloudier climate than that of the European continental lands farther east and south limits the productivity and variety of crops that can be grown. The soils, moreover, are only moderately fertile, and only 30 percent of the total area of Great Britain is arable. Most of the arable land is in the south and east, on the lowlands (Fig. 20.3).

Despite these handicaps Great Britain before the industrial revolution was quite self-sufficient in agricultural products. Indeed, the original prosperity of the country was based on the agriculture of the southeast plain, once it had been cleared of its forest

Fig. 20.3—Country Village of Southeast England. (Courtesy, British Information Services.)

cover. With industrialization and the great growth in population that accompanied it, however, Britain became increasingly unable to satisfy its food needs. Despite the attention given to expanding domestic food production during World War II the country can satisfy at present only two-fifths of its food needs. It is the greatest food-importing nation of the world.

Intensive farming is, of course, the rule, and, although different crops predominate in the various districts, there is little specialization on individual farms. Mixed farming is typical.

Agricultural Products. Among the cereals **oats, wheat,** and **barley** rank in that order of importance. The temperature limit of wheat runs near the Scottish border, but the excessive dampness over most of Britain limits the significant wheat output to the drier southeast corner of the country. Oats are important in the drier eastern sections, but as they can stand both damper and cooler conditions the leading district is eastern Scotland.

As in Germany, **root crops** are grown to take advantage of the low average temperature. **Sugar beets** and **potatoes** are produced for human use on those arable lands where the cereals are less suited to the climate, and **turnips** and other root crops are produced for fodder. **Hay** is grown wherever possible.

Peas, beans, and **truck vegetables** are produced in the more populous southern part of the country. Temperate **fruits** and **berries** are important in various restricted areas.

The same circumstances that handicap the raising of crops are responsible for the great importance of the grazing industries in Great Britain. One-quarter of the total land area is fit only for rough grazing use, and another fifth is in permanent pasture. **Sheep** are most important among the livestock. Despite its small size Great Britain, with more than 20 million sheep, is exceeded in sheep population by few countries. The grasslands and moors provide rich pasturage for these animals, and the cool climate stimulates **wool** growth. Britain's high-quality breeds have been used to improve local stocks throughout the world. Sheep are raised in almost

every corner of the country, but the outstanding districts are the Southern Uplands, Wales, and extreme southeast England.

Cattle are also raised on the fodder crops and pasture lands. The total population of 10 million is about equally divided between **dairy** and **beef** cattle. Although cattle are also rather widespread they are concentrated in western England. With the exception of milk, none of the products of the grazing industries is sufficient for domestic needs.

Fisheries. Several circumstances combine to make the **fisheries** of Britain important. The island is surrounded by shallow seas that constitute excellent fishing grounds. The abundance of small harbors on the indented coastline early encouraged the development of a fishing industry. Indeed, the great maritime tradition of Britain, exemplified in the British navy, was founded in no small degree on the seamanship acquired through fishing. Lastly, as a domestic product fish constitute an important part of the diet in a country that must import so much of its meat.

Mineral Products. The outstanding mineral resource and product of Great Britain is **coal.** Among the world's nations Britain has the largest reserves of coal in proportion to its area. The country's extensive deposits occur in three main districts: (a) on the flanks of the Pennines, especially the east and south, (b) the Central Lowlands of Scotland, and, (c) southern Wales. About one-fifth of the Welsh coal consists of anthracite. British coal is, however, becoming increasingly difficult to recover because of the depth and thinness of the seams (Fig. 20.4).

Iron ore is Britain's only other significant mineral resource. The major occurrences, low in grade but easily worked, are in the eastern and northwestern sections of the Midland Plain. Iron ore also occurs interbedded in many of the coal fields, but these resources, although formerly much used, are now of little account.

Manufacturing. As the birthplace of the industrial age Great Britain was until the twentieth century the outstanding industrialized nation. Although now outranked by the United States and the Soviet Union in terms

Fig. 20.4—British Coal Miners at Work. (Courtesy, British Information Services.)

Pennines and in the western portion of the Central Lowlands in Scotland. The **woolen** industry is centered in the southern Pennines, and in the valley of the **Tweed River** at the eastern end of the Scottish border, which has given its name to the high-quality woolen goods produced there.

The second industry of Britain is **iron and steel,** in the production of which the country is exceeded only by the United States and the Soviet Union. There are several important centers, including northeast England, the central Midlands, southern Wales, and the western portion of the Scottish Central Lowlands. Through no mere coincidence these centers are in or adjacent to the important coalfields.

As is characteristic of the great industrial nations, the number and variety of manufacturing enterprises in Great Britain is too great to be considered in more than general terms here. The iron and steel centers are also sites of large concentrations of heavy industry such as the production of **locomotives** and other **machinery.** The presence of large estuaries plus the marine tradition fostered the development of several large **shipbuilding** centers (Fig. 20.5). A large metal **smelting** industry is located in South Wales, founded on metallic ore deposits anciently important but now practically exhausted.

of volume of output it exceeds both countries in the proportion of its working population engaged in industry. The ratio of industrial workers to agricultural workers in Great Britain is nine to one.

Britain's premier industry is **textiles.** The industrial revolution began in the British textile industry, and was fostered initially ·by the availability of waterpower (the direct use of the power of water wheels, not hydroelectric power) as well as the domestic supply of wool, and by the suitability of the moist climate to the processes of spinning and weaving. (High humidity makes the fibers and threads pliable and easily worked rather than stiff and brittle.) Subsequent expansion was, of course, based on the great coal resources. Although Britain remains one of the leading textile countries of the world it has been outstripped in terms of bulk by some of its former customers. The British textile industry is now known chiefly for the high-quality goods it produces.

The manufacture of **cotton goods** is at present the most important of the textile industries. Britain is consequently the major cotton-importing nation. The cotton industry is concentrated on the Midlands west of the

Fig. 20.5—Shipbuilding on the Clyde River, Great Britain. (Courtesy, British Information Services.)

CITIES OF GREAT BRITAIN

Name	Type	Population (1951)
London	Seaport, governmental, industrial	4,400,000
Birmingham	Industrial	1,100,000
Glasgow	Industrial	1,090,000
Liverpool	Seaport, industrial	790,000
Manchester	Industrial, seaport	703,000
Sheffield	Industrial	513,000
Leeds	Industrial	503,000
Edinburgh	Governmental	467,000

Cities. **London** (Fig. 20.6), the capital of the United Kingdom, was for many years without a close rival as the world's greatest city. It was the largest in population, the capital of the most powerful nation (and thus most important politically), and the capital as well of the world's finance and commerce. Although London is no longer supreme in the first two (ranking second to New York and Washington, D.C., respectively) and must share the lead with New York in financial and commercial importance, it is still outstanding among the world's cities.

London is located in the southeast corner of England in the center of a lowland district known as the London Basin. It is on the **Thames River** some 40 miles inland from the estuary mouth of the stream. The name "London" applies to three distinct political and geographical entities. The City of London is an area of one square mile corresponding to the medieval city. It occupies the heart of the present city and contains most of the famous landmarks and historical points of interest. It is analogous to the lower tip of Manhattan Island in New York City. The County of London is a roughly circular district some 12 miles in diameter surrounding the City and constitutes the modern city of London. Extending some 20 miles out, a surrounding ring of suburbs together with the County constitutes Greater London. It is on the basis of the Greater London population of 8,300,000 that the city disputes with New York for the rank of largest city on earth.

It is difficult to characterize London. It is

seaport more technically than otherwise, for the docks that comprise the Port of London extend for 55 miles down the Thames from Tower Bridge in the heart of the city. They constitute one of the world's greatest ports, though part are outside London proper. London is also the internal commercial center of Britain, for it is at the hub of the country's rail and highway systems. As a governmental city London is equally important, serving as the seat of both Parliament and the royal court, and hence constitutes the capital of

Fig. 20.6—London, England. Big Ben and Houses of Parliament, the Thames, and London Bridge. (Courtesy, British Information Services.)

the British Commonwealth of Nations. London is also an industrial city, since the County contains in its eastern half such a bewildering variety of industrial establishments as to comprise one of the major industrial concentrations of the country. Only textiles are absent, but London is the major center of the clothing industry. In atmosphere, however, London is predominantly commercial. In the City the streets are lined with the commercial, banking, and insurance houses that conduct world-wide businesses.

Accounts of the great fogs for which London is notorious are not exaggerated as to degree, but fogs are not so frequent as is commonly thought. They occur only a few times each year during February and March. Unlike American city fogs, induced by industrial smoke and dust, the London fogs are due to the soot from countless thousands of soft-coal fires in open fireplaces, with which Londoners persist in heating their homes and apartments.

Birmingham (Fig. 20.7) is Britain's second city and greatest center of industry. It lies 100 miles northwest of London in the heart of the Midlands and is the nucleus of a large collection of manufacturing towns and cities developed on the basis of the coal fields of the district. The great quantities of soot from the many factories early caused the district to be known as the "black country" because of its drab and grimy aspect.

Glasgow, Scotland's largest city, is situated on the **Clyde River** about 10 miles upstream from its estuary mouth. It is the core of the Scottish industrial district based on the coal fields of the Central Lowlands. The banks of the deep Clyde are the locus of the world's greatest center of shipbuilding, and the industries of the district, including the manufacture of steel, to a great extent serve that industry.

Fig. 20.7—Birmingham, England. Center of the chief industrial district of England. Note smoky background. (Courtesy, British Information Services.)

Liverpool and **Manchester** are two cities of the northeast Midlands industrial district on the west coast. The former is situated at the mouth of the **Mersey River** and as Britain's second port handles most of the trade from the Atlantic. Liverpool was for a long time hampered by the great range of the tides of the Mersey estuary, but now a large lock system maintains the high-tide level within the port. Manchester, 30 miles east of Liverpool, is the latter's great rival. As an industrial city Manchester was handicapped by the necessity for transshipment of its raw materials and products at Liverpool and to obtain that trade for itself constructed a ship canal that brings ocean ships to its doors. Liverpool's industries include the processing of the food and raw materials imported through it. Manchester is the world's greatest cotton textile center. The rivalry between the two cities has stimulated the development of the commerce and industry of both.

Sheffield and **Leeds** are a pair of cities 25 miles apart in the great industrial district and coal field on the southeastern flanks of the Pennines. Sheffield, one of the first centers of British iron and steel manufacture, early acquired a world-wide reputation for its fine cutlery. Although it has since lost its original advantage of nearby resources and must, in fact, import its iron ore from abroad, the Sheffield name has enabled it to continue as an important iron and steel city. The reputation of Leeds also dates from early times. Since the Middle Ages it has been the world's greatest center in the manufacture of woolen goods, its original advantage having been good soft water. In modern times the manufacture of heavy machinery has also become significant.

The city of **Edinburgh** lies in the Central Lowlands of Scotland, about 50 miles east of Glasgow and four miles inland on the south shore of a large estuary known as the **Firth of Forth**. Present-day Edinburgh is difficult to classify as a city. It is listed herein as governmental, and, although it is still the capital of Scotland as a part of the United Kingdom, its significance as a city stems from its former role as capital of the independent Scottish kingdom. Its industries have declined in the face of competition from Glasgow, and its port has little commercial standing. This is not to say, however, that Edinburgh is a decadent city. It functions today as the center of Scottish culture; it is the site of the national university and other educational institutions, many national monuments, and certain national political bodies such as the Supreme Court of Scotland. It presents a pleasant atmosphere of quiet residential life in comparison to the commercial and industrial bustle of Britain's other major cities.

Great Britain as a Whole. The economy of Great Britain is founded to the same great extent as that of the Low Countries on international trade. Britain became the dominant world power by virtue of importing raw materials and exporting manufactured products. Its exports plus the earnings of its overseas investments, its large merchant fleet, and its world-wide banking and insurance services served to pay for its food imports and to provide a good standard of living.

In the years since World War I the British position has deteriorated in several ways. The nation was forced to meet the competition in world markets of other countries which industrialized later and consequently possessed newer, more efficient industrial facilities. Many of its markets, notably the textiles market, dwindled as former customers began to supply their own needs. Its overseas investments were largely liquidated to help pay for the two World Wars, especially the second. Coal, its sole important raw material export, declined in importance as output dwindled owing to growing inefficiency of production and as the world's shipping converted to oil for fuel.

All of these events and circumstances produced a crisis in the British international economic position after World War II. To some extent the British have overcome their handicaps through the development of new industries producing chemicals, aircraft, electronic equipment, and specialized machinery, in which they are in the forefront rather than in the rear of technological progress. The fact remains, however, that much of British industry is reluctant to modernize plant and equipment and to change its accustomed ways. The spirit of aggressive competition so prevalent in American industry is the exception in Britain, where the prevailing attitude is to be content with one's established position in an industry and to "get along" rather than to expand.

There is little question that the British nation will survive these circumstances as it has previous crises of other kinds. The basic industrial strength and unrivaled commercial advantages (see Chapter 1, p. 9) still exist. And, although the reëstablished international economic position may not be maintained without further crises, the resourceful, hard-working British people will probably be successful in their own way in overcoming their troubles.

6. IRELAND

General Aspects. Ireland, the other large island of the British Isles, has a total area of 32,000 square miles, slightly more than that of Maine. It is divided politically into two separate countries: **Northern Ireland,** a part of the United Kingdom comprising the northeast corner of the island, and the **Irish Republic** (Fig. 20.1). The Irish Republic constitutes over four-fifths of the total area.

Topography and Climate. Ireland's topography can be generalized as that of a shallow basin. Much of the island is a low plain under 500 feet in elevation, with a discontinuous rim of highlands which rise on the average to over 1000 feet and in the extreme southwest reach 3000 feet. Isolated higher masses also occur throughout the central plain. The country is dotted with lakes and bogs which reflect poor natural drainage due to the low gradients in the basin and to the topographic irregularities of the thick deposits left by the ice age glaciers.

Situated in an exposed western position relative to Great Britain and the European continent, Ireland experiences a pronounced development of the marine west coast climate. Winter temperatures average 40° F.,

summer temperatures 60° F. Rainfall is heavy and uniformly distributed throughout the year. It is fortunate that the mountains of Ireland are low and few, for if they were high the island might be glacier covered even today.

The People. The population of the Irish Republic, Ireland, is 3 million and that of Northern Ireland 1.4 million. The peoples of the two countries not only differ in temperament, political outlook, and religion but have a violent antipathy for each other based on their attitudes toward Britain. The inhabitants of Northern Ireland are intensely loyal subjects of the British Crown. Although the Irish Republic has been a fully independent, sovereign nation since 1922, its people cannot forget the indignities and, at times, oppression suffered under British rule in preceding centuries. So bitter is the feeling that although English was the common language when the state was founded, Gaelic, the ancient Irish tongue, was resurrected and adopted as the official language of the country. The people of Ireland are so preoccupied with things Irish that they have little interest in what is happening in the rest of the world.

The enmity between the two countries of the island is furthered by the feeling of the Irish Republic that it should include all of Ireland, and that the Irish of Northern Ireland are therefore traitors to their own kind. The Republic, moreover, is strongly Catholic, while Protestantism is dominant in Northern Ireland.

Agriculture and Products. Ireland is almost exclusively an agricultural country. Some three-fifths of the land is in crops and pasture. The cool, humid climate favors the growth of plants not requiring much sun or high temperatures. It is especially good for grasses, and the year-round cover of their lush green growth warrants the name "Emerald Isle" commonly given to Ireland.

The leading crop is **hay**, grown for the large livestock population. **Root crops** such as **potatoes** and **turnips** are next in importance, with the cereals **oats, wheat,** and **barley** following in that order. **Cabbage** is also a major field crop.

The grazing industries, formerly subordinate to the raising of potatoes as the chief agricultural activity, are now dominant. The extensive grasslands and moors, supplemented by the hay crop, provide lush fodder for livestock. The Republic possesses over 4 million **cattle** and nearly 3 million **sheep;** Northern Ireland has almost one million cattle and 900,000 sheep. The **pig** population, fed on root crops, is also large. Pigs are more important in Northern Ireland, where 700,000 equal the number in the larger Irish Republic. These livestock populations are unusually high relative to the size of the island.

About one-third of the cattle are dairy cows, and beef from the other two-thirds is an important Irish export. Meat for export is also the major product of the sheep and pig-raising industries. Eggs from a large poultry population are another major export item. Together, the food products from the livestock industries constitute the bulk of Irish exports.

Mineral Resources and Manufacturing. Ireland is very poor in mineral resources. A little coal of poor quality occurs, but the major fuel is **peat.** Northern Ireland contains most of the manufacturing of the island. **Linen** and **shipbuilding** are the two major fields of enterprise. The linen is made partly from domestic flax, but in the main from imported material from the Low Countries. The Republic has a variety of small, light industries that process the domestic products of the country. Virtually all the manufacturing is concentrated in the center of the east coast.

CITIES OF IRELAND

Name	Country	Type	Population (1951)
Dublin	Irish Republic	Governmental, seaport	522,000
Belfast	Northern Ireland	Industrial, seaport	444,000

Cities. **Dublin** (Fig. 20.8), the capital and most important city of the Irish Republic, is on Dublin Bay, an arm of the Irish Sea in the middle of the east coast of Ireland. The city has experienced a turbulent history in modern times, as it was the site of many serious

Fig. 20.8—Dublin, Ireland. Air view of the government buildings. (Courtesy, Embassy of Ireland.)

disorders and uprisings in the long struggle for Irish independence. It is thus the center of Irish patriotism and culture. It contains many historic monuments and buildings of Irish history, institutions of higher learning, and an important theater. Dublin's chief activity is, paradoxically, trade with Britain. Its leading industries are brewing and distilling.

Belfast, approximately 100 miles northeast of Dublin on the eastern coast, is the capital and port of Northern Ireland and the only other major city on the island. Belfast is noted for its shipbuilding and linen industries.

Ireland as a Whole. The Ireland of today is a far different country from that of the past. In the early nineteenth century the island contained a population twice as large as at present, dependent almost entirely on the potato crop for food. A series of disastrous harvests culminating in complete failure of the crop in 1846 owing to blight caused a serious famine and resulted in the emigration of Irishmen by the hundreds of thousands to America. The emigration plus a low birth rate (the Irish Republic has the highest proportion in the world of unmarried adults in its population) so reduced the population that today the country verges on being underpopulated. The switch in agricultural emphasis to livestock, moreover, has provided a sounder agricultural basis in recent decades.

From a geographical point of view Ireland should unquestionably be a single country. Unification, however, is very unlikely and if it were achieved would have no great economic consequence. The danger in Ireland is that the preoccupation of the Irish Republic with the former great days of Irish culture and with the unification issue will handicap progress. Ireland is a backwater in the modern world—a place where nothing happens. Under such circumstances its ambitious young men are inclined to emigrate. The country is quaint and charming but of little significance in the world at large.

QUESTIONS. Describe the chief topographic features of Great Britain. What are the general climatic features? Discuss the national character and background of the English, Scots, and Welsh. Compare the type and extent of the transportation facilities in Great Britain with those of the continental countries of Europe previously discussed. Discuss the general setting of agriculture in Great Britain and compare present circumstances with those of the past. Name the major crops. Discuss the importance of the grazing industries. Why are the British fisheries unusually significant in the life of the country?

What is Britain's outstanding mineral resource? Name the major manufacturing industry. In what way is its importance related to the British climate? What are the two major types of products of this industry? What is the second-ranking industry of Britain? In what way are its major population centers related to the country's mineral resources? Discuss the position of Great Britain among the nations of the world, noting the circumstances responsible for that position. Explain why London is important as a seaport, a governmental, and an industrial city. What are the "three Londons"? Why is the region around Birmingham known as the "black country"? Glasgow is the world's leading center of what industry? Explain how Liverpool and Manchester complement each other as both seaports and industrial cities. In what respect is Edinburgh unique among the larger cities of Great Britain?

Name the political divisions of Ireland. Describe the island's topography. Contrast the characteristics and outlook of the people of the island's two political divisions and explain the reason for the ill feeling between them. Name Ireland's important crops. Why are the grazing industries so important? What are the chief products of those industries? What is the common fuel of Ireland? Where are the major manufacturing centers located? Contrast the present position of Ireland with its circumstances in the nineteenth century.

7. DENMARK

General Aspects. The Kingdom of Denmark consists of the peninsula of **Jutland** (which extends north from the center of the German coast) and the islands that lie immediately to the east of the peninsula (Fig. 20.9). Its total area is 16,000 square miles (a little

Fig. 20.9—Denmark, Norway, and Southern Sweden. The inset compares the area of the region with that of California, which is approximately equal.

particularly heavy glacial deposit that has been worked over by the sea and converted into sand dunes along the coast. This part of the country is agricultural wasteland that has been planted with forests to keep the dunes in place.

With its low elevation, and because it is surrounded by the sea except on the south, Denmark experiences rather typical marine west coast climatic conditions. But as the waters are the North Sea and the Baltic rather than the warmer waters of the North Atlantic Drift the annual temperature range is greater than is appropriate to a completely representative occurrence of this climate. Thus the winters are more rigorous, the summers milder than those, for example, of Brittany.

The People. The Danish population of over 4 million is a very homogeneous group descended from prehistoric peoples who inhabited the same region and evolved into the Danish branch of the northern, fair-haired Nordic stock. The homogeneity of the people is reflected in their single religious affiliation—the Lutheran Church. The Danes are a quiet, hard-working nation with a marked capacity for coöperative effort. They have profited by a long period of political and social stability. As is true of all the Nordic countries, the health and cultural levels are very high. Both birth and death rates are low, and so close together that there is a comfortably low rate of population growth. A high percentage of the population receives high-school and university training. Indeed, a particular problem in Denmark is to find suitable occupations for all the persons graduated from the schools of higher learning.

Agriculture and Products. Agriculture in Denmark is in many respects similar to that in the Low Countries: small holdings and intensive cultivation. In addition, however, there is a characteristic Scandinavian touch —governmental insistence on quality production, administered through the farm coöperative. Nowhere else do farm coöperatives have such great national significance.

About three-fourths of all the land is under cultivation, and, although the soils are not

more than twice the size of Massachusetts). The islands, spread out to within a few miles of Sweden on the east, dominate the entrance to the Baltic Sea. The passage between Jutland and Sweden is known as the **Kattegat,** and that on the north, between Jutland and Norway, is called the **Skagerrak.**

Denmark is a low country with little relief (Fig. 20.10). Its entire area is between zero and 500 feet altitude. Like Ireland and northern Germany its topography was fashioned by the extensive deposits left by the ice age glaciers, and, although the land is in general a plain, it is dotted with the small hills and depressions that form the surface of the glacial debris, the latter the sites of lakes and swamps. Western Jutland has a

especially fertile, yields are high because of the scientific farming methods. The most productive areas are eastern Jutland and the islands.

There is only slight exaggeration in the characterization of Denmark as one great dairy farm. With typical careful reasoning and logical action the Danes decided that high specialization in quality food products was the answer to their problem of small size. Denmark is, as a consequence, the **dairy**

sugar beets are grown for human food, turnips and other root crops for fodder.

As might be expected from the maritime location, Danish **fisheries** are important in the country's economy, although the Danish catch is well down the list among those of the European countries.

Industries. The country is so devoid of fuel resources that it depends to a large extent on electricity delivered by submarine cable from Sweden. **Food processing** is Den-

Fig. 20.10—Denmark. Farm scene showing typical low relief of the country. (Courtesy, Danish Information Service.)

country of the world, with a cattle population of 3 million almost equal to its human population. Along with its world-famous **butter** and **cheese** it produces **eggs** from its hen population of 25 million and high-quality **bacon** from the more than 4 million pigs. These specialty food products are exported in large quantities, with Britain the best customer. Denmark is Britain's "butter and egg man."

The crop production is directed toward support of the livestock industries. **Barley** is the chief cereal, followed in rank by oats, rye, and wheat. In terms of acreage **root crops** are second to barley. **Potatoes** and

mark's major industry. The processing of cheese, butter, and bacon is carried on in large plants. Other activities are on a smaller scale. The textile and chemical industries are in second place, with a value of output equal to that of food processing. In addition, beer is brewed from the country's barley, there is small-scale shipbuilding, and there is some manufacture of dairy equipment and precision instruments.

City. **Copenhagen** ("Merchant's Harbor"), the capital, commercial and industrial center, and only large city of the country, is on the eastern side of the large island of **Zealand,** across the narrow strait from Sweden. In few

CITY OF DENMARK

Name	Type	Population (1950)
Copenhagen	Governmental, seaport	975,000

countries of the world is a single city so dominant in the national life. A very pleasant city, Copenhagen has several distinctive characteristics. Its residential suburbs consist of one-family dwellings with surrounding lawns and gardens, as in the United States. This is a rarity in Europe. As its site is almost perfectly level the chief means of transportation is the bicycle (Fig. 20.11). Cyclists move in great waves as the traffic lights change at street intersections, in an odd parallel to the congested automobile traffic of American cities. Relics of the past stemming from its highly strategic site controlling the entrance to the Baltic Sea are the fortifications that dominate the city and its harbor.

Denmark as a Whole. Denmark is a shining example of what can be done by a small country with limited resources. The deliberate specialization has carried with it the risks that go along with a one-crop or one-industry economy, yet it has enabled Denmark to enjoy a standard of living impossible on any other basis. Moreover, the high repute enjoyed by the Danish dairy products assures the country of a steadier market than would be the case if those products were of average quality and had to meet general competition. There is no reason why Denmark should not maintain its solid position as the dairyman of Europe.

8. NORWAY

General Aspects. Norway occupies the western margin of the **Scandinavian peninsula** which dangles from the Arctic Ocean on the north to points opposite Denmark and Germany at its southern end (Fig. 20.9). Norway is, like Chile, a "strip country," 900 miles long, less than 100 miles wide throughout most of its length, widening to 200 miles in the south. Its area of 125,000 square miles

Fig. 20.11—Copenhagen, Denmark. Street scene with typical bicycle traffic. (Courtesy, Danish Information Service.)

is a little greater than that of New Mexico. Its northernmost point, **North Cape,** is at latitude 71° 12′, several hundred miles north of the Arctic Circle and the most northerly point on the European continent.

Topography. The Norwegian terrain is rugged and inhospitable. It consists almost entirely of a plateau much dissected into mountains on its abrupt western edge but with a gentler eastern slope. A large part of the country stands at elevations of over 2000 feet; the highest summits in the southwest reach 8500 feet. The streams of Norway in consequence are short, swift torrents, with many spectacular waterfalls.

Norway may thus be said to consist of two countries: the summit levels of the high plateau, sparsely inhabited and utilized only in the extraction of forest and mineral resources, and small, scattered lowland areas, on which the bulk of the population, the agriculture, and industry are situated.

The dominant feature of the landscape is the fiord. Norway is the type fiord country, as its entire western coastline is indented by these great valleys with steep rock sides and occupied by long, deep arms of the sea that reach scores of miles inland.

Low, rock islands extend as a fringe all along the bold, high, fiord coast. This is the *skerry* (island) guard that acts as a breakwater against the high storm waves of the North Sea and provides channels of protected water routes for much of the length of the country.

Climate. Norway's marine west coast climate is the most impressive product of the North Atlantic Drift. Under its influence the country enjoys a uniformly moderate climate throughout its unusual length and despite the high latitudes. In the southern quarter of Norway the average winter temperature is above freezing. The harbors of the entire country are ice free the year round. In the mountains of most of the country, however, altitude tells, and the heavy precipitation produces a thick snow cover. Several large glaciers are reminders of the epoch when the region was the center of the enormous glacier that spread over much of Europe.

Summer days are very pleasant and cool, so that the country ranks high as a European summer resort, especially for the British. Along the coast outdoor lunches may be enjoyed on sunny days as late as mid-September.

The People. The Norwegians are truly products of their environment. The inhospitable, infertile land and the sheltered fiord and skerry coast early pushed and pulled the inhabitants into maritime activity. The exploits of the Vikings, the ancestors of the modern Norwegians, in trade, exploration, and foreign conquest are famous in history. It was in the calm waters of the skerry channels and fiords that they early acquired their seafaring knowledge. Today Norway carries on the maritime tradition (Fig. 20.12) with a merchant fleet of world importance far out of proportion to the size and status of the country among the world's nations.

Modern Norway has also evolved a very

progressive, alert, and homogeneous society. The 3.3 million inhabitants enjoy a high health level, art and literature flourish, great interest in Norwegian history and archaeology is everywhere manifest, and the country in general is a notable contributor to the intellectual life of Europe.

Agriculture and Other Resource Activities. Agriculture in Norway is carried on under unusual circumstances. Almost three-quarters of the total area is unproductive and largely uninhabited. Less than 4 percent of the land is actually under cultivation; most of this consists of small tracts near sea level at the heads of the fiords, and of restricted patches on low shelves and shoulders of the moun-

Fig. 20.12—Ship Chandler's Store, Alesund, Norway. (O. D. von Engeln.)

tain areas (Fig. 20.13).

Offsetting these disadvantages are the advantages of climate and latitude. Norway is famous as the "Land of the Midnight Sun"— in that portion of the country above the Arctic Circle the sun never sets during the height of the summer and throughout the remainder of the country summer is a season of very long days and short nights. With so many hours of daylight crops mature rapidly.

The largest single crop of Norway is **hay**. This fodder crop is grown in every available nook and cranny of level ground, often on

Fig. 20.13—Norwegian Farm on Steep Side of Hallingdal Valley. (Courtesy, Norwegian Information Service.)

shoulders above slopes so steep that the harvested hay has to be let down from the field with ropes and pulleys. Because of the wet climate it is regularly cured by loose stacking around poles instead of being spread out on the ground as is the practice in drier climates. **Potatoes** follow hay in importance, after which come in order of rank **oats, barley, wheat,** and **rye.** Although dairying and other livestock industries are practiced they are not of the same importance as those of such other countries of the region as Denmark, Ireland, and the Netherlands.

Almost one-quarter of Norway is forest covered (mostly with conifers), and forest products are important in the country's economy. **Pulpwood** and **paper** are the major products from the forest resources, followed by **lumber.** All the forest products are significant exports.

In line with the maritime tradition previously noted, Norway's **fisheries** are of great importance. Although fishing ranks below agriculture in the country's economy, Norway is exceeded only by Japan and the United States in the size of its annual fish catch; and in the field of **whaling** (Fig. 20.14), which ranges over the world, Norway has no rival. This international position of the Norwegian fisheries and whaling industry is trib-

ute to the seafaring abilities of the Norwegian people.

Another "animal product" is furs, from mink and several varieties of fox. Fur farms are becoming an increasingly important source of the valuable pelts.

Norway's mineral resources are modest in size and variety. Iron ore, the only significant resource, is mined at various places, including a point on the extreme northeast Arctic coast.

Norway's only fuel resource is peat, important in so many of the European marine west coast countries. Its lack of coal, however, is counterbalanced by its enormous **hydropower** resources. Norway stands about fifth in the world in the production of hydroelectricity, an impressive position for a country of its size. Yet even this level of output represents the development of only one-fifth of the country's total hydropower potential.

The importance of this abundant and cheap power (Norway's electricity is among the world's lowest-cost energy supplies) in the development of the country is obvious. Five-sixths of the population enjoys electricity in its homes—a high proportion for any country. It may readily be imagined how much this has added to the cheerfulness of life in the remote fiord villages and farms, in a region where darkness prevails for twenty or more hours of the day during winter.

Fig. 20.14—Norwegian Whaling Ship, a Vast Floating Meat-Packing and Oil-Extraction Plant. (Courtesy, Norwegian Information Service.)

Manufacturing. Norway, like Denmark, is an example of the intelligent use of available resources, for Norway has put most of its electric power to work in specialized industries for which cheap, abundant electricity is the major requirement and cost factor. Norway is an important refiner of aluminum, magnesium, and nickel, all major **electrometallurgical** industries. Equally significant is the production of nitrogen fertilizers and other products of **electrochemical** industries. The **pulp and paper industry** is also a large consumer of electricity.

CITIES OF NORWAY

Name	Type	Population (1952)
Oslo	Governmental, seaport, industrial	441,000
Bergen	Seaport	113,000

Cities. **Oslo** (Fig. 20.15), the capital and chief city of Norway, is located in the southeastern corner of the country at the head of a

Fig. 20.15—Oslo, Norway. The large building in center is the town hall. The columned building in left middle background is the royal castle. (Courtesy, Norwegian Information Service.)

60-mile fiord. Oslo has a sort of Parisian charm, but with a slower pace to its life. The city contains many striking examples of modern architecture and as a result of extensive public housing developments is devoid of slums. It is the cultural center of Norwegian

Fig. 20.16—Picturesque Street With Wooden Houses in Old Part of Bergen, Norway. (O. D. von Engeln.)

life as well as the center of a manufacturing district using nearby sources of hydroelectricity.

Bergen is the only other Norwegian city over 100,000 population. It is the country's second port and major fishing center, nestled at the base of great fiord cliffs on the North Sea coast almost due west of Oslo. It is a city of wooden buildings and its center has suffered much and often from fires. The outskirts, however, still preserve the Old World charm of picturesque wooden dwellings and steep, narrow, irregular streets (Fig. 20.16). The American visitor is impressed with the care expended in cultivating goldenrod as a garden flower and for florist's bouquets.

Norway as a Whole. Despite the great hydropower resources Norway is on the whole a poor country whose standard of living does not compare too favorably with that of its neighbors. This follows logically from the fact that Norway is basically an agricultural country but with a climate and topography that handicap agricultural activity. Were it not for the existence of the great merchant marine, large fisheries, the rational emphasis on electricity-consuming industries, and a tourist trade of growing significance, Norway's standard of living would be low indeed.

On the other hand, the outlook for further progress and development is favorable. Norway is fortunate in that its greatest resource is inexhaustible, and with a further realization of the hydropower potential the country's wealth can be substantially increased. With cheap electricity more necessary than ever in the world because of the growing emphasis on electrometallurgical and electrochemical industrial processes, there need be no doubt that Norway's advantages on this score will yield the country increasing benefits.

9. Southern Sweden

General Aspects. Only the southern fifth of Sweden is within the marine west coast climatic region of Europe (Fig. 20.9). Southern Sweden is part of the great north European plain. Like Denmark and Northern Germany its topography has been determined by the deposits left behind by the ice age glaciers. It is a land of smiling farms, lakes, and clear streams alternating between placid, deep flow and rushing waterfalls. The lakes and streams are so numerous that it has been possible to engineer a water route across the whole width of the country by connecting a series of lakes and streams with a minimum of canal excavation.

The climate is more continental than Norway's, in the same manner that Germany is more under the continental influence than is France. On the other hand, the slight southerly latitudinal advantage and the fact that the southwest winds can get in across Denmark from the North Sea make the winters only slightly more severe.

Agriculture in marine west coast Sweden is very similar to that of Norway but is not so handicapped by lack of arable land. Hay, the hardier cereals, and root crops predominate. Dairying is carried on at about the same level of importance as in Norway.

CITIES OF SOUTHERN SWEDEN

Name	Type	Population (1954)
Göteborg	Seaport, industrial	368,000
Malmo	Seaport	202,000

Cities. **Göteborg** is the largest city of marine west coast Sweden and the country's chief port for overseas trade. It lies five miles up a small stream on the west coast, opposite the northern tip of Denmark. It owes its importance to its position as the only Swedish port whose Atlantic trade does not have to pass through Danish territorial waters, to its good rail connections with the rest of Sweden, and to its location as the western terminus of the trans-Sweden canal referred to above. Göteborg is a canal city, reflecting its early settlement by the Dutch. Its industries are shipbuilding, machinery, sawmills, cotton mills, and other light industries.

Malmo, another Swedish port, is at the southwest tip of the country only 17 miles across the strait from Copenhagen, Denmark. Its growth has been blighted by the proximity of that rival city on the strategic entrance to the Baltic. Malmo, like Göteborg, contained an early Dutch population and thus also has its canals.

QUESTIONS. Describe the general topography of Denmark. What are the major characteristics of the Danish people? Account for Danish national solidarity. On what products is Danish agriculture concentrated? How is it organized? How does Denmark obtain its energy? What danger is inherent in Denmark's specialization? What are the distinctive characteristics of Copenhagen?

Characterize the topography of Norway. What is the dominant topographic feature? How does climate counteract latitude in Norway? Describe how climate and topography have affected human settlement and activities in Norway. What are the advantages and disadvantages for agriculture in Norway? What are the major crops? Characterize Norwegian national traits. What nonmanufacturing activities are important in Norway? Name the chief natural resource of the country and discuss Norway's position among the countries of the world with respect to it. How has this resource been utilized in the specialization of Norwegian industry? Why is the future of Norway favorable despite the general paucity of resources? Compare the size of the chief Norwegian cities with those of the Low Countries and Denmark.

What part of Sweden is within the marine west coast climate? Compare the agriculture of this part of Sweden with that of Norway. Explain Göteborg's status as Sweden's chief port.

CHAPTER 21

The Marine West Coast Climate: Pacific Regions

Fig. 21.1—U.S.-Canadian Pacific Coast Region.

B. THE UNITED STATES–CANADIAN PACIFIC COAST

The marine west coast climate in North America occurs on the Pacific coast as a narrow strip (some 100 miles in average width) which extends from north of San Francisco Bay to the base of the Alaskan peninsula (Fig. 21.1). It includes the coastal districts of northern California, Oregon, Washington, of the Canadian province of British Columbia, and the Alaskan Panhandle.

Topography. Topographically the region presents the typical Pacific coast elements of two north-south mountain ranges with a central valley between. The Sierra Nevada range of California (see Chapter 16, p. 318) is replaced farther north through Oregon and Washington by the geologically unlike **Cascade Range,** a broad arch surmounted by a string of volcanic peaks, and, across the international boundary, by the **Coast Ranges,** sharp-crested mountains that rise almost directly at the coast along the shoreline of Canada and the Alaskan Panhandle. The summits of the Cascades and Coast Ranges are not quite so high as those of the southern Sierras. **Mount Rainier,** in Washington, is the highest peak in the Cascades, with an altitude of 14,400 feet. All the higher elevations are snow covered throughout the year, and small glaciers are numerous. In the Coast Ranges at the northern end of the region some of the largest and longest valley

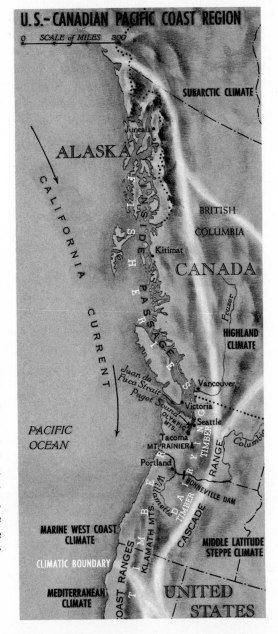

glaciers in the world descend 40 miles and more through mountain valleys to the sea. The conspicuously developed fiord coast affords magnificent scenery to voyagers who sail along it and is little changed from its primeval condition.

The Coast Ranges of California (see Chapter 16, p. 318) are likewise continuous northward through Oregon and Washington, culminating in the **Olympic Mountains** at the international boundary. North of these is a gap, the **Juan de Fuca Strait,** beyond which the Coast Ranges continue as a chain of islands parallel to the mainland. The southernmost of these islands, **Vancouver Island,** is the largest and most important.

The central valley of California is not continuous with the valley to the north. The **Klamath Mountains,** a dissected plateau, bridge the tract between the Coast Ranges and the Sierras in the vicinity of the California-Oregon border. This is a rugged and sparsely inhabited region. In the **Puget Sound** region the central valley is drowned and becomes an arm of the sea through Juan de Fuca Strait. The central valley continues north in Canadian and Alaskan territory as the ice-eroded and fiorded **Inside Passage,** a more or less sheltered water route between the island chain and the mainland.

There are only two major breaks that provide easy access from the coastland to the continental interior across these mountain ranges. The more important of these is the valley of the **Columbia River,** which forms the Oregon-Washington boundary. (A tributary of the Columbia, the **Willamette,** flows northward in the southern end of the central valley.) In Canada the valley of the **Fraser River** cuts across the Canadian Coast Ranges just north of the boundary.

Climate. Because of the high altitude of most of the region precipitation is even greater than is normal in marine west coast regions. The portion within the United States receives more rainfall than any other part of the country (up to 180 inches a year on the mountains). There is, however, a tendency toward dry summers, for the cool moist air from the ocean then encounters warmer land. Thus, paradoxically, droughts may occur in an exceptionally humid region.

Temperatures are typically marine west coast—the summer average is 60° F., the winter average 40° F. The moderating marine influence is heightened by the **California Current.** This is the prolongation of the warm Kurosiwo or Japanese Current, which is turned into the Gulf of Alaska by the Aleutian Island barrier and hugs the west coast of North America as it flows south from there. Along the Alaskan coast it is still relatively warm, but farther south it interposes a belt of cool water between the coast and the open sea. Accordingly, the coastal lands are warmed in the high latitudes and cooled farther south by reason of the westerlies blowing across the current before reaching the continental shore.

Natural Resources. 1. The **forests** of the marine west coast region of North America are the resource of first importance to the inhabitants of the area and are of very considerable significance to both the United States and Canada. The combination of topography and climate within the region is the ideal environment for certain species of conifers, which occur in dense forests covering thousands of square miles (Fig. 21.2). In size the trees exceed the giants of the equatorial rainforests and are among the largest trees on earth. The stands are often so thick that there is perpetual twilight beneath the canopy of foliage. The undergrowth consists of ferns and other moisture- and shade-loving plants. Mosses carpet the floor. The huge, vaulting trunks, clean of branches almost to the top, give the same cathedral-like atmosphere to the forests as in the rainforests of the equatorial regions. The drip of water is constantly heard. Most such forests occur in uplands and on the well-drained slopes of the mountains and foothills. On less rapidly drained lowlands it may be too moist even for the trees; there thick green grass covers the ground.

In a word, the world's finest coniferous forest mantles the slopes of the two mountain ranges of the region. It comprises some 200,000 square miles of the richest timber

Fig. 21.2—Rainforest of the Marine West Coast Climate in the Olympic Mountains, Washington. (Courtesy, U.S. National Park Service.)

Fig. 21.3—Sequoias in the Mariposa Grove, California. (Courtesy, U.S. National Park Service.)

resource on earth. Almost one-third of the **saw timber** remaining in the United States and a large proportion of that of Canada are in this tract.

The coniferous forests contain different varieties of pine, cedar, hemlock, and spruce, but the majority of the trees, especially those in Oregon and Washington, are *Douglas firs.* These trees average between 175 and 200 feet in height, with a diameter of three to six feet. Douglas firs of such size constitute 90 percent of many timber stands, growing perfectly straight and without branches ex-

cept at the top. They provide timber of the highest quality available, in logs so large they are handled with difficulty even when modern logging equipment is employed.

In northern California the western slopes of the Coast Range are the particular locale of the *redwood,* a tree even larger than the Douglas fir. The redwood seems to be restricted to the area of summer fogs. It is not the tallest tree on earth (the eucalyptus of Australia grows even higher—see Chapter 13, p. 235), but some specimens grow more than 300 feet high and have a diameter of 10 feet or more at the base. The redwood grows in stands as thick and uniform as those of the Douglas fir; in terms of timber yield per acre these stands constitute the richest to be found anywhere.

(Somewhat farther to the south in certain sheltered valleys on the western side of the Sierras are isolated groves of the greatest giants of them all, the *sequoias* (Fig. 21.3). The largest of these trees are considered to be the oldest living things on earth.)

Unhappily the exploitation of much of these forests has been ruthless and short-sighted. The few remaining sequoias and some small stands of redwood are now under government protection, as are areas of Douglas fir to the north. Those who first worked the privately owned lands made little or no provision for reforestation. This conservation practice has now, however, been adopted by the larger lumber companies. The natural second growth unfortunately consists of cedars and other varieties of far less value or use. Forest fires that occur during the drought periods continue to take a heavy toll of the remaining stands of virgin timber.

Lumbering nevertheless remains the dominant industry of the Northwest coastal lands. Lumber is a major item of commerce; sawmills and lumber mills are the important establishments; wood is the main household fuel of the region.

2. The **fisheries** of the region rival the lumber industry in value and spectacular aspects. Many of the better-known marine food fish, such as tuna and halibut, are caught in the usual manner here, but the take of **salmon** is the outstanding feature of the industry (Fig. 21.4). It is so large as to make salmon the third most important food fish in the world.

The salmon fisheries have suffered from an exploitation comparable to that which depleted the forests. Originally every river from California to central Alaska had its salmon "run," when the big fish would return from the open sea and head upstream to spawn and die. The California streams have been completely denuded of fish; other streams showed a continual decline in yield

until 1920, when the first governmental regulations came into effect. In recent years the catch has been maintained or has increased, but the industry is subject to a new menace. Great dams erected for power and irrigation purposes, especially on the Columbia and its tributaries, bar the fish from their spawning grounds. "Fish ladders," which permit the salmon to by-pass the dams, have proved inadequate for maintenance of the runs, and the coasts of British Columbia and Alaska to the north have taken the lead from the Columbia River system in the production of canned salmon. In 1951, however, it was proved that the fish hatched from salmon eggs transported to suitable spawning beds of other streams would return to their birthplace when mature, thus providing for potential salmon runs at many new sites.

3. The **hydropower** resources of the region are its third major natural resource. These, too, are vast. The region shares with that to the east one of the greatest hydropower potentials in the world. **Bonneville Dam,** across the gorge of the Columbia where it passes through the Cascades, is the largest dam of its kind in the world; other large dams have been built still farther to the east. Much power, however, remains undeveloped.

Agricultural Products. Because of the climate and the small area of level land agri-

Fig. 21.4—Salmon Drying, Indian Catch, Near Valdez, Alaska. (Courtesy, Stanley C. Mosser, Jr.)

culture is relatively unimportant. The only noteworthy agricultural district is the Puget Sound–Willamette Valley lowland, together with the lower valley and delta of the Fraser River. The Willamette Valley had no primeval forest cover; it was the promised land at the end of the Oregon Trail. It now comprises over one-half the total farm land of Oregon. North of the Columbia stumps of the great trees in the lumbered areas had to be destroyed before the land could be used. As the soil and drainage are poor much of this land is still unsettled.

Almost every kind of temperate crop is grown in the valley belt. In the vicinity of the large cities it is more profitable to concentrate on mixed farming to supply local markets with a variety of foods than to raise bulk crops for long-distance shipping. A substantial **dairy** industry is one aspect of such production for local markets.

It is nevertheless possible to specify certain products for which the district is known beyond its borders. **Berries** and **fruits** of the kinds that thrive in the cloudy, humid climate, such as cherries, peaches, and pears, are canned and preserved for eastern markets on a considerable scale. In addition nuts, cranberries, potatoes, and hops are important.

Manufacturing. The preparation and processing of locally produced raw materials—the canning, paper, lumber, furniture, and flour-milling (of wheat from east of the Cascades) industries—are the leading activities. The salmon-canning industry is carried on primarily in isolated plants along the Canadian-Alaskan coast, but there is also a notable concentration on the Columbia. Most of the Columbia catch is canned in Oregon.

World War II brought about a spectacular growth in the **shipbuilding** and **aircraft** industries, both of which have remained important. Another new industry, **aluminum** refining, has been established since World War II, based on the ample power available from the large hydroelectric stations in the upper reaches of the streams. The **Kitimat** aluminum and power project of British Columbia is the greatest enterprise of its type. Still newer latecomers are other electrometallurgical and electrochemical industries.

Generally speaking, the region has been developed thus far on the basis of its extractive industries, so that it has something of the frontier quality in the United States portion and around the Canadian border. It is definitely a frontier region along the British Columbia coast and in Alaska. As the resources are unique, varied, and vast, the position strategic both commercially and politically, the hydropower resources only partially developed, and the climate favorable, more than one writer has suggested that it may eventually become one of the dominant regions of the continent.

The major disadvantage is isolation. In the United States one or two commercial routes connect with the eastern part of the country, but north of the Fraser River the isolation of the coast from the interior is nearly complete. However, Puget Sound and the Inside Passage provide excellent north-south transportation arteries.

Cities. **Vancouver** (Fig. 21.5), the largest Canadian city of the region, is the third-ranking city of all Canada. It is also the only important west coast port of Canada and, as the terminus of both Canadian transcontinental rail lines, plays an important commercial role for the western part of the country. The city is located on the south shore of an inlet on the Fraser River delta and has an excellent harbor. It is a large wheat export center, shipping the product of the interior plains behind the mountains both west across the Pacific and east to Europe via the Panama Canal. Vancouver almost doubled in size as a result of the stimulus provided by World War II.

Seattle, the largest city in the region, is on the eastern shore of Puget Sound some 140 miles south of the Canadian border and about the same distance from the open sea. The city is set on a group of hills several hundred feet high, between the Sound and Lake Washington on the east. It has magnificent harbor facilities, including a fresh-water port on the lake, developed by means

Fig. 21.5—Vancouver, British Columbia. (Courtesy, George Hunter, Ottawa.)

CITIES OF THE UNITED STATES–CANADIAN PACIFIC COAST

Name	State, Province, or Territory	Type	Population
Vancouver	British Columbia	Seaport, industrial	345,000 (1951)
Seattle	Washington	Seaport, industrial	468,000 (1950)
Portland	Oregon	Seaport, industrial	374,000 (1950)
Tacoma	Washington	Seaport, industrial	144,000 (1950)
Victoria	British Columbia	Governmental, seaport	51,000 (1951)
Juneau	Alaska	Governmental	6,000 (1950)

of a canal from the Sound. Seattle is a major commercial center by reason of its position as a transcontinental rail terminus with north-south rail connections, and the major west coast port closest to the Orient. The city is thus the leading port for trade with both Japan and Alaska. It is also the commercial, industrial, and financial capital of the Northwest. It is one of the leading centers of United States aircraft production and has a variety of industries attracted by its low-cost power and superb commercial location.

Portland is the largest city of Oregon and the commercial capital of the Columbia River basin. It is astride the Willamette River 14 miles from its confluence with the Columbia and 108 miles from the latter's mouth. Extensive dredging at the mouth of the Columbia has made Portland accessible to ocean shipping. Like Vancouver, Portland has a large export trade in wheat as well as lumber.

Tacoma, the second port of Puget Sound, is located 25 miles southwest of Seattle on the eastern shore of the Sound. It functions as a commercial center for the products of the surrounding districts. It is also a metal-smelting center and is the site of lumber industries, shipyards, and electrochemical plants.

Victoria is the capital of British Columbia and is located on the south tip of Vancouver Island about 80 miles south of the city of Vancouver. It has a large but not too well-protected harbor and, lacking a rail connection with the mainland, can never hope to compete with Vancouver in commercial importance. Its trade is restricted to the products of the region, such as lumber, fish, and coal from deposits on the island. Vancouver has almost the complexion of an American city, but Victoria, probably because of its relative isolation and original status of crown colony, has been called "the most British city in Canada."

Juneau is situated 1000 miles north of Seattle near the northern end of the Inside Passage. The city is built between the foot of a 3000-foot mountain and the water and is only a few blocks wide. It deserves mention only as the capital of the territory of Alaska, although it is the only modern city of the Panhandle. Government services account for virtually all activity in Juneau.

C. SOUTHERN CHILE

The marine west coast climatic region of South America extends for more than 1000 miles along the west coast of the continent at its southern end (Fig. 21.6). This strip is some 100 miles wide in the north, nearly 200 miles wide in the southeast. With the exception of a small area of Argentine territory in the extreme southeast it is all part of Chile.

Topography. The topography remarkably resembles that of the North American region. There are the same three major elements: two parallel mountain chains with a valley between. The coastal "mountains" here are, however, rather low (see Chapter 16, p. 312), whereas the Andes, on the east, are considerably higher than the Sierras and Cascades. The coastal highlands terminate in the south at a strait, beyond which they are present as a chain of islands, the most northerly of which, **Chiloe,** is the most important. The central valley corresponds to the Willamette Valley–Puget Sound lowland, and at Chiloe Island disappears under the sea to form the equivalent of the Inside Passage of the North American coast. The southern mountain-island topography corresponds to the coast of British Columbia and the Alaskan Panhandle. Glaciers and rock-

Fig. 21.6—Southern Chile. The inset compares the area of the region with that of California, which is approximately equal.

walled fiords are the characteristic elements of the landscape.

In the extreme south, where the continent takes an easterly trend, the resemblance ends. The mountains are lower (the highest peak is only 7000 feet) and the island chain terminates in the large island of **Tierra del Fuego,** separated from the mainland by the **Strait of Magellan.** The eastern half of the island is Argentine territory. **Cape Horn,** famous as the southern tip of the South American continent, is a small island south of Tierra del Fuego.

Climate. This South American region is the harsh expression of the marine west coast climate. In the central portion of the region the Andes attain their greatest altitudes and the westerlies are excessively strong (see Chapter 6, p. 95), a combination of extremes that gives rise to one of the few regions on earth practically uninhabitable because of excessive rainfall. Even at sea level precipitation exceeds 100 inches yearly. The measure of the much higher volume in the mountains is not known because so much of the country is unexplored. For 900 miles north and south the land is a misty, sodden morass; the forests drip moisture continually. Fogs are as thick and as frequent as in the North American region. Temperatures are somewhat lower, so that glaciers come down to the sea at a latitude corresponding to that of the Columbia River. In the extreme south the land and temperatures are both lower and the precipitation is less.

Forests. The typical marine west coast forest cover is well developed in the Chilean region (Fig. 21.7). Evergreens predominate —on the lowlands broad leaf trees, on the higher slopes conifers. As in North America the trees are large and the stands close. Unfortunately, however, the trees are less useful than the North American species. Only some 3 million of the 30 million acres of forest in Chile can support lumbering. Exceptions are a variety of pine that is much like the valuable Parana pine (see Chapter 17, p.

Fig. 21.7—Forests of Marine West Coast Region, Southern Chile. (Courtesy, Panagra.)

345), and a tree that resembles the California redwood. But the most abundant tree is the *coihué,* a variety of beech useless for either lumber or fuel.

Despite the rugged topography and poor yield there is some lumbering in the extreme northern and southern portions of the region —at the southern end of the central valley in the region of the Strait of Magellan.

The People. The inhabitants of the northern portion of the region have been described above (see Chapter 16, p. 316). In the southern portion the native inhabitants are the *Fuegian Indians,* a primitive hunting and fishing people who eke out a miserable, near-starvation existence in a raw climate and an environment deficient in food resources.

Agriculture. The agriculture of the northern part of the region is the counterpart of that of the Willamette–Puget Sound Valley. Where the stumps have been removed and the soil is fertile, wheat, oats, peas, and fruits are the important products. Dairying is also a significant activity; potatoes are grown on the mainland and especially on Chiloe Island. Cattle raising is a leading occupation, based on the lush grass in the pastures.

The southern portion of the region is almost ideal **sheep** country. The pasture is good and the uniform, moderate temperatures favor the development of heavy fleece. Tierra del Fuego and the lands surrounding the Strait of Magellan are thus the site of an important sheep-raising industry. Curiously, the industry is conducted not by the Indians, the Chileans, or the Argentines but by Europeans. The owners of the sheep *estancias* are British; the herders are recruited from western Europe sheep country.

CITY OF SOUTHERN CHILE

Name	Type	Population (1952)
Punta Arenas	Seaport	34,000

City. **Punta Arenas** is worthy of note as the most southern city of the world. It is about midway along the Strait of Magellan, a far outpost in a desolate, dreary landscape —the nearest city of equal size is almost 500 miles away. It is modern in aspect, however, despite its isolation. Punta Arenas serves as a way station for traffic through the Strait and handles the products of the local sheep-raising industry. As it is in the rain shadow of the Andes it has a steppe, rather than a marine west coast, climate.

QUESTIONS. What states, provinces, and territories of the United States and Canada are wholly or partly within the marine west coast climatic region of North America? Describe the major topographic features of the region. What phenomenon of the Pacific Ocean influences its climate? Describe the forests of the region. Name the three kinds of trees in the forests that are especially noteworthy. What is the second great natural resource of the region? What aspect of current development is imperiling this resource? What is the third great natural resource of the region? Name the leading agricultural activity of the region. What characteristic do the major industries of the region have in common? Compare the location and commercial significance of Seattle and Tacoma, Vancouver and Victoria.

In what ways are the marine west coast regions of North and South America similar in topography? Explain why the climate of the South American region is "the harsh expression of the marine west coast climate." Compare the character and usefulness of the forest resources of this region with that of the North American region. What is the major agricultural activity of the region?

D. THE SOUTHEAST COAST OF AUSTRALIA

General Aspects. At first thought it would seem a contradiction in terms for a west coast climatic region to be situated on the east coast of a continent. The explanation is that only the projecting southeastern tip of Australia extends far enough south to reach into the latitudes of the marine west coast climate. Most of the state of Victoria, a small portion of New South Wales, and the island of **Tasmania**, some 150 miles south of Victoria, are so situated (Fig. 21.8).

A resemblance of the topographical pattern to that of the North American region, though not so complete as that in South America, is nevertheless discernible. The major mountain range parallel to the coast (the southern coast in this instance) is the westerly extension of the Eastern Highlands. The high peaks of the **Australian Alps** in the Victoria–New South Wales border district form the eastern portion of the range; the western portion is a plateau of lower elevation (1000 to 3000 feet) known as the **Dividing Range** (Fig. 21.9). This range separates Victoria into northern and southern parts. The northern portion was previously discussed as part of the Murray Basin (see Chapter 13, p. 235). South of the Dividing Range the **Great Valley** extends parallel to the mountains, corresponding roughly to the Willamette–Puget Sound Valley of North America. South of the valley are two small, isolated plateaus, the equivalent of the Coast Ranges but on a much smaller scale. They are separated in the center by a great indentation of the coast—**Port Phillip Bay**—which reaches north almost to the mountains.

Fig. 21.8—Southeast Coast of Australia. The inset compares the area of the mainland region and of Tasmania with Idaho and West Virginia, which have approximately equivalent respective areas.

SOUTHEAST COAST OF AUSTRALIA

Fig. 21.9—View in the Great Dividing Range in Southeastern Australia. (Courtesy, Australian News and Information Bureau.)

Tasmania is a mountainous island slightly larger than West Virginia (26,000 square miles) with a maximum elevation of 5000 feet and considerable relief. It is structurally a southern extension of the Eastern Highlands on the mainland.

Because the latitudes in which it is situated are lower than those of the regions on other continents the Australian marine west coast climate is warmer than the normal development. The temperature ranges between a winter average of 50° F. and a summer average of 70° F. Rainfall is distributed rather evenly throughout the year.

Agricultural Products. The outstanding activity in marine west coast Australia, and the dominant single activity in the country as a whole, is the raising of **sheep.** About three-quarters of Australia's sheep population of 113 million is grazed within the region, along a great arc following the mainland highlands, and in Tasmania. The products of the industry, especially **wool,** are of the greatest importance in the economy of the country. Wool is the largest single export item by value, at times amounting to almost one-half the total value of Australian exports. Australia is, moreover, the world's first-ranking producer of wool, accounting for more than one-quarter of the total annual output. In terms of the higher-quality merino wool in which Australia specializes it accounts for over one-half of world production. On this score alone, the marine west coast region of Australia, although one of the smaller climatic regions of the country, is the most important of all in its contribution to the nation's income.

The coastal portions of the region (including the north shore of Tasmania) are also the site of a considerable segment of the Australian **dairy** industry, contributing **milk, butter,** and **cheese** to the country's exports as well as to the markets of the populous east and southeast coast.

Apples constitute the principal crop of the region. Over half the total Australian output comes from Tasmania alone, and on the mainland the chief center is around Port Phillip Bay. Apples are also exported in quantity.

The marine west coast region contains a good portion of the Australian **timber** resources, the best of which are in Tasmania and on the southeast flanks of the Eastern Highlands.

Mineral Products. The region ranks high in Australian mineral production. The most important resource is **lignite,** produced from enormous beds up to 200 feet thick at **Yallourn,** east of Port Phillip Bay. A small amount of bituminous coal is also obtained from the same general region. Other mineral products include copper from Tasmania, lead, zinc, tungsten, and tin from Tasmania and southeastern New South Wales, and gold from all three states of the region. The original gold strike of the continent was made northwest of Port Phillip Bay, but the output of the region has long since been eclipsed by that of the Western Australia gold fields (see Chapter 13, p. 237).

CITIES OF MARINE WEST COAST
AUSTRALIA

Name	State	Type	Population
Melbourne	Victoria	Seaport, governmental	1,420,000 (1953)
Hobart	Tasmania	Seaport, governmental	95,000 (1954)

Fig. 21.10—Melbourne, Australia. River Yarra in foreground. (Courtesy, Australian News and Information Bureau.)

Cities. **Melbourne** (Fig. 21.10) is the capital of Victoria, the second largest city of Australia, and was for the first quarter of this century the capital of the nation. It is on a small plain at the head of Port Phillip Bay, which provides it with a large, excellent harbor. The city is the greatest wool-trading center of the world and handles the bulk of Australia's wool exports. It also deals in the products of its large hinterland, which includes part of the Murray Basin to the northwest and a good part of New South Wales. Although Melbourne has varied industries it is not industrialized to the same extent as are the other large ports of southern and southeastern Australia.

Hobart, the capital of Tasmania, is situated in a scenic setting on a long, narrow bay at the base of a 4000-foot mountain. The bay constitutes a good harbor, and the city is not only the chief port of the island but also the site of considerable industry, such as metal works and food-processing plants.

Australia as a Whole. The descriptions of the various climatic regions of Australia are here concluded. From the accounts as a whole it will be apparent that Australia is an "empty continent." An area of just under 3 million square miles—almost exactly equal to that of the continental United States—contains fewer than 9 million people, compared with the United States population of 165 million. Australia is also a dry continent. Not only does the major portion of its area consist of steppe and desert climatic regions, but great undependability of rainfall is characteristic of its Mediterranean and humid subtropical regions as well.

The fact that economic activity in Australia is concentrated in the borders of the continent and, indeed, confined to certain portions of those outer belts is responsible for many unique features of Australian geography. Southwest and southeast Australia are separated from each other by a long stretch of uninhabited country; similarly, the small centers of activity on the northern coast are even more isolated from the southern and eastern coasts by the central desert. Only the east coast is a continuously populated area (except in the extreme north).

Moreover, the development of the country entirely within the age of railroads has resulted in the concentration of almost one-half the total population in a few large cities. The first established ports became the focal centers of the local railroad systems and the manufacturing and political centers as well.

Australia has one of the most homogeneous populations in the world; only 2 percent of the inhabitants are not of British origin. Because of this the British tradition is strong, and the ties with the mother country are close and firm.

On the other hand, the isolated position of Australia, the fact that it has been a pioneer country continually from the time the first British settlers landed in 1788 until the present, and the environment with its unique animal and plant life have jointly fostered the development of some distinctly un-British customs and national traits. The language is full of odd-sounding names and idioms. The people are hearty extroverts, with a strongly democratic spirit and outlook like that engendered by the frontier tradition in the United States. Sports are highly popular, and everything from horse racing to cricket is engaged in with tremendous enthusiasm. Australians are thus very much like Americans and as a nation they feel a natural affinity for the United States.

For a long time Australians believed that the parallel between the two countries extended to their resources, and that the destiny of Australia was to grow in wealth like the United States as the resources of the continent were developed. This belief has been replaced by the more sober realization that much of Australia remains undeveloped not because it takes time to accomplish the utilization of great areas but simply because of a relative dearth of natural riches.

Although much can still be done in the development of resources, such as the expansion of irrigation projects and the further discovery and exploitation of mineral deposits (especially uranium and petroleum), it would seem that Australia is economically maturing. The emphasis is now on industrialization, and on diversification of trade in terms both of its constituent items and of the countries with which it is carried on. The industrialization has progressed rapidly, but there can be no overlooking the fact that Australia is fundamentally an agricultural, raw-material-producing country, and in the absence of abundant, diversified resources and an adequate supply of labor industrialization can proceed only so far. The greatest necessity for further development is a larger population, to provide more efficient industrial production and a larger home market. Australian insistence that immigration be restricted to readily assimilable racial and national stocks in order to insure the continued homogeneity of the population prevents rapid expansion of numbers but serves to preserve freedom from the problems unrestricted immigration would undoubtedly raise.

E. NEW ZEALAND

The Dominion of New Zealand is a part of the marine west coast climatic region of Australia and Tasmania but is separated from those lands by 1200 miles of open ocean. New Zealand consists of two large islands, one minor one, and several small island groups a few hundred miles away. The two large islands, of roughly equal size, known by the unimaginative names of **North Island** and **South Island,** form an arc over 1000 miles long from north to south, separated by **Cook Strait,** a gap 20 miles wide (Fig. 21.11). The area of the Dominion as a whole is slightly over 100,000 square miles, about equal to that of Colorado.

Topography. The dominant topographic feature of the islands is a central mountain range. On South Island the range is west of the center of the island. The South Island mountains are called the **Southern Alps;** their highest peaks, **Mount Cook** and **Mount Tasman** are, respectively, over 12,000 and 11,000 feet in elevation. Several volcanic peaks also occur near the center of the island. Lakes are numerous, and the mountains support large glaciers. The southwest flank of the mountains is deeply fiorded. Together these features create impressive scenic panoramas.

On North Island the mountains are near the east coast, and the peaks reach 9175 feet in elevation. West of the mountain range in the central portion of the island is a volcanic area with higher peaks, hot springs, and gey-

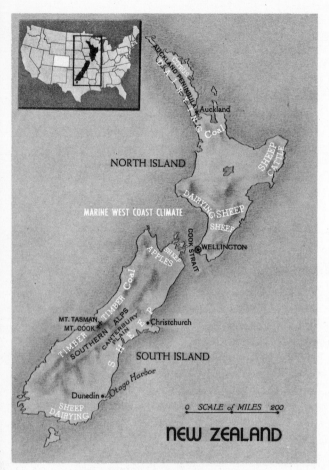

Fig. 21.11—New Zealand. The inset compares the area of New Zealand with that of Colorado, which is approximately equal.

sers. Earthquakes are rather frequent in this district.

Plains comprise only small, isolated portions of both islands. The most important is the **Canterbury Plain,** an area roughly 40 miles wide and 175 miles long on the east central coast of South Island. On the west coast fertile valleys run back into the mountains. On North Island the plains areas are more extensive, comprising most of the southern coast and all of the northwestern, or **Auckland Peninsula.**

Climate. Of all the marine west coast regions, New Zealand has the most equable and agreeable development of the climate. In the central portion of the 1000-mile arc the average temperature does not go much below 50° F. in the winter or above 60° F. in

the summer. The southern extremity, because of its higher latitude, has an average below 40° F. for its coldest month; the temperatures of the northern portion of the Auckland Peninsula, on the other hand, are almost subtropical.

Precipitation is favorably moderated by the mountains. These rise athwart the westerlies and condense over 70 inches of rain annually on their windward slopes. On the eastern side precipitation falls below 50 inches yearly on North Island, 30 inches on South Island. The islands are so narrow that on the one hand a full rain-shadow effect is not developed, and on the other they escape the excessive rainfall that characterizes the similar climatic regimes of the Western Hemisphere regions.

Forests. The combination of high mountains, ample rainfall, and moderate temperatures, here as elsewhere in the marine west coast regions, results in luxuriant forest growth (Fig. 21.12). Evergreens predominate, chiefly pines at the higher altitudes, with broad-leafed beeches occupying the lower slopes. "Tree ferns" provide an unusual type of undergrowth. Growing up to 50 feet in height, they give the forests an exotic and strangely beautiful appearance. One tree, the *kauri* pine, reaches 300 feet in height and ranks with the Douglas fir, redwood, and eucalyptus as a giant among the trees of earth. It is found only on the Auckland Peninsula. Gum from this tree is used as a varnish base.

The exploitation of these extensive timber resources makes **lumbering** an important industry in New Zealand. Unfortunately, the New Zealanders have been as short-sighted and wasteful as the people of the United States in utilizing this valuable natural wealth. Logging was formerly wastefully practiced in connection with the clearing of land for agricultural use. Such clearing was extended beyond useful limits, and as a consequence New Zealand has only one-quarter of its original timber resources left after only three generations of occupation, plus a good deal of deforested land that cannot be profitably cultivated. About one-fifth of the total area of the country is still forested. Most of the remaining timber is in the Southern Alps.

Once aware of the situation the New Zealand government, with more acumen than has been shown in the United States, initiated an intensive reforestation program second only to that of Japan (see Chapter 18, p. 374). All timber waste has now been stopped. It will be some time, however, before a substantial yield of timber can be obtained from the second growth. In the meantime New Zealand is a lumber importer.

The People. The people of New Zealand are even more homogeneous than those of Australia. Ninety-nine percent are of British origin. The country is also young (it was not settled until 1840 and has been self-governing only since 1852); it is thinly populated (total population is only 2.2 million); and it is a frontier region. The great difference between New Zealanders and Australians stems from the different size of the countries

Fig. 21.12—Beech Forest at Milford in the Southern Alps, South Island, New Zealand. (Courtesy, New Zealand Embassy.)

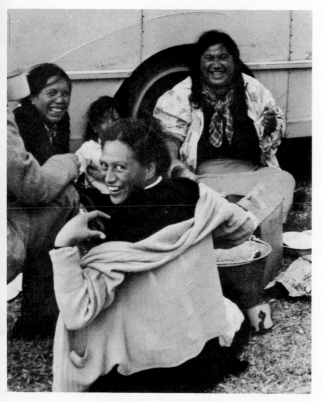

Fig. 21.13—Maori Women, New Zealand. (Courtesy, New Zealand Embassy.)

and the correspondingly different population densities. New Zealand's compact islands contrast strongly with Australia's wide open spaces.

New Zealand has become known for its advanced social legislation. It was a leader in adopting woman suffrage, old-age pensions, public housing, and similar social measures. Social security is so all pervasive that the government dispenses not only Old Age and Unemployment Benefits, as in the United States, but also Family Benefits, Invalid's Benefits, Miner's Benefits, Orphan's Benefits, and Widow's Benefits!

The health level of New Zealand is the highest in the world, and the standard of living also ranks high. The latter probably results from the comparatively low population density and the excellent yield of agricultural products, circumstances which provide for abundant food and high per capita wealth. Thus New Zealand stands well to the fore in such measures of material well-

being as the number of people per motor vehicle and telephone.

The native population, the *Maoris* (Fig. 21.13), deserve special mention. The Maoris, racially similar to the Hawaiians, were the most advanced people of the southern Pacific and fought the encroaching colonists bitterly until 1871, when they realized the futility of further struggle. The whites, on their side, recognized that fair treatment of the Maoris would prove mutually advantageous. An enlightened native policy has given them representation in the government and resulted in a substantial increase in their numbers in recent decades. New Zealand is one of the few countries in the world in which whites and the native people whom they conquered live together with mutual trust and esteem.

Agriculture and Products. Agriculturally, New Zealand is very similar to the parent country, Great Britain. The moderate, humid climate favors grass growth and permits year-round pasturage (Fig. 21.14). Low population density makes possible large ranch holdings. These circumstances have made the raising of **sheep** the leading industry of New Zealand. The climate and topography are so good for sheep that there are 36 million of them, an extraordinary number for so small a country. The chief sheep regions are on the eastern sides of the islands, in the districts where the rainfall is 50 inches or less a year.

The industry began with the emphasis on **wool** and **tallow**. These are both imperishable and valuable enough to endure and repay the long voyage to the European market. When refrigerated ships became available **mutton** could also be profitably exported. (New Zealand is the lowest-cost mutton producer in the world.) The breed of sheep now raised is a type that provides a high yield of all three items.

The **dairy** industry, second in importance, is concentrated in those areas that are too wet for sheep and below 1000 feet in elevation, notably the Auckland Peninsula and the plain to the south of it. The 5 million dairy cattle in New Zealand are also an impressive number considering the limited area.

The dominance of the pastoral industries is measured in many ways. Almost half the total area of the country is used for pasture. With almost three-quarters of the output of the livestock industries destined for sale abroad, wool and butter constitute more than half the total value of all exports and, together with cheese, ham, mutton, casein, and tallow, account for more than four-fifths of the value of the country's export trade. The importance of New Zealand in the world markets for these commodities is indicated by its status among the first three exporters of mutton, cheese, butter, and wool. The great bulk of these exports is to Great Britain.

New Zealand has accomplished this position through highly mechanized and scientific agriculture. Imported grasses have contributed to the building up of rich pastures; almost all the dairy farms have milking machines and cream separators; sheep shearing and meat packing are done efficiently on a large scale.

Under such circumstances field crops are, naturally, of secondary importance. **Wheat,** the ranking crop in both acreage and production, is grown in the warmer areas and on the richer lands, especially on the Canterbury Plain. **Oats** and **barley** are grown in the colder areas and on the poorer soils. **Apples** are the chief crop of the northern end of South Island. The Auckland Peninsula has a warm enough climate for citrus fruits. Most of these products, as well as those of the truck farms of the country, are chiefly for local consumption.

Other Aspects of the Economy. The only important mineral resource of New Zealand is **coal.** Small coal beds of various thicknesses and quality occur at many places on the islands, the most important being the good-quality bituminous on the west coast of South Island. Output is sufficient to satisfy household needs and a portion of those of industry. New Zealand may be considered deficient in mineral resources in general.

Hydropower resources are large for such a small area, a consequence of the heavy rainfall and mountainous topography. All

Fig. 21.14—Sheep on Year-Round Pasturage at Hawke's Bay, New Zealand. (Courtesy, New Zealand Embassy.)

hydropower facilities are government owned and developed, and the distribution of power is handled by government at the local level. With such good resources power is cheap, and electrification has been extended throughout the rural districts.

Despite the high relief of the islands inland transportation is adequately provided for. All the important centers on each island are linked by state-owned railroads. The narrowness of the islands necessitates only short spurs to get the products of the farms, ranches, and mines down to the main lines and to market; however, the railroads are narrow gauge, with light equipment, and the service is expensive. Coastal shipping between and around the islands provides an adequate supplement to the rail system.

As would be expected, the chief field of manufacturing enterprise is **food processing** —packing and freezing plants, cheese and butter factories, and so on. In addition, New Zealand's isolation from the major industrial centers of the world was from the beginning

a strong stimulus to the establishment and maintenance of a variety of manufactures to supply the many products utilized by modern civilization. This was given further impetus by the lack of import sources during World War II.

The result is a remarkable diversity of manufacturing, considering the paucity of domestic resources and the smallness of the domestic market. Many of these industries can, of course, exist only with government help or subsidy of some kind. New Zealand thus produces (and even exports on occasion) such items as barbed wire, engines, and radios. Local metal works, sawmills, and textile plants (especially for woolen goods), on the other hand, have a sounder basis and are actually more important in the economy.

Cities. Because it is such a young country New Zealand has been able to plan and build its cities with modern understanding of their functions and the warranted expectations of growth and expansion. The scenic beauty of the country is so general and

Fig. 21.15—Auckland, New Zealand. The air view shows the superb harbor. (Courtesy, New Zealand Embassy.)

CITIES OF NEW ZEALAND

Name	Type	Population (1954)
Auckland	Seaport	362,000
Christchurch	Commercial	186,000
Wellington	Seaport, governmental	140,000
Dunedin	Seaport, industrial	99,000

widespread that all its cities are in pleasing surroundings. Without exception they have wide thoroughfares, many parks, and marked cleanliness.

Auckland (Fig. 21.15), the largest city and leading port of New Zealand, is on North Island at the base of the Auckland Peninsula at a place where the island is only six miles wide. The harbor on the east side is superb, that on the west is unfortunately shallow, so that large ships from the south must come around the island to dock at the city. Auckland is the major center of New Zealand's foreign trade. It was the original capital of the country, serving in that stead from 1840 to 1865. Its chief industries are dairies and sawmills.

Christchurch is the largest city of South Island, five miles inland from the east coast roughly midway along the island's length. It is the commercial center of the Canterbury Plain. Although the city contains New Zealand's finest cathedral, its unusual name has no connection with this fact but was chosen by the founding settlers of the district, a semireligious group known as the "Canterbury Pilgrims." Christchurch's industries are chiefly meat freezing and the manufacture of woolen goods.

Wellington is New Zealand's second port and has been the capital of the country since 1865. It was the original white settlement on the islands. It is at the extreme southern tip of North Island and has a spacious harbor. With its central location, Wellington is the focal point of the national maritime commerce and is also a rival of Auckland in international trade.

Dunedin, New Zealand's fourth largest city, is intermediate in size between the three largest cities and the other cities and towns of the country. It is on the east coast of South Island, not far from its southern end, at the head of a narrow, 15-mile-long bay known as **Otago Harbor.** Dunedin serves as the chief coastal port for the southern end of South Island and is also a manufacturing center for textiles and clothing as well as for the local development of the ubiquitous New Zealand meat-freezing business.

New Zealand as a Whole. New Zealand is like Denmark—one of the small countries of the world with a small population and a high income level based on agriculture, hence a country where a high standard of living is possible and where social problems are relatively simple. The large measure of dependence on Great Britain as a market for its products is the chief weak point in New Zealand's position.

New Zealand is not wealthy in the sense that it has a large industrial establishment or extensive mineral resources. It is a rich land, nevertheless, in that it enjoys an invigorating climate which has been taken advantage of by an alert, industrious, and intelligent population. There appears to be adequate room for an indefinite continuation of the unspectacular but steady expansion of the country's population, industry, and agriculture.

QUESTIONS. Explain why marine west coast Australia is located on the southeastern coast of the continent. What states or portions of states are within the region? Name the region's major topographic features and compare them with the general topography of the Western Hemisphere marine west coast regions. Why is the climate of the region somewhat warmer than in the normal development of the climate elsewhere? Give as many facts as you can to demonstrate the dominant importance of the sheep-raising industry in Australia. Name the second-ranking agricultural activity. What is the major crop? The most significant mineral resource? Why can Australia be characterized as an "empty continent"? What implications does this have for the Australian economy and the country's future progress? Describe the major traits of the Australian national character.

Explain the nature and basis of Australia's immigration policy.

Name the two major islands of New Zealand. Describe their general topography. In what way is the climate of New Zealand unlike that of southern Chile? Compare the extent and utilization of the forest resources of New Zealand and the marine west coast region of North America, as to both similarities and differences. Describe the general standard of living in New Zealand. What is unusual about the present-day relationship of the native people of New Zealand and the descendants of the white colonists? Name the major industry of New Zealand and give as many facts as you can to illustrate its dominance. Explain why this industry is so well developed in New Zealand. Name the major crops of the country. What is its only important mineral resource? How is the domestic dependence on this resource lessened? Name the major types of manufacturing enterprise. Explain why manufacturing is unusually diversified in New Zealand relative to the paucity of the country's resources. Why may New Zealand be compared with Denmark? In what respects is New Zealand wealthy despite its small size and limited resources? What characteristics do New Zealand's major cities have in common? Name the two largest cities and chief ports of the country. What advantages does one have for foreign trade, and the other for domestic trade?

Middle-Latitude Dry Climates

CHAPTER 22

Middle-Latitude Deserts and Steppes: Eastern Hemisphere

■ DEFINITION AND CAUSES OF MIDDLE-LATITUDE DESERTS AND STEPPES

Tropical regions of warm dry climate are the product of the trade winds, intensified in some coastal areas by cold ocean currents alongshore. The regions of middle-latitude dry climate are primarily a phenomenon of "continentality," i.e., they exist because of the extremely large land masses present in the middle latitudes. Middle-latitude dry climates are best developed in the central portions of the Northern Hemisphere continents. There the distance from the sea in every direction is so great that little or no atmospheric moisture generated over the oceans is likely to reach them.

The extent and configuration of the middle-latitude deserts and steppes are likewise greatly dependent on the presence, position, continuity, and altitude of mountain ranges and the effectiveness of the rain shadows they cast toward the interior regions. Thus there may be more than one desert area within a given middle-latitude region of dry climate. Moreover, the steppe margins of such deserts are likely to be discontinuous because of interruptions by mountain ranges.

■ CLIMATIC CHARACTERISTICS

PRECIPITATION

In Chapter 12 (p. 203) it was noted that the distinction between humid and arid conditions is based on whether there is more or less than 20 inches of annual rainfall, respectively, in warm climates, and more or less than 10 inches in cool climates. The lower evaporation rate at lower temperatures permits the existence of a continuous plant cover at lower precipitation levels. The middle-latitude dry climates are actually less arid than those of the tropical latitudes because of two circumstances: (1) The middle latitudes are within the westerlies belt of air mass movements and cyclonic storms. This alternation makes possible more frequent rains. (2) In winter the precipitation occurs as snow, and though it may not amount to much, such snow as does fall may evaporate or melt comparatively slowly; hence there is a chance it will be absorbed by the soil.

The seasonality of precipitation depends on location. Where the continental influence is strongest there is likely to be a summer concentration due to the strong inblowing monsoon developed by the heated continental mass. Destructive thunderstorms and hail-storms are likely to be frequent then. The summer rainfall concentration is a fortunate circumstance, since it coincides with the growing season for crops.

On the other hand, where the Mediterranean climatic influences are sufficiently strong, precipitation may be concentrated in winter. This occurs where the middle-latitude dry climate, in its lower latitudinal extent, adjoins a Mediterranean climatic region.

TEMPERATURE

Temperature is the major distinction between the middle-latitude and lower-latitude dry climates, a difference sharply defined by the fact that the middle-latitude dry climates have a winter season with freezing temperatures. Although, as in the warm dry climates, the diurnal temperature range is large—and for the same reasons (see Chapter 12, p. 204)—the really wide temperature variation is that between summer and winter. Extremes of heat and cold are reached in the absence of the moderating marine influence.

In summer the middle-latitude dry climates can attain the high temperatures of the lower-latitude deserts and steppes, and in winter may go far below zero degrees Fahrenheit. Because these climates extend across a latitude belt within which the effect of latitude on temperature is strong, no typical set of temperatures can be cited. One clear generalization, on the other hand, is that because of the extreme temperature ranges living conditions are generally less pleasant than those of other middle-latitude climates.

DESERT CHARACTERISTICS

Middle-latitude deserts generally occur in continental interiors surrounded by mountains. They are basin regions of interior drainage. The basic characteristic—low altitude behind barriers to winds from the exterior—promotes high temperatures in the summer, so that the weather and living conditions then duplicate those of the warm deserts.

The much lower winter temperatures, on the other hand, with the possibility of a snow cover if only for brief periods, may permit the growth of sufficient vegetation to afford pasturage for livestock for part of the year. The utility of the middle-latitude deserts in this respect is thus far greater, area for area, than that of the warm deserts.

STEPPE CHARACTERISTICS

In the warm climates the large, well-known deserts are surrounded by relatively narrow steppes, whereas middle-latitude deserts are themselves relatively small and unimportant but are surrounded by large steppe regions. Steppe development is the dominant expression of middle-latitude arid climate. In general, these regions receive their rainfall from occasional cyclonic storms, those which, because of exceptionally large diameter, can "swirl" in moisture-laden air from directions that are normally to the leeward. An example is the rain produced in the North American region by cyclones bringing in humid air from the Gulf of Mexico. In Asia the monsoons are at times sufficiently strong to carry rain to the steppe regions (Fig. 22.1). Thunderstorms are everywhere occasionally a source of rainfall.

The occurrence of the middle-latitude steppe climate over large expanses of plains and plateaus, especially in North America, permits the development of unusually strong winds. An extreme case is the *blizzard* phenomenon of the North American steppe region. A blizzard combines exceptionally low temperatures, high winds, and a blinding snowstorm. There is, on the other hand, a dry winter wind which descends from the mountains, known in North America as the *chinook*. Because of its descent it is warm. The chinook can, in fact, raise temperatures by 50° F. within an hour in the middle of winter. But in summer the chinook, unhappily, is like a searing draft from a fire. To ward off the withering blasts of the summer chinook windbreaks consisting of successive rows of trees are used to reduce its force and so protect crop areas to leeward from being scorched.

Fig. 22.1—Steppe Region of Asia. Kabadian, Turkestan. (Courtesy, W. Rickmer Rickmers.)

REGIONAL ASPECTS

Like the warm steppes, the middle-latitude steppes are grasslands. The precipitation is too low for trees to survive. These occur only along streams or in low places where more water is available. Although the typical transition from the neighboring humid climate through steppe to desert that appears in lower latitudes is lacking, there is nevertheless a progression within the middle-latitude dry climates starting with the tall grass of the prairie (which is in a humid climate) through short grass, with tufts farther and farther apart as the desert core is approached. In the desert itself brush, shrubs, and cacti replace the grasses.

Since grass is the omnipresent fodder, it follows that animal life must be chiefly of the grazing kind. In North America the steppe region (Fig. 22.2) was the land of the bison, which roamed the country in herds of incredible size. Antelope were also numerous. Although the bison has disappeared except in isolated preserves, the wolf

and coyote that preyed on it have unfortunately persisted and are now a menace to domestic animals. Smaller animals of the North American steppe include such rodents as gophers, jack rabbits, and prairie dogs, which also still abound sufficiently to be agricultural pests.

In the South American region the dominant pre-Columbian form was the rodent. Currently the larger wild-life forms are the rhea, an ostrich-like bird, and the guanaco, a camel-like animal. In the Asian regions the major steppe animals are the antelope, wild horse, bactrian (two-humped) camel, and gazelle.

■ UTILIZATION OF MIDDLE-LATITUDE DESERTS AND STEPPES

The middle-latitude steppes are noted for their fertile soils, developed as a result of many thousands of years under grass cover. It is generally considered that these steppe regions, especially their humid margins, have

Fig. 22.2—Middle-Latitude, Short-Grass Steppe Country in North America, Former Range of the Bison. Eastern Montana. (Courtesy, A. D. Falck, Jr.)

a richer soil than is present in any other climatic type. Their high productivity, together with the location of the steppes immediately adjacent to the densely populated humid climatic regions of middle latitudes, has resulted in more intensive utilization of these lands than of their warm counterparts. Even so, they remain among the sparsely populated types of climatic regions.

Pastoral activity is most common and widespread in the middle-latitude arid regions. Farming tends, however, to push its way into such regions. One of the characteristics of steppe precipitation, as noted, is its erratic fluctuation from year to year. A succession of high rainfall years encourages farmers to venture farther and farther into the steppe country. Return to more normal precipitation conditions, or a swing to prolonged drought, then brings about economic disaster. Moreover, in accordance with the rule that the lower the average precipitation the more undependable it is, the farthest margin of the pioneering agriculture gets hit the hardest.

The raising of **sheep** is the most important pastoral pursuit. Not only are sheep well adapted to crop the coarse grasses of the steppe, but their thick fleece also enables them to withstand the winter cold. **Cattle** are of great importance in the humid dis-

tricts of the regions. Large-scale ranching for beef production is the typical mode of operation.

Wheat is the outstanding crop where precipitation consistently suffices for agriculture. Although wheat is produced in large quantities in other climatic environments, the product of the steppe regions is of superior quality in that it is hard, high-protein grain, whereas wheat grown in humid regions is starchy and soft. Dry climates, moreover, limit the prevalence of the plant diseases to which wheat is subject.

The other basis of the dominance of the middle-latitude steppes in the world's wheat production is the great expanse of level or rolling land included in such regions. These favor mechanized farming on an enormous scale. In places the rippling grain extends like the sea from horizon to horizon.

Owing to the great latitudinal extent of the middle-latitude steppes two types of wheat are planted. *Winter wheat* is sown in the fall, grows during the winter, and is harvested in late spring. This type is raised where the coldest month does not average below 20° F. In the colder, higher latitudes *spring wheat* is the crop, planted after the frost has left the ground and harvested in late summer. Thus a forward-rolling wave of harvest activity from low latitude to high latitude marks the progression of the seasons in the middle-latitude steppe lands.

Because the invasion of the steppe regions

by agriculture is a phenomenon of the present century, steppe-land farming has a certain frontier aspect. Man is still engaged in learning the most suitable agricultural techniques for these regions. Dry farming, for example (see Chapter 12, p. 207) has made possible the utilization of arid lands on which irrigation for one reason or another is not possible.

■ MIDDLE-LATITUDE DESERT AND STEPPE REGIONS AND COUNTRIES

The middle-latitude desert and steppe regions occur between 30° and 50° latitude, approximately, and are developed to a significant extent on only four continents: Europe, Asia, North America, and South America. (Although South America is the only Southern Hemisphere continent that extends to sufficiently high latitudes to permit development of a middle-latitude desert and its surrounding steppe, certain portions of the steppe lands of southern Africa and southern Australia are technically middle-latitude rather than warm steppe regions.) (See Fig. 22.3.)

The regions of these climates in the Northern Hemisphere occur in more or less continuous areas, but these are so irregularly defined that they tend to defy systematic treatment of their spread except as this is undertaken in great detail. Mountain ranges largely determine the extent of the regions, but the complex spatial pattern is also notably related to the basic cause of the climate, that is, continentality in the westerlies belt. Tropical dry climates are due to the steady trades and their regular seasonal shifts; middle-latitude dry climates occur within the westerlies belt, which is dominated by migrant warm and cold air masses and irregularly developed cyclonic storms. In consequence precipitation varies greatly over the years. Boundaries of the regions therefore can be defined only in terms of "average climate." Any one locality in the border districts may have one of several climates in a given year or short period of years. Thus the regions discussed in this and the following chapter are much more generalized than those previously treated, and the inclusion of countries and portions of countries is somewhat more arbitrary.

So qualified, the regions of middle-latitude desert and steppe climate are **central Asia and extreme southeastern Europe,** most of the **western United States,** and **western and southern Argentina.**

Fig. 22.3—World Distribution of Middle-Latitude Desert and Steppe Climatic Regions.

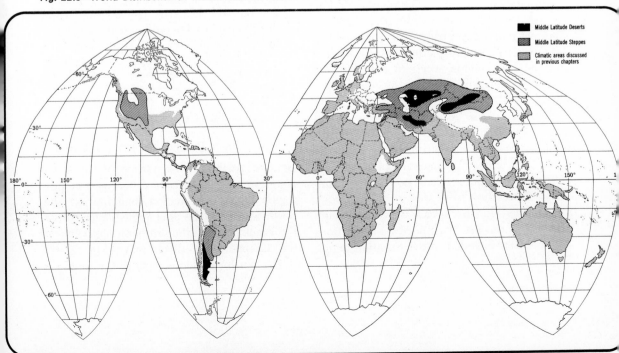

A. CENTRAL ASIA AND EXTREME SOUTHEAST EUROPE

Since Asia is the largest continent and since "continentality" is the dominant factor in determining the characteristics of the middle-latitude desert and steppe climates, the Asian development is the largest of such regions. Technically, however, not all the area here included has a desert or steppe climate, for many thousands of square miles consist of mountain country where vertical zoning (see Chapter 8, p. 132, and Chapter 13, p. 230) rather than areal climatic distribution is predominant.

There are three major desert areas within the region. One occupies the entire reach between the Caspian Sea and Lake Balkhash. No name is applied to this area as a whole, but the extreme of arid conditions is experienced in the part called the desert of **Kara Kum** just east of the Caspian and south of the Aral Sea. Farther to the east is the **Taklamakan Desert** occupying the Tarim Basin north of Tibet. This, the most continental of all existing deserts, is one of the most desolate and inhospitable places on earth. Still farther to the east is the **Gobi Desert** of Mongolia, which lies between China and Siberia.

Most of the region is isolated and little known even today. In part, this lack of knowledge is due to its remoteness, but in regard to the portion under the direct or indirect political control of the Soviet Union the paucity of information results from a firm Soviet denial of access by outsiders and a policy of secrecy on all matters concerning those areas.

Politically, the Asian region can be divided approximately into halves. The northern half comprises territories of countries within or under the influence of the Soviet Union, the southern half non-Soviet countries. Proceeding from west to east through the former, and back, east to west, through the latter, the list of countries and portions of countries included in the Eurasian region is as follows:

Northern Half
1. Southern Russia and the Caucasus
2. Soviet Central Asia
3. Mongolia
4. Sinkiang

Southern Half
5. Afghanistan
6. Iran
7. The Anatolian Plateau (not considered separately in this chapter but discussed under Mediterranean Turkey in Chapter 14)

QUESTIONS. Contrast the basic "causes" of the warm dry climates with those of the middle-latitude dry climates. Where are the middle-latitude dry climates best developed, and for what reasons? Why are they less arid in general than their warm climatic counterparts? What is their outstanding temperature feature? What is their characteristic topographic feature? Explain the terms "blizzard" and "chinook."

Why is there a tendency toward greater utilization of the middle-latitude steppes than of the warm steppes? What is the leading occupation of the middle-latitude steppe regions? Name the chief agricultural products. Why is wheat especially associated with the middle-latitude steppe regions? Explain the difference between winter wheat and spring wheat. Why must the boundaries of the middle-latitude dry climatic regions be generalized? Describe the general world distribution of these regions. Name the major desert areas within the Asiatic region of middle-latitude dry climate. What political divisions and subdivisions are included within it?

Countries of the Eurasian Region

1. SOUTHERN RUSSIA AND THE CAUCASUS

General Aspects. This portion of the great Eurasian middle-latitude desert and steppe region has a right-angled configuration, the northwest leg of the right angle lying north of the Black Sea and the southeast leg between the Caspian and Black seas (Fig. 22.4). The northwest leg comprises the southern half of the country known as the **Ukraine** (borderland) and the northern half of the **Crimea,** the peninsula that juts down from the north coast of the Black Sea. Politically, the northwest leg includes the Moldavian Soviet Socialist Republic (a small area located on the Rumanian border, formerly the Rumanian province of Bessarabia) and the southern half of the Ukrainian Soviet Socialist Republic, which virtually coincides with the natural geographic region of the Ukraine. The Soviet Socialist Republics are the major political subdivisions of the Union of Soviet Socialist Republics. Theoretically they have somewhat more sovereignty than the states of the United States. Actually, they function merely as the highest-level administrative units of the U.S.S.R., with no sovereignty whatever.

The southeastern leg of the right angle is the region known as the **Caucasus,** a land bridge from Europe to Asia situated between the Black Sea and the Caspian Sea. The southern half of the Caucasus comprises

Fig. 22.4—Southern Russia and the Caucasus. The inset compares the area of the region with an equivalent area of the United States (states in white).

three political subdivisions: the Georgian, Azerbadjan, and Armenian Soviet Socialist Republics along the border with Turkey and Iran.

The "corner" of the right angle is not known by any regional name. This area and that part of the Caucasus outside the previously named Soviet Socialist Republics are within the core unit of the Communist state, known as the Russian Soviet Federal Socialist Republic, which constitutes three-quarters of the total area of the Union of Soviet Socialist Republics.

Topography. The Ukraine and the "corner" to the east is predominantly a plains area, averaging some 500 feet in elevation and sloping gently toward the Black Sea. Running from northeast to southwest across the lowland is a line of low hills up to 1000 feet in elevation. The major river of the Ukraine is the **Dnieper,** which flows south until it encounters the hill land, then eastward for some distance along the base of the hills before making an abrupt turn to the south and southwest across the hills to its mouth in the Black Sea. The west bank of the Dnieper is consistently high and rather steep, whereas

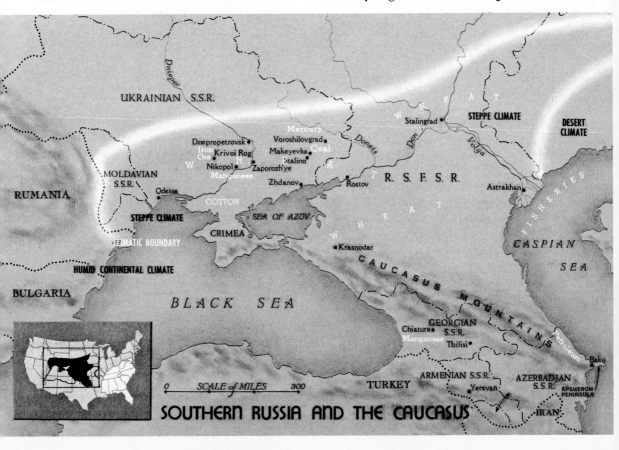

SOUTHERN RUSSIA AND THE CAUCASUS

the east bank is low and flat. Crossing the hilly belt introduces a series of rapids in an otherwise placidly flowing stream.

The northern half of the Crimean peninsula is a continuation of the Ukrainian plains, but the southern portion is mountainous, an extension of the mountains of the Caucasus. The mountains so effectively protect the southern coast of the peninsula from the continental climatic influences that it has a Mediterranean climate. Topographically and climatically it is thus much like the French Riviera and is well patronized as a vacation resort.

A belt of low hills trending north-south borders the Ukraine on the northeast. Another large river, the **Don,** hugs the eastern side of these hills until, making a wide circle at their southern end, it empties into the northeastern corner of the **Sea of Azov,** an arm of the Black Sea. A large tributary of the Don, the **Donets,** repeats this pattern between the Dnieper and the Don before it joins the larger stream. The contact of the Don with the hilly land gives rise, as with the Dnieper to the east, to a high west bank and a low eastern one, but the Don does not transect the hills.

East of the Don a third north-south trending hilly region is bordered on its eastern side by a third large river, the **Volga.** At a point opposite the great bend in the Don, where the two rivers are about 50 miles apart, the Volga makes a sharp bend to the southeast to empty into the Caspian Sea.

The northern half of the Caucasus region is mostly lowland. The southern half constitutes a group of three mountain ranges trending northwest-southeast. The ranges are very rugged, with many peaks of over 15,000 feet elevation, and are separated by narrow valleys. The mountain country is one of the vertically zoned climatic regions referred to previously.

The People. The term "Russian" is a misnomer when collectively applied to the people of the U.S.S.R. Within the Soviet Union there are more distinct nationalities and separate racial stocks than in any other country. The true "Russians" are a group of

Slavic peoples of eastern European origin in which are included the "Russians" as most Americans think of them, the *Great Russians.* The Great Russians, or "Muscovites," are the original inhabitants of central European Russia north of the Ukraine. Their name stems not from their size but from their prowess, as the most aggressive of the Russians, in uniting the group as a whole into the original Russian nation.[1]

Fig. 22.5—Two Members of the State Ukrainian Folk Chorus. (Courtesy, Soviet Embassy.)

The predominant people of the Ukraine are the *Ukrainians,* who are "cousins," so to speak, of the Great Russians but are stockier and swarthier in appearance (Fig. 22.5). The Ukrainians have always been rather resentful of the Great Russians' dominance in the Russian nation. A proud, independent people, they have repeatedly attempted to assert their political independence, but to no avail. Indeed, Great Russians are found throughout the Ukraine, and in the western parts there are admixtures of Hungarian and other Slavic groups.

South of the Ukraine, in Crimea, Great Russians predominate, but about one-quarter of the population are *Tatars,* whose presence is testimony of the great Mongol invasion of southern Russia in the thirteenth century.

[1] It is thought that the word "Russian" derives from "rus," which may refer to the fair hair of the Great Russians.

In the eastern "corner" of southern Russia Great Russians are mingled with the *Kazakhs,* a central Asiatic stock whose religion is Buddhism and whose other characteristics are equally Oriental. The Kazakhs are nomads who pasture their herds of sheep, camels, goats, and horses mostly on lands east of the Volga. This area is also the home of the *Cossacks,* the ferocious fighting horsemen of Russian history. The Cossacks are a mixture of Great Russians and Ukrainians, together with some Tatar and Turkish stock.

The complex racial composition of the U.S.S.R. reaches its extreme in the mountainous parts of the Caucasus, where the number and interrelationships of races defeat any attempt at a simple description. A dozen or more different stocks are recognized on the basis of language, and the official Soviet census lists 50 nationalities. Some of the peoples, such as the *Georgians, Armenians,* and *Azerbadjans,* are recognized by the Soviet regime through the establishment of "republics" with those names. But in addition to a conglomeration of Slavic, Mongoloid, and Semitic (Arab) stocks there are numerous unidentified racial groups related to none of these three. Their origin is a mystery and they are termed, for want of a better name, "Caucasians." This tangle of races, languages, and nationalities is the result of countless migrations and invasions since prehistoric times from Asia to Europe. It has been preserved and fostered by the corresponding complexity of topography of the Caucasus, which allowed ancient languages and customs to remain undisturbed in the isolated valleys and highlands of the region.

Mineral Resources. Southern Russia and the Caucasus are the repository of the greater portion of the Soviet Union's significant mineral resources. The world's largest **manganese** deposits occur at **Nikopol** in the central Ukraine; the second in rank at **Chiatura** in the Georgian S.S.R. **Iron ore** deposits of major importance are found at **Krivoi Rog** in the central Ukraine. Just to the east, in the Donets Basin (or **Donbas,** as the Russians call it) are the most important **coal** deposits of the U.S.S.R., with large reserves including both anthracite and coking coal. The Donbas is also the leading Soviet source of **mercury.** The Caucasus is a major Soviet source of **petroleum,** from fields on the west shore of the Caspian and the northeast shore of the Black Sea.

Agriculture. Southern Russia is one of the world's great **wheat** districts. The level steppes of the Ukraine are the site of vast, state-owned farms on which the Russians have concentrated their efforts to mechanize agriculture. In the southern Ukraine, just north of the Crimea, the Russians have succeeded in adapting cotton to dry-farming methods. Plantings are extensive, but the yield is rather low.

To the east, the farmers of the lower Volga are plagued not only by low rainfall but also by poor seasonal distribution of the precipitation. Rain after harvest time is of no benefit to agriculture no matter how heavy it may be. On the other hand, years of relatively low rainfall may be good crop years if rain comes during the growing season. The rainfall disadvantage is partly overcome by growing **sunflowers** (for seeds to yield oil) and **corn** to utilize the summer rains.

Other crops include **castor beans** and **soybeans** in the northern Caucasus, **citrus fruits** and **tobacco** in those districts of the southern Caucasus where local climatic conditions permit.

The Caucasus and Ukraine also produce **beef cattle,** which are raised on farms rather than the open range. **Hogs** are raised in the Ukraine on grain and agricultural waste, and in the Caucasus on corn.

Southern Russia is in addition the scene of the most important **fisheries** of the country. The Caspian Sea provides unusually good fishing grounds, especially for the sturgeon, whose eggs are famous as caviar.

Industries. As one would expect from the mineral resource catalogue of the Donbas, it is one of the chief industrialized regions of the U.S.S.R. The excellent combination of iron ore, coking coal, manganese, and hydroelectric power has formed the basis of a large industrial complex. **Iron and steel,** heavy machinery, and **metallurgy** in general are the predominant industries, with **glassmaking** and the production of basic **chemicals** also important.

CITIES OF SOUTHERN RUSSIA AND THE CAUCASUS

Name	Type	Population (Estimated, 1946–48)
Baku	Lake port, governmental, industrial	900,000 (1955)
Odessa	Seaport	600,000
Tiblisi	Industrial-governmental	540,000
Dnepropetrovsk	Industrial	500,000
Stalino	Mining-industrial	500,000
Rostov	Industrial	500,000
Stalingrad	River port-industrial	400,000
Astrakhan	River port	300,000
Zaporozh'ye	Industrial	300,000
Makeyevka	Industrial	300,000
Yerevan	Industrial-governmental	255,000
Krivoi Rog	Mining-industrial	200,000
Zhdanov	Industrial-seaport	200,000
Krasnodar	Industrial-commercial	200,000
Voroshilovgrad	Industrial	200,000

Cities. The outstanding city phenomenon of southern Russia is the great urban complex of the Ukraine. Like the Pittsburgh-Detroit-Buffalo area of the United States and the Ruhr-Saar complex of western Europe, it is based on the combination of an abundance of basic raw materials, a dense population, and the establishment of giant heavy industrial plants and associated chemical works. The great steel mills are at **Zhdanov** and **Makeyevka** in the Donbas, and **Krivoi Rog**, **Zaporozh'ye** and **Dnepropetrovsk** in the Dnieper district. The accompanying heavy machinery industry is typified by the locomotive works at **Voroshilovgrad** and the railroad car plant at Dnepropetrovsk.

Stalino, the largest city of the Donbas, is a coal-mining center in addition to having metallurgical and chemical industries. Makeyevka with its huge steel mill is a few miles to the northeast. In the Dnieper district Dnepropetrovsk and Zaporozh'ye are very similar to the Buffalo–Niagara Falls industrial concentration in this country. The great dam (Fig. 22.6) near the latter city is the largest power source in Europe. Besides supporting its own heavy industry the great power resources of Dnepropetrovsk have made the city a center of aluminum refining.

Baku (Fig. 22.7), the largest city of the area, is the capital of the Azerbadjan S.S.R. and fifth largest city of the Soviet Union. The **Apsheron** peninsula on the west coast of the

Fig. 22.6—Dnieper Dam Near Dnepropetrovsk. Note the large industrial plants in the distance. (Courtesy, Soviet Embassy.)

Fig. 22.7—Nizami Square, Baku, Azerbadjan S.S.R. (Courtesy, Soviet Embassy.)

Caspian, on which it is situated, is an oil field, so that the city's major activity is refining and shipping petroleum.

Odessa is one of the leading seaports of the U.S.S.R., on the northern coast of the Black Sea near the extreme southwestern tip of the country. It handles the Black Sea trade between the Caucasus and all of western Russia and is also the major Soviet port for Mediterranean and South American commerce.

Rostov, just above the Don's mouth, was originally a commercial city at the intersection of important trade routes. It is now an industrial city by virtue of its large factory for agricultural machinery, its machine tool and automobile assembly plants, and its shipyards.

Stalingrad (Stalin City) and **Astrakhan** are the two great lower Volga ports, the former situated where the river comes closest to the Don, the latter at the apex of the Volga delta. Stalingrad is famous as the site of one of the decisive battles of World War II. It is important in its own right, however. Extending over a distance of 30 miles along the river (Fig. 22.8), the city is an important transshipment point for petroleum and coal. Its industries reflect the varied commercial activities of the city. These in-

Fig. 22.8—Volga River Embankment, Stalingrad, Showing Characteristic High West (Foreground) and Low East Bank of the South-Flowing Russian Rivers. In the right foreground is a bathing beach and swimming pool. (Courtesy, Soviet Embassy.)

clude a large tractor plant, metallurgical works, shipbuilding, chemical, and lumber industries, and oil refining. Astrakhan is the chief fishing center of Russia and possesses a variety of light industries 'related to its fishing and agricultural trade.

Krasnodar is the chief city of the northern Caucasus. Its industries range from oil refining to food processing. **Tiblisi** (Fig. 22.9) and **Yerevan** are the capitals of the Georgian and Armenian S.S.R.'s, respectively. Both were formerly minor local administrative centers now transformed into important industrial cities by the development of local hydropower resources.

Fig. 22.9—Scene in Tiblisi, Georgia S.S.R. (Courtesy, Soviet Embassy.)

2. Soviet Central Asia

General Aspects. The Eurasian middle-latitude desert and steppe region continues eastward beyond the Caspian Sea to the borders of the Chinese political sphere in what is here called, for lack of better terminology, Soviet Central Asia.[2] This area in the heart of Asia encompasses more than 1.5 million square miles (over half the area of the United States) and comprises the following countries: **Kazakhstan** (land of the Kazakhs), the northern two-thirds of the area; **Turkmenistan,** the lands east of the Caspian and north of Iran; **Uzbekistan,** the region north and east of Turkmenistan, and extending from Afghanistan to Lake Aral; **Tadzhikistan,** situated to the east on the Afghanistan and Sinkiang borders; and **Kirghizstan,** along the northern Sinkiang border[3] (Fig. 22.10).

These odd-sounding names, with strange spellings due to transliteration from languages wholly alien to English, may well evoke visions of remote, mysterious lands and utterly foreign peoples. Such a reaction is not unwarranted, for the lands and peoples of the heart of Asia have always been among those least known to Western civilization. Their inhabitants have for centuries adhered to a fanatical tradition of isolation and enforced it through the enslavement or murder of outsiders who ventured within their territories. When these regions were conquered by the czars in the nineteenth century this policy was retained, and the Soviets have maintained it even more rigorously than did their czarist predecessors.

Although the area, accordingly, remains isolated and is in large part empty desert, it is not one that can be dismissed as of little geographic significance, for it contains a population of perhaps 20 million people who have been organized by the zealous enterprise of the Communist regime to achieve a productive development of their by no means meager natural resources.

Topography. The general topography of the area is that of a flat lowland ringed on

[2] The old term "Russian Turkestan" came closest to designating this area.

[3] Tadzhikistan, Kirghizstan, and southeast Kazakhstan are also mountainous areas within the region where vertical zoning is predominant over areal climatic pattern.

the south and east by lofty mountain ranges. Almost the entire extent of this **Turan Lowland** is true desert, with sand or clay surface. It includes the eastern portion of the Caspian depression and a series of plains and low plateaus ringed around the Aral Sea. Listed in counterclockwise order these topographic units are the **Emba Plateau** on the northwest, the **Ust-Urt Plateau** in the west, the **Kara Kum** (Black Sands) plain in the south, the **Kizil Kum** (Red Sands) plain in the southeast, the **Hunger Steppe** in the east, and the **Turgai Plain** in the northeast. The **Amu Darya** (Fig. 22.11) (river) separates the Kara Kum and Kizil Kum, the **Syr Darya** runs between the latter and the Hunger Plain. In the north a low line of hills, the southernmost extension of the Urals, separates the Emba Plateau and the Turgai Plain. East of the Hunger Plain is still another lowland area, the **Balkhash Basin,** surrounding the lake of that name. Northeast of the plains

Fig. 22.10—Soviet Central Asia. The inset compares the area of the region with an equivalent area of the United States (states in white).

portion is the **Kazakh Upland,** a district of low hills. The eastern portion of the mountain rim is within the region and consists of the **Altai, Tien Shan,** and **Pamir** ranges, in order from north to south.

People. The mixture, admixture, and evolution of the various stocks of this part of the world have produced an extraordinarily complex ethnological assemblage. The majority of the peoples present today are of Turkic and Iranian heritage, with Islam as the common religion. The chief groups, recognized in the administrative units (the Soviet Socialist Republics) established by the Soviets, are the Kazakhs, Uzbeks, Turkmen, Kirghiz, and Tadzhiks (Fig. 22.12). The first four are the Turkic element, the latter the Iranian. All are fierce, violent people whose work and recreation are both strenuous.

The territorial extent of the various S.S.R.'s corresponds only loosely to the distribution of the various peoples, and the language pattern is even more confused. The Kazakhs account for a little over one-half of the Kazakhstan population (Russians and Ukraini-

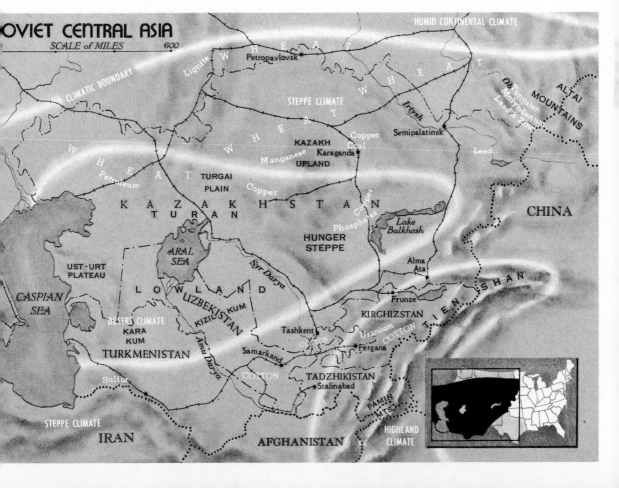

Fig. 22.11—Amu Darya or Oxus River, in the Kizil Kum. (Courtesy, W. Rickmer Rickmers.)

ans account for another third), and Uzbeks constitute more than a majority of the population of the other S.S.R.'s.

The Kazakhs typify the nomadic element. Formerly the inhabitants of what is now northwestern Kazakhstan practiced transhumance over a route up to 800 miles long, to the Altai Mountains. Under the Soviet regime, however, they were forced to abandon their nomadism in favor of a semi-nomadism in which only the herdsmen accompany the herds.

Mineral Resources. Kazakhstan is especially important to the U.S.S.R. as a source of the nonferrous metals—**copper, lead,** and **zinc.** The major copper deposits of the Soviet Union are located within the Kazakh Upland, and those of lead and zinc in the Altai Mountains. The latter district is also a large producer of **tungsten** and **molybdenum** for the U.S.S.R. Kazakhstan also contains additional manganese resources supplementing

the great deposits to the west. Vital **uranium** deposits are reported in a belt through the south central portion of the area. The most important source of this element is in west central Kirghizstan, near the Uzbek border.

Fuel resources include both **coal** and **petroleum.** The coal fields of **Karaganda,** northwest of Lake Balkhash, supply good coking coal and rank third in the country. The oil fields are northeast of the Caspian Sea on the Emba Plateau. The significant nonmetallic resources include **phosphate rock** in northwest Kazakhstan and **sulfur** in the Kara Kum district of Turkmenistan.

Agriculture. As in all desert regions, agriculture in Soviet Central Asia is on an irrigation basis, using the natural water supply of oases and along watercourses, or that provided by dams and reclamation projects. The Soviets have devoted great energies to the construction of dams and associated irrigation systems in this area, just as the United States has done in its own West where climate and topography are similar. Large projects have been undertaken on both the major rivers as well as smaller streams throughout the area. Outstanding in this respect is the **Fergana Valley** of eastern Uzbekistan, very similar in fertility and products to the lush Imperial Valley of southern California.

The chief crop of the irrigated farms is **cotton,** produced in sufficient quantity to make the area the leading Soviet source of the fiber. The oases also produce a rich variety of other crops, including **sugar beets, rice,** lesser known **rubber** and **fiber plants,** and all kinds of **fruits.**

Fig. 22.12—Tadzhik Tribesmen of the Tadzhik S.S.R. (Courtesy, W. Rickmer Rickmers.)

In the northwest of Kazakhstan the agriculture is like that of the lower Volga district. Dry farming produces spring wheat and sunflower seed. Where conditions are too arid for agriculture, pastoral activities are carried on through semi-nomadism, with **sheep** and **camels** the chief animals. In the mountain pastures of the south and east **cattle, goats,** and sheep are raised.

Industries. Soviet Central Asia was one of the fortunate portions of the Soviet Union that were spared the destruction of World War II, and benefited also by special development as a new, strategically safe industrial center. As a result Kazakhstan now possesses a large new **nonferrous metallurgical** industry, smelting and refining the locally produced copper, lead, and zinc ores with local supplies of fuels and hydroelectricity. Local nonmetallic resources also support **chemical** and **fertilizer** industries using salt, phosphate, and borax. Other industries of the area include those devoted to **food processing,** especially **meat packing** and **beet sugar refining.**

Transportation. Although the area remains isolated from the rest of the world it is no longer cut off from easy commerce with the rest of the Soviet Union. Until 1927 there was only a single railroad, the Turksib (Turkestan-Siberian) spur line from the Trans-Siberian Railroad, which provided a rather roundabout route to Russia. The railroad development has been supplemented by highway construction. Nevertheless the caravan is still an important factor in internal commerce.

CITIES OF SOVIET CENTRAL ASIA

Name	Type	SSR	Population (Estimated, 1946–48)
Tashkent	Industrial-governmental	Uzbek	600,000
Alma Ata	Governmental-industrial	Kazakh	300,000
Karaganda	Mining	Kazakh	220,000
Samarkand	Industrial	Uzbek	150,000
Frunze	Governmental-industrial	Kirghiz	140,000
Ashkhabad	Governmental-industrial	Turkmen	120,000
Stalinabad	Governmental-industrial	Tadzhik	110,000
Semipalatinsk	Commercial	Kazakh	100,000
Petropavlovsk	Commercial	Kazakh	100,000

Cities. **Tashkent,** the capital of the Uzbek S.S.R., was an ancient commercial city of central Asia that has been converted by the Soviets into the major industrial metropolis of the area. It is in northeast Uzbekistan on a river whose waters make it an oasis. Its industries include metallurgy, textiles, and machinery.

Alma Ata, the capital of the Kazakh S.S.R., is in the extreme southeast corner of Kazakhstan in the foothills of the Tien Shan range. It is in the midst of a large apple orchard district, hence the name "Father of Apples." Its industries range from heavy machinery, through textile mills, to tobacco factories. It is also the cultural capital of the republic.

Karaganda is a good example of the youthful Soviet city deliberately created to take advantage of local resources. In 1926 the population was 150. The city lies in the center of coal fields and, as a result of the development of a large industrial complex based on the mineral resources of the district, it is now the metropolis of the many mining and industrial cities surrounding it.

Samarkand, like Tashkent, is a river-based oasis. It is in the east central section of the odd-shaped Uzbek S.S.R., of which it was formerly the capital. Samarkand is the oldest city of central Asia, with an age of some 5000 years. It was the capital of Tamerlane, the destructive conqueror of the fourteenth century, whose monumental public buildings have survived and give an air of exotic antiquity to the city.

Frunze, Ashkhabad, and **Stalinabad** are the capitals of the Kirghiz, Tadzhik, and Turkmen S.S.R.'s, respectively. Frunze is situated in northern Kirghizstan about 125 miles southwest of Alma Ata. Stalinabad is in western Tadzhikistan and Ashkhabad in southern Turkmenistan, only a few miles from the Iranian border. All three are the industrial and cultural as well as administrative capitals of their republics. Their common industries are those that process the local agricultural products—cotton and silk mills, and meat packing. In addition, Stalinabad manufactures electrical machinery; Ashkhabad makes glass and is one of the sites of the Soviet motion-picture industry.

Semipalatinsk and **Petropavlovsk** are commercial centers in northeastern and northern Khazakhstan. The former is at the intersection of the **Irtysh River** and the Turksib railroad; the latter is the meeting place of the Trans-Siberian and Trans-Kazakh lines. Both have the usual agricultural processing industries.

3. Mongolia

General Aspects. Climatically, this subdivision of the middle-latitude desert and steppe region in Asia consists of the Gobi Desert and encircling steppe lands (Fig. 22.13). It corresponds in general to the old geographic region known as Mongolia, which was further divided into Inner and Outer Mongolia. The terms "inner" and "outer" referred to positions relative to China, which lies to the southeast, and reflected a traditional Chinese political and cultural orientation of the inhabitants. Circumstances are now much changed, however. Outer Mongolia, i.e., that portion more remote from China proper, became nominally independent from China in

1913 and formally so in 1946. Its new title is **Mongolian People's Republic**, a phraseology that suggests its status as a *de facto* part of the Soviet Union, whose political control is complete. Strategically, this "republic" serves as a useful buffer zone to protect the vital Trans-Siberian Railroad, which parallels the Mongolian border for a considerable distance in these parts. Thus Outer Mongolia covers about 600,000 square miles (equal to the states of California, Washington, Oregon, and Texas) and comprises the greater part of the Gobi subdivisions of the desert-steppe region as a whole.

Inner Mongolia cannot be so simply defined, but may conveniently be assumed to include most of the Chinese border provinces of Jehol,[4] Chahar, Suiyuan, and Ningsia. These have an area of 400,000 square miles (equivalent to that part of the United States east of the Mississippi and north of the Mason-Dixon line). The farther border of Inner Mongolia is roughly marked by the outer line of the famous **Great Wall of China** (Fig. 22.14) (in many sections the Great Wall is multiple), which was built to repel raids on China by the inhabitants of the Gobi region. Climatically considered, there should also be included here the western

[4] It was reported in 1955 that Jehol province was abolished and its territory incorporated in neighboring provinces.

Fig. 22.13—Mongolia and Sinkiang. The inset compares the area of the region with that of the United States.

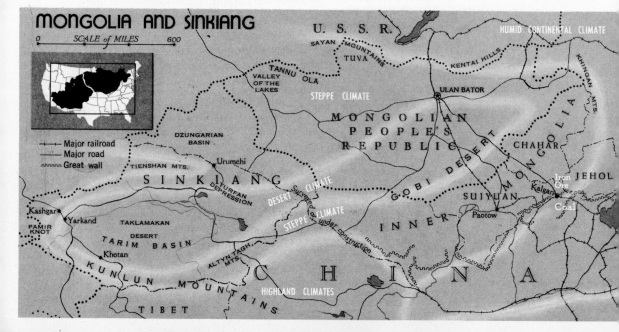

border portion of Manchuria and, in the northwest, most of **Tuva,** a mountain basin 65,000 square miles in extent (somewhat smaller than the state of Washington) at the geographical center of Asia. Tuva became a part of the U.S.S.R. in 1944, having been an "autonomous" People's Republic for some years before then.

Topography. Most of Mongolia is a flat plain with wide areas of exceptional levelness. The plain averages one mile in elevation in the south and rises to over 6000 feet in the north, but, in general, the region is a basin with a gradual rise from the center to the rimming mountains. Much of the surface of the basin is bare rock or has only a thin gravel cover; sand dunes are present in limited areas, mostly in the southwest.

The **Altai Mountains** extend southeastward from Central Asia to form the most promi-

Fig. 22.14—The Great Wall at Nankow. (Courtesy, American Geographical Society, photograph by F. G. Clapp.)

nent portion of the mountain rim. The Siberian frontier consists, from west to east, of the **Tannu Ola,** the **Sayan Mountains,** and the **Kentai Hills.** The Tannu Ola separate the Tuva basin from the Gobi. South of the Tannu Ola is a collection of basins known as the **Valley of the Lakes.** The **Khingan Mountains** of Manchuria on the east, and assorted lesser mountain ranges and hills curving southwest along the border of Inner Mongolia complete the rim. Inner Mongolia is a grassy plateau of 4000 feet elevation in the north, and a zone of lower altitude and varying topography in the south, 250 miles

wide in the center, narrowing to a few miles on the east and west.

People. The Mongols, after whom the land is named, are the dominant people of the Gobi Desert region. The population of the People's Republic is variously reported at from 800,000 to 2 million, of which Chinese and Russian minorities number perhaps 100,000. The bulk of the inhabitants live on the north side of the Gobi. Inner Mongolia has a population in the neighborhood of 5 million, in which a high proportion of Chinese is included as a result of large-scale Chinese colonization in the early decades of the twentieth century. The Tuvinians are a national group related to the Kirghiz, and number about 150,000.

The Mongols are descendants of the warrior nomad followers of Genghis Khan and Kublai Khan, who at one time held sway over most of Asia, ruled China for a period, and even threatened Europe. The present-day Mongols retain the strong nomadic traditions, but their warlike tendencies have been curbed and they are steadily being coaxed into a more sedentary life by the Communist leaders of the People's Republic. The typical nomad with his rugs and *yurts* (felt tents) and his identification with his flocks and herds may well become a relic of the past, although the utter dependence on grass, wherever it may be found, makes some form of movement of the livestock essential. The religion of the Mongols is lama Buddhism, a form of the religion in which monks (lamas) and monastery life are the outstanding features. It also differs from Buddhism in countenancing the slaughter of animals for food and other useful products—as well it must for people who are herdsmen!

Mineral Resources. During most of recent history Mongolia has been only slightly less isolated and unknown than Soviet Central Asia. Moreover, the discovery and development of mineral resources has been at a slower pace than those of Central Asia, where the circumstances were both more urgent and more favorable. **Coal** is known to exist, however, in the People's Republic at three points—in the north central district, in the east near the Manchurian border, and in the Altai Mountains. The coal is lignite of low quality, but modest production is reported from the north central deposits, where reserves are substantial. Those near Manchuria are also reported as developed, because they are of superior quality.

Mineral resources of Inner Mongolia include deposits of high-grade **iron ore** and some coal in Chahar province. Tuva is said to have rich mineral resources. Exploitation of all these resources is just beginning, however, owing to lack of transport facilities.

Agriculture. Most of the People's Republic is too arid and too cold to permit farming on any significant scale. Still, some grains, hay, and vegetables are produced. Farming is better in Inner Mongolia, along the fluctuating border between the arid climate and the more humid climate to the south; there 70 percent of the population is engaged in tilling the soil. Irrigation is practiced locally on a small scale; without it, subsistence farming is the rule. Mixed crops of grains, oilseeds, vegetables, and fruits are raised. In Tuva grains are produced with some irrigation.

Pastoral activities are, of course, the main pursuit of the steppe dwellers. The tendency, as noted above, is a shift from unfettered nomadism to ranch life. The People's Republic contains animal populations of several million each of **sheep, goats, cattle,** and **horses,** in descending order of abundance. In addition there are many hundred thousand camels. Much of the yield of the stock raising is consumed by the Mongols themselves as food and for clothing, housing, and fuel (by burning dried dung). Both wool and hides are exported to the Soviet Union. The inhabitants of the northern portion of Inner Mongolia also raise livestock, exporting their products to China.

The hunting tradition of the Mongols is preserved in the **fur** industry. Marmots, squirrels, foxes, and other fur-bearing animals are abundant in the mountains, steppes, and forests. Furs comprise a considerable portion of Mongolian exports.

Industries. Industry is almost nonexistent in the Mongolian region save for the mining activities previously noted. The Soviets have been markedly successful in converting the Mongol nomads into mine workers, but how much pressure and outright force were involved in bringing about such conversion is not known. There is a small "industry" in wool, leather, and felt preparation located at the capital of the People's Republic. Miscellaneous light industries have also been established to satisfy local demands.

CITIES OF MONGOLIA

Name	Type	Population
Ulan Bator	Governmental-commercial	100,000 (1950)
Kalgan	Commercial	151,000 (1947)
Paotow	Commercial	82,000 (1948)

Cities. **Ulan Bator** (Red Hero) is the capital and commercial center of the People's Republic. It is the site of the industries mentioned above, and the chief lignite mine is located 20 miles to the southeast. The Soviet urge to develop the country has resulted in considerable modernization of the city. The government has established a theater, a high school, a university and technical colleges, all housed in modern buildings.

Kalgan and **Paotow** are the two chief cities of Inner Mongolia. Both are Chinese. The former is in Chahar province only 100 miles northwest of the Chinese capital, Peiping. Paotow is in Suiyuan province 250 miles farther west. Both are gateway cities to the Mongolian steppe lands. Indeed, Kalgan means "gate" or "barrier." The city was formerly at the main gate in the Great Wall for entrance into China from Mongolia. Paotow is inside Mongolia 100 miles beyond the Great Wall. Its commercial position stems from its being the western terminus of the railroad from the Chinese capital.

QUESTIONS. Describe the major topographic features and political divisions of southern Russia and the Caucasus. Describe the ethnic and national composition of the population. Name the outstanding mineral resources of the Ukraine; the Caucasus. What is the major crop of the Ukraine? Locate the important fishing district of the area. Explain the great industrial concentration of the Donbas. Why are the cities of Dnepropetrovsk and Zaporozh'ye like Buffalo and Niagara Falls? Explain the importance of Odessa, Baku, Astrakhan, and Stalingrad.

Name the peoples of Soviet Central Asia. Explain how they are related to the political subdivisions of the area. Describe the major topographic features. What are the chief mineral resources and why are they especially significant to the Soviet Union? What is the chief crop? Explain the similarity between the Fergana and Imperial valleys. What is the relation between the industries and the local resources? What is the historical significance of the cities of Tashkent and Samarkand?

Explain the terms "Inner" and "Outer" Mongolia and name the present political units to which they refer. Describe the general topography of Mongolia. Identify the Mongols. What is the chief occupation in Mongolia? Explain the political spheres of influence within Mongolia.

4. SINKIANG

General Aspects. Sinkiang ("New Frontier") has been nominally a province of China for over 2000 years, though Chinese authority has usually been rather tenuous. But since the 1930's Sinkiang has been under progressively stronger Soviet control. The country's 700,000 square miles (twice the area of the three Pacific coast states) comprise an area of great strategic and commercial importance. For centuries Sinkiang was the gateway to China on the overland route from the Western world. It was also astride north-south trade routes and commanded the main mountain passes for all this trade. Abundant ruins testify to a past period of large population and great activity. Its strategic site is demonstrated by its borders—Mongolia on the north, China on the east, Tibet and India-Pakistan (the disputed Kashmir state) on the south, Afghanistan and Soviet Central Asia on the west (Fig. 22.13). It is truly a nodal point for international interests in central Asia.

Topography. Sinkiang is composed of a double basin separated and surrounded by high mountains on all sides save the east, where the two basins coalesce with the basin of the Gobi. The **Tarim Basin** in the south averages 3000 feet in altitude and occupies the major portion of the country; it is the site of the **Taklamakan Desert**. The smaller **Dzungarian Basin** is in the north. A portion of the Tibetan plateau on the south is also politically a part of Sinkiang.

The greatest of the encircling mountain ranges is the **Tien Shan** ("Celestial Mountains"), which run east-west from the Pamirs and are the highlands that separate the two desert basins. The Tien Shan attain altitudes of almost 24,000 feet. Also extending from the Pamirs are the **Kunlun** in an arc on the south. These rise to over 20,000 feet, the northernmost of the series of ranges that culminate in the Himalayas. On the east the **Altyn Tagh** ranges complete the southern arc. They curve northeast from the main Kunlun line. Various ranges on the west north of the Pamir Knot bar access from the U.S.S.R. except by way of three passes. The Dzungarian Basin is rimmed on the north by the Altai Mountains.

The extreme remoteness of the Tarim Basin and the height of the surrounding mountains make the Taklamakan the driest of all Asiatic deserts. Although precipitation is rare within the basin the surrounding mountains do accumulate ice and snow which feed many streams coursing down their slopes. All but one of the torrents on the southern mountains either sink into the earth on reaching the basin proper or are fully depleted by irrigation use on the way. Those on the west and north, however, contribute to the main river of Sinkiang, the **Tarim**. This stream flows from west to east along the northern edge of the basin floor, following a shifting channel through the sandy desert wastes (the Taklamakan is the sandiest of all inner Asian deserts), until it ends in the salt lake **Lop Nor** in the east.

The Dzungarian Basin is much less arid; it is more like the Gobi. Nevertheless it also lacks a major stream. Small streams either sink into the ground or maintain individual salt lakes at their terminals.

The Tarim Basin, in short, is a country of physical and climatic extremes. The Tien Shan look down on the **Turfan Depression,** several hundred feet below sea level. Rainfall ranges from virtually nothing in the desert to 30 inches a year on mountain slopes. Temperatures of 128° F. and −25° F. have been recorded in the Taklamakan.

People. Various estimates (there are no census figures) place the number of inhabitants of Sinkiang at about 4 million. Three-quarters of these are members of a collection of tribes of Iranian stock known as the *Uighur,* who are oasis farmers. The nomads of the grasslands are chiefly Kazakhs (who make up 10 percent of the population), Kirghiz, and Mongols (3 percent). The Chinese account for less than 10 percent of the population and are mostly town dwellers. Population is densest in the southwest corner of the country.

The dominant religion of Sinkiang is Islam, the rise of which in the tenth century resulted in a steady drift away from the Chinese orbit. From the racial, national, and religious make-up of the country it is apparent that the strongest ties are with the west —herein termed Soviet Central Asia. Indeed, these two areas were formerly known jointly as Turkestan, divided into Chinese Turkestan on the east and Russian on the west.

Mineral Resources and Transportation. A varied assemblage of mineral resources is known to exist in Sinkiang. Relatively rich oil fields occur in Dzungaria; coal, iron, tungsten, copper, and gold are also found within the country. Some of the deposits are mined for local needs, and primitive refineries even produce kerosene and gasoline for local use.

The ancient silk routes of the overland trade with China are still largely used for commerce. The "North Road" on the northern side of the Tien Shan was improved for truck transport as a supply route to China in World War II. It connects with the Turk-Sib railroad on the northwest and the Chinese railhead to the southeast. The southern route along the northern edge of the Tarim Basin is suitable for cars, but trade over the passes to Afghanistan and Kashmir is limited to what can be moved by pack mule and human porterage.

Agriculture. Agriculture in the basins is confined to the oases bordering their edges. The most productive developments are in a U-shaped zone in the western Tarim Basin and in a belt along the southern edge of the Dzungarian Basin. Some of these oases are associated with the small streams that course down the mountain slopes. Others, as in the Turfan Depression, are supplied by irrigation tunnels or "horizontal wells," called *Karez* (see Chapter 11, p. 184). Such tunnels are used instead of open ditches to avoid evaporation loss. Crops produced under oasis cultivation include cereals, vegetables, fruit, tobacco, and cotton.

In Dzungaria the northern slopes of the Tien Shan receive sufficient rainfall to give rise to a belt of grassland, meager but adequate to support nomadic grazing activities. The total animal population of Sinkiang is around 11.5 million each of sheep and goats, 1.5 million cattle, 900,000 horses, and almost 100,000 camels. Their yield enables the country to export wool and leather in addition to silk and cotton.

CITIES OF SINKIANG

Name	Type	Population
Yarkand	Commercial	60,000 (1945)
Kashgar	Commercial	50,000 (1945)
Khotan	Commercial	25,000 (1945)
Urumchi	Commercial-governmental	70,000 (1947)

Cities. **Yarkand** and **Kashgar** are both river oases and ancient caravan cities. They are at the western end of the Tarim Basin about 100 miles apart. Like Tashkent and Samarkand their names have featured in much of the history of that part of the world. **Khotan** is still another river oasis some 200 miles southeast of Yarkand. It has the further distinction of being what could be called Sinkiang's industrial capital, as it is the center of silk production and of felt and carpet manufacture. It is also known for metal craftsmanship. **Urumchi** is the administrative capital of Sinkiang and is located on the North Road on the north side of the Tien Shan, midway along their length through the country.

The Soviet Sphere of Middle-Latitude Arid Asia as a Whole

As noted at the beginning of this chapter, the northern portion of the middle-latitude desert and steppe region in Asia is either part of Soviet territory or under the political domination of the U.S.S.R. The ultimate import of this control has not yet been realized by the Western world. But the reader has perhaps become aware of the enormous significance of a single fact, namely, that *the entire area is being aggressively industrialized*. Countries and regions that history had, so to speak, long since by-passed are being brought within the sphere of Western technology and scientific knowledge. This is not always occurring with the full consent of the people. Cultures, customs, and traditions that had persisted for centuries and even millennia are, under compulsion, being drastically modified or swept away (Fig. 22.15). On the other hand, latent nationalistic sentiments are being played upon by promotion of the formation of new national governments and the reëstablishment of group artistic traditions. This process has reached an advanced stage in the Soviet Socialist Republics of the Caucasus and Central Asia; it is well started in Mongolia and is in the initial stages in Sinkiang.

The significance of these developments is, of course, that new centers and sources of economic and political power are being created. Whatever the motives of the Soviets and however reprehensible their methods, it is apparent that the population in this part of the world is being utilized in building the strength of the Soviet nation.

5. AFGHANISTAN

General Aspects. In Afghanistan there is a shift from consideration of the Soviet sphere of influence in the Asiatic middle-latitude

Fig. 22.15—"Miners' Palace of Culture," Karaganda, Kazakh S.S.R. This is roughly the equivalent of a civic auditorium in the United States. The design of the arches reflects local architectural tradition, but the whole is dominated by the heroic figures typical of Soviet monumental architecture. (Courtesy, Soviet Embassy.)

dry climatic regions to that of Britain. Afghanistan formerly had the same strategic buffer importance for British India as Mongolia had for Russian Siberia. The Kingdom of Afghanistan was created as an independent state in 1747 by the amalgamation of various tribes under one ruler. For most of its history it has been completely under British influence. Modern Afghanistan only attained full independence in 1919.

Afghanistan's 250,000 square miles (equal to Montana and Wyoming combined) lie between Iran on the west, the U.S.S.R. on the north, and Pakistan on the east and south (Fig. 22.16). There is also a boundary with Sinkiang at the end of a long, narrow corridor (at one place only nine miles wide) that extends to that country. This corridor separates the Soviet Union from Pakistan and is evidence of the former value of a buffer state to both Russians and British in a region

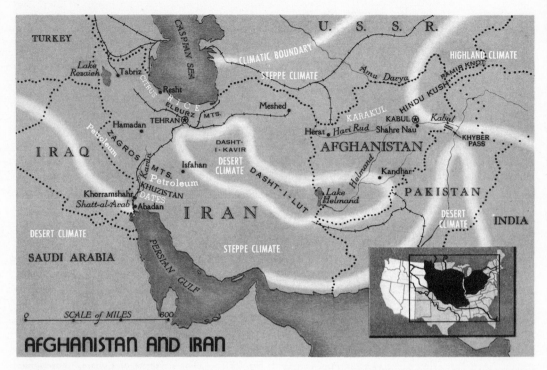

AFGHANISTAN AND IRAN

where ill-defined boundaries caused constant friction.

Topography. The dominant topographical feature of Afghanistan is the great **Hindu Kush** mountain system that runs southwest from the Pamir Knot (in the northeast corner of the country) and fans out into several subsidiary ranges 150 miles in width across the center of the country. The elevation of the mountains diminishes from over 23,000 feet in the northeast to a few thousand feet in the southwest. On the north are plains across which ran the ancient Silk Road. In the south, southeast, and southwest are desert basins with salt lakes.

The central mountain region is the source area of several large streams. The **Amu Darya** (Fig. 22.11) rises in the Pamirs at the east of the Hindu Kush, and the line of its course forms most of the northern boundary of the country. The major topographic feature of the west is the valley of the **Hari Rud** (river). The **Kabul,** a tributary of the Indus, is the principal eastern stream, and the **Helmand** drains the southeast. Of all these only the Kabul waters reach the sea; the others all end in salt lakes.

Fig. 22.16—Afghanistan and Iran. The inset compares the area of the region with an equivalent area of the United States (states in white).

People. The people of Afghanistan (estimated to number between 7 and 12 million) are, like those of Soviet Central Asia, predominantly Turkic and Iranian. Indeed, in the north there are tribes of Uzbeks and Tadzhiks who were outside the borders of the Soviet republics named for them when these were set up. The limits of previous Russian expansion in these parts did not extend to the ethnic boundaries. Some 2 millions of the population are nomadic tribes (*Kuchis*) who winter in Pakistan. The religion of Afghanistan is Islam, and tribal customs and traditions are still strong. Thus military activities are held in high esteem. These are the tribesmen who made the North-West Frontier of British India for long the scene of conflict.

Resources and Agriculture. Afghanistan is not a rich country, and what resources it possesses are largely undeveloped. Most of the country is as yet unsurveyed for mineral resources, although there are known deposits of coal, salt, iron, and lead. The Afghans are chiefly pastoral people whose livestock graze on rather barren hills. The livestock population is large and includes an odd native breed of fat-tailed sheep, the fat from which is used as a butter substitute. The country is renowned for its production of the fur, *karakul* (Persian lambskin), obtained especially in the north.

Farming is limited in general to those districts that can be irrigated. In addition to irrigation from the streams the Afghans also employ the *karez*, or tunnels, unique to the arid lands of Asia. Wheat is the staple crop; a variety of other grains and vegetables is also grown. Fine fruits are produced in certain of the more fertile districts.

CITIES OF AFGHANISTAN

Name	Type	Population (1948)
Kabul	Governmental-commercial	206,000
Kandhar	Commercial	77,000
Herat	Commercial	76,000

Cities. **Kabul,** the largest city of Afghanistan, is the political, commercial, and cultural capital. It is at an altitude of 6000 feet astride the river of the same name, in the east central portion of the country 150 miles west of the Khyber Pass. The surrounding country is a fertile agricultural district. Kabul is really two cities; the Old City or original Kabul lies on the south side of the river; across from it a well-planned modern city, **Shahre Nau,** is fast expanding.

Kandhar is the "coming city" of Afghanistan. Lying in the southeastern corner of the country 70 miles from the Pakistan border, it seems destined to become the chief commercial city, as a rail head exists at the Pakistan border and it is the closest city to a seaport (Karachi). Kandhar is already developing a fruit-processing industry for export trade.

Herat is an old caravan town on the Hari Rud in the west. It is also in a rich agricultural district and is known for its fine gardens and historical buildings.

Afghanistan as a Whole. The economic and political effects of World War II on this part of the world are largely responsible for an awakening of the Afghan people similar to that stimulated by the Soviets in their territories and sphere of influence. The developmental task facing the country is indicated by the transportation situation. There are no railroads, only 2200 miles of roads passable by motorcar, and even caravan trails total only 18,000 miles.

The government has, however, vigorously attacked the development problem. An American engineering firm was engaged to build roads, dams, irrigation works, and hydroelectric plants. The United Nations and the United States have also given much assistance in introducing Western technology. There are ambitious plans for general education, the establishment of a banking and commercial system, the construction of railroads and airports, and the modernization of agriculture. If these plans are at all successful, Afghanistan should be able to maintain itself as a self-supporting national unit.

6. IRAN

General Aspects. The Empire of Iran ("Land of the Aryans") is the present-day successor to the earlier Persia. Its 628,000 square miles (almost twice the area of the Pacific coastal states) lie between the Caspian Sea and the Persian Gulf. Its neighbors are Pakistan and Afghanistan on the east, the U.S.S.R. on the north (Turkmenistan to the east of the Caspian, the Caucasus to the west), Turkey and Iraq on the west (Fig. 22.16).

Although Iran is herein discussed with the middle-latitude desert and steppe lands, only its northern half is actually within that climatic province. Its southern half has a warm desert and steppe regime and its southern coastline can be considered part of the Arabian Desert. Iran comprises, nevertheless, a single desert region and its surrounding steppe, and on the basis of physical, ethnic, and social characteristics has a greater similarity with the countries of inner Asia than with those of the Arabian Desert region.

Topography. Iran is mostly plateau country with elevations between 3000 and 8000 feet. It shows many resemblances to the basin and range province of the western United States, made up of a series of interior valleys surrounded by mountain ranges. In Iran the chief ranges are the **Elburz Mountains** on the north and the **Zagros Mountains** on the west and south. The former constitute a barrier across the entire northern border of the country. The latter extend over the full length of the Iraq border and continue southeast along the entire coastline. Thus mountains effectively isolate all the interior of Iran.

Two small lowland regions exist on the north and south. One is the southern end of the Caspian Depression, between the Elburz and the waters of the inland sea. The other, **Khuzistan,** is at the extreme southwest corner, a continuation of the low Iraq plain.

The only Iranian stream of any size is the **Karun River** in the southwest, which empties into the head of the Persian Gulf. As is commonly true in deserts, most of the drainage is to the interior and consists of small streams ending in salt lakes. The largest of these is **Lake Rezaieh** in the far northwest, about the same size as Great Salt Lake in Utah. **Lake Helmand,** on the Afghan border, is the terminal lake of the river of that name, the last few miles of which are within Iran.

The desert districts of Iran account for one-sixth of the area of the country. The two main deserts form a belt that extends for some 800 miles north to south in the eastern section. The northern one is known as **Dasht-i-Kavir** ("Salt Desert Plain"), the southern one as **Dasht-i-Lut** ("Barren Plain"). Both are among the most arid places on earth. The latter is especially desolate and contains sand dunes attaining the extraordinary height of 700 feet.

Most of the Iranian plateau receives a rainfall of less than 12 inches a year, but the extreme northwest gets as much as 15 to 35 inches. The Caspian lowland receives 40 to 60 inches and with its steaming marshes and jungle growth is actually an area of humid subtropical climate. The precipitation is all Mediterranean winter rainfall, brought by the westerlies.

Latitudinal differences are great enough to put northern Iran on the cool side, while southern Iran is definitely hot. Summer days in the north may be warm but never approach the 130° F. readings common during the summer on the southern coast. Accompanied by high humidity from the Persian Gulf the coastal temperatures are well-nigh unbearable for humans.

People. The population of Iran is variously estimated to be between 15 and 20 million. About 90 percent are Aryans. In appearance these resemble Italians or Greeks, are brunets with dark hair and eyes and medium height and frame, but in head form they approach Nordic characteristics in possessing long heads, high foreheads, and narrow noses.

The remaining 10 percent of the population is made up of a bewildering variety of tribes and racial and religious minorities. In the northeast are Kurds and Turkmen; in the northwest are Azerbadjani of the same group as their brethren over the border in a Soviet republic; in the southwest are the Arabs and in the southeast Baluchi. Religious groups include Armenians, Jews, Christian Assyrians, and even Parsis, or Zoroastrians. The last are fire worshipers who perpetuate this, the ancient religion of Persia. Islam, however, is the religion of 98 percent of the population; and despite the numerous tribes and minorities Persian culture and traditions are very strong.

Mineral Resources. Iran possesses a variety of mineral resources but has been identified with only one—petroleum. Surface indications of oil fields in the form of bitumen, oil seeps, and gas leakage were known to the early civilizations of the country, and the bitumen was used as asphalt is used today. Iran in the early part of this century became the first Middle East oil country and immediately after World War II was the fourth-ranking producer of the world. The producing fields are in the southwest corner of the country at the head of the Persian Gulf (Fig.

Fig. 22.17—Oil Refinery (Upper Center), Abadan, Iran, at the Head of the Persian Gulf. This is the largest refinery in the world. (Courtesy, Iranian Embassy.)

22.17), and near the western frontier where Iran protrudes farthest into Iraq. Reserves are still large, and petroleum should continue to be the major mineral resource for many years.

Other minerals include bituminous coal in the Elburz Mountains, currently being mined, copper and iron ore produced in small quantities, and reported occurrences of precious metals, ferroalloy metals, and various salt deposits.

Transportation. Iran has from very early times been well traversed by roads. The ancient civilizations established trade routes to the Mediterranean that have remained more or less in active use to the present. Iran is one of the countries on the Silk Road to China, so that east-west caravan routes are also of long standing.

Modern roads for wheeled vehicles were built in the nineteenth century, and since 1925 there has been a program of motor road construction. The 1954 mileage of first-class roads is 9000 miles, with another 15,000 miles of second- and third-class roads. Much of the first-class mileage was paved during the development of the southern supply route to the U.S.S.R. in World War II.

Construction of trunk railroads was also undertaken in the 1920's. In a monumental construction feat the Trans-Iranian line from the Persian Gulf to the Caspian Sea was completed in 1938. The hundreds of bridges and 47 miles of tunnels in the mountain sections were financed within the country at great national strain. During World War II this line was vitally important in keeping the U.S.S.R. supplied with munitions from the United States.

Spur lines have been built east and west from the Trans-Iranian so that the major cities of the country are almost all connected by the rail net. The intention is to tie in the

Fig. 22.18—Line of Shafts Descending to *Karez*, Adrar, Iran. The underground course of the *karez* is excavated by digging from one shaft to the next. (Courtesy, American Geographical Society.)

Iranian system ultimately with the systems of all neighboring countries.

Agriculture. Two-thirds of Iran is rugged mountain or desert land and hence not naturally arable. But the melt-water from mountain summit snows feeds many oases, and descending streams are tapped by the ubiquitous *karez*, here encountered at their origin, for they are a Persian invention. The 20 miles or more in length of Iranian *karez* gives the country first place in utilization of the device (Fig. 22.18).

In the northwest dry farming is practiced at elevations of 6000 feet or more, with yields depending on the frequency of yearly rainfall. As in Iraq, many of the old irrigation systems are no longer functioning. They were allowed to fall into disuse in the previous two centuries during a period of population decline.

Wheat, barley, and **rice** are the staple grains, in that order of importance. Wheat is grown wherever possible, accounting for 80 percent of the cropland. On the humid Caspian lowland rice is the leading crop. Many kinds of **vegetables** are grown. Iran is famous for its **melons** and fine **fruits** of all sorts. **Grapes** are also widely cultivated on the plateau; it is said that wine was first made here. Iran is the fifth-ranking producer of **raisins.** Other dried fruits are also significant export items.

Cash crops also include **olives** from a small district on the north side of the Elburz mountains, **dates** from huge groves in Khuzistan, **citrus** fruits from the Caspian district, and **cotton, tobacco, sugar beets, tea,** and **opium poppies** from various districts.

About one-quarter of the population is seminomadic, so that livestock are also significant. Estimates of the animal population are 13 million **sheep,** 7 million **goats,** 2 million **cattle,** and smaller numbers of horses, donkeys, and camels.

Industries. The leading industry of Iran is **oil refining.** The British company that had the oil concession in Iran constructed the world's largest refinery on **Abadan Island** at the head of the Persian Gulf. The second-ranking industry is **textiles.** Cotton ginning, spinning, weaving, and garment making are all carried on in factories. Many other less

Fig. 22.19—Drying New Rugs on a Rock Ledge, Iran. (Courtesy, American Geographical Society, photograph by F. G. Clapp.)

important industries were established under the modernization program of the 1920's. A traditional industry—**rug weaving**—continues, however, to account for more than a third of the total value of exports (Fig. 22.19). Persian rugs have been famous the world over for centuries.

CITIES OF IRAN

Name	Type	Population
Tehran	Governmental-commercial	1,000,000 (1949)
Tabriz	Commercial	272,000 (1949)
Isfahan	Commercial	192,000 (1949)
Meshed	Commercial	191,000 (1949)
Hamadan	Commercial	122,000 (1949)
Resht	Commercial	110,000 (1949)
Khorramshahr	Seaport	20,000 (1947)

Fig. 22.20—Tehran, Iran. Ministry of Posts and Telegraph. (Courtesy, Iranian Embassy.)

Cities. Architecturally all of the Iranian cities reflect the distinctive Persian culture. They are characterized by numerous mosques, by flat-roofed buildings, and by miles of bazaars (streets under arcades). **Tehran** (Fig. 22.20) is the capital, principal industrial city, and hub of the transportation system. It has an unusually Western appearance because of the modernization program. It is in central Iran 70 miles south of the Caspian Sea, on the south side of the Elburz Mountains.

Tabriz, the chief commercial center of the northwest, is 400 miles northwest of Tehran. It is another of the old trade cities of the Silk Road. The city is dominated by magnificent ruined mosques.

Isfahan is a commercial center 250 miles south of the capital. It was, however, the former capital and contains many beautiful examples of Mohammedan architecture, including the second largest public square in the world. (The largest is Red Square in Moscow.)

Meshed, a commercial city in the northeast corner of Iran 470 miles from the capital, is the religious center and Mecca of Iran. It contains the shrine of a moslem martyr.

Hamadan and **Resht** are two "industrial" cities, the former a silk center and the latter the principal rug-weaving center of Iran. Both are basically commercial cities, however. Hamadan is 180 miles southwest of Tehran, Resht 225 miles to the northwest, in a rice district on the Caspian lowland.

Khorramshahr is the seaport of Iran and leading port of the Persian Gulf. It is located at the head of the Gulf on the Shatt-al-Arab, the boundary stream between Iraq and Iran at this point. It is the southern terminus of the Trans-Iranian railroad and benefited greatly from extensive port improvements made by the Allies during World War II.

Iran as a Whole. Present-day Iran is a paradox. In past times it was the home of great civilizations, and many refinements of its present culture indicate the rich tradition on which this culture rests. During the twentieth century its flood of oil production provided an enormous national revenue in the form of royalties paid by the British operating company to the Iranian government. In the period before World War II, this income enabled a start to be made on the extensive modernization of the country. Yet in the years following World War II Iran reached a state of near anarchy and collapse, and its future has become clouded.

The immediate cause of Iran's troubles was the emergence of a fanatic nationalism, due partly to the social and economic dislocations of World War II, partly to the political shock of protective occupation by the

Allies during the war. The nationalism led to the expulsion of the British oil company and the nationalization of the industry. In the resulting disruption of production Iran found that it had lost, at least temporarily, the financial benefits that had flowed from the industry and on which it had become dependent. Although the problem was resolved by the subsequent formation of an international operating company, the severe economic strain the country thus suffered will have repercussions for some time to come.

Basically, however, Iran's troubles are less the result of mismanagement of a national resource than they are an expression of serious flaws in the social and economic structure of the country. Despite the constructive use made of a good portion of the oil income, the great bulk of the population experienced no improvement whatever in their lot, either directly from the oil income itself or through the public works it financed. Iran remains a country of wretchedly poor peasants. Agriculture engages 80 percent of the population, yet over half the farmers are landless. The bulk of the farm land is held by a few hundred absentee landlords for whom most of the peasants labor on a share-crop basis. Productivity and yields are low because of the continued use of primitive methods, for under the existing system the landlords see no advantage to them in the introduction of modern methods and equipment. As a consequence the poor, illiterate peasantry has developed an intense nationalism that makes for great political instability.

QUESTIONS. Locate Sinkiang and name its principal desert. Describe the outstanding features of the topography. Compare the climate of Sinkiang with that of Mongolia. Compare the racial compositions and religions of the respective populations. Compare the degrees of modernization in each. Locate the chief agricultural and pastoral districts of Sinkiang. Discuss the strategic implications of Soviet control and influence over the greater portion of middle-latitude arid Asia.

Locate Afghanistan and explain its strategic significance. Describe the country's general topography. Describe its population. What are the major products? Describe the transportation situation. Why is the future outlook good for this country?

Locate and give a topographic description of Iran. Describe the climate, the population make-up. Describe its transportation system. What are *karez* and why are they so important in arid inner Asia? What are the chief agricultural products of Iran? Name a product for which Iran has always been famous. What are the two major Iranian industries? Discuss the future of Iran in the light of developments since World War II.

CHAPTER 23

Middle-Latitude Deserts and Steppes: Western Hemisphere

B. WESTERN UNITED STATES

Introduction. The middle-latitude steppe and desert region of North America is more readily and concisely defined than that of Eurasia. In brief, the steppe country is the **Great Plains** province to the east of the Rocky Mountains; the predominantly desert region may be broadly referred to as the intermontane basin, range, and plateau region in the United States between the Rockies on the east and the Sierra Nevada and Cascade ranges on the west. The boundary lines of these tracts are thus clearly indicated and they comprise distinctive units of vast size (Fig. 23.1).

These differences from the dissociated, less clearly outlined Asiatic occurrences are due to the subordination of *continentality* in North America to *mountain barriers* as the chief determinant of the desert-steppe region. In other words, the steppe and desert tracts of North America are in the rain shadow of continuous, high mountain ranges with a north-south orientation. This disposition of the mountains places them directly athwart the basic air flow of the westerlies, whereas in Asia the main trend of the mountains in the same latitudes is east-west. The east-west extension of the Asiatic ranges does block the southern monsoon from the interior of the continent, but the monsoon itself is a phenomenon of continentality. Moreover, as the mountains interfere only partially with the southeast monsoon they contribute to the overall irregularity of precipitation in the interior regions and hence to the discontinuity and random distribution of the Asiatic desert and steppe lands.

In North America the steppe country of the Great Plains is not only in the rain shadow of the Rockies but also in the lee of the wide belt of desert country which intervenes between the Rockies and the Pacific coast. Thus the westerlies are relatively dry even at high altitudes before they reach the crest of the Rockies. The Great Plains region is redeemed from desert conditions only because masses of moist air from the south and southeast have easy access to it. Continentality is nevertheless sufficient to reduce the rainfall potential such invasion suggests. In other words, the Great Plains are too far inland from both the Atlantic and the Gulf of Mexico to have abundant moisture reach them from these sources.

The middle-latitude desert region of North America is an extension northward of the warm, low-latitude desert bordering it in the United States and continuing into Mexico (see Chapter 13, p. 247). The extremes of aridity which give rise to desert conditions in the middle-latitude belt are due to its being a gigantic corridor between lofty mountain ranges. Thus the region is in the rain shadow of the High Sierra (Fig. 23.2) and Cascade ranges on the west and is cut off by the Rockies from random masses of moist air originating in the Gulf of Mexico.

477

MIDDLE LATITUDE DESERT AND STEPPE REGION
IN NORTH AMERICA

Fig. 23.2—Cima Dome, Mohave Desert, California, in Rain Shadow of the Sierra Nevada. (Courtesy, Eliot Blackwelder.)

1. THE GREAT PLAINS PROVINCE

Size and Location. The Great Plains extend over some 300,000 to 400,000 square miles, or approximately one-tenth to one-eighth of the United States. Their width ranges from 200 to 400 miles (greatest in the north), and they are about 1200 miles long. The province is bounded on the west by the base of the Rockies and on the east by the 100th meridian. Starting in the north it includes a small part of **Alberta** and **Saskatchewan** in Canada and much of **Montana,** and extends across western **North** and **South Dakota,** northeastern **Wyoming,** western **Nebraska,** eastern **Colorado,** western **Kansas,** northwestern **Texas,** and eastern **New Mexico**—a truly vast region (Fig. 23.1).

Topography. Almost all the Great Plains area has an apparently level surface. Actually the summit tracts slope eastward about 10 feet to the mile. At the base of the Rockies the altitude of the plain ranges from 3000 to 5000 feet; its eastern edge is about 1500 feet above sea level. The northern part, Montana and the Canadian lands, is an exception to the rule of general levelness. There the upland surface is made irregularly rolling and hummocky by glacial deposits (Fig. 23.3). Elsewhere the land was originally a smooth, unbroken apron of deposits

Fig. 23.1—Middle-Latitude Desert and Steppe Region in North America. In order to avoid excessive detail in climatic boundaries, no distinction is made on the map between the middle-latitude desert and middle-latitude steppe regions.

spread out from the base of the Rockies in the recent geologic past. Vast tracts of such level surface are still present. But subsequent erosion has developed a large number of valleys dissecting the upland plains. These valleys are narrow and deep (100 to 300 or more feet) near the mountains, shallow and wide (5 to 20 miles) near the eastern border of the province.

Other irregularities include such areas as the **sand hills** (Fig. 23.4) in northwestern Nebraska, built up by windblown materials from the dry beds of the shallow river valleys during periods of low water. A second is the **Bad Lands** of southwestern South Dakota at the eastern edge of the plains. There deep and intricate rain gullying has converted a wide area of originally level upland into a maze of sharp, barren ridges and dry, V-shaped troughs. Further, at the foot of the mountains in Colorado, streams have created a broad lowland with a surface considerably below the level of the plains to the east of the belt.

Another notable interruption of the general monotony of form and surface of the Great Plains is the **Black Hills** district of western South Dakota and northeastern Wyoming, a circular mountain mass rising many thousand feet above the general level of the surrounding surface. (The highest summit has an altitude of 7216 feet.) In the central area of the Black Hills the updomed plains rocks have all been eroded off; around the borders of the mountains the upthrust edges of these rock layers stand out as encircling ridges.

Special Climatic Characteristics. The Great Plains conform to the pattern of middle-latitude steppe regions in that precipitation is low, undependable, erratic in occurrence, and marked by occasional violent downpours. Seasonal and daily temperature extremes are also characteristic features.

Precipitation ranges from 10 inches in the north, farthest inland, to 26 inches in the south. With respect to plant growth these figures are equivalent, as the higher temperatures and hence greater evaporation in the south offset the greater rainfall there.

Fig. 23.3—Great Plains in Alberta, Canada. Cattle crossing Milk River in southern Alberta on their way to summer pasture. (Courtesy, National Film Board of Canada.)

In general, 70 percent of the annual rainfall comes during the growing season, chiefly as thunderstorms. Drought periods and years are frequent, especially in North and South Dakota, Kansas, and New Mexico.

Throughout the Great Plains temperatures of 100° F. and higher are experienced in summer. In winter the northern states, particularly Montana, Wyoming, and South Dakota, suffer from blizzards. Cold waves with temperatures below zero are common in winter as far south as Nebraska. In the belt of lands at the immediate base of the Rockies in Montana, Wyoming, and Colorado winter temperature rigors are offset by chinook winds. South of Nebraska summer heat waves provide the temperature extremes. Thus 20 to 25 successive days of 100° F. temperatures are experienced in Kansas. On the other hand, blizzards may sweep as far south as Texas.

A noteworthy climatic phenomenon of the Great Plains is the constancy of wind movement, a result of the vast expanses of level surface over which the air may sweep uninterruptedly for hundreds of miles. When

Fig. 23.4—Sand Hill Region of Nebraska. (Courtesy, Division of Nebraska Resources.)

the wind descends from the west down the slope of the plains it is, moreover, hot and drying. Shelter belts of trees planted athwart the course of the wind have been found appreciably effective in modifying its force over limited areas in their lee. They also reduce evaporation and heat loss from houses and afford some relief from the nerve strain induced by the wind's incessant sweep. Much more serious is the effect when, in association with prolonged drought, the dry, hot wind lifts up and carries away cubic miles of soil from lands in the southwest sections of the plains. These are the circumstances of the *dust bowl* development which spell ruin for the inhabitants of those areas. Tornadoes are also frequent in this section, but the total destruction one of these causes is limited to a narrow belt that may completely miss towns and homes.

The growing season on the Great Plains ranges from a low of 120 days in the far north to 180 days in Texas and New Mexico.

Agriculture. Much of the Great Plains area was once regarded as the "Great American Desert" (see Chapter 13, p. 247). Pioneer settlers bound for Oregon and California crossed them and the mountain barriers on their western border as fast as they could. Once it was realized, however, that the treeless *long-grass* prairie plains which had earlier been looked upon with suspicion were almost ideal agricultural areas it took only 50 years—1820 to 1870—to bring them completely under cultivation. There seemed to be no reason why the *short-grass* lands of the Great Plains, into which the prairies merged westward, would not prove equally productive. The government would give 160 acres for a homestead there as it had in the prairie country. But recurrent droughts proved disastrously that the short-grass lands were not the agricultural Eden they seemed.

It is now known that 600 to 2400 acres are needed to support a farm family on the arable parts of the plains, that agricultural practices different from those of the humid lands must be followed, and that much of the country is suitable only for grazing. In particular, dry farming and irrigation are the requisites for success.

The present agricultural utilization of the Great Plains is based on the recognition that, despite their general uniformity of climatic characteristics and topographic expression, their parts vary sufficiently to require the employment of different practices and products in different places for their successful exploitation. Beginning at the north with the Canadian section, where it includes southern Saskatchewan and the southeastern corner of Alberta, and extending southward across Montana, North and South Dakota, and part of eastern Colorado, is the **spring wheat** section. Here wheat is planted in the spring, after which the farmer waits and hopes through the summer that the rainfall will suffice for a crop.

In Wyoming, Colorado, Nebraska, Kansas, and Texas, with greatest production in Kansas, **winter wheat** is grown. These states have sufficiently mild winters to permit the grain to be sown and germinate in the fall and survive as green plants until spring, when the wheat grows rapidly to ripeness.

Thus the wheat harvest, which starts early in spring in Texas, moves progressively northward until it ends in late fall in the Canadian areas, where the decline to a minimal number of growing days limits the northward extension of production.

In Canada the Great Plains wheat fields reach to the base of the Rockies. In the mountain states south of Montana—that is, in Wyoming, Colorado, and New Mexico—wheat is grown only over the eastern parts of the region. The plains belt between the wheat fields and the mountains in these states is short-grass grazing country or is utilized agriculturally through irrigation projects. Thus in Colorado large acreages of irrigated lands are devoted to the production of **sugar beets** (Fig. 23.5). Elsewhere the forage crops **alfalfa** and **sorghum** are grown. Except for irrigation projects, the farther south, the greater the prominence of **cattle** raising. In this Texas is supreme, as it is also in **sheep.** In more arid New Mexico, however, sheep take precedence over cattle. The sand hill country of Nebraska is another important center of cattle raising. In the early 1950's the Texas Panhandle became a significant irrigated agricultural district, yielding wheat, sorghum, and alfalfa through the use of water from wells 200 to 400 feet down.

Fig. 23.5—Sugar Beets Being Carried From Storage Pile to Factory in Stream of Warm Water. (Courtesy, Sugar Research Foundation, Inc.)

Mineral Resources and Products. With the exception of Nebraska all the Great Plains states and the Canadian provinces are large-scale producers of **petroleum** and **natural gas.** Texas leads in both, and much of the gas that has superseded coal for home heating in the northeastern United States comes by pipe line from Great Plains fields. Although enormous deposits of **coal** underlie wide areas of the Great Plains, most of this is not of much value except to supply local needs. An exception is the coal of Colorado, some of which is anthracite.

The Black Hills situated in the middle of the Great Plains are highly mineralized. **Gold** was discovered there in 1875; today the district is the largest United States source of the precious metal.

There are also immense amounts of **salt** and some **potash** under the Great Plains. Both are mined in considerable quantity, the potash in New Mexico and the salt in Kansas.

Transportation. Transportation over the Great Plains has been from the start and still remains primarily a matter of east-west crossing. It began with the covered wagon and the Oregon Trail and California Trail, and was followed by the railroads, also with the west coast as their objective. Then came highways and air routes, again primarily to bridge the gap between the densely populated and humid East and the comparably well-settled moist west coast lands. There was never developed a trunk railroad or automobile route north-south over the plains. The nearest such route toward the east parallels the Mississippi River; in the west there is none until the Pacific coast is reached. Trunk railroad lines do follow diagonal routes southwestward across the plains, but their objectives are Pacific coast terminals. In brief, there is little demand for transportation of either goods or people across the north-south dimension of the Great Plains.

Industry. Other than processing food locally produced and consumed, and providing local services such as railroad repair shops, most of the cities and towns of the Great Plains have no noteworthy industrial developments. There are some significant exceptions to this generalization, however. Thus large **sugar refineries** are associated with sugar beet raising in northern irrigation districts; **copper smelting** and **refining** is carried on where ore from the mountains can be advantageously treated at sites of great hydroelectric developments. In western Colorado the close association of iron ore, coking coal, and limestone is the basis for a **steel** industry which has a large part of the entire Great Plains region as a home market not readily open to competitors from faraway centers of steel production. The mining developments of the Black Hills provide a similar opportunity for manufacturers of mining machinery and supplies to industries in towns at their base. It will be noted that aside from the sugar refineries these industrial developments are quite unrelated to the utilization of the Great Plains regions as they are conditioned by climatic factors.

wide area, serving particularly the mountain districts to the west and the extensive irrigation developments at the base of the mountains, to the east. It is the state capital and houses many agencies of the Federal government. But Denver owes much of its fame to its attractions as a resort city. It averages 175 to 200 frost-free days per year, far above the number at the same or lower latitudes on the Great Plains. This long growing season indicates moderate temperatures throughout the year; severe cold and high heat are the exceptions. There is free-

CITIES OF THE GREAT PLAINS

Name	State or Province	Type	Population (1950)
Denver	Colorado	Commercial, governmental, resort	416,000
Calgary	Alberta	Commercial-industrial	129,000
Amarillo	Texas	Commercial-industrial	74,000
Lubbock	Texas	Commercial	72,000
Regina	Saskatchewan	Commercial-governmental	71,000
Pueblo	Colorado	Industrial-mining	64,000
Colorado Springs	Colorado	Resort	46,000
Great Falls	Montana	Industrial-hydropower	39,000
Cheyenne	Wyoming	Commercial	32,000
Billings	Montana	Commercial	32,000
Odessa	Texas	Mining	30,000
Roswell	New Mexico	Commercial	26,000
Rapid City	South Dakota	Mining	25,000

Cities. In view of their remoteness both from large markets and from the sources of most raw materials it is apparent why large industrial centers have not been built up on the Great Plains. Aside from the home industries of food processing and packing regularly present in all market towns of a region of agricultural production, there are few exceptions to this general rule. These are at sites where some raw material or combination of materials permits manufactures of other kinds for local consumption.

The metropolis of all the Great Plains is **Denver,** Colorado (Fig. 23.6). Denver is advertised as "The Mile-High City" (altitude 5280 feet), truly a distinctive characteristic for a metropolitan center of its size. Despite that size, Denver conforms to the pattern of the Great Plains cities in that manufacturing for a national market is almost nonexistent. On the other hand, Denver is the dominant commercial center of a

Fig. 23.6—Denver, Colorado, Business District. (Courtesy, Advertising & Publicity Department, Colorado.)

dom from the high winds of the plains at the base of the mountains, and almost unlimited sunshine. In these parts Denver is a "natural" as a tourist haven.

In common with the other Great Plains communities situated along the base of the

Rockies, Denver may appropriately be designated a "portal city," a gateway to the mountain regions farther west. In fact, with its surpassing size compared to the others, it may be regarded as *the* portal city.

Calgary, Alberta, is another portal and market center, termed by its inhabitants "The Sunshine City of the Foothills." It has a further considerable industrial development based on the mining and oil activities of its district. **Great Falls,** Montana, is similarly a portal city and is also industrial because of the power developed by the falls of the Missouri River and used for copper refining and fabricating. **Helena,** still another portal, is the capital of Montana and the commercial center for the rich copper-mining district in the adjacent mountains. **Colorado Springs,** the site of the Air Force Academy, is a portal city 65 miles south of Denver and its rival for resort business. Yet another portal city is **Pueblo,** Colorado, 100 miles south of Denver and the outstanding industrial city of the Great Plains. It is situated where iron ore, coking coal, and limestone deposits are immediately accessible. With the three essentials for steelmaking thus locally available Pueblo has become the steel mill and heavy manufacturing center for the northwestern Great Plains. Besides being a portal city, **Roswell,** New Mexico, is the supply center for a wide area of ranch country and the nearby irrigation developments.

Billings, Montana, is primarily a market town for noteworthy irrigation districts; the emphasis is on sugar beets. Even more definitely, **Regina,** Saskatchewan, is a trade center in the spring wheat section, the "Queen of the Plains" in local acclaim. It has not experienced specialized industrial developments because it is too remote from large markets and from easy access to the supplies of a large variety of raw materials. The two Canadian cities Calgary and Regina have both expended considerable effort in planting trees, damming local streams to make lakes, and laying out pleasant parks. These features greatly enhance the attractiveness of the cities.

Rapid City, South Dakota, is the supply center for the mining developments of the Black Hills. **Amarillo, Lubbock,** and **Odessa,** Texas, are oil towns, although Amarillo and Lubbock are perhaps basically the great market towns and focal railroad points of the cattle ranch country of the Texas Panhandle.

QUESTIONS. Where are the middle-latitude steppe lands of North America? The middle-latitude desert lands? How is each bounded? How do their climatic causal conditions differ from those of similar lands in Asia? How do these differences affect the occurrences on the two continents?

State the dimensions of the Great Plains. What provinces and states are partly within them? What is their major topographic expression? List the departures from this general aspect. Characterize each exception briefly. In what respects do the Great Plains conform to the general climatic pattern of steppe lands? What is the range of temperatures? Of precipitation? What percentage of precipitation is received in the growing season? What wind phenomenon is characteristic of the Great Plains generally?

Account for the concept of the "Great American Desert." What difficulties were encountered in the agricultural conquest of the Great Plains? How are their different parts now utilized? What are the major mineral resources of the Great Plains? What is the significant characteristic of transportation on the Great Plains? Name industries of the Great Plains region that produce for external markets.

Account for Denver as a metropolis. Name three portal cities, stating for each some additional urban function that promoted population growth. Name two market towns for irrigation districts; for the spring wheat section; for mineral production.

2. THE DESERT REGION— THE INTERMONTANE PROVINCE

Size and Extent. Although what proves to be truly middle-latitude desert in North America is only a limited part of the former "Great American Desert," this remainder is nevertheless a region of impressive size. It includes practically all of Utah and Nevada and considerable portions of New Mexico,

Arizona, California, Washington, Oregon, and Idaho. Altogether the desert territory extends over 600,000 square miles, a region 12 times the size of New York State. It is evident that on the basis of size the potentials of this vast tract would be enormous if it were relieved of the handicap of a desert climate. But even as a desert country it has become a region of notable significance in the economy of the United States.

An east-west line drawn through the headwaters of the Little Colorado River would serve as an approximate southern border of the middle-latitude desert areas which are arid because of topography and continentality. The Sierra Nevada and Cascade ranges are their western limits, the Rockies their eastern margin, and the Spokane River their northern terminus (Fig. 23.1).

Topographically and geologically the desert belt has three main subdivisions. From south to north these are the **high plateaus** of Arizona, New Mexico, and Utah, the **basin and range province** (or **Great Basin**) centered over Nevada and Utah, and the **Columbia lava plateaus** of Oregon, Idaho, and Washington.

The High Plateaus

Topography. The high plateaus are usually

referred to as the **Colorado Plateau** because the course of the Colorado River across Arizona is the region of their most impressive development. The plateaus of Utah and New Mexico are of the same nature, however. The highest plateau surfaces have altitudes of 11,600 feet; the lower levels reach 5000 feet. Throughout this area a vast platform of hard, nearly flat-lying rocks has been dissected into an intricate maze of deep canyons and towering cliffs. Overland travel across much of this country verges on the impossible; transport except by animal or human porterage *is* impossible.

The greatest of the canyons is the **Grand Canyon** of the Colorado (Fig. 23.7), over a mile deep and in places 15 miles wide. Except to express dimensions words do not suffice to describe it; it is recognized by many world travelers as the outstanding scenic wonder on earth. Standing on its rim the observer is confronted with a vast abyss of dreamy silence; the rushing river is seen as a thread at the bottom of the gulf but no sound of its flow can be heard at the canyon top. Across the canyon the light falls on an unending series of cliffs and shelves—giant stairways leading only to an ever changing pattern of sun and shadow.

Elsewhere the topographic marvels of this country are so many that even magnificent monuments can receive only passing men-

Fig. 23.7—Grand Canyon of the Colorado. (Spence Air Photos.)

Fig. 23.8—Bryce Canyon, Utah. (National Parks Service.)

tion. Here may be seen, among others, such scenic wonders as **Bryce Canyon** (Fig. 23.8), a panorama of castles and cliffs of lacework in stone; **Rainbow Natural Bridge** (Fig. 23.9), a natural arch of surpassing grandeur; **Monument Valley** (Fig. 23.10), a weird assemblage of monoliths suggesting the ruins of a lost world; the **Painted Desert,** a wide carpet and drapery of vivid poster colors (Fig. 2.5); **Zion Canyon,** with enormous bastions of white rock set on bases of deep red; and **Coon Butte,** an enormous circular depression, probably due to the impact of a great meteorite. All are on such a gigantic scale that extravagant adjectives only faintly convey the awed impression made on those privileged to view their splendor.

Fig. 23.9—Rainbow Natural Bridge, Utah. (National Parks Service.)

Climatic Features. Although the westerlies have been drained of their moisture in reaching the Colorado Plateau, the air is not completely devoid of water vapor; hence exceptional heating and its rise to high altitudes, with resulting expansion and cooling, cause precipitation in violent thunderstorms and cloudbursts. These are, of course, very irregular in both time and place of occurrence. A region recorded as having five inches of rainfall annually may get it all in one downpour only several hours long. Then ordinarily dry gullies become raging torrents for a short period. Much more dependably and consistently, on the other hand, the flow of air across the summit levels of the plateaus effect sufficient cooling to bring about gentle precipitation in both summer and winter.

The level of precipitation ranges progressively from five inches in the lowest valley floors to 25 inches on the summits of the highest plateaus. This is a fortunate distribution, for it affords, in places at least, a trickle of water for springs and streams at the lower elevations. Water holes along the stream beds survive the dry periods and are the source of supply for sheep and cattle and for small irrigation developments on narrow valley floors.

Temperature changes follow a pattern that in a sense matches that of precipitation. The extremes are experienced on the low-altitude areas, on the hot rather than cold side. Temperatures of 100° F. and over are common; the nights are cool—40° to 50° F. Because of the cool nights and low humidity the high temperatures are much more easily endured than they are in most regions. The almost unfailing sunshine also contributes to the general agreeableness of the climate.

The natural vegetation cover corresponds to these climatic elements. Cactus and sage-

Fig. 23.10—Monument Valley, Arizona. (Courtesy, *Stage Coach,* Walter Wanger Production.)

brush occupy the lowlands; the lower slopes have a bunch grass cover; at higher levels scattered and stunted small trees grow; and the highest plateau summits are covered with a substantial forest of conifers. These trees are so inaccessible for commercial lumbering that they serve only the needs of local inhabitants.

Agriculture. Other than small-scale irrigation developments on valley floors based on springs and trickles from the summit lands, agriculture is nonexistent in the Colorado Plateau district. This is grazing country, primarily for **sheep** and to a lesser extent for **cattle.** The sheep are pastured in the higher altitudes in summer, on the lower slopes in winter. There the grasses dry to natural hay which is highly nutritious. **Wool** is a sufficiently high-value product to permit transport by pack animal to railheads and hence to provide a meager cash income to the "desert" people.

Mining and Industry. Copper mining was traditionally the most important activity in the desert area, but since the opening of the atomic age the rocks of the plateaus have been found to contain large deposits of **uranium** minerals. Most of the mines are small and short lived, but constant new discoveries and an expansion of processing facilities to keep pace with the finds have made the plateau area one of the world's major sources of uranium. The uranium rush has helped spark a general booming development of the entire area.

People. The Colorado Plateau may well be regarded as the last stronghold of the American Indian in the United States. Elsewhere Indian reservations are small and situated in the midst of lands occupied and utilized by white people. In Arizona and New Mexico, however, there are large regions of the plateau area not open to settlement by whites. In these wide territories *Apache, Hopi, Navajo, Zuñi,* and *Pueblo* Indians still maintain their tribal life and customs (Fig. 23.11). They are the chief sheep raisers of the country. Only Oklahoma (formerly Indian Territory) has a greater Indian population than either Arizona or New Mexico.

Other than the mining populations the white inhabitants of the Colorado Plateau are mainly the farmers in the irrigation districts, some cattle and sheep men, and those serving the **tourist** business. This last group is large. Besides the attraction of the Indian cultures and the magnificent scenic phenomena, the dry air, bright sunshine, and mod-

Fig. 23.11—Taos Pueblo, Northern New Mexico. Ancient adobe structure. Indian is clothed in his light summer blanket. (Courtesy, New Mexico State Tourist Bureau.)

erate temperatures of the plateau district attract hundreds of visitors whose health is adversely affected by the climatic conditions of more humid lands.

CITIES OF THE PLATEAU DISTRICT

Name	State	Type	Population (1950)
Albuquerque	New Mexico	Resort, commercial	97,000
Santa Fe	New Mexico	Resort, governmental, commercial	28,000

Cities. The two large cities of the Colorado Plateau are situated on the southern boundary of the district, where the transcontinental railroads traverse the states of New Mexico and Arizona. They owe their recent great growth to increasing popularity as winter resort centers.

Albuquerque, the largest city of New Mexico, is another tourist center located on the upper Rio Grande. **Santa Fe,** in mountains 55 miles to the northeast, is one of the oldest cities in the United States and is the capital of the state. It was founded in 1610 by the Spanish. Both cities have also preserved the "pueblo" architecture from earlier periods.

The Great Basin

Topography. The Great Basin or basin and range province extends over most of Utah and Nevada and includes that part of California east of the Sierra Nevada (Fig. 23.1). As the phrase "basin and range" suggests, the topography of this section of the middle-latitude desert area consists of disconnected, short mountain ranges separated by level-floored basins (see Chapter 2). Collectively, the ranges have a general north-south trend but do not occur in continuous lines; rather, they are irregularly offset so that they are spaced fairly evenly over the whole of the area. Within the basin some ranges rise to 10,000 feet or more. The summits of the higher ones are lifted out of the desert climate and may be crowned with forests. As in the Colorado Plateau the low temperatures of the heights condense enough moisture to maintain trees on the mountaintops, green meadows in upland valleys, and running streams down the mountainsides. The larger of these streams persist to the levels of the desert basins, where they afford water for irrigation of tracts of limited extent.

The region as a whole is one of interior drainage, but the basins between the ranges stand at different levels and are, for the most part, disconnected.

The most famous of the basins is **Death Valley,** containing the lowest point in the United States. In addition to its desert features Death Valley has a variety of volcanic phenomena—lava flows, cones, and craters. Its evil reputation was earned when most of the members of an 1849 gold rush party on their way to the California gold fields perished from thirst in an attempt to cross the valley.

Two areas, on opposite sides of the basin, get exceptional supplies of water. In the far southwest the **Owens Valley** parallels the eastern base of the Sierra Nevada. The combined volume of the streams coursing down the mountainsides suffices to maintain the Owens River for 120 miles along the axis of the valley. Its flow supports a considerable ranching and irrigation development which was somewhat curtailed, however, by the requisitioning of a large volume of the water flow for the Los Angeles city water supply.

A similar situation exists at the far northeast corner of the basin province. There the **Wasatch Mountains** are the water source. Streams from them fill **Lake Utah,** which overflows into the **Jordan River,** much of whose water is diverted to irrigate wide tracts of land. The rest empties into **Great Salt Lake.**

Climatic Characteristics. The climate of the basin province is colder than that of the Colorado Plateau because of the higher latitude. On the other hand, the highest temperature ever recorded in the United States —134° F.—was on the floor of Death Valley. In midwinter, however, even Death Valley is pleasantly cool, with a 70° temperature at midday.

Agriculture. The highest mountain summits, as previously noted, are covered with open forest. Upland valleys are meadows; and the lower slopes of the mountains and the higher basins support scattered growths of bunch grass (Fig. 23.12). Wherever a watering hole or spring is available **cattle** are grazed. It is a common practice to pasture the cattle at high altitudes in summer and bring them down in winter to graze on the bunch grass or hay-feed them in corrals. In view of the sparseness of the natural fodder the number of cattle that can be carried on the range is severely limited. Accordingly,

Fig. 23.12—Bunch grass, scattered growth, Deep Springs Valley, California. (O. D. von Engeln.)

ranches are isolated and far apart. Noteworthy also are the large flocks of **sheep** pastured on the steep eastern slopes of the Sierra Nevada.

There are extensive irrigation districts fed by water from lakes and reservoirs in the northeast and northwest of the basin at the foot of the Wasatch Mountains and the northern Sierra Nevada, respectively. In these areas **sugar beets, fruits, vegetables, potatoes, corn** for ensilage, and **alfalfa** in support of a **dairy** industry are commercially produced. But for the most part the irrigated lands are small plots based on the diversion of mountain streams persisting to the level of the basin floors.

Mineral Resources. The basin province had an early history of bonanza gold mining which left behind "ghost" towns when placer and vein deposits were eventually worked out. Since then mining in the basin has become much more enduringly stabilized through the exploitation of enormous masses of low-grade **copper** and **silver-lead** ores. **Bingham Canyon** in northern Utah and **Ely** in eastern Nevada are representative of the copper deposits, the **Tintic** district of Utah of the silver-lead type. Only Chuquicamata in Chile (see Chapter 13, p. 240) has greater reserves of copper ore than the Bingham deposit. In the early 1950's the extension of the **uranium** boom from the plateau country affected this area as well.

People. Unlike the plateau province the Great Basin contains only a small Indian population. In considerable part the pre-Columbian Indians of the plateau country were enterprising peoples dependent chiefly on irrigation agriculture for their subsistence. For hunters and collectors, such as the Great Basin Indians were, the desert lands could sustain only a sparse population.

The white population of the more remote ranches is of the frontier type. In these parts the cowboy tradition of the United States is probably best preserved. Whereas the Great Plains ranches now are mostly fenced lands, much of the basin desert is still open range.

In the large irrigation districts and in the mining towns the assemblage of American types closely resembles that encountered in similar communities elsewhere in the United States. An exception is the *Mormon* population of Utah, centering around Great Salt Lake. In 1848 a large colony of people united by strong religious convictions settled there as a body and began irrigation agriculture. They were so successful that their settlement was self-sustaining from the start. The coherence of the Mormons has endured, and they have created a rich and populous oasis in this part of the basin desert.

Industry. The **smelting** of **ores** and **refining** of **metals, sugar,** and **oil** are about the only large-scale industries in the Great Basin province. In common with cities and towns elsewhere the basin communities have the "domestic" industries concerned with food processing. In addition there are such manufactures as stoves, soap, candy, and printing.

CITIES OF THE GREAT BASIN

Name	State	Type	Population (1950)
Salt Lake City	Utah	Commercial, governmental, industrial	182,000
Ogden	Utah	Commercial, industrial	57,000
Reno	Nevada	Resort	38,000
Provo	Utah	Commercial-resort	29,000
Las Vegas	Nevada	Commercial-resort	25,000

Cities. The growth of **Salt Lake City** in a desert region to become a metropolitan center bespeaks the extent and high productivity of the irrigated lands at the western foot of the Wasatch Mountains. The size of these tracts and the high yields obtained from them are indicative of the large volume of water here available for irrigation use. Salt Lake City also profits by its industrial activities: sugar refining based on the oasis production of sugar beets; ore processing, smelting, and refining of the large recovery of metallic minerals in nearby districts; oil refineries; printing and publishing. As a governmental center it is the capital of the state. It is the headquarters of the Mormon Church and is significant as an educational center through the presence of two universities. In brief, by absorbing to itself practically all the varieties of city functions Salt Lake City has acquired its size and metropolitan status in a region that on first appraisal would not be expected to support an urban center of such magnitude.

Ogden, the city next in size, is only one-third as large as Salt Lake City and is the only other significant urban center in a territory four and a half times as large as New York State. Ogden owes its rank to the fact that it functions as a "railport" for the metropolis 35 miles to the south. It is the largest railroad center between the Rockies and the Pacific coast, and its location, like that of Chicago and Winnipeg, is related to a lake

barrier. Great Salt Lake is so shallow, however, that the east-west transcontinental route goes right across it on a trestle. Hence Ogden is not situated at the end of the lake but at the middle of its eastern side where the trunk railroad comes, as it were, into port.

Reno is the largest city of Nevada, on the Truckee River where it affords hydropower. The setting is scenically and climatically delightful, circumstances that have promoted its development as a resort. Nevada's liberal laws regarding gambling and divorce attract a large transient population and provide the basis for a boisterous civic exuberance typified in the municipal slogan "The Biggest Little City in the World." Reno is, further, the market town for the surrounding cattle-raising country and adjacent mining districts.

Provo is in a rich irrigation district, serves nearby mining centers, and is a notable summer resort. **Las Vegas** is the focal point of the Hoover Dam utilization of the Colorado River, because of which, in part, its size increased by 12 times between 1920 and 1950. Like Reno it has also became a notable gambling resort.

QUESTIONS. What states are as a whole or in part included in the middle-latitude desert region of North America? How is it bounded? What are its subdivisions? What are the chief topographic characteristics of the Colorado Plateau region? What is the range of altitudes there? Name scenic wonders other than the Grand Canyon in the plateau area. How does the precipitation of the lowlands and summits of the plateaus differ? What are the precipitation seasons? Discuss temperature ranges; distribution of natural vegetation. What agricultural utilization is made of the plateau lands? Why is sheep raising so general? What are the two chief mineral products of the plateau district? What is the status of the American Indian in the district? Name the three large cities. What geographic conditions are common to all three?

What is the nature of the mountains in the basin and range province? Of the basins? Where and why are exceptionally large supplies of fresh water available for irrigation in the province? Why are cattle ranches far apart in the province? Why are modern copper-mining developments relatively durable enterprises? Account for the notable success in the utilization of the Great Salt Lake district. Compare transportation in the Great Basin with that in the Colorado Plateau district. What are the large-scale industries of the Great Basin? Account for the large size of Salt Lake City. How does Ogden resemble Chicago and Winnipeg? Account for the prosperity of Reno.

The Columbia Lava Plateaus

Topographic Features. The northern division of the desert region, the Columbia lava plateaus, is the creation of prehistoric volcanic activity. Here lava was poured out, layer on layer, in such enormous volume as to engulf completely a region of 100,000 to 200,000 square miles. Where they have since been cut through by streams the lava flows appear as layers piled up to thicknesses of 3000 feet or more (Fig. 23.13).

The Rockies are the eastern boundary of the Columbia lava plateaus, but the Cascade Range takes over from the Sierra Nevada as the western boundary of this section of the desert country. The 42nd parallel is the southern boundary of both Oregon and Idaho, and by coincidence is also the southern Columbia plateau border. On the north the international boundary between the United States and Canada also happens to coincide with the border of the lava plateaus, which here abut against a westerly offshoot of the Rockies (Fig. 23.1).

As could be expected from the origin of the surface of the region, much of the country is remarkably level. This is especially true of the **Snake River Plains** of southern Idaho. There the eruptions took place so recently, geologically speaking, that the surface of the land is the bare top of the cooled and hardened lava. Over much of this surface only a thin layer of soil has developed. But there are places where soil deposited from adjoining highlands is present.

In the same latitudinal belt in southeastern Oregon is the **Harney Basin,** 8000 square miles in extent, a region of interior drainage. Its western part is so barren that it has

earned the name "Great Sandy Desert." Although the Harney Basin, like the Snake River Plains, is underlain by horizontal lava layers, these have sagged to produce the basin development. Moreover, the cover material is not the hard lava rock but volcanic dust so loose, porous, and thick (70 feet) that all precipitation sinks underground as soon as it falls.

Wedged between the Harney Basin and the Snake River Plains, thus occupying southeastern Oregon and southwestern Idaho, is the **Payette Section.** This is a region of lava layers alternating with old lake beds.

North of the Payette Section, from which it is separated by lesser mountains, is the **Palouse Country,** the core of a wider area in these latitudes referred to as the **Inland Empire.** The Palouse Country is a region of rolling hills composed of fine-textured soils 50 to 75 feet deep. The upper levels of this material are evidently composed of wind-blown dust derived from drier country to the south and west.

On the north side of the Palouse Country there is an extensive area known as the **scab lands,** an extremely desolate region made up of interlacing, wide, steep-sided, and dry channels. These are the old watercourses of an enormous volume of melt-waters from the great ice age glacier of these parts. The channels are known as "coulees," the largest of which is **Grand Coulee** (Fig. 23.14). Much of the region is sandy desert.

The Columbia plateau district is dominated by the mighty **Columbia River** that enters it from the north. The **Snake River** from the south rivals the Columbia in size and has a magnificent gorge. At the base of the Cascades the **Yakima River** in Washington and the **Deschutes** in Oregon are notable watercourses. These streams derive their large volumes from the high mountains surrounding and within the plateau country. The orographic precipitation in summer in addition to the spring and summer melting of the mountain snow cover contributes much to maintain the volume of flow in the streams.

Climatic Characteristics. Although the

Fig. 23.13—Eroded Lava Beds of the Snake River Area of the Columbia Lava Plateau. Twin Sisters Peak near Wallula, Washington. Snake River Valley floor in the distance. (Courtesy, Washington State Advertising Commission.)

Fig. 23.14—Grand Coulee, Washington. (Spence Air Photos.)

great streams of the Columbia plateaus derive their volume chiefly from the mountains in which they rise, their persistence through the desert lands is favored by the climatic factor of decreased evaporation due to lower average yearly temperatures. The arid regions of Washington average only 60° to 65° F. in July.

Moreover, the influence of altitude on precipitation is much more pronounced in these northern parts. Although the high altitudes of the level plateau summits are relatively ineffective in squeezing moisture from the air, any slightly higher elevation within the plateau tends to induce precipitation. Thus, while the Cascade Range casts a rain shadow that is responsible for the general aridity of the province, it does not entirely prevent moisture from the Pacific from reaching the interior areas of the Columbia plateaus states.

Again, latitude places these regions outside the oppressive heat of the desert belt farther south, but a residue of marine warmth conveyed across the Cascades barrier makes the winter cold much less rigorous than would be expected at those latitudes. Winters in eastern Washington are distinctly mild in comparison with those of Montana at the same latitude. This softening of the severities of winter in Washington is reflected in the number of frost-free days in the two states: 120–140 on the plains of northern Montana, 160–180 at the same latitude in Washington.

Agriculture. In its pristine state practically all the Columbia plateaus province was grazing land. Bunch grasses and water were available almost everywhere. Much of the country is still range land on which large herds of **cattle** find sustenance.

Special conditions of climate, soil, and water supply, however, have permitted the reclamation of vast tracts to higher agricultural use. Whereas dry farming and irrigation are practices of large importance in the Colorado Plateau and Great Basin provinces of the middle-latitude desert region they reach their acme of significance in the Columbia plateaus province.

Outstanding in this connection is the Palouse Country as a **wheat**-growing district with dry-farming techniques. There the climatic regime is ideally suited to winter wheat. The heaviest precipitation is received in winter and spring. Temperatures are high enough through the cold months to preclude winterkilling of the fall-sown grain. During the cold months the grain makes its green growth, and the deep, silty soil retains sufficient moisture during the early summer to foster the maturing of the wheat. In the dry summer months the kernels fill out and ripen. Moreover, the yellow fields of ripened grain can stand unharmed a long time awaiting the harvester. Though the land in the Palouse Country is rolling rather than level the slopes are so gentle that all operations from sowing to reaping can be done by machine. As a consequence the Palouse Country is one of the leading wheat regions of North America. The yield per acre is higher than anywhere else on the continent. Unfortunately the precipitation is not high enough to permit annual cropping, so dry farming is necessary and in the Palouse Country is a reliable practice.

Irrigation is practiced in all the Columbia plateaus province where streams that descend from the enclosing and interior highlands supply the water. The streams have been utilized on a progressively grander scale through the construction of enormous dams to create huge reservoirs for both irrigation and generation of hydroelectricity.

These developments are too numerous to permit separate mention of each, but the **Grand Coulee** project (Fig. 2.12), as perhaps the most representative example of reclamation of the desert lands of the Columbia plateaus, indicates the general significance of such undertakings for the agricultural utilization of the province.

Just north of the scab lands district a dam 550 feet high has been erected across the Columbia River, forming a 27-mile lake. Part of the flow of the river is used to develop enormous hydroelectric energy, which in turn operates pumps capable of lifting great volumes of water from the lake level 1280 feet over the barrier between the lake and the head of the Grand Coulee. One hundred gallons of water going through the turbines lifts 80 gallons from the lake into the Grand Coulee. This water is then distributed down the Coulee by irrigation canals and ditches. The amount available suffices to irrigate over a million acres of land formerly only sagebrush plain. The chief crop is **alfalfa hay** for winter feeding and fattening of the cattle and sheep of the district. Sugar beets and grain sorghum can also be profitably grown. At the dam a large surplus of power beyond that needed for pumping the irrigation water is available to the Pacific Northwest and incidentally to power the largest **aluminum** plant in the United States.

The irrigated lands at the eastern base of the Cascades are largely utilized for orchard crops. Outstanding is the production of **apples**; up to one-fifth of the total United States crop is harvested here. Other fruits such as **pears** and **cherries** are also important. A special item is **hops** for the brewing industry.

Industry. Aside from the food-processing plants common to market towns in every region of the United States the industries of

more than local importance in the Columbia plateaus province are nearly all related to the availability of large amounts of hydroelectricity at low cost. Thus there are **aluminum** and **magnesium** reduction plants, the former in some instances utilizing material which had its source in the Caribbean. Flour milling for sales outside the province, based on the great wheat yield of the Palouse Country, on ample hydropower, and on access to trunk railroad transportation is also of considerable importance. Since the bulk of flour is almost as great as that of raw wheat, transportation costs of the processed material are hardly greater than for the raw grain. So also with a **textile** industry based on the local supply of **wool**. Timber from the surrounding mountains supports lumber mills and furniture factories.

CITIES OF THE COLUMBIA LAVA PLATEAUS

Name	State	Type	Population (1950)
Spokane	Washington	Commercial-industrial	162,000
Yakima	Washington	Commercial	38,000
Boise	Idaho	Governmental-industrial	34,000
Pocatello	Idaho	Commercial-industrial	26,000

Fig. 23.15—Spokane, Washington. Air view showing Spokane River and falls. (Courtesy, Washington State Advertising Commission.)

Cities. **Spokane** (Fig. 23.15) is the only city of really large size in the Columbia plateaus province. Its preëminence derives from its function as the commercial center for the rich Inland Empire and its large wheat production. The high falls of the Spokane River at the city site early fostered flour milling. Enormous additional volumes of power available from the Grand Coulee development, and already existing city and railroad facilities made Spokane an appropriate location for large aluminum and magnesium plants. Rolling mills and railroad and machine shops add to the industrial activity. In the decade between 1940 and 1950 Spokane increased in size by one-third. The indicated great expansion of irrigated lands within the Inland Empire, together with the capacity of the hydroelectric developments to supply all needed power, promises continued rapid growth for Spokane.

Yakima, Boise, and **Pocatello** are all three market towns for their districts. Yakima and Boise serve large irrigation districts. Boise, as the capital of Idaho, has also a large governmental population. Pocatello is primarily a railroad center.

3. THE ROCKY MOUNTAINS

Topography. The Rocky Mountain system is comprised of a great number of separate ranges that overlap sufficiently to make a continuous north-south belt of highland country from the southern United States almost to the Arctic Ocean in northern Canada. There is no easy passage across this belt. In the United States it intervenes between the steppe lands of the Great Plains and the arid regions of the Colorado Plateau, Great Basin, and Columbia Plateaus (Fig. 23.1).

Although not the greatest mountains of the West, the Rockies rise to far greater elevations and are much more rugged than any of the mountains in the eastern parts of North America. Range altitudes of 12,000 feet are common; many peaks in Colorado are above 14,000 feet. The Rockies are of exceedingly diverse structure; all kinds of rocks in all kinds of attitudes are present.

Certain features and phenomena do, however, stand out. One of these is the occurrence of so-called "trenches" or "parks" within the ranges. The trenches are a development of the northern Rockies and occur especially behind what is termed the **Front Range** in Colorado. They are wide, unobstructed, linear depressions with floors at altitudes of 7500 to 9000 feet or more—troughs that extend for long distances between the ranges. The high altitudes of their floors and their wide expanses of level land in the midst of the mountains makes the "parks" favorite recreation areas. **Estes Park, North, Middle,** and **South parks,** and the **Bitterroot Valley** are among those widely known.

Another feature of the Rocky Mountain region is the **Yellowstone National Park** with its geysers and hot springs. Although these occur elsewhere in the world, at no other place is there so great and varied an assemblage of such phenomena. The men who first reported the existence of this wonderland of 3400 square miles (over two-thirds the size of Connecticut) at the northwest corner of Wyoming were considered tellers of outrageous tall stories.

Climatic Aspects. As is true of lofty mountains everywhere, climates in the Rockies are vertically rather than horizontally patterned. The lower slopes are, like the adjoining plains and basins, arid. With increasing altitude and higher precipitation trees appear as a belt at heights only moderately greater than the desert floors. At altitudes where the winter cold does not permit trees to survive, mountain meadows are developed. These in turn give way to bare rock ledges and slopes littered with boulders in the summit tracts. Snow-capped peaks do not appear in the southern Rockies of the United States but are the rule in the Canadian ranges. Drifting winter snows suffice, however, to maintain small glaciers in a few places in the United States, of which **Glacier National Park** in Montana is best known. Elsewhere, especially at **Sun Valley,** Idaho, deep powder snow, moderate cold, clear clean air, and bright sun make ideal winter sports resorts.

Fig. 23.16—Georgetown, Colorado, an Old Rocky Mountain Mining Town. Note the tailings (waste rock) from prospect holes and mine entrances on the side and at the base of the mountain. (Courtesy, Colorado Advertising & Publicity Department.)

Mineral Resources. The whole extent of the Rockies is dotted with mining developments (Fig. 23.16), but for the most part they are small and their number is steadily declining. When a vein or lode runs out there is nothing to do but abandon the workings. Thus **Leadville,** Colorado, had its greatest production of silver in 1879, when it was a community of 35,000 people. In 1950 the population had declined to 4000.

Montana, Colorado, and Idaho are now the leading Rocky Mountain mining states. Montana ranks first because of the greatest exception in the Rockies to the rule that ore deposits are rather limited. This exception is the great **copper** deposit at **Butte,** Montana, where the whole of a low mountain is a mass

of veins and lodes. From it over $2 billion worth of copper, silver, and gold have been recovered since 1880, and it is estimated that the area can be profitably mined until the year 2000.

The mineralized areas usually occur in districts. In Idaho one such district is that of **Coeur d'Alene,** at the north end of the state, a large producer of **lead, zinc,** and **silver.** In Colorado there are three important districts, of which **Cripple Creek,** south of Denver, is representative. In 1950 Cripple Creek had a population of only 1427.

Although the Rockies have been well combed over by prospectors it is not to be assumed that their mineral possibilities have been exhausted. The new finds, however, will probably be of types of minerals not earlier in demand. Thus over 70 percent of the world's supply of **molybdenum** is obtained from the largest single mine in North America at **Climax,** Colorado. Again, finds of **cobalt** and **thorium** have been made in Idaho. Especially active search goes on for uranium minerals, unknown or valueless when the copper, gold, and silver deposits were discovered.

Forest Resources. The forest resources of the Rockies are far less than those of the mountains bordering the Atlantic and Pacific coasts. Lack of moisture on the lower slopes and killing cold at the higher altitudes severely limit the extent of forests in the Rockies. Only in northern Idaho are there trees up to three feet in diameter. More than 30 percent of Idaho is forest covered, however, and **lumbering** is an industry of considerable importance in the state. Elsewhere the Rocky Mountain forests are composed of small trees in thin stands.

In general, exploitation of the forests is to satisfy regional demands. Mine timbers are wanted in almost every Rocky Mountain locality. The mountain forests are also the local source of lumber to meet the needs of the populations adjacent in the treeless Great Plains and desert provinces. Local lumber mills at the base of the mountains at many sites convert the logs to the forms required for construction purposes and furniture manufacture.

Agriculture. Grazing of **cattle** and **sheep** is the major agricultural activity of the Rocky Mountain province. In many localities there is a migration of the herds and flocks to high-altitude mountain pastures in summer. On the way up in spring and down in fall the open forest lands are cropped. This commonly results in overgrazing and soil erosion, however, as the timber belts will not support the number of animals that can be maintained on the highland meadows.

Rather surprisingly there is also considerable crop production at remote sites within the mountains. The relatively level, high-altitude "park" lands have a long enough growing season to permit the maturing of barley, potatoes, and a variety of vegetables. Fresh vegetables are in great demand by the mining populations. Barley is fed to pigs to produce bacon, a mainstay in the diet of the prospector.

CITIES OF THE ROCKY MOUNTAINS

Name	State	Type	Population (1950)
Butte	Montana	Mining-commercial	33,000
Missoula	Montana	Mining-commercial	23,000
Coeur d'Alene	Idaho	Mining	12,000
Rock Springs	Wyoming	Mining	11,000

Cities. In view of Rocky Mountain topography, climate, and resources it could be expected that cities within the province would be few and small. In other provinces communities of the size here listed would fail of notice. The small Rocky Mountain cities are all mining centers. **Butte,** Montana (Fig. 3.7), is referred to as the largest mining town in the United States. Its size and relative permanence indicate the size of the copper deposits on which it is based. On the other hand, even though Butte is also the commercial and industrial center of Montana, its population has declined since 1930.

Missoula, Montana, with copper and lead mines, is in the midst of the mountains on a valley floor at the junction of two streams. A wide acreage of arable land there provides for large agricultural and horticultural production, and enough beet production to maintain a sugar factory. Missoula is also on the main line of a transcontinental railroad.

Coeur d'Alene, Idaho, is the center of the mining district to which it gives its name. **Rock Springs'** mineral background is coal.

C. SOUTHERN AND WESTERN ARGENTINA

General Aspects. The middle-latitude desert and steppe region in South America covers 750,000 square miles of southern and western Argentina, over two-thirds of the total area of the country and equivalent to more than three times the combined areas of the Pacific coast states (Fig. 23.17). Just as the Atacama region (see Chapter 14, p. 239) is a rain-shadow product of the Andes in the trade wind belt, so the Argentine region is a rain-shadow product of the south-

SOUTHERN AND WESTERN ARGENTINA

Fig. 23.17—Southern and Western Argentina. The inset compares the area of the region with an equivalent area of the United States (states in white).

ern Andes in the westerlies belt. The narrowness of the continent in the middle latitudes, however, makes the region climatically rather untypical. Continentality is less pronounced; since the region borders on the ocean, the marine influence is proportionately greater. Temperatures on the whole are more moderate than in the other regions of the climate. In the north, however, lower latitude and interior location result in higher average temperatures. Technically the northeast corner of the region is a warm steppe.

Like the North American region, that of South America may be regarded as constituting two distinct physical provinces, the **Northwest,** north and west of the Pampa (see Chapter 17, p. 349), and **Patagonia,**[1] south of the Pampa. Patagonia is predominantly desert, like the intermontane province in the United States; the Northwest is mostly steppe land, like the Great Plains.

Topography. Patagonia is rugged, with a general eastward slope from the Andes to narrow coastal plains on the Atlantic. South of the Pampa is a large plateau, with a series of separated smaller plateaus running southward. Some areas are, like the Columbia plateau, lava covered. Large tracts are rocky wastelands. The plateau canyons run east to the sea but in many places there is local interior drainage. Between the plateaus and the mountains on the west there is a belt of lower land as much as 2000 feet below the plateau levels. The small plains areas of this belt are grass covered and far more hospitable regions than the plateaus. The Andes west of Patagonia are on the average much lower than in the north, with numerous passes and stretches where the crest line is below 10,000 feet. Glaciation during the ice age carved many depressions now occupied by clear mountain lakes, especially in the southeast along the Chilean border. This "lake country" of southwest Argentina is a well-developed resort area, much like the "parks" of Colorado.

The Northwest, which has great topographic diversity, is physically more like the intermontane desert province of the North American region than its steppe climatic counterpart. The Andes, on the west, here begin to widen and to develop the **Altiplano,** or intermontane plateau, that is so significant in the Andean countries farther north. In the west central section the Andean mass attains

[1] Patagonia means "Big Feet," an allusion to a characteristic of the original inhabitants that impressed the first explorers. The term has been dropped from official Argentine usage but is still convenient as designating a geographic area.

its greatest elevation and here rises the highest peak on the continent, **Mount Aconcagua,** to a 23,000-foot elevation.

East of the Andes the region is a patchwork of plains and plateaus. The plain-plateau district is the largest interior drainage basin of the region. Just northwest of the Pampa is the **Sierra de Cordoba,** a low mountain mass with 5000-foot altitudes. Many oases are scattered throughout the Northwest and have large economic significance.

Vegetation. The typical vegetative cover of the region is sagebrush and other drought-resistant plant types. In the Sierra de Cordoba an assemblage of such plants, known as the *Monte* (grove) has developed. It consists of stunted trees, and thorny shrubs and bushes interspersed with cactus.

On the slopes of the Andes west of Patagonia the greater precipitation at higher altitudes has fostered the development of large pine and beech forests. These have some economic value as well as scenic beauty. Between the forests and the desert growths farther east there is a narrow borderland of grasses. In the Northwest the oases, with their thick groves of trees and lush undergrowth, stand out in sharp contrast with the drab brown of the surrounding arid vegetation.

Agriculture and Associated Activity. Patagonia is one of the important **sheep** centers of the world. Its sheep population is on the order of 20 million. It is concentrated especially in the south and gives Argentina third rank among the world's sheep countries. Although cattle and **goats** are raised (the latter in the area just south of the Pampa), Patagonia is essentially too dry for stock other than sheep. **Cattle** are more important in the Northwest, together with lesser numbers of sheep and goats.

Some farming is carried on in the northern part of Patagonia along the valleys of the streams that flow through to the sea. Here irrigation projects have created fertile acres devoted to orchards, vineyards, and fields of **alfalfa. Pears, apples,** and **grapes** are important Argentine exports.

The Northwest is agriculturally the more important district, however. Through dam construction and the wide distribution of oasis water, irrigation on a scale comparable to that of the earlier United States projects has created large productive areas. The leading crops are **wine grapes,** especially in **Mendoza** and **San Juan** provinces, and **sugar cane** in the north central part of the region, centered in the province of **Tucuman.** These irrigated districts and their products are an important element in the agriculture of all Argentina, for wine is the national drink and the country ranks fifth in the world in the production of wine. The production of sugar is sufficient for all domestic needs.

Tucuman, the smallest of the Argentine provinces, is the paragon of the oases, commonly known as the "garden spot of Argentina." It not only is the center of the sugar industry but in addition has large yields of citrus fruits, tobacco, corn, and rice among other crops.

Mineral Resources and Products. In contrast with its North American counterpart the South American steppe region is only a small producer of metallic ores. It is, however, the only area of Argentine **petroleum** output, minute in amount by world standards but of sufficient volume to provide for almost two-thirds of the country's needs. There are four oil fields, the largest and most important at **Comodoro Rivadavia** on the coast of southern Patagonia. The oil from this field furnishes the fuel for the great Argentine railway system (see Chapter 17, p. 349), and a pipe line supplies Buenos Aires with the premium fuel for house heating: natural gas. A second field in **Salta** province in the extreme north is a small producer of high-quality petroleum. Two other fields occur west and southwest of the Pampa. The western and northern oil fields have been significant factors in speeding up the extension of rail facilities to districts otherwise not sufficiently productive to justify the cost. Farmers of these districts now benefit by cheap transportation to market. The oil resources, moreover, have been of fundamental significance nationally in view of the complete absence of other fuels in Argentina.

Production of metals in Argentina is limited to **lead** and **zinc,** which occur at several places on the eastern side of the Andes. The largest and richest deposits are at Aguilar in the extreme northwest corner of the country. The other deposits are little developed, as the output from a single Aguilar mine, despite its remoteness and transportation difficulties, is sufficient to satisfy Argentina's needs, and because national policy is to hoard the surplus natural resources rather than export them.

Other metals are known to exist in the long stretch of the Andes, but remoteness has hindered both exploration and development. But in view of the mineral richness of this great mountain system throughout most of its length the prospects are favorable for significant future discoveries.

CITIES OF SOUTHERN AND WESTERN ARGENTINA

Name	Type	Province	Population
Cordoba	Commercial-governmental	Cordoba	352,000 (1947)
Tucuman	Commercial-governmental	Tucuman	235,000 (1953)
Mendoza	Commercial-governmental	Mendoza	110,000 (1947)
Bahia Blanca	Seaport	Buenos Aires	93,000 (1945)

Cities. **Cordoba,** the third largest city of Argentina, lies 430 miles west of Buenos Aires on the edge of the Pampa where the Sierra Cordoba rises. It is an old town with a strong Spanish heritage; it was founded in 1573 and has a university dating from 1613. It has also been influenced by the later European immigration to Argentina because of its superior communications ties with the Pampa cities to the east. Its commercial significance stems from its position on the route to the Northwest. It is also the capital of its province.

Tucuman is the metropolis of the north and, as the capital of its province, the center of the best developed of the western oases. The subtropical vegetation and bright sunlight give it an unusual Mediterranean air for a city of the steppe region. Tucuman is a commercial center on the railroad routes to the far northwest and is also the focus of sugar refining.

Mendoza is also the capital of its province, and an oasis city. Its surrounding district yields many fruits grown by recent immigrants from Spain and Italy. Large quantities of dried fruits and wines are shipped both to the Pampa and abroad. Mendoza's site is highly strategic; it lies due west of Buenos Aires on the direct route to Santiago, Chile, at the eastern entrance to a major Andean pass.

Bahia Blanca is about 530 miles south of Buenos Aires on the border of the steppe and humid subtropical regions, at the southern edge of the Pampa. It is the export center for the Patagonian wool clip and also for the wheat harvest from the surrounding dry margin of the Pampa. Bahia Blanca is actually several miles inland, with no less than five port sites distributed along the shores of its bay to handle the docking of ships.

QUESTIONS. How do the three sections of the middle-latitude desert belt in North America differ topographically? How are the Columbia plateaus bounded? What is the nature of the Harney Basin? Of the Payette Section? Of the Palouse Country? Account for the "coulees" of the scab lands. Name the important rivers of the Columbia plateaus province. Account for the low evaporation of the province. For the relatively high winter temperatures. For what crop is the Palouse Country famous? List the factors favoring this crop there. What factor limits irrigation development in the Columbia plateaus? Describe the Grand Coulee development. What kinds of crops are grown at the eastern base of the Cascade Range? List the industries of the Columbia plateaus province. Name the important cities of the province. Account for the prosperity of the largest of these.

Locate and characterize the Rocky Mountains. Characterize the structure and composition of the Rockies in two short phrases. What is the nature of Rocky Mountain "parks"? What are the attractions of Sun Valley, Idaho? Give the history of Leadville, Colorado, and the implication this has for Rocky Mountain mining cities in general. Why is Butte famous? What minerals are now sought by prospectors? Where are the largest Rocky Mountain forests? Describe stock raising in the Rockies. Where is a Rocky Mountain farm prosperous? Discuss the size of Rocky Mountain cities.

Locate the middle-latitude desert and steppe region of South America. In what respects does it differ climatically from the regions of the Northern Hemisphere? What are its two major physical provinces? Compare these with the major subdivisions of the North American region. What is the predominant economic activity in Patagonia? In the Northwest? Explain the difference. Name the chief products of each of the two provinces. Where is the "garden spot of Argentina"? Where are the Argentine oil fields? Why are they of such extreme importance to Argentina? What are the two major metallic mineral products? In what way has the development of the oil fields and mineral districts aided the agriculture of Argentina? What characteristics do the cities of Cordoba, Tucuman, and Mendoza have in common?

Low-Temperature Humid Climates: The Humid Continental Climate

CHAPTER 24

The Humid Continental Climate: Eurasian Region (Long-Summer Phase)

■ DEFINITION AND CAUSES OF THE HUMID CONTINENTAL CLIMATE

The designation of the group of climates that includes the humid continental type as "low temperature" does not necessarily imply low average temperature but rather the occasional occurrence of low temperatures. Distinctions are made within the group on the basis of the frequency and duration of low temperatures—i.e., how low the average temperature is.

As indicated by its name, the humid continental climate is one in which precipitation is adequate if not ample, and continentality is the dominating element. It is developed on the eastern sides of continents in the latitudes of the westerlies belt and its procession of unlike air masses. On the eastern sides of continents the marine influence is absent because of remoteness from the western oceanic source. The procession of air masses, alternating between the low-pressure cyclone bringing both clouds and precipitation, and the high-pressure anticyclone with its clear skies, results in extremely variable weather and possible sudden changes in temperature. Moreover, the higher the latitude, the lower the average temperatures.

As the regions of this climate have a wide latitudinal extent they can be divided into two types or phases. The northern type, in the higher latitudes, is termed the *short-summer* phase; the southern type of the lower latitudes is the *long-summer* phase.

Where mountains on the western side of a continent produce an interior rain shadow, the humid continental climate is developed east of a middle-latitude arid climate. Where no mountain barriers are interposed, the humid continental climate gradually succeeds a marine west coast climate and represents the eastward replacement of the marine regime by the continental. On the high-latitude side the climate merges with a cold climate; on the low-latitude side the boundary climate is typically the humid subtropical type, and in a special instance the Mediterranean type. Where the humid continental region is projected eastward to the border of the continent it is subject to some modification by the adjacent ocean waters despite their being to the leeward. Technically this produces a third variety of the climate that is not considered separately in this simplified discussion.

■ CLIMATIC CHARACTERISTICS

PRECIPITATION

The term "humid" with reference to this climate should not be understood to mean really wet. The rainfall is, on the average, moderate but not heavy. Precipitation varies within the regions, tending to be greater near the eastern bordering ocean, where one is present, and toward the low-latitude

505

margin. The total annual rainfall will range from below 20 inches in a particular year (it will be recalled that 20 inches is the minimum that separates humid from arid climates, but this refers to the *average* over a period of years) up to 40 or 50 inches. The average for the climate, accordingly, is roughly 30 inches.

The rainfall is well distributed throughout the year; winter precipitation is mostly as snow; in summer thunderstorms account for most of the rainfall. In the long-summer phase the freeze-and-thaw alternation during winter gives rise to water-saturated muddy fields and prevailingly wet pavements in cities, conditions that may create the impression that winter is the wet season of the year. Actually, precipitation from April to September averages four inches per month, whereas for the six cold months it averages only two inches per month.

Although there is no pronounced seasonality of precipitation, summer is normally the season of greater rainfall because of several circumstances: (1) The characteristic continental air is more humid (i.e., the absolute humidity is higher—see Chapter 6, p. 96) at the high temperatures of summer. (2) Continentality promotes a summer monsoonal inflow and winter antimonsoonal outflow. (3) The air in summer is subject to convectional updrafts and cooling at high altitudes that cause its moisture to condense whether it is of continental or marine origin.

TEMPERATURE

Given continentality as the dominant factor in determining the nature of the climate, it follows that the humid continental regions will suffer from temperature extremes in all seasons. And because of the strength of the latitudinal temperature influence the low temperatures are more extreme and hence the winters are severe. Again, since the extremes are due to the absence of a moderating influence that would also lessen the frequency of fluctuations about the average or norm, variations from year to year are also extreme.

The humid continental regions, then, are the lands of the "cold wave" and "heat wave." It is no coincidence that the well-known statement "Everybody talks about the weather but nobody does anything about it" first appeared in a Connecticut newspaper editorial, published in a humid continental region. In these regions weather is a commonplace topic of conversation, whereas in climatic regions where constancy of weather is characteristic the weather does not provide a universal subject for small talk.

The four seasons of the year are most completely expressed in humid continental regions and are developed in close parallelism with the progressive change in the angle of the sun's rays during the year. Winters are sufficiently cold to kill all annual plants and at times when temperatures fall well below zero degrees Fahrenheit match those of arctic climates. The approach of spring is leisurely, often with false starts but eventually arriving at settled warm weather. Summers are definitely hot; temperatures may rise to 100° F. or higher. It can thus be both hotter and, on occasion, even more humid than wet tropical lands. Summer is relatively long over the whole belt, short-summer phase as well as long-summer phase. Fall is a period of gradual cooling off, when annuals wither and die, and leaves fall from the deciduous trees.

The climatic characteristics for the two subtypes of humid continental climate may be summed up as follows: The short-summer phase has severe winters and hot summers, but heat waves are infrequent and cloudiness is common. Precipitation is moderate and snow remains on the ground for long periods during winter. The long-summer phase has hot summers with frequent heat waves. Its winters are moderate, with thaws between the cold waves, so that the snows melt rather than accumulate. Precipitation is somewhat greater.

■ REGIONAL ASPECTS

There is no one natural vegetative cover expressive of the humid continental regions as a whole. Certain major types of growth are, however, representative. (1) In the drier districts grasslands prevail. Technically these are termed *prairies* to distinguish them from the steppes of still drier grasslands. (2) In border districts between the drier and more humid portions of a region the *wooded steppe* is the dominant feature. This is roughly comparable to the savanna (see Chapter 9, p. 139) with its alternating grassland and forest. (3) In the areas of heaviest rainfall true *forests* exist. In the long-summer phase the broadleaf or deciduous trees, especially hickory, oak, and maple, are predominant. In the higher latitudes of the climate there is a gradual transition from the broadleaf, hardwood forest to one of conifers such as pine, fir, spruce, and hemlock. These take over more or less completely as the high-latitude boundary is reached. The broadleaf birch, however, is still present at the farthest north reaches.

Hardwood forests at one time covered virtually the entire extent of the long-summer phase of the humid continental regions. In only a few extremely restricted areas, however, do remnants of these great forests remain. Although the forest lands were occupied by widely dissimilar peoples and civilizations on the several continents, the inhabitants have everywhere all but obliterated the original tree growth. In some regions the forests were destroyed because they occupied land that was more valuable for agricultural uses. In others, the great timber resources were over-exploited because of their high utility.

The wild animal life of the humid continental lands was originally abundant and varied. Rather surprisingly a considerable remainder of this population has survived in all such regions despite decimation by man. The prairies still harbor a large burrowing rodent population such as gophers, prairie dogs, and woodchucks, and a great assemblage of smaller animals and birds still populate areas of the second-growth forests and the primeval tracts that remain.

■ UTILIZATION OF HUMID CONTINENTAL REGIONS

The marine west coast climate was described in Chapter 19 (p. 382) as coming "nearest of all the climates to the ideal circumstances for spurring human activity." The humid continental climate is only slightly less stimulating. Indeed, in two regions of humid continental climate the level of human activity may be said currently to surpass that of the European marine west coast region. Although correlating human endeavor with climate can only be inferential, there is general agreement that with respect to human activities in the regions of humid continental climate the following generalizations are warranted:

1. The climate, although not always stimulating and invigorating, is generally conducive to a high level of human enterprise.

2. The regions of the climate include no mountainous areas that are hindrances to economic activity; on the contrary, by far the greater portion of the areas having humid continental climate is plains land.

3. The regions contain the bulk of the world's high-grade coal resources and excellent iron ore resources; thus the basic requirements of modern industrial development are provided for.

In other words, in the humid continental regions there coexist favorable topography, rich natural resources, and an easily endurable if not actually benign climate. The influence of the first two is commonly so dominant that the particular characteristics of the climate become of subordinate importance for complex human activities. To be sure, farming, forest occupations, and the like remain significant elements in the economy, but they are far from dominant even though climatic conditions for agricultural endeavor may be ideal. In brief, industrialization and commerce have been developed to their highest levels in the humid continental regions.

Despite its secondary status agriculture in the humid continental regions perhaps more perfectly reflects climate than it does in any of the other types of climatic environment. The division of the humid continental regions into short-summer and long-summer phases is expressed in relation to agriculture. This is because the growing season is of basic importance to agriculture and for practical purposes measures the length of the summer. The growing season of the short-summer phase ranges from 100 to 150 days; of the long-summer phase, from 150 to 200 days.

Another factor of major importance to agriculture in the humid continental regions is the summer concentration of rainfall. Water is provided when it is most needed for plant growth. The summertime thunder-shower rainfall is, however, localized, and if, because of its random incidence, particular areas fail to get their normal quota in a given year, serious droughts and crop failures may result. As the 20 to 40 inches of average annual precipitation in the climate is not high, any considerable deficiency is critical.

The typical crop of the long-summer phase is **corn**, for which the optimum conditions of high temperatures and a growing season between 150 and 180 days are realized. In North America corn is the leading crop in this phase, in certain areas almost to the exclusion of all others. In eastern Europe **wheat** has the premier status, associated with mixed farming of such cash crops as **sugar beets** and **tobacco**. In Asia **soybeans** and **kaoliang** (a kind of sorghum) vie with wheat. In corn regions **hogs** are the notable farm animal, because they most efficiently convert corn into meat, ordinarily affording a higher yield than sale of the grain.

The short-summer phase is the ideal climate for **spring wheat**. Over three-quarters of the world's supply of wheat is grown in spring wheat districts. Other crops include the smaller cereals **rye** and **oats**, and **potatoes**—all crops that thrive in cool summers and growing seasons as short as 100 days, as well as on the poorer soils that are so common in hilly regions affected by glacial

activity in the ice age. **Flax** is the great cash crop in such parts. Also, because of the cooler conditions much **hay** is grown, and for the same reason plus the availability of the hay, **dairying** is important wherever urban concentrations provide good markets for fluid milk.

■ HUMID CONTINENTAL REGIONS AND COUNTRIES

The humid continental climate occurs on only three of the continents—North America, Europe, and Asia (Fig. 24.1). Only South America among the Southern Hemisphere continents extends sufficiently poleward to attain the appropriate latitudes, but owing to its southerly taper South America is there so diminished in east-west extent that the continental influence is not strong enough to overbalance the marine influence of neighboring oceans.

The three great regions of humid continental climate are: **east central Europe and west central Siberia**, the **central Pacific coast of Asia**, and **central and east central North America**.

A. EAST CENTRAL EUROPE AND WEST CENTRAL SIBERIA

The Eurasian region of humid continental climate has the shape of a huge wedge with its wide end on the west and its tip on the east. The western portion covers all of eastern Europe from the eastern corner of the Baltic south to the fringe lands of the north Mediterranean shore. The wedge extends east from this line across central Russia and into central Siberia to about the 85th meridian east. At its widest north-south extent the wedge measures some 1300 miles; its maximum east-west extent is about 3200 miles.

This region is the single occurrence abutting a marine west coast region on the west without the interposition of an interior arid region. Moreover, it begins in central rather than eastern Europe. The situation is due to the absence of any European mountain system sufficiently high and extended to pro-

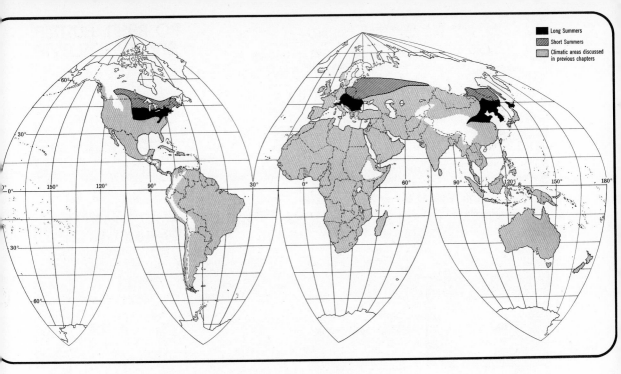

Fig. 24.1—World Distribution of Humid Continental Climatic Regions.

duce a rain-shadow arid climate east of its ranges. The region thus merely represents a modification of the Atlantic marine influence —the cyclonic disturbances off the Atlantic, in passing eastward over Europe, gradually lose their moisture. At the critical distance inland the resulting precipitation is less than the defined limit for the marine west coast climate, and there the humid continental region begins. The western boundary of the region accordingly parallels the trend of the Atlantic coast of Europe.

Specifically, the Atlantic cyclones come through the Baltic corridor, and their (relatively) warm humid air gradually loses its heat and moisture as it moves east. The region, moreover, pinches out because of cold on the north and aridity on the south. Before these factors terminate the wedge the Urals are sufficiently a barrier to make the Siberian portion somewhat colder and drier than that to the west.

This transitional sequence is expressed in the forest composition of the region. Mixed deciduous and coniferous forests occur in Russia. These are the projection eastward of the broad-leafed tree stands in the warm, more humid climates to the west. Different species disappear progressively. First to drop out is beech, which barely penetrates into

Russia, then in turn ash, maple, and oaks— the latter just reaching the Urals. Finally there remains only the linden, which continues partly into Siberia.

Agriculturally the Eurasian humid continental region accounts for most of the world's production of potatoes, rye, and flax and ranks second as a supplier of corn.

For convenience in discussion of the countries of the region the two phases of climate are considered separately, although the line between them does not even approximate political boundaries. The long-summer phase includes northern Italy, all of Austria, all of Yugoslavia except the Adriatic coast, and all or virtually all of Bulgaria, Rumania, Hungary, and Czechoslovakia. The short-summer phase includes Poland, the Baltic States, central Russia, and west central Siberia.

1. NORTHERN ITALY

Topography and People. The **Apennines** that form the "backbone" of the Italian peninsula veer westward at their northern end. Humid continental Italy is Italy north and east of the Apennines up to the Yugoslavian border (Fig. 24.2). The district is a distinctive topographic unit surrounded by mountains on three sides: the great **Alps** barrier on the

Fig. 24.2—Po Basin, Austria, and Yugoslavia. The inset compares the area of the region with an equivalent area of the United States (states in white).

north, the **Maritime Alps** which curve south to the Mediterranean on the west, the Apennines on the south. Roughly it comprises the drainage basin of the **Po River,** which flows eastward for 250 miles into the head of the Adriatic Sea. The major part of the area of the Po Basin consists of a plain. When the mountain slopes adjoining the plain are included there are three topographic divisions to be considered: the **Piedmont** or upper basin; **Lombardy,** the middle Po; and the delta district at its eastern end. The basin in general is low; even the Piedmont averages only 600 feet in elevation. The plain is practically flat and stands only slightly above sea level. The steep slopes of the surrounding Alps provide a sharp contrast to these lowlands areas, and the beautiful scenic settings of some of the glacial lakes on their southern margin, such as that of **Lake Como,** are world famous.

The people of northern Italy are markedly unlike their southern countrymen in appearance and characteristics. A mixture of different stocks has resulted in a north Italian taller, lighter in complexion and hair, and more energetic and industrious than the south Italian.

Resources and Economic Activities. Northern Italy has better mineral resources than the rest of the country, consisting of newly discovered and developed **petroleum** and **natural gas** fields along the middle Po which have come into prominence only since 1950. Gas has been found in sufficient quantity to warrant pipe-line construction to convey it as cheap fuel to the industrial centers of the region.

The best farm land of Italy is this northern part of the country. The fields are intensively cultivated with modern techniques and equipment. **Wheat** and **corn** are the leading crops, the latter under irrigation where possible. **Hog** raising goes along with the corn. **Rice** is grown in the Piedmont and Lombardy; the yield is of such volume as to make Italy the leading European producer. Other important crops are **sugar beets** and **hemp.** **Vegetable** growing has a relatively minor place in the farm economy but **peaches** are an important fruit crop. Extensive vineyards for **wine** production are present, especially in the Piedmont. In the northeast the vines are trellised on and between mulberry trees whose leaves provide food for **silkworms.** A substantial **dairy** industry utilizes the rich pastures of the Alpine slopes.

Agriculturally prosperous, humid continental Italy is industrial Italy as well. Almost 80 percent of the country's manufactures come from the Po Basin, which is a major industrial center of Europe. Although Italy lacks large coal and iron deposits the Alps provide very large hydropower resources that have been fully utilized. Italy is the leading producer of electricity in Europe. But because of their general lack of mineral resources the Italians have been handicapped in developing heavy industry. **Textile** manufactures have long been significant; silk, cotton, and rayon cloth are all produced in quantity. **Automobile** making has in recent decades been highly successful, however, because of the Italian flair for good engineering and styling. Even more recently this talent in machine design has resulted in a marked growth of **typewriter** and **sewing machine** manufacture for export markets.

CITIES OF NORTHERN ITALY

Name	Type	Population (1951)
Milan	Industrial-commercial	1,275,000
Turin	Industrial-commercial	720,000
Venice	Resort	323,000
Trieste	Seaport	271,000

Cities. **Milan,** the chief city of humid continental Italy, is second to Rome in size. It is in the central Piedmont at the intersection of the east-west route across the Po plain with the main route north from Italy through the Alps. This early commercial situation is now subordinate to Milan's status as the major industrial center of Italy. The city is well known for its textile manufactures and ceramics and is also the Italian financial capital. It has a stock exchange and branches of many great international banking concerns.

Turin, by its situation in the western Piedmont on the main route to France, also has its origin as a commercial city. But, like Milan, its modern significance derives from its industries. It is best known for its automobile manufacture. It also makes textiles and machinery.

Venice (Fig. 24.3) is one of the most remarkable cities of the world. In the days when overland trade with the Orient was a major commercial activity of the continent it was one of the few great cities in Europe because of its function as the seaport at the head of the Adriatic. Now it is primarily a tourist center with rich treasures of art, architecture, and artistic manufactures. Venice is celebrated also for its canals, 177 of them.

Fig. 24.3—Venice, Italy. View along one of the "side street" canals. (O. D. von Engeln.)

Other cities are traversed by waterways but none is so completely canalized as is Venice. Transportation within the city is entirely by water. There are pedestrian walks through the city, but one cannot ride in a wheeled vehicle because the bridges over the canals are approached by steps.

Trieste, at the extreme north end of the Adriatic, is now the chief seaport of the region. In part because of its commercial significance, the city has been disputed and fought over for most of the twentieth century. The inhabitants are chiefly Italians but the trade relations are mainly with Yugoslavia and Austria.

Italy as a Whole. What prestige and rewards Italy derives from the productivity of its humid continental portion and the enterprise of its people are more than offset for Italy as a whole by the poverty and inertia that prevail in the rest of the country (see Chapter 14, p. 276). Italy's almost desperate economic status may be ascribed chiefly to a single circumstance: overpopulation. The resources of the country are simply inadequate to support the population of 48 million, which, moreover, continues to grow at an alarming rate. Most farmers produce barely enough for subsistence at a near-starvation level and industrial unemployment outside the humid continental portion is chronic. Emigration has traditionally been the outlet for the surplus population, but the numbers who leave do not keep pace with the rate of population growth; hence the situation continually worsens. Lower mortality rates due to improved sanitation accentuate the problem.

There are, of course, other factors that contribute to Italy's national difficulties. Despite the high repute Italians have as gardeners and viniculturalists, and the intensive cultivation practiced in many localities, yields are commonly low owing to centuries of abuse of the land. Much of the damage can be corrected in time, but not within a generation even if comprehensively undertaken. A further trouble is that much land is held in vast, private estates. On these there is little incentive for either full utilization or efficient working of the acres under cultivation. Some progress has been made in eradicating this evil by redistribution of the land so as to provide small peasant holdings that are intensively worked.

It is true that the economic status of Italy as a whole is better now than it ever has been, and this after practically the whole length of the country was ravaged by war. Postwar American aid fostered great improvements in agricultural practices and brought about a spectacular rejuvenation of Italian industry. The discovery of natural gas fields has accelerated the industrial development. A $2 billion development program for the south was begun in 1950. But even with intensive development of specialized industries and the complete rehabilitation of agriculture it is difficult to see how the adverse factor of runaway population growth can be offset. On the other hand, Italy is not necessarily headed for national disintegration. It will probably continue to struggle along, beset by chronic social and economic problems.

QUESTIONS. What is meant by "low temperature" climates? Explain the significance of the following in the occurrence of humid continental regions: (1) the eastern side of continents; (2) the westerlies belt; (3) the latitude. What are the two types of climatic regions found to the west of the humid continental regions? Why? What are the two types to the south? Describe the general aspects of precipitation in the humid continental climate. Why is summer the season of greater precipitation? Why does the tendency toward temperature extremes result in more severe winters than summers? Why are the humid continental regions regions of weather, not climate? Contrast the climatic characteristics of the "short-summer" and "long-summer" phases.

What are the three types of natural vegetative cover found in humid continental regions? What are the chief types of trees? Why is so little of the original forest cover found? Discuss the relation between the humid continental climate and the level of human activity. Why is agriculture such a clear reflection of climate in humid continental regions? Name the typical crops, distinguishing between long-summer and short-summer phases.

Describe and explain the general world distribution of the humid continental regions. Explain the occurrence of the Eurasian humid continental region. Name the countries and portions of countries included in it.

Describe the topography of northern Italy and name the outstanding features. Contrast the people of northern and southern Italy. Name the important mineral resources, crops, and industries of northern Italy. Name two of its important industrial cities. What is Italy's greatest single problem? How do the problems of agriculture aggravate the basic problem? Is Italy now better or worse off than before World War II?

2. AUSTRIA

General Aspects. The Republic of Austria is a small, landlocked country a little larger than Maine (32,000 square miles). On the map it has the shape of a plump tadpole heading east. The tail (most of which is the district known as **Tyrol**) extends westward where Switzerland comes between Italy and Germany (Fig. 24.2). The body portion is surrounded by Czechoslovakia, Hungary, and Yugoslavia on the north, east, and south, respectively. The overall east-west length of the country is 400 miles.

Austria is an Alpine country in the sense that two-thirds of it is mountainous and that the mountains are part of the Alps. Fortunately for its economic functioning two large east-west valleys in the Tyrol allow convenient access to the "tail" section. In the north and northeast, where the foothills of the Alps give way to a plateau country of low mountains, there are forested uplands. The southeast and east are lowland basins. The only significant river is the **Danube**, which crosses the country from west to east in a sharply defined valley between the Alpine foothills and the plateau.

The people of Austria number 7 million, are 95 percent Roman Catholic, and speak German. The Austrians resemble and have much the same ethnic backgrounds as the Germans of southern Germany. Though industrious, they are at the same time gay and fun-loving, with the enviable knack of making life enjoyable for themselves even under adverse circumstances.

For such a little country Austria is surprisingly well endowed with mineral resources. Small **petroleum** fields occur, mostly in the northeast corner. The best **iron ore** of central Europe is found in the center of the country at **Eisenerz** (Iron Ore). There is in addition a modest production of other metals. Other important nonmetallic minerals are **graphite** and **magnesite,** found in the center of the country near Eisenerz. Austria accounts for over one-half the world production of the latter material.

With so much mountainous terrain Austria

is clearly not capable of large-scale agricultural production. Although the arable land is intensively utilized the country is able to supply only about three-quarters of its food needs. The chief crops are **rye, wheat, oats,** and **barley,** in that order, along with **potatoes,** which are the staff of life for all Germanic peoples. **Dairying** is an important activity in the Alpine districts.

More than one-third of Austria is forest covered, mostly in pine and spruce, with beech at the lower levels in the east. The forest growths permit a steady output of lumber and pulpwood under rigidly observed conservation practices.

Austria also has excellent hydropower possibilities in most parts of the country. These are already well developed, and further utilization is projected. Despite the lack of coal resources hydroelectric energy provides the basis for substantial industrial activity. **Iron and steel** manufacture relies on the domestic ore supply. Other important industries are **fertilizers** (atmospheric nitrogen plants using electric power), **aluminum refining** (another electric power-consuming industry), **glass,** and **textiles.**

Although the manufactured products of Austria comprise a long, varied list, the lack of bulk raw materials has led to a concentration on quality rather than on heavy goods.

Fig. 24.4—Picturesque Fishing Village on Altausee (Lake) in Styria, Austria. (Courtesy, Austrian Information Service.)

The Austrians specialize in export commodities in whose production their expert craftsmanship is utilized. Even so, the most important "industry" is **tourism.** The Alpine districts are developed to provide resort attractions throughout the year. In the winter skiing and other winter sports are available; in summer mountain scenery and cultural festivals lure visitors from abroad (Fig. 24.4).

Cities. **Vienna** (Fig. 24.5), where "The Blue Danube Waltz" was written (actually the Danube is a yellow, sediment-laden stream), is a city sentimentizing wistfully over its memories of the Good Old Days. As capital of the Austro-Hungarian Empire Vienna was the governmental center of a nation of 60 million people. It was then a city of cosmopolitan glitter that rivaled Paris as a focal point of European culture. During

Fig. 24.5—Vienna, Austria. Air view with the Danube River in the distance and the Ringstrasse, site of the old moat, curving around the inner city. (Compare with Fig. 3.5.) (Courtesy, Austrian Information Service.)

CITIES OF AUSTRIA

Name	Type	Population (1951)
Vienna	Governmental, commercial, industrial	1,616,000
Graz	Industrial-commercial	226,000
Linz	Industrial-River port	185,000
Salzburg	Resort	103,000

this period it was the home of more outstandingly great composers than any other city either before or since. Today Vienna is "a capital without a country." It remains however, a center of commerce between eastern and western Europe owing to its focal location and is Austria's largest manufacturing center, especially for textiles.

Graz and **Linz** are the two other major

industrial centers of Austria. The former is situated in the southeast near the Eisenerz, the latter far up the Danube in the northwest section of the country. **Salzburg** is on the Bavarian border just north of the Austrian "tail." In recent decades it has become the cultural capital of Austria, noted especially for the great summer music festival staged there annually. This attracts music lovers from all over the world.

Austria as a Whole. The foregoing description of Austria should suggest a country enjoying modest good fortune. This is true as far as geographical equipment is concerned, yet Austria is actually an unfortunate country. Through little fault of their own the Austrians found themselves on the losing side of two World Wars and have been dealt with politically and economically almost as harshly as were those nations responsible for the conflicts. Their misfortune derives solely from the circumstance that Austria occupies the strategic center of Europe.

Austria today is only the core of an Austro-Hungarian Empire that covered a wide region of central and eastern Europe but was dismembered after World War I. Then, in 1938, Nazi Germany forcibly annexed the core area. After World War II the country was, until 1955, jointly occupied by the Soviet Union and the western Allies. During their occupation the Soviet forces systematically removed from their zone a large portion of the industrial equipment and forced the plants which remained to produce for Russia. These appropriations and compulsions were justified as "reparations" for alleged Austrian war damages. Now that the country is again free it faces a hard struggle to attain a sound economic basis. Tourism will probably continue to be its chief "industry."

3. YUGOSLAVIA

General Aspects. The "Federal People's Republic of Yugoslavia" is composed of six republics (**Slovenia, Croatia, Serbia, Macedonia, Montenegro,** and **Bosnia-Herzegovina**) and two provinces, all theoretically autonomous, or self-governing units, but actually merely administrative divisions. It is the largest of the south European countries collectively referred to as the "Balkan States." Its area (just under 100,000 square miles) is slightly greater than that of Wyoming. Yugoslavia is located on the eastern side of the Adriatic Sea and has boundaries with Italy on the northwest, Austria and Hungary on the north, Rumania and Bulgaria on the east, Greece and Macedonia on the south (Fig. 24.2). Its coastal district, known as **Dalmatia,** has a Mediterranean climate, but is of such slight regional importance as not to merit mention in the chapters on the Mediterranean climate or more than passing reference at this juncture.

Topography. Yugoslavia, like Austria, is a land of mountains, notable for their ruggedness and confused pattern rather than for their elevation. A group of ranges running the full length of the country parallel to the Adriatic coast, known as the **Dinaric Alps,** is the dominant topographic element. In the northwest the Dinarics curve westward into the **Slovenian Alps,** which in turn connect with the true Alps of which the entire system is an extension. The Dinaric Alps average only 4000 to 6000 feet in altitude but are very rugged, with no good passes across them. The Dalmatian coastal belt is thus isolated from the interior of the country, and, as the mountains rise virtually from the sea, the region is also very narrow (Fig. 24.6). The lime rock of which the Dinarics are composed is subject to solution and underground escape of water, so that systematic surface drainage is lacking. Hence there are no connecting valleys and the soil cover is thin or absent except in pockets. Altogether, the Dinaric district is an extremely inhospitable area of little economic value.

In the southeast of Yugoslavia the Dinarics are succeeded by a confused assemblage of mountains and basins. On the northeast, however, the mountains are lower, the soil and drainage are better, and heavy forests are present. The altitudes, in general, diminish northeastward down to the level of the plains that constitute the northeast section of the country.

Fig. 24.6—Dinaric Alps and Coastal Belt, Makarska, Yugoslavia. (Courtesy, Embassy of the Federal Peoples Republic of Yugoslavia.)

The major stream of Yugoslavia is the **Danube,** which traverses the northeast corner. The plains area there, in fact, consists for the most part of the valley floors of the Danube and its tributaries. The largest of these tributaries is the **Save,** whose course extends west to east across the entire northern section. Just before the Danube leaves the country at the eastern boundary it is joined by the **Morava** from the south. The Morava Valley is lined up across a low divide with that of the **Vardar River,** a south-flowing stream that drains through Macedonia to the Aegean Sea. The two valleys provide a readily negotiated passageway through the mountainous jumble of the southeast Balkans.

People. The Yugoslavs (southern Slavs) number 16 million people divided between three important national groups. The largest is that of the *Serbs,* who live in the eastern portion of the country and who comprise over half the population. The *Croats* who occupy the Save Valley account for about one-quarter of the population. The *Slovenes* in the west make up about one-tenth of the

people. Another tenth consists of a variety of national and racial minorities ranging from Italians to Turks. Three languages are spoken; religions include Roman Catholicism, two branches of the Orthodox Eastern Church, and Islam.

The three major population groups are ancestrally from the same basic stock but each has developed a separate identity with distinctive traditions because of different histories. The Croats were part of the old Austro-Hungarian Empire and so absorbed some of the cultural aspects of that Germanic state. The Slovenes, the most advanced group economically, were strongly influenced by their contacts with their north Italian neighbors. The Serbs were for a long time under the oppressive rule of the Turks and are the most backward group economically.

Mineral Resources. The mineral riches of Yugoslavia's mountains compensate in part for the reduction in agricultural land and the difficulties for transportation their presence interposes. The country is second only to Russia as a European producer of **copper, lead, silver, antimony,** and **chromite.** The copper is obtained from a large deposit at **Bor,** in the east. Lead and silver, along with zinc, are found at several places in the mountains. Antimony comes from the center of the country and chromite from the extreme south. In addition Yugoslavia is an important producer of **mercury** from the **Idria** district in the extreme northwest, ceded by Italy after World War II, and of **bauxite** obtained along the Dalmatian coast. There are even some fuel deposits—lignite in many localities and petroleum along the central course of the Danube. Development of these resources is still in an early stage, however.

Agriculture. Despite the high yield of minerals Yugoslavia is essentially an agricultural country. The subsistence type of farming is predominant in the mountain districts. **Wheat** and **corn** are the chief crops grown on the northern plains; **plums** from orchards in the northeast are important for conversion into prunes, jam, and an alcoholic drink. **Tobacco,** raised in the south, is the leading cash crop.

Industries. Manufacturing is of relatively small importance in Yugoslavia, even though iron and steel, nonferrous metallurgy, machinery, chemicals, textiles, and a wide range of other industries exist. All of them are small and, aside from the refining and processing of the mineral resources, are chiefly for partial satisfaction of domestic needs. There are no outstanding industrial concentrations, nor any specialized industries whose products are internationally significant.

CITIES OF YUGOSLAVIA

Name	Type	Population (1953)
Belgrade	Governmental-River port	470,000
Zagreb	Commercial	350,000
Ljubljana	Commercial	138,000
Sarajevo	Commercial	136,000
Subotica	Commercial	115,000

Cities. **Belgrade** ("White Castle") (Fig. 24.7) is an old Danubian port on the south bank of the river where the Save joins it. The capital and chief city of Yugoslavia, it was formerly the old Serbian capital. Considering the long isolation of the region it is surprisingly modern in appearance.

Zagreb, on the upper Save, is the capital of Croatia. It is a center of many light industries. **Ljubljana,** still farther west at the headwaters of the Save, is the Slovenian capital. This city with a name which looks unpronounceable has metallurgical, textile, and glass industries.

Sarajevo is in the center of the country in the most populous district of the Dinarics. It is the largest city outside the northern lowlands and its population is one-third Moslem. Sarajevo is famous as the site of the assassination of the Austrian Archduke in 1914 which precipitated World War I. **Subotica** is a peasant market city in the far northeast.

Yugoslavia as a Whole. Yugoslavia is unique in being the only Communist country not under political and economic bondage to the Soviet Union. This is a matter of great importance, for it means that Yugo-

Fig. 24.7—Belgrade, Yugoslavia. Air view showing Danube River in the distance. (Courtesy, Embassy of the Federal Peoples Republic of Yugoslavia.)

slavia is free to develop its resources independently, without being geared to Soviet needs and desires.

The handicaps to such development are great. World War II did much to arouse a national consciousness, but national traditions and ambitions date only from the time of Yugoslavia's creation after World War I, whereas the constituent peoples of the country have a history of quarreling and petty warfare among themselves that goes back for centuries. National fusion outside the strictly political sphere has not yet occurred.

In accordance with basic Communist doctrine that industrialization (more or less regardless of the resource base) is essential for progress, Yugoslavia is striving to expand manufacturing at a pace emulating its furious growth in the Soviet Union. Emphasis is placed on development of fuel and power resources, as well as on the building up of a transportation system adequate to the needs of an industrial state.

The furtherance of this program has behind it the dogged determination of the Communist government to bring it to success and an unusual (Communist) readiness to modify doctrine in the face of realities such as the Yugoslav peasant's insistence on remaining an independent farmer. The greatest handicap to its rapid achievement, on the other hand, is the "lost time" that must be made up. The Yugoslav peoples are all unfamiliar with Western technology. While western Europe was evolving the existing industrial society the Yugoslavs were isolated and subject peoples.

4. SOVIET SATELLITES

General Aspects. The remaining countries of the long-summer phase of the Eurasian region of humid continental climate are geographically closely associated with Yugoslavia but politically separated from it by a phenomenon unique in modern times—that of the satellite state. The four countries here considered—Czechoslovakia, Hungary, Rumania, and Bulgaria—were all independent nations at the end of World War II. Some were the victims of Nazi aggression; others were partners in the aggression. But whether victims or partners, these countries within two or three years after World War II found themselves, through Communist political

machinations, with Communist governments. Their situation is unique in that an elaborate fiction of individual sovereignty is maintained, whereas in reality each country is little more than an administrative unit of the Soviet Union.

The four satellite countries occupy a belt stretching from the center of Europe to the Black Sea. **Czechoslovakia**, on the northwest, is a remnant of the Austro-Hungarian Empire. The size of North Carolina, it covers an area of 49,000 square miles east of Germany, south of Poland, and north of Austria (Fig. 24.8).

South of Czechoslovakia is **Hungary**, formerly the "other half" of the Austro-Hungarian Empire. Its area of 35,000 square miles (about that of Indiana) borders on the Soviet Union in the northeast, Austria on the west, and Yugoslavia on the south.

Rumania, southeast of Hungary, is the largest of the four satellite countries. Its area of 91,000 square miles is twice that of Penn-

Fig. 24.8—Czechoslovakia, Hungary, Rumania, and Bulgaria. The inset compares the area of the region with an equivalent area of the United States (states in white).

sylvania. About half of its territory was formerly Austro-Hungarian. On the other hand, the portion of the Soviet Union on its northeast border was part of Rumania until the boundary "adjustments" after World War II were made. Its western boundary is with Yugoslavia; on the east Rumanian territory extends to the Black Sea.

Bulgaria lies south of Rumania on the Black Sea coast and is situated between Yugoslavia on the west and Greece and European Turkey on the south. Its area of 43,000 square miles is slightly greater than that of Tennessee.

Topography. The dominant topographic feature of all four countries is a large reversed "S" formed by the series of ranges that constitute the eastern portion of the great mountain system of southern Europe of which the Alps are the central mass. The Balkan segment of the Alpine system begins in eastern Czechoslovakia and arcs south through Rumania as the **Carpathians,** a rugged mountain chain with peaks over 6000 feet in altitude. This arc continues around to the southwest as the higher and even more rugged **Transylvanian Alps.** The curve then reverses, first to the southeast and back to the northeast through northern Bulgaria. These are the **Balkan Mountains,** from which the countries of south central Europe get their name. The Balkans gradually decline in altitude toward their eastern terminus near the Black Sea.

There are two other significant highland areas. Western Czechoslovakia is the **Bohemian Plateau,** which consists of a central upland between 1500 and 1600 feet in elevation ringed about by mountains. These are in the northwest, at the German border, the **Erz Gebirge** (Ore Mountains); on the northeast the **Sudeten Mountains,** which form the Polish border. On the southwest are the **Bohemian Mountains.** The other highland is the **Rhodope Mountains** of southern Bulgaria, trending east-west along the Greek border.

Inside the Carpathian arc, in western Rumania and eastern Hungary, is the hilly **Transylvanian Basin.** South of the Transyl-

vanian Alps is the **Wallachian Plain** of southern Rumania.

Save for the Bohemian Plateau the entire area of all four countries is drained by the great **Danube.** The river enters through a gap between the east end of the Alps and the west end of the Carpathians, forming part of the Czechoslovak-Hungarian border. It then turns south across the center of Hungary into Yugoslavia, emerging from that country through a rock-walled gorge between the Transylvanian Alps and the Balkans known as the **Iron Gate.** The river continues east, forming first the Yugoslav-Rumanian and then the Rumanian-Bulgarian borders before turning north across eastern Rumania and finally east, as the Rumanian–Soviet Union border, before emptying into the Black Sea.

A tributary of the Danube, the **Morava** (not to be confused with the Yugoslavian Morava) flows south across Czechoslovakia between Bohemia and Slovakia forming an important lowland corridor known as **Moravia.**

People. All four Soviet satellites duplicate on a larger scale the ethnic, language, and religious mosaics that occur in Yugoslavia. As in Yugoslavia the broken nature of the Balkan lands—rugged mountain barriers separating isolated basins—together with their historical position in the path of Asiatic invaders, led to the intrusion of diverse stocks and their preservation through either amalgamation or isolation.

The 14 million people of Czechoslovakia are divided, as the name indicates, between Czechs in the west and Slovaks in the east. Both these groups, unlike other Balkan peoples, are descended from the prehistoric inhabitants of the area. Their present differences have historical and cultural origins and are not due to separate stocks. The population is 90 percent Czechoslovakian and almost entirely Roman Catholic, but there has never been a strong sense of national unity. The Slovaks have always disliked the Czech domination of the country, and there was a chronic strong separatist tendency in Slovakia.

Fig. 24.9—Hungarian Folk Dance in National Costume. (Courtesy, Legation of Hungarian People's Republic.)

Hungary has a population of 9 million and is predominantly Roman Catholic in religion. From 85 to 90 percent of the people are *Magyars* (Fig. 24.9). The original Magyars came from central Asia, and the Hungarian language, as a member of the "Finno-Ugrian" group, manifests its alien origin by differing basically from the other languages of Europe. There is also present a strong Turkish element, the result of several centuries of Turkish rule, and lesser similar European infusions from the soldiers of occupying garrisons of other nations. Only about 30 percent of the present population is of pure Magyar descent. The physical characteristics of the Hungarians are not very indicative of their Asiatic origin, but such traits as hot tempers and fatalism reveal the heritage.

Rumania has a population of 16 million people. Rumanians as such are the descendants of a mixture of Roman (later, Latin) colonists and native Slavs, along with Turkish, Tatar, and still older invaders. Now the inhabitants of the country are seven-eighths Rumanians. The small remainder is made up of German, Gypsy, Magyar, Jewish, Turkish, and other minorities. The language shows the Latin influence, but Slavic culture prevails. The common religion is Eastern Orthodox.

Bulgaria, with its 7 million population, also presents a mixture of Asiatic (Mongoloid) nomad invaders with a local Slavic people. There is, further, a Turkish minority of about 10 percent testifying to former Turkish rule. The name "Bulgar" is of Finno-Ugrian derivation; like the Hungarians, the Bulgars show their Asiatic ancestry by temperament and attitudes, and retain traces of their steppe origin in their dress and food preferences. Eighty percent of the people adhere to the Eastern Orthodox Church; 15 percent are Moslems.

Mineral Resources. In mineral wealth and output Rumania has first importance; Czechoslovakia has by far the greatest variety; Hungary has a single important resource; Bulgarian resources are insignificant.

Rumania leads in mineral wealth because of its petroleum resources. In both reserves and output the country is second in Europe —the most important producer west of the Caucasus. The largest field is around **Ploesti** on the Wallachian Plain. Another field is located farther north, to the east of the Carpathians. **Natural gas** also occurs at Ploesti and in a separate field in the Transylvanian Basin. The gas is used locally; the oil is exported to Russia. Metallic mineral deposits found in the Carpathians include gold, silver, copper and lead, and iron in large quantities, but they are as yet undeveloped.

The **coal** resources of Czechoslovakia are the most important mineral resource of that country. In terms of reserves they exceed those of France. The major source is the field of upper Moravia, part of a larger coal province centered in Poland. This field yields both anthracite and bituminous coal. Coal is also mined in the center of the Bohemian Plateau and east of the Erz Gebirge. Second in importance are the **uranium** deposits of **Jachymov** in the Erz Gebirge. These famous old mines produced the ore from which radium was first obtained. The Soviets are working them frantically with slave labor, but it is believed that reserves are nearing exhaustion. The Erz Gebirge also yield significant quantities of **graphite.** Other mineral products are small amounts of iron ore, antimony, and magnesite, and larger quantities of high-grade **china clay** and the raw materials for glassmaking.

Hungary's outstanding mineral resource is the largest reserves of **bauxite** in Europe, located in the western portion of the country. Other resources consist of small coal fields— an **anthracite** area at **Pecs** on the Yugoslav border and a **lignite** belt along the northern border.

Bulgaria's meager mineral resources consist of small lignite deposits in the center of the country, with a modest output.

Agriculture. The agriculture of Czechoslovakia reflects the country's transitional position between the marine west coast climate, the humid continental climate, and the two phases of the latter. About two-fifths of the population are engaged in agriculture, which is of the peasant, small-holding type. The Bohemian and Moravian farms are better cared for than those of Slovakia to the east. Indicative of the transitional climatic location of the country is the absence of any dominant crop. **Wheat, rye, oats, barley,** and **potatoes** all have about the same acreage; the cereals collectively occupy a little more than half the cultivated land.

Special crops include **hops** in western Bohemia and **sugar beets** in northern Bohemia and Moravia. Czechoslovakia is one of the leading sugar producers of Europe. **Grapes** are also important in both these districts.

Czechoslovakia has ample and well-managed timber lands. Coniferous forests clothe the upper slopes; beechwoods occupy the lower levels. Together these afford adequate supplies of both lumber and pulpwood.

In Hungary over one-half the population is engaged in agriculture and almost two-thirds of the area of the country is arable,

the highest such proportion in Europe. Farming in Hungary is of two general types. One is centered about peasant, or "garden," towns (Fig. 24.10), with vegetable plots adjacent to the houses and the outlying lands used for field crops. Formerly there were wide reaches of pasture and wasteland between one and the next of the cultivated areas ringing the garden towns. The utilization of these unoccupied tracts is the second general type of agriculture. Techniques and equipment are still backward, an inheritance from feudal days of large estates. The Communist drive to institute state and collective farms meets with stubborn peasant resistance. The Hungarian rural workers are doggedly opposed to any sort of change.

Corn and **wheat** are the two chief crops, with about the same acreage. Fields of these two grains occupy more than one-half the total area of the country. Wheat tends to be centered in the east; corn, along with barley and oats, is distributed throughout the country. **Tobacco** is important in the northeast, sugar beets and grapes in a number of separate districts. **Rice** growing is concentrated in lowlands along the **Tisza,** a south-flowing tributary of the Danube in eastern Hungary, where irrigation works have been constructed to provide and control the flooding essential at one stage in the production of this grain.

A specialty crop of Hungary is **paprika,** a kind of red pepper introduced by the Magyars. Livestock raising, of small importance in Czechoslovakia, has a large place in Hungarian agriculture. Among the fowls, **geese** are particularly favored.

In Rumania three-quarters of the population depend on farming for a livelihood; about one-half the land is arable. Rumanian agriculture is of the peasant type characteristic of this part of Europe, with small landholdings, poor practices, and low yields. Between the World Wars the old feudal estates were broken up, and collectivization is now also in progress, although at a slower pace than the Communists would like. As befits the long-summer phase of the climate, **corn** is the dominant crop, in both acreage and out-

Fig. 24.10—Hungarian Peasant Garden Town. (Courtesy, Legation of Hungarian People's Republic.)

put. The great center of production is the Wallachian Plain, which is almost one vast cornfield in summer. The crop has long been grown for local consumption, since cornmeal is the staple food of the people, but the Communists are endeavoring to make corn the export grain instead of **wheat,** the second crop, which has traditionally been sold abroad. The chief center of wheat production is the Transylvanian Basin. Some **oats** and **barley** are grown. Beans and peas are raised between the corn rows in Wallachia; sugar beets are important in the west.

Since World War II there has been a considerable expansion in the growth of **oilseeds** because of an active demand due to the general shortage of vegetable oils in eastern Europe. Sunflowers, rapeseed, soybeans, and linseed are the important items of this kind. Grapes, apples, plums, and pears are grown on the south-facing slopes of the rugged districts. Stock raising has a significant place in Rumanian rural activities. The water buffalo, almost unknown elsewhere in Europe as a domestic animal, is common in Transylvania.

Bulgaria, like Rumania, has 75 percent or more of its population engaged in agriculture. Only two-fifths of the land area is arable, however, and one-fifth is truly wasteland, more than in any of the other three countries. Cultivation is of the outmoded peasant type, with low yields. As elsewhere in these Balkan states the Communists have endeavored to substitute collectivization and nationalization of agriculture but with only indifferent success because of peasant resistance.

Agriculture in Bulgaria is transitional between that of the humid continental climate and that of the Mediterranean climate. Thus in the north there is an extension of the Rumanian **corn** and **wheat** districts where the land rises toward the Balkan Mountains. In the south corn is less important, but **fruits** and **grapes** are grown along with wheat. Some **cotton** is produced in a basin between the Balkan and Rhodope mountains.

Tobacco from the Rhodopes is a major export crop; it is a special aromatic type used in world tobacco centers for blending purposes. A very unusual product which has its chief source in Bulgaria is **attar of roses,** rose essence made by crushing the petals of the flowers grown as a "field crop." The **sheep** population of 10 million is the largest in the four countries. Along with **goats,** the sheep are raised in the mountains. Pigs and cattle are found in the corn-growing areas. The water buffalo here also appears as a draft animal.

Industries. Czechoslovakia is by all odds the most completely industrialized of the four countries. Its industrial development dates from before World War I, when the present state was the manufacturing center of the Austro-Hungarian Empire. Accordingly, there is in Czechoslovakia complete familiarity with modern processing and assembly practices, together with ample skilled manpower, managerial ability, and know-how. Factories are concentrated in Bohemia and Moravia, especially in a belt along the inner side of the Erz Gebirge and Sudeten Mountains. The Czech industrial districts, however, are not urban concentrations as is regularly the case in the larger industrial countries of Europe, but instead are small town developments and commonly consist of numerous small, scattered plants. Czech industry resembles that of the great powers, on the other hand, in the very wide range of its activities and products. Practically every kind of manufactured article is made in Czechoslovakia.

Iron and steel and **heavy machinery** are the two leading industries, the latter including plants making machine tools, aircraft, locomotives, and armaments. Although the volume of iron and steel production is small it is significant because it is based on local supplies of ore and fuel. Under Communist control efforts are being made to integrate the Czechoslovakian iron and steel industry with that of neighboring Poland, where large amounts of coal are available.

Textiles, both cotton and woolen, rank next after heavy machinery; then come the ceramic industries—**chinaware** and **glass.** The textile raw materials are largely imported, but those for ceramic manufacture are of local origin. Mention needs also to be made of the extensive **chemical** industry, which includes both drugs and fertilizers, and a **brewing** industry that produces world-famous high-quality beer.

Hungary is much less intensively industrialized than is Czechoslovakia. Although it supports some heavy industry, this is not known for any specialized products. A small iron and steel works antedating World War II was supplemented in 1950–51 by a large mill erected as part of the development program undertaken by the Communists. The two plants apparently strain the very modest local raw material base on which the industry was originally established. Most Hungarian factories are engaged in agricultural processing: breweries, sugar beet mills, flour mills, and the like. A small textile industry supplies local needs on the basis of imported raw materials. Industry is concentrated in three regions: one in the center of the country, where a wide variety of consumers' goods is produced, agricultural processing is done, and metallurgical products are made; one in the northwest, with textile mills, cement and china manufactures; and one in the northeast, where machinery and armaments are made.

Rumania remains an almost completely agricultural country, since less than 10 percent of the population is engaged in manufacturing. Most of these few are engaged in craft industries. Leatherworking, spinning, weaving, and embroidery are all regularly represented in the peasant towns. The colorful national costumes attest to the high skill that has been developed in these arts. Factories as such are chiefly devoted to agricultural processing, but there is a small nucleus of heavy industry. The iron and steel mill essential for this is based on local coal and iron deposits found in the southwest corner of the country.

Bulgaria's industrial status is nearly identical with that of Rumania. About the same proportion of the population is engaged in manufacturing. There are the beginnings of heavy industry with the necessary iron and steel plant. Most factories, however, are engaged in agricultural processing.

CITIES OF CZECHOSLOVAKIA, HUNGARY, ROMANIA, AND BULGARIA

Name	Country	Type	Population
Budapest	Hungary	Governmental, commercial, industrial	1,100,000 (1948)
Bucharest	Rumania	Governmental, commercial	1,000,000 (1952)
Prague	Czechoslovakia	Governmental, commercial, industrial	922,000 (1947)
Sofia	Bulgaria	Governmental, commercial	437,000 (1950)
Brno	Czechoslovakia	Industrial	273,000 (1947)
Ostrava	Czechoslovakia	Industrial	181,000 (1947)
Bratislava	Czechoslovakia	River port-industrial	173,000 (1947)
Szeged	Hungary	Commercial	140,000 (1948)
Plovdiv	Bulgaria	Commercial	127,000 (1950)
Debrecen	Hungary	Commercial	126,000 (1948)
Pilsen	Czechoslovakia	Industrial	118,000 (1947)
Cluj	Rumania	Commercial	118,000 (1948)
Timisoara	Rumania	Commercial	112,000 (1948)
Miskolc	Hungary	Industrial	109,000 (1941)
Ploesti	Rumania	Commercial	96,000 (1948)
Iasi	Rumania	Commercial	94,000 (1948)

Cities. **Budapest** (Fig. 24.11) is the largest city of the four countries and is the capital of Hungary. It is on the Danube at the intersection of its north-south course with an east-west trade route. Like Vienna, it is a relic of the days of the old empire, is a governmental city too large for its country, but does have the advantage of being situated near the center. The place is really two cities linked together. Buda, the citadel and administrative center, occupies the hills west of the river; Pest, the market center, is situated on the lowland across the river on the east. Buda remains the cultural and administrative center and Pest is the busy commercial river port. Most of the industry of Hungary is centered in Budapest, and it is the greatest center of flour milling in Europe. The center of the city has an old, monumental look that stands out in sharp contrast with the garish newness of the eastern suburbs.

Bucharest, the capital of Rumania, is the second largest city of the four countries. It is in the southeast section of Rumania a few miles north of the Bulgarian border and is the cultural and commercial center of the country. Like Budapest, it has the look of a modern urban place in its central section but this aspect deteriorates abruptly to dirt roads and a squalid countryside in the outer zones of the city and its immediate environs.

Fig. 24.11—Budapest in Winter. (Courtesy, Legation of Hungarian People's Republic.)

Prague ("Ford") is the capital of Czechoslovakia (Fig. 24.12). It grew up originally

Fig. 24.12—View of the Center of Prague. (Courtesy, American Geographical Society.)

as a commercial center at the intersection of trade routes in the center of the Bohemian Plateau at the point where there was a ford across a small stream. Like the other capitals of east central Europe, Prague is the dominating urban center of its country. It is at once the focus of all governmental, industrial, commercial, and banking activities of Czechoslovakia. It is also a beautiful city, with many cultural monuments.

Sofia, the capital of Bulgaria, is the smallest of all European capital cities. It is nevertheless rather modern in appearance. Aside from being the Bulgarian capital its only other significance is that of its position on the main railroad between Istanbul and western Europe.

In Czechoslovakia there are four other cities with populations of 100,000 or more. Brno, the second city, is situated in the center of the country. It is noted for its textile manufactures, especially of woolens. Nearby is one of the largest shoe factories in the world. Ostrava is a center of heavy industry in the northern coal fields. It is often called the "Pittsburgh of Czechoslovakia." Bratislava, on the southern border 40 miles down the Danube from Vienna, is the country's chief Danubian port and largest Slovakian city. Pilsen, 50 miles southwest of Prague in the Bohemian Basin, is a major industrial

center, known for such diverse items as the *Skoda* plant, one of the greatest European armament factories; high-quality glassware and paper; and Pilsener beer, a premium brew that is widely imitated in the United States.

Besides Budapest, other Hungarian cities with populations of 100,000 or over are Szeged, Debrecen, and Miskolc. The first two are local market towns that represent the consolidations of several small peasant villages. Szeged is also a center of flour milling. Miskolc has iron mines nearby and in consequence boasts some heavy industry.

Major Rumanian cities are: Cluj, the second city of the country, an old market center of the Transylvanian Basin; Iasi on the northeast border, a local market center with a predominantly Jewish population; Timisoara, a commercial city of the southwest in a mining district; and Ploesti, the oil-field center 35 miles north of Bucharest.

The single major city of Bulgaria other than its capital is Plovdiv, an ancient commercial center 80 miles southeast of Sofia in the center of a fertile valley between the Balkans and the Rhodopes, and also on the railroad to Istanbul.

Czechoslovakia, Hungary, Rumania, and Bulgaria as a Whole. Were the plight of the people in the four satellite countries not so distressing the present political and economic situation might be regarded simply as a perversion of human endeavor. Until after World War II this whole region had remained economically backward because it was divided into too many independent nations, none of which was a geographic unit. If these nations had been mutually coöperative, as Canada and the United States are, boundary handicaps to effective utilization of resources could have been overcome. Instead there was complete lack of amity. The countries bickered constantly over boundaries, over the use of the Danube, and over many other problems. Now, as satellites of Soviet Russia, they find themselves collectively in the same unpleasant predicament. It is ironic that under the effective, unified control which exists and which permits the political boundaries that made the former difficulties to be ignored and geographical units to be treated as such, the people and the countries are worse off than before.

This is because it is the basic policy of the Russian Communists to exploit all satellite countries in order to build up the economic and military power of the U.S.S.R. To achieve these ends they introduce and enforce state-owned, collectivized agriculture and promote the industrialization of each country. The result in agriculture to date has been unhappy. The "breadbasket of Europe," as the region was formerly termed, now has trouble feeding its own people. The decline in agricultural output despite some progress in farm mechanization is due partly to the elimination of incentives for production, partly to the Russian insistence on the development of mining and industry, which involves the transfer of labor from the land to the mines and factories. Moreover, the emphasis on building up heavy industry at the expense of manufacturing to supply consumer needs and wants has resulted in a decline in the standard of living despite an increase in industrial output.

In all this, geographical circumstances have not been completely ignored. It is true that now Czechoslovakian chemicals can be made from Rumanian oil, and Rumanian oil production is dependent on supplies of Russian and satellite materials. But however realistic these adjustments are, they have as their major and almost sole purpose the build-up of Soviet strength, and the industrialization of Rumania and Bulgaria is being pushed too fast for people who have been economically backward for so long.

QUESTIONS. Locate Austria in Europe. Describe its topography; its people. What is its most important industry? What kind of goods has Austria tended to specialize in? Explain why Austria is an "unfortunate country." Why is its future uncertain? Briefly characterize Vienna.

Why is Yugoslavia officially known as a "Federal People's Republic"? Name the major mountains, the chief streams. Describe Yugoslavia's mineral resource status, its agriculture, its manufacturing. What are the three major peoples of the country? Why is Yugoslavia unique among the Communist nations? What are difficulties in the way of establishing a nationalist Yugoslavia? What are the urges to hasten the country's industrialization? Name the capital of Yugoslavia.

Explain the term "satellite" as applied to certain east European countries. Locate Czechoslovakia, Hungary, Rumania, and Bulgaria in relation to one another. Describe the general topographic aspects of the four countries, naming the major units. Discuss the peoples of the four countries, noting their similarities and differences. Characterize the mineral resource position of each of the countries. Name the major mineral resource of Rumania, of Czechoslovakia, of Hungary. What is the most significant present-day product of the Erz Gebirge? Compare the agriculture of the four countries in terms of: importance within the country, major crops, techniques. Locate the most important districts for each of the outstanding crops.

Name Czechoslovakia's chief industries. Where are they located? In relation to their past, what is ironical in the present economic situation of the four countries? What are the objectives and what has been the result of Communist development policies? Describe Budapest. In what way is Bucharest similar to Budapest? What is unique about Sofia? Why is Ostrava known as the "Pittsburgh of Czechoslovakia"? Name two things for which Pilsen is famous. What product is associated with Ploesti?

CHAPTER 25

The Humid Continental Climate: Eurasian Region (Short-Summer Phase) and Asian Region

■ EURASIAN REGION— SHORT-SUMMER PHASE

1. POLAND

General Aspects. The "effective" area of Poland since World War II has been 121,000 square miles, or about the size of New Mexico. The word "effective" is used to indicate that most of Poland's boundaries have remained a matter of dispute since the end of World War II. In the absence of internationally negotiated treaties the existing borders are those established by the Communists, but these are not recognized by the non-Communist nations. The Communist boundaries of Poland are Germany on the west, Czechoslovakia on the south, the Soviet Union on the east and northeast (Fig. 25.1). The Soviets have also allotted Poland a considerable length of coastline along the Baltic Sea.

Further, as established by the Communists, Poland now includes a number of former German territories: **Pomerania** in the northwest, about one-half of former **East Prussia** on the northeast, **Lower Silesia** on the southwest, and **Upper Silesia** in the south center. On the east an area larger than that taken away from Germany was appropriated by the Russians. Polish territory was thus moved 120 miles west of its prewar extent and reduced about one-fifth in area by these Soviet adjustments.

Fig. 25.1—Poland and the Baltic States. The inset compares the area of the region with an equivalent area of the United States (states in white). The boundaries of the Baltic States represent their present boundaries as Soviet Socialist Republics within the Soviet Union. The Kaliningrad district is now a part of the major political unit of the Soviet Union, the Russian Soviet Federal Socialist Republic.

POLAND AND THE BALTIC STATES

Topography. The overall topographic aspect of Poland is extremely simple. There is a wide plain that rises gradually from the Baltic coast toward the south until it reaches a highland belt that extends east-west across the whole country. The Baltic coast is straight and shallow, festooned with lagoons and backed by sand dunes. Inland the surface relief becomes confused and irregular and is the expression of glacial deposits from the ice age. Lakes and hills up to 800 feet in elevation are distributed throughout the western portion. Streams wander erratically, and the poor drainage is indicated by marshy tracts.

Farther south the effects of the glacier are less evident; the drainage is better organized and hence the land is drier. The land continues to rise gradually until the highland belt is reached. In the west this consists of the **Sudeten Mountains,** continuing in the east as the **Silesian** and **Polish plateaus.** South of the plateaus are the foothills of the **Carpathian Mountains** and finally the Carpathians themselves, along the eastern part of the southern border.

There are relatively few major streams. The **Vistula** follows an approximately northerly course through the center of the country. Its largest tributary, the **Bug,** forms the central portion of the eastern boundary of the country. The **Oder** constitutes most of the western border. Its upper reaches have their source in Silesia to the southeast, so that the western border is continued southward along a north-flowing tributary of the Oder, the **Neisse.**

People. The 25 million people of Poland are Slavs. The Poles belong to the western Slavs, as their forebears were among those who ranged farthest west during the great Slavic invasions of ancient times. As presently constituted the country has an unusually homogeneous population. Previous to World War II there were large enclaves of Russians and Germans, but after the war the Soviet-fixed boundaries, migrations, and forced population movements resulted in a Poland for the first time almost completely Polish. Practically all Poles are Roman Catholics. The large prewar Jewish minority was all but exterminated during the Nazi occupation.

The turbulent history of their country, which includes repeated dismemberment and even elimination of the nation as such, has made the Poles fanatically patriotic. This served to keep Polish culture and traditions alive during the eclipses of the Polish state but when the nation was powerful it led to arrogance and territorial greed. The Poles never hesitated to take advantage of the weakness of neighboring states when they were able to do so.

Mineral Resources. Poland's highly important mineral resources are almost entirely concentrated in Upper Silesia. What was probably the richest prize wrested from defeated Germany after World War II was the acquisition by Poland of the second largest **coal** deposits of Europe. Prior to World War II Poland had held a portion of the Silesian fields but sharing them with Germany and Czechoslovakia involved Poland in even more complicated political and economic problems than those of the Saar-Luxembourg, Franco-Belgium complex in the West. The Silesian coal deposits include both anthracite and good-quality coking coal (accounting for one-fifth of the total output) and are easily mined. Lignite fields of minor extent are distributed over the west and center of the Polish plain. The leading **zinc** source of Europe is also in Silesia. The district known as **Galicia** has a natural gas field, small oil resources, and large salt deposits.

Agriculture. Although the name "Poland" means "Land of the Fields" the country does not have soils that yield bounteous crops. Nor is Poland statistically an agricultural country, for less than half the population is engaged in farming. Nevertheless, about one-half of Poland is arable, and Polish landscapes are characteristically rural. Like all the countries of eastern Europe, Poland until after World War II labored under the yoke of a feudalistic system of great estates preserved intact from medieval times. While much progress was made between the World Wars in parceling out the vast single landholdings to individual farmers, it was the Communist government after World War II that brought about the breaking up of the remaining large tracts. On the other hand, the Communists also initiated their customary collectivization program.

Subject to climatic limitations the glacial soils that cover much of Poland determine the major crops. Thus **potatoes** come first in tonnage produced and are the staple food of the country. They are grown practically everywhere. The chief cereal and leading crop in terms of acreage planted is **rye,** most of which is grown in Galicia and Pomerania. **Wheat,** the second cereal, is still ahead of potatoes in acreage; the leading regions are Silesia and the lower Vistula. **Oats** and **barley** are also grown everywhere, with concentrations of the former in Galicia and the latter in Silesia. Other important crops are **sugar beets** in the south, where it is warmer and the soils are better, and **flax** in the northern coastlands.

Poland has a substantial livestock population. Its 10 million **pigs** give it the second rank among the hog-raising countries of Europe. Polish hams are internationally famous for their savoriness. There are about 7 million cattle; **dairy farming** is an important activity. The hog-cattle sections are in the west of the country. Some sheep raising is carried on in the east.

Forests cover about one-quarter of the Polish area. Coniferous trees predominate on the sandy soils of the north and in the Carpathians. Lumber is a significant item among Polish products, much of it a harvest from former German forest lands where good conservation practices had long been followed.

Industries. Industry in Poland is rather closely restricted to three well-defined districts in the center and south of the country owing to the concentration of raw material resources in those parts. The most important district is, accordingly, Upper Silesia. The basic resources of coal and iron ore found there are being exploited at the feverish pace characteristic of Communist industrial operations (although the bulk of the ore supply must come from imports). The Silesian district is thus a booming center of heavy industry, with **iron and steel** mills, associated **coke** ovens and **chemical** plants, factories for making **machinery, lead** and **zinc** smelters, and **glass** factories.

The second industrial district is located in the center of the country and is given over chiefly to **textile** manufacturing. Here cotton and woolen textiles are produced in large factories. Other fibers—silk, flax, hemp, jute, etc.—are also processed. Most of the textile industry is based on imported raw materials.

The third industrial district is in Galicia, on the north side of the Carpathians. There **chemicals,** based on the local resources of petroleum, natural gas, and salts, predominate.

CITIES OF POLAND

Name	Type	Population
Warsaw	Governmental, commercial, industrial	800,000 (1952)
Lodz	Industrial	615,000 (1952)
Krakow	Commercial-industrial	347,000 (1950)
Poznan	Industrial	342,000 (1950)
Wroclaw	Commercial-industrial	279,000 (1950)
Gdansk	Seaport	170,000 (1950)
Szczecin	Seaport	159,000 (1950)
Bydgoszcz	Industrial	156,000 (1950)
Stalinogrod	Mining-industrial	156,000 (1950)
Chorzow	Mining-industrial	131,000 (1950)
Zabrze	Mining-industrial	128,000 (1950)
Czestochowa	Industrial	115,000 (1950)
Gliwice	Mining-industrial	114,000 (1950)
Bytom	Mining-industrial	112,000 (1950)
Gdynia	Seaport	111,000 (1950)

Cities. There are two unusual circumstances relating to the cities of Poland. One is the great number with new names that appear on maps in place of their famous old German names (in the account which follows the old names are given in parentheses). The other is the fact that many of them are smaller now than they were prior to World War II. The latter circumstance is due partly to the expulsion of the German population from the cities in the former German territory, and partly also to the extermination of Poland's prewar Jewish population which was concentrated in the cities.

Thus the 30 percent of the former population of the capital city that was Jewish no longer exists.

Warsaw, the capital and largest city of Poland, had a prewar population of 1,300,-000. It is centrally situated on the Vistula River just above the entrance of the Bug. Warsaw was the most completely destroyed of all the large cities of Europe in World War II. It endured a siege and two internal rebellions, and in the final battle, when it was captured by the Russians, it was battered to pieces. It will probably show the scars of war longer than any other European city of large size. Warsaw is the commercial hub of Poland and has a great variety of light industries.

Lodz, the second city, is the great textile center of Poland and is often compared to the English textile centers, which it resembles in importance and atmosphere. It is on the Polish plain 75 miles southwest of Warsaw.

Krakow in the southeast is the traditional Polish capital and because of its cultural treasures represents the spirit of Polish nationality. As a Communist city its cultural importance has been subordinated to that of a new industrial concentration. It has a chemical industry based on the nearby salt mines, and a new iron and steel plant is located in a suburb projected to be one of the largest in all Europe.

Czestochowa is an industrial center 60 miles northwest of Krakow. Its industries are textiles and iron and steel. **Poznan** (Posen), **Wroclaw** (Breslau), and **Bydgoszcz** (Bromberg) are three cities which grew large and acquired importance while they were German. The first has a chemical industry independent of local resources; the second was the old provincial capital of Silesia, now a textile and electrical equipment center, with a new huge freight-car plant; the third is a woodworking center using lumber brought down the Vistula.

The industrial complex of Upper Silesia maintains five large cities in an area 15 by 25 miles: **Stalinogrod, Chorzow, Bytom** (Beuthen), **Gliwice** (Gleiwitz), and **Zabrze,**

(Hindenburg). The first two retain their previous Polish names, but Stalinogrod (Stalin City) was called Katowice until 1953. The new name is in line with the Communist intention to make this city the new metropolis and transportation center of Upper Silesia.

At the other end of the country along the Baltic coast are three seaports with interesting histories. **Szczecin** (Stettin), at the mouth of the Oder, was formerly the greatest of the Baltic ports of Germany. It now has little more than half its former population. **Gdansk** (Danzig) was a German port established as a free city in the Versailles Treaty to provide Poland with a seaport without actually donating a German city. The Poles refused to be satisfied with this half measure and built the all-Polish port of **Gdynia** a few miles to the north. Now that both ports are Polish, Gdansk is the chief port of the country and the outlet for Vistula commerce. Gdynia is the center of passenger traffic and the export trade in Silesian coal. All three ports are shipbuilding centers.

Poland as a Whole. Bringing the whole of the great Silesian resource-industry complex together in one country and placing it under forced development has provided Poland with an exceptionally good balance between agricultural and industrial activities. But as far as the Poles are concerned, little benefit has come to them in consequence of this union and its energetic exploitation. Like the other satellites of the Soviets the Poles have experienced a declining standard of living while this was going forward. For them there was little comfort to be found in the progress that was taking place.

With Silesia included in its territory Poland is unquestionably the most important of the satellites to the U.S.S.R. Before the Soviets are through Silesia may well rank with the Ruhr in the size and development of its industrial complex. Silesia also gives Poland significant exportable surpluses of coal and zinc which can be used to advantage in trade with western and northern Europe for the iron ore and textile raw materials on which Polish industry is almost completely dependent.

On balance the new Poland presents another of the Soviet satellite paradoxes. Geographically the nation is on a sounder basis than ever before: boundaries make ethnographic sense; resources are greater and more diversified; and economic development is well advanced (the severe wartime damage has been to a great extent overcome). Yet there is no future for the Poles as Poles until the day when Poland is again a free, sovereign nation or the member of a free association of nations, a United States of Europe.

2. The Baltic States

General Aspects. The "Baltic States" comprise three small countries in the corner of the European mainland that constitutes the east coast of the Baltic and the south coast of the Gulf of Finland. From north to south and in order of increasing size, the countries are **Estonia, Latvia,** and **Lithuania.** Together they total 74,000 square miles, or roughly the size of South Dakota (Fig. 25.1). They are bounded on the east by the Soviet Union and on the south by Poland. In the southwest, on the coast, the northern half of former East Prussia is now a special enclave of Soviet territory. (This area is included in the following discussion.)

Actually, the three states are also part of the Soviet Union, having been incorporated into the Communist nation in 1940, ostensibly to protect these territories from German occupation. As Soviet Socialist Republics in the Soviet Union they are theoretically independent states, even in the field of foreign affairs. Actually they have no sovereignty whatever. As the non-Communist world has never recognized the Soviet annexation the countries are here considered separately from the rest of the Soviet Union.

Topography. Topographically the lands of the three states are like those of northern Poland, for they are a continuation of the low Baltic Plain. The region is covered with glacial deposits that in certain districts rise to form hills 1000 feet in elevation. Most of the land is below 500 feet, however. The drainage is quite unsystematic, and the landscape is dotted with swamps and lakes. The largest lake is **Lake Peipus,** situated along most of the eastern border of Estonia. Because of the poor organization of the drainage all the rivers are short. The **Narva** which drains Lake Peipus has a 100-foot drop to the Gulf of Finland and is an excellent source of hydroelectric power. The **Dvina** in Latvia also has developed power resources.

The coast continues north from Poland with the smooth, shallow characteristics it has in that country. In Latvia a very large bay, the **Gulf of Riga,** penetrates a hundred miles inland. Still farther north the Estonian coast is higher and more irregular, with many islands offshore.

People. The people of the three countries are quite distinct, as indicated by the fact that different languages are spoken in each. The one million Estonians, or *Ests,* are racially closer to the Finns north of them than to their immediate neighbors on the south. The Estonian language and racial stock is Finno-Ugrian. On the other hand, the racial background of the 2.7 million Lithuanians and 1.8 million *Letts* of Latvia is the same as that of the other major peoples of Europe. Their different languages are not, however, directly related to any other language on the continent.

The religious pattern is odd, reflecting the influence of the several neighboring countries during the past. Thus the Lithuanians, next to Poland, are almost all Roman Catholics. Only one-fifth of the Latvians are of this faith, another fifth adhere to the Eastern Orthodox Church, and the majority is Lutheran. The dominance of the Protestant Lutheran faith indicates the former strong German influence. The Estonians, for the same reason, are four-fifths Lutheran and one-fifth Eastern Orthodox.

Resources and Economic Activity. There is only one mineral resource of any consequence, the Estonian **oil shales** north of Lake Peipus. These are extensive deposits very easily mined; some of the beds are so close to the surface that the covering earth and rock can be stripped away. The oil shale is ground up and then distilled to obtain "shale oil," a liquid similar to but not the same as petroleum. It can, however, be processed for fuel, tar, and various chemicals. Estonia is one of the three places in the world where oil shale is exploited.

About one-half the land is cultivated, and agriculture is the chief occupation of the people. The crops are the type assemblage suited to glacial soils and the harsher extremes of the short-summer phase of the humid continental climate—oats, rye, barley, potatoes for human subsistence; hay along with the grains as feed for livestock; flax as a cash crop. Dairying supplies butter, and hogs, raised on root crops, yield bacon, both formerly export items.

Another quarter of the land is forested, and lumbering is a common activity. The industries are mostly small and all are related to locally produced items. They process shale oil, sugar beets, flax, linseed, and lumber.

CITIES OF THE BALTIC STATES

Name	Type	Population (1946–48)
Riga	Seaport	390,000
Tallinn	Seaport	190,000
Vilna	Commercial-industrial	163,000
Kaliningrad	Seaport-industrial	150,000
Kaunas	Industrial	110,000

Cities. **Riga** (Fig. 25.2) and **Tallinn** are the Latvian and Estonian capitals, respectively. Their significance as ports is that, although frozen over in winter, they can be kept open with icebreakers. Both are the "industrial" centers of their countries.

Vilna and **Kaunas** are Lithuanian cities. The former, in the southeast corner of the state, was the ancient Lithuanian capital. A much-disputed rail center, it was held by Poland between the World Wars. Kaunas thus became the capital during the period of modern independence after World War I. Like Riga and Tallinn, Kaunas is the "industrial" center of its country.

Kaliningrad, although not the largest city of the area, is the most important. As Königsberg, it was the former capital of East Prussia. It is now the center of the district the

Fig. 25.2—Scene in Riga, Latvia. (Courtesy, Soviet Embassy.)

Russians have annexed, a territory 6100 square miles in area with a total population of 600,000. The city has always had shipyards, machine shops, and an associated naval base. Feverish construction activity there since World War II indicates that the Soviets mean to make Kaliningrad one of the major Baltic centers of military power.

The Baltic States as a Whole. In the past the Baltic States have been more or less a forgotten corner of Europe. Although Lithuania was an important medieval kingdom the three states knew independence in modern times only after World War I. They began at that time the task of catching up culturally and economically with the rest of Europe. They were making quiet progress until they were again brought under subjection in World War II.

Their absorption into the Soviet Union has unusually ominous implications. To the Soviets this area is no forgotten corner but an important strategic zone. Commercially it is important in providing year-round open ports on the Baltic, which the Russians had lacked. To insure that the Baltic States will be permanently Soviet territory and that yearning for independence will never get out of hand a large proportion of the local populations has apparently been forcibly deported to Siberia.

Even more significant is the incorporation of the northern half of East Prussia into the

Russian Republic as part of the Soviet Union, together with the mass eviction of the old German population. A simpler means of dealing with the newly acquired territory would have been to award it to either Poland or Lithuania. It would appear that the territory was deemed strategically too important to be entrusted to anyone other than Russians.

Grim as is the future that the larger satellite countries face, it cannot equal the tragic probability of national extinction that appears to be in store for the people of the small Baltic States.

QUESTIONS. Explain the status of Poland's boundaries as they have existed since World War II. What has been the effect of the new boundaries on Poland's location, size, resources, industries, and population? Describe the general topography of Poland. What are Poland's two outstanding mineral resources? Name the district in which both are produced. Name the chief crops of Poland. Locate the major industrial concentrations within the country. Name the leading products of each district. Why is Poland probably the most valuable of the Soviet satellites? Why is the population of many Polish cities smaller than before World War II? Name the Polish capital, the center of Polish culture, the chief port.

Name the Baltic States and explain their present political status. Describe their topography. Distinguish between the people of the three states. Name the only mineral resource of any importance. Discuss the implications of Soviet control of this area. Explain the situation of Kaliningrad and relate it to the answer to the previous question.

3. CENTRAL RUSSIA AND WEST CENTRAL SIBERIA

General Aspects. The great Eurasian wedge of humid continental climate is still of sufficient width in western Russia to include almost the entire western border of the country from the Gulf of Finland to Rumania (Fig. 25.3). To the east the wedge narrows by gradually trending south of the 60th parallel and north of the 50th until it terminates several hundred miles north of where Kazakhstan, Mongolia, and Sinkiang come together.

Politically the climatic region extends over most of the Russian part and the southwest portion of the Siberian part of the **Russian Soviet Federal Socialist Republic.** On the west it also includes the northern half of the **Ukrainian Soviet Socialist Republic** and, in the central portion of the Polish border, the **Belorussian S.S.R.** Altogether there is involved an area of some 2 million square miles, or two-thirds that of the continental United States. It is the climatic region which constitutes the core of the Soviet Union.

Topography. The humid continental portion of the U.S.S.R. cuts across many diverse topographic elements. The western border of Russia is part of the large plain south of

Fig. 25.3—Central Russia and West Central Siberia. The inset compares the area of the region with an equivalent area of the United States (states in white).

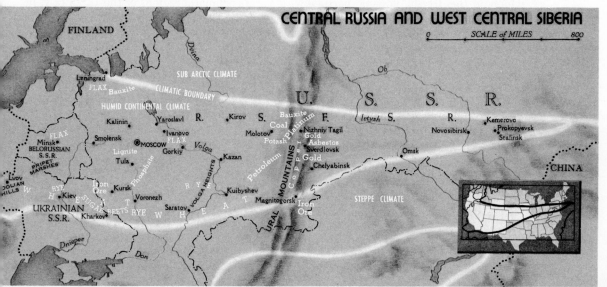

the Baltic Sea save for the **Podolian Hills,** which rise in the southwest corner. Just to the north of the hills is the largest swampy area of Europe, the **Pripet Marshes,** most of which lie in Belorussia. Central Russia is also mostly a low plain, with a district of low hills crossing its middle from north to south. East of the hills but still near the center of the plain is another hilly section, the **Volga Heights.** Most of Russia down to the southern edge of this climatic region has surface features which give evidence that the great continental glacier of the ice age advanced over the area.

The plains of central Russia are bordered on the east by the north-south line of the **Ural Mountains,** the conventional boundary between Europe and Asia. East of the Urals the humid continental region includes the southern portion of another plains area that extends over most of western Siberia. Of all the "billiard table" areas on earth this is probably the largest. The poor drainage resulting from its near horizontality gives rise in these Asian parts to the most extensive swamp district in the world.

As the climatic region cuts across the general drainage pattern no streams are specifically associated with it. In the west it includes the upper portions of the great Ukrainian rivers, the **Dnieper** and **Don,** and the middle and upper reaches of the major stream of Russia (and of all Europe), the **Volga.** East of the Urals the region comprises the upper portion of the large river system of the **Ob** and its tributaries, chief of which is the **Irtysh,** flowing northwestward from Sinkiang. The region is bordered on the south by the Kazakh Upland and at its eastern extremity reaches the western end of the Altai and associated ranges (see Chapter 22, p. 461).

As this region merges on the south with the middle latitude steppe lands of the U.S.S.R. its southern portion is a representative tract of "wooded steppe" (see Chapter 24, p. 507). The fertile, so-called "black earth" region of the wooded steppe runs the full length of the region from east to west and accounts for two-thirds of the total ara-

ble land of the Soviet Union. The richest soil of the black earth region is in the northern Ukraine.

People. Central Russia is the homeland of the *Great Russians* (see Chapter 22, p. 456). These are by far the dominant element in the population of the humid continental region of the Soviet Union. The *Ukrainians* of the Ukraine have also been discussed previously (see Chapter 22, p. 456). Belorussia is populated by 8 million people of that name. The Slavic Belorussians are like the Ukrainian group to the south, a sort of "cousin" group to the Great Russians. They were formerly known as "White Russians," apparently an allusion to the peasant custom of dressing all in white; but with the introduction of political connotations to the words "red" and "white" their current official designation of Belorussians is probably more acceptable.

The Ural-Volga district is the home of an ethnic hodgepodge comparable to those of the Caucasus and Soviet Central Asia (see Chapter 22, p. 461). Between the Volga and the Urals live most of the *Tatars* of the Soviet Union. Distributed around them are several Finno-Ugrian peoples, mixtures of blond Finns and dark Mongolians in varying degree, whose language is Turkic. The Finno-Ugrians include 1.4 million *Mordva,* 600,000 *Udmurts,* and 500,000 *Mari.* The chief Turkic peoples are the 1.4 million *Chuvash* and 850,-000 *Bashkirs.*

On the whole the humid continental region is the most densely populated of the various climatic regions of the U.S.S.R. It includes the heaviest population concentration of all (that occupying the central Russian plain), as well as the large centers on the Baltic coast, in the central Volga district, the Urals, and on certain tributaries of the Ob.

Mineral Resources. The middle-latitude arid region of the U.S.S.R. has the most important mineral resources of the country, but the humid continental region runs it a close second. This high rank is due to the unusual abundance and variety of the mineral resources found in the Urals. The region also contains the largest and best reserves of coal at its far eastern end, in a district around an upper tributary of the Ob known as the **Kuznets Basin,** or as the Russians call it, "Kuzbas." The Kuzbas beds are the best of all Soviet coals and include both coking bituminous and anthracite. The coals are easily mined, and production ranks second to that of the Donbas. Coal also occurs at several other places in the region: in the **Moscow Basin** south of the center of the Russian plain, on the west side of the central Urals, and on the east side of the southern Urals. The central Ural coal is too high in sulfur to be a good metallurgical coal; the Moscow and southern Ural coals are lignites. Nevertheless the Moscow and Ural districts follow the Kuzbas in volume of production, since they are so convenient to the centers of Russian activity.

Petroleum, the other basic fuel, is produced in a large district embracing the area between the Volga and the Urals. In output and reserves it is of such importance that it is known as the "second Baku" (see Chapter 22, p. 458).

The region also closely matches the arid region of the U.S.S.R. in **iron ore** resources. The most important are those of the southern Urals, at **Magnitogorsk,** where the ore occurs in the iron-rich mineral, magnetite. A deeply buried low-grade deposit occurs in the central hills of the northern Ukraine at **Kursk.** Low-grade ores are found in the Moscow Basin and the central Urals, and some small deposits occur in the Kuzbas.

Nonferrous mineral resources are present in significant but not outstanding quantities. **Bauxite** of poor quality is mined in the northern part of the hilly belt on the Russian plain and in the Urals. The Urals also contain widespread but poor-quality **copper** deposits as well as sources of the ferroalloy metals **nickel, vanadium,** and **chromium.**

The truly notable mineral resource of the Urals, however, is **platinum,** the basis of the chief mining industry there under the czars. Russia, in fact, has always been the leading platinum producer of the world. **Gold** also is mined in the Urals.

Nonmetallic resources of importance include: **phosphate** rock in the center and east center of the Russian plain; **potash** and **asbestos** in the central Urals. Reserves and production of all three are large.

Agriculture. The agricultural products of the humid continental region of the U.S.S.R. are those characteristic of the climate, except that **wheat** growing is emphasized along the southern border of the region because of the urgency of the Soviet drive to move crops up to their northern limits. This is the champion **rye**-producing district of the world, and the other hard cereals **oats, barley,** and **buckwheat** are also commonly raised. In the south **millet** and **lentils** are field crops. Among the vegetables **potatoes, cabbages, cucumbers,** and **carrots** are the most important. Indeed, from the frequency of cabbage dishes in the Russians' diet this vegetable could be considered their staff of life. Other common crops in the south are **hemp, sunflowers,** and the fruits **apples, cherries, plums,** and **berries. Flax** predominates in the northern portion of the region. Here are districts that account for more than one-half the world production. Hogs, cattle, and other domestic animals are kept on the farms wherever there is fodder.

Particular concentrations of production appear by districts. In the Ukraine sugar beets are a large planting, along with the typical humid continental crops. In Belorussia the glacially diversified soils and a surface dotted over with swamps and lakes yield only poor returns, but rye, oats, and root vegetables are nevertheless cultivated as well as may be. Flax is the nonfood crop there. Farther north potatoes, hemp, and flax are grown. In the upper Volga district the list includes rye, hardy varieties of spring wheat, potatoes, cabbages, sunflowers, and flax.

In Siberia the special effort to extend wheat growing northward has made spring wheat the dominant crop in the region. Grain elevators punctuating the horizon line of the western Siberian plain duplicate the landscape aspect of the great wheat plains of the United States and Canada.

Cattle are raised throughout central Russia and West Central Siberia for both **dairy** and meat products, the dairy cows especially in the northern sections in both Russia and Siberia.

Industries. Almost the entire northern section of the humid continental region in Russia is a single great industrial district. In this it is comparable to the part of the United States extending from Massachusetts and New Jersey to Wisconsin and Illinois. There are, however, three districts within the Russian region where industrial concentrations are exceptionally notable.

The **Moscow** or **central industrial district** is located in the center of the Russian plain. It is the great **textile** center of the U.S.S.R. and has been so from czarist times. In addition the Communist regime has established there a heavy-industry complex that includes even **steel** production from the local ores and Donbas coke. The district specializes in making **heavy machinery** and **precision tools.** Chemical manufacture is also important. Other industries of the Russian plain within the limits of the humid continental region include **linen** manufacture in the territory west of the Moscow district and **sugar refining** in the Ukraine.

The **Ural industrial district** was the first great new industrialization achieved by the Soviets. On the basis of local iron ore and Kuzbas coke a large **steel** industry was founded, and subsequently expanded and specialized on the basis of the resources of alloy elements found in the Urals. Other industries of importance in this area are **chemicals, paper,** and a **lumber** industry based on forests along the Volga tributaries.

Both Moscow and Ural districts are at a disadvantage because of a lack of high-grade metallurgical coke. This necessitates the use of charcoal, a practice which the rest of the steelmaking world has long since abandoned.

The third great industrial district is that of the **Kuzbas.** This is an even more impressive *tour de force* by the Soviets than that of the Urals, for in the period of only a few decades a large heavy-industry complex was created where previously there was only empty steppe. Originally the Kuzbas area was nothing more than a local source of coal

for the Trans-Siberian Railroad. The first step in its industrialization was the establishment of a **steel** industry based on local coal and Urals ore. The transportation problem this posed was solved by setting up a grandiose shuttle service. Ore was shipped east to the Kuzbas and coal west to the Urals—thus steel could be produced at both places. The cost of the rail haul this required, a distance of over 1200 miles, would make an American steelman shudder. Even the Russians realized that it was an uneconomic approach. Accordingly, they shortly turned to the Karaganda coal fields (see Chapter 22, p. 462) as a source of coal for the Urals, and developed local Kuzbas iron deposits to supplement the ore from the Urals. These substitutions should eventually make the shuttle service unnecessary. In addition to steel the Kuzbas sector produces large quantities of **heavy machinery** and **chemicals.**

Transportation. The humid continental region of the Soviet Union is noteworthy in that a very large part of all Soviet transportation facilities are within it. A rail map of Russia shows a spiderweb of lines radiating from the Moscow industrial district, with circumferential connecting lines at appropriate distances out from Moscow. This rail net is in fact the only well-developed transportation system in the U.S.S.R. In Siberia most of the eastern end of the Trans-Siberian line lies within the humid continental region.

Besides the railroads the humid continental region of Russia is also served by the majority of the river routes, of which the Volga is outstanding. Indeed, the Volga is the greatest artery of commerce in all Russia, for it links such large economic centers as the Moscow industrial district, the Urals, the Ukraine, and the agricultural districts to the south and east. In addition, an extensive interconnecting canal system duplicates the spiderweb pattern of the railways on the Russian plain (see Chapter 2, p. 18).

Cities. It is remarkable that in this impressive list of cities with populations numbering from hundreds of thousands to millions there are many of such recent origin as to be completely lacking in significance for the Western world. This drab obscurity derives not only from their newness and their location

CITIES OF THE HUMID CONTINENTAL REGION IN THE SOVIET UNION

Name	Type	Population (1946–48)
Moscow	Governmental, commercial, industrial	4,800,000 (1955)
Leningrad	Seaport-industrial	3,200,000 (1955)
Kiev	Governmental, commercial, industrial	990,000 (1955)
Gorkiy	Commercial-industrial	900,000
Kharkov	Commercial-industrial	900,000
Novosibirsk	Commercial-industrial	750,000
Kuibyshev	Commercial-industrial	600,000
Sverdlovsk	Commercial-industrial	600,000
Chelyabinsk	Commercial-industrial	500,000
Kazan	Industrial-governmental	500,000
Saratov	Commercial-industrial	500,000
Omsk	Commercial-industrial	500,000
Molotov	Industrial-commercial	450,000
Lvov	Commercial-industrial	400,000
Yaroslavl	Industrial	300,000
Ivanovo	Industrial	300,000
Tula	Industrial	300,000
Voronezh	Industrial	300,000
Kalinin	Commercial-industrial	300,000
Kirov	Commercial-industrial	250,000
Nizhniy Tagil	Mining-industrial	250,000
Minsk	Governmental, commercial, industrial	230,000
Magnitogorsk	Mining-industrial	200,000
Stalinsk	Industrial	200,000
Kemerovo	Mining	200,000
Prokopyevsk	Mining	200,000
Smolensk	Commercial-industrial	150,000

behind the Iron Curtain but also from their nature. It will be noted that nearly all of them are here classified as commercial-industrial, industrial, mining, or mining-industrial. In other words, they function as district manufacturing and trade centers. They are an expression of the explosive conversion of Russia under Soviet compulsion from an agrarian to an industrial country. Such a shift is, to be sure, a phenomenon of almost world-wide incidence, but nowhere has it taken place with the feverish haste characteristic in the Soviet Union.

Moscow is the great international city of the Soviet Union. It is international in the sense that it is the only Russian city to which foreigners have a degree of access equivalent to that customary in all Western cities. It is a super metropolis not merely because of its very large population but in being far and away the supreme urban expression of Russian character and culture. As the capital of the leading Communist state Moscow has extraordinary political, social, and economic significance for all the world. Moreover, it functions as the commercial and industrial capital of the Soviet Union in its own right. Its position at the center of the Russian plain makes it the focus of the region's commercial activities, a position that has been fully exploited. The small river on which the city is situated has been connected with the Volga by a canal, so that Moscow has adequate water transport connection with the whole country. Not only is it technically an inland port, but its volume of water-borne traffic is impressively large.

Moscow is also the rail hub of the country. It is the terminal of radial trunk lines and is completely encircled by belt lines. The city is also a great industrial center. A larger variety of products are made there than in any other Soviet city. These range from heavy transportation equipment and rolling stock to clothing and books.

Like all cities of world renown Moscow is quite unrepresentative of the rest of the cities of its country. The Soviets have been lavish in providing it with cultural monuments and have maintained those inherited from czarist times. The grim **Kremlin** (citadel), the palace of the old Russian rulers and now of the Soviet dictators, dominates the city and is a world-famous landmark. So also is the neighboring **Red Square,** the largest public square in the world, with its tomb of the embalmed Soviet demigod, Lenin, and his disciple, Stalin. The Red Square is the site of the gigantic parades and demonstrations through which the Soviet hierarchy gives visual demonstrations of its power. To these architectural inheritances from the past there have been added the most elegant (though short) subway yet constructed anywhere (Fig. 25.4) and numerous ornate public buildings (Fig. 25.5) and large apartment houses. Little of such décor appears in other Soviet cities. And, in common with all metropolises

Fig. 25.4—A Moscow Subway Station. (Courtesy, Soviet Embassy.)

of world fame, Moscow consists chiefly of block after block of dingy apartments, small shops, and factories.

Beyond the actual suburbs of the city, but still within the industrial district of which Moscow is the core, are three manufacturing centers—**Tula, Yaroslavl,** and **Ivanovo.** At slightly greater distance out there are three other cities which were originally commercial centers in their own right but are now highly industrialized. Of these **Smolensk,** on the west, has light industries; **Kalinin** and **Gorkiy,** in the northwest and east, respectively, have heavy industries.

Three hundred miles northwest of Moscow is **Leningrad,** the second largest city of the Soviet Union and the seaport of northern Russia. Leningrad is situated at the extreme eastern end of the Gulf of Finland on the 60th parallel; thus it is at the same high latitude as the southern tip of Greenland. This makes Leningrad the northernmost of all cit-

ies inhabited by a million or more people. For 200 years before 1918 this city was the Russian capital. It is now an industrial center rivaling Moscow, with large factories producing machinery, electrical equipment, shoes, and rubber products. It was beleaguered during most of World War II and although it did not surrender it survived capture only through the superhuman endurance of its inhabitants.

Kiev and **Kharkov** are the two largest cities of the Ukraine, the one in the north center of the area, the other in its northeast sector. Kiev is an old Russian city that was long a rival of Moscow; it is the present capital of the Ukrainian S.S.R. (Kharkov was the former capital). Both cities were completely destroyed in the surging battles of World War II and have since been rebuilt. Both have been converted to manufacturing centers as part of the general industrialization of the Ukraine.

Other major cities of the south and west are **Lvov, Voronezh,** and **Minsk.** The first-named is the largest city of the western

Fig. 25.5—Moscow View Showing Soviet Skyscraper Architecture. (Courtesy, Soviet Embassy.)

Ukraine; prior to World War II it belonged to Poland. Voronezh is an industrial center in the black earth belt, north of the Ukraine. Minsk is the capital of Belorussia.

On the eastern edge of the Russian plain, in the Volga region, there are four cities of considerable consequence. **Kuibyshev,** the largest of these, is on the middle Volga at the most easterly point of the course of the river. It was a secondary industrial and commercial center until World War II, when many industries were moved to it at the time the Russians were being forced back by the German army. Indeed, for a brief period Kuibyshev acquired almost the status of the capital of the U.S.S.R. Foreign embassies and many governmental departments actually transferred to it, but Moscow held, and a formal shift was never made. **Kazan,** the second city in size, is the Tatar cultural and administrative capital. **Saratov** is situated farther down the Volga on the southern edge of the humid continental region. Its chief industries are the processing of agricultural products. **Kirov,** the fourth city, is an industrial center of the northern part of the region.

In the Urals the largest city and commercial and industrial capital is **Sverdlovsk,** on the eastern side of the mountains in about the center of the humid continental region.

It makes mining and electrical equipment and processes part of the products of the many mining centers around it, although each of these, in accord with the Soviet policy of placing factories at the mines wherever possible, has its own industry. Typical of such mine-mouth centers is **Nizhniy Tagil,** an iron-mining city that has its own steel mill. The second city of the district is **Chelyabinsk,** 125 miles south of Sverdlovsk and the western gateway to Siberia on the route of the Trans-Siberian Railroad. It has considerable industry based on raw materials supplied to it by rail transport. **Molotov,** northwest of Sverdlovsk on the western side of the Urals, is another large industrial concentration that includes chemical industries. Finally there is **Magnitogorsk,** situated in the center of the Urals southwest of Chelyabinsk. Magnitogorsk was the first large planned industrial center established by the Soviets. It is a parallel of the creation of Gary, Indiana, and Fairless, Pennsylvania, by private capital in the United States. The largest steelworks of the Urals is located in Magnitogorsk. It smelts the local iron ore and processes the metal into tractors, automobiles, and railroad equipment.

The growth and development of the Siberian cities, like those of the Urals, were greatly stimulated during World War II by transfers of industries to them and by giving the cities priority in the establishment of new industries. At the eastern end of the Siberian humid continental region the cities of the Kuzbas had been expanding even before the war through the exploitation of the great local coal resources. **Stalinsk** (originally Kuznets) was the site of the first iron and steel works, established there in 1932 as a unit of the Kuzbas-Urals shuttle operation. It is now the second largest steel center in the U.S.S.R., surpassed only by Magnitogorsk. In accord with Soviet planning there are associated metallurgical plants and heavy equipment factories. **Kemerovo** and **Prokopyevsk,** the other large cities of the Kuzbas, are coal-mining centers. The former has a large coking works, and chemical plants to treat the by-products of the coking process.

There are two large cities on the Trans-Siberian line between the Kuzbas and the Urals. Originally these were commercial centers, but they have been industrialized as an insurance against the dangers that threatened Soviet production west of the Urals in World War II. **Novosibirsk,** "the Chicago of Siberia," is one of the largest cities of the country. Its commercial significance, like that of Chicago, is as a focal point of railway transportation. Both the Turksib railroad and the spur line to the Kuzbas connect with the Trans-Siberian route at Novosibirsk. The city has the ubiquitous steel rolling mill and both agricultural processing and heavy manufactures. Midway between the Kuzbas and the Urals is **Omsk.** Its industries are mostly agricultural processing but there are also automobile assembly, locomotive, and tire plants.

QUESTIONS. Describe the extent of the humid continental region within the Soviet Union. Outline the major topographic features. What is the formal name for the so-called "White Russians"? Describe the population make-up of the Ural-Volga district. Locate and explain the significance of the Kuzbas. Where is the "second Baku" and why is it so termed? Locate the major iron ore resources of the humid continental region of the Soviet Union. What is the outstanding and first-known mineral resource of the Ural Mountains? In what agricultural product does this humid continental region lead the world? Name the other outstanding crops.

Name and locate the chief industrial districts of the region and list the leading products of each. Explain the economic relationship between the Kuzbas and the Urals. How does the transportation system of the Soviet Union as a whole compare with that of this climatic region of the country?

Characterize Moscow as a world city, as the commercial and industrial center of Russia, and as the capital of the Soviet nation. Locate Leningrad and explain its present importance. Name the two chief cities of the Ukraine. For what are they noted? Name the chief city of the Urals industrial district. What do Magnitogorsk and Stalinsk have in common? Why is Novosibirsk called "the Chicago of Siberia"?

■ ASIAN REGION

B. THE CENTRAL PACIFIC COAST OF ASIA

The Asian development of the humid continental climate is the smallest of the three such regions. Unlike the Eurasian region the Asian one has steppe lands on its western border; hence the precipitation over much of its area tends to be deficient. The southern, long-summer phase of the climate borders a humid subtropical region and has characteristics that derive from the strong development of monsoon air circulation over Asia.

These characteristics are extremes of difference in the volume of annual precipitation. The long-summer phase of the Asian humid continental region is subject to both serious droughts and great floods. As a consequence the chief crops are not those typical in the other regions. They are wheat and kaoliang rather than corn. Kaoliang is better able than corn to endure either drought or standing water.

In the short-summer phase of the Asian region the winters are more severe than is typical of the climate, despite the maritime location. This is owing to the cold **Okhotsk Current** from the north that parallels the coast offshore. The chief crop, soybeans, is again untypical in that it largely supplants wheat. In fact, the enormous production of soybeans in this portion of the region is remarkable, especially as the district in which they are grown is a relatively small part of the whole region.

Politically the region includes extreme southeast Siberia (and the island of Sakhalin), all of Manchuria[1] except the west central portion, Korea except for its southern tip, and the northeast corner of China proper (Fig. 25.6). The two phases of the climate

[1] Although Manchuria is commonly thought of as a separate country it is in every sense an integral part of the Chinese nation. Manchuria is used here as a geographic term referring to a well-defined area. It is a much better understood term for this purpose than would be the Chinese names of the provinces which constitute it.

are roughly equal in area but are not considered separately in what follows.

1. SOUTHEASTERN SIBERIA

General Aspects. The Siberian portion of the Asian humid continental region consists of all the territory east from Manchuria to the sea. This area is roughly the same as that which the Russians term the "Maritime Province." It covers 428,000 square miles, almost equal to the combined area of Texas, Oklahoma, Louisiana, and Arkansas. Although little known, it is a region of considerable strategic significance.

The principal topographic feature of the district is the **Amur River,** the second longest river in the Soviet Union. The Amur forms the northern boundary of Manchuria until it turns north to flow into the Okhotsk Sea. From the turning point the Manchurian border trends south up a tributary of the Amur, the **Ussuri.** North of Manchuria there is an upland area which rises northward and culminates in the **Bureya Mountains,** a range that attains altitudes of 13,000 feet. West of this range a plateau slopes southward to the Amur, and east of the range is the valley of the lower Amur. The eastern coast is bordered by a range of mountains, still largely unexplored, known as the **Sikhote Alin** (a corruption of the Chinese name meaning "Great Range of Rivers Flowing West"). These are low mountains not much over 6000 feet in elevation at their southern end. In the southwest corner of the area, in the upper Ussuri Valley, there is a large lake, **Lake Chanka.** Sakhalin Island, which in its northwestern portion is only five miles from the mainland, is comprised of two low, parallel mountain ranges. Mixed deciduous-coniferous forests cover large areas of the entire district.

Most of the inhabitants of the district are Russian and Ukrainians, with an admixture of Chinese immigrants from the south. Remnants of the original inhabitants, various *Tungus* tribes (renamed *Evenki* by the Soviets) of Mongol stock, make up about 10 percent of the population. The Soviets sponsored an interesting settlement experiment on the middle Amur. In 1928 this **Birobi-dzhan** district was made available to Russian Jews as a colonial home within the Soviet Union. It was successful to the degree that Birobidzhan is now a significant center of textile and leather manufacture, but there has been no great concentration of Jewish population there.

Southeastern Siberia is still chiefly a frontier district, with **furs, fish,** and **lumber** the principal products. On the other hand, important mineral resources exist and substantial progress has been made in their exploitation. The most significant of these developments is the recovery of petroleum in northern Sakhalin. The Bureya Mountains contain deposits of both **iron ore** and **coal,** the latter of coking quality and in good quantity. It is axiomatic in Soviet planning that an **iron and steel** plant should rise on that basis. Other coal deposits occur in the extreme south of the region and on Sakhalin Island. Copper, lead, zinc, tungsten, and molybdenum are also produced in moderate amounts.

CITIES OF SOUTHEASTERN SIBERIA

Name	Type	Population (1946–48)
Khabarovsk	River port-industrial	300,000
Vladivostok	Seaport-industrial	300,000
Komsomol'sk	River port-industrial	150,000
Voroshilov	Commercial	150,000

Cities. **Khabarovsk** is at once the chief city of the district and the commercial capital. It is a river port at the junction of the Ussuri and Amur and is also the transshipment terminus on the Trans-Siberian Railroad for the district as a whole. Some of its many industries are machinery, assembly plants, and oil refining (based on Sakhalin petroleum).

Vladivostok is the great seaport of Far Eastern Siberia and the eastern terminus of the Trans-Siberian Railroad. It is also the point of departure for ships following the "northern sea route" to Russia via the Arctic Ocean. Vladivostok is concerned solely with maritime activities. Besides its business with overseas shipping it is the headquarters for the Pacific fishing and whaling fleets, and cans, refrigerates, and otherwise processes their catches.

Voroshilov is situated 50 miles north of Vladivostok where a Manchurian railroad from the west joins the Trans-Siberian line. It is a local agricultural processing center, especially for soybeans and their products.

Komsomol'sk ("City of Youth") is 200 miles down the Amur from Khabarovsk. It is another example of Soviet founding and developing cities by fiat. The city was started in 1932 with an initial population of 4000, all members of the Young Communist League, and is still literally a city of young people. It boasts its having the only iron and steel mill in southeastern Siberia.

2. KOREA[2]

General Aspects. Korea (*Chosen*—"Calm Dawn Land"—as it is called by its inhabitants) occupies a peninsula 400 miles long that juts south from the Asiatic mainland (Fig. 25.6). Its base, 150 miles wide, adjoins Manchuria, and in the far northeast corner it is in contact with the Soviet Union for a few miles. At its southern tip the peninsula approaches within 100 miles of the main islands of Japan. Korea is a small country; its 85,000 square miles of area is only a little greater than that of the state of Utah.

Very little of the Korean land is either low or level. Four-fifths of the country is actually mountainous; more than half the area rises above the 3000-foot contour. The highest mountains attain altitudes of 9000 feet in the **Paik-to-San** ("Long White Mountain") range in the northern center along the Manchurian border. Most of the north and northeast of the peninsula is occupied by the **Kaima Plateau,** so much dissected by streams that the relief is rugged. Midway down the peninsula it is traversed by a conspicuous rift valley (see Chapter 9, p. 147). South of this valley the mountains continue along the east side of the peninsula in ranges that are not much over 5000 feet in elevation but are very rugged in places. Along the eastern

[2] The political division of Korea in 1953 is ignored in this account of the land and the people.

coast the mountain slopes are steep; on their west sides the land descends gradually to the indented, island-studded western coast, behind which most of the Korean lowlands occur.

The major streams are the **Yalu,** flowing west from the Paik-to-San along the northern border of the country to the Gulf of Korea;

Fig. 25.6—Southeast Siberia and Korea. The inset compares the area of the region with an equivalent area of the United States (states in white).

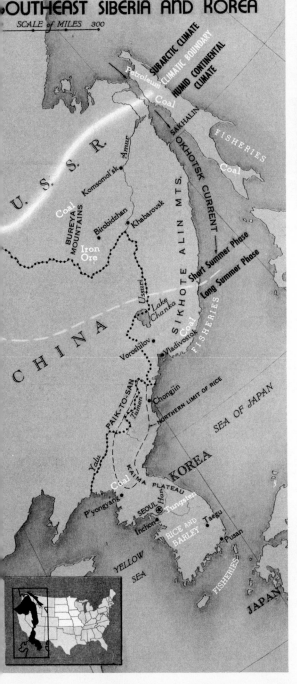

Fig. 25.7—Korean Farmer Resting for a Smoke While Transporting His Rice Crop From the Field. (Courtesy, U.N.K.R.A.)

the **Tumen,** rising on the east slopes of the same highland region to become the remainder of the northern boundary to the point where the river empties into the Sea of Japan; and the **Han,** which flows across the west central part of the peninsula.

Although Korea is within the long-summer phase of the Asiatic humid continental region its considerable latitudinal range and high altitudes give the northern part of the country very severe winters. The average temperature of this section is below freezing for five months of the year. Elsewhere in Korea winters are short. On the other hand, summers are hot, humid, and unpleasant owing to the monsoon. Precipitation is ample or more than ample everywhere.

People. Korea's rather dense population of 30 million people in a country only a little

Fig. 25.8—Korean Farmhouse in Field of Chinese Cabbage. (Courtesy, U.N.K.R.A.)

larger than Utah is concentrated in the southern half. The highlands of the northeast are almost uninhabited. The Koreans are of Tungus, or Evenki, stock. Their general appearance is Oriental (Fig. 25.7), but such aberrant traits as brown hair and white skins are often seen. Koreans are larger than Japanese and have more finely chiseled features.

The Koreans have both a distinctive culture and a national tradition despite their geographic position between the larger and more energetic Chinese and Japanese populations, and the fact that for most of its history the homeland has been under foreign domination. Korean culture is manifested by the design of the national dress (in which white is conspicuous) and in house construction. Korean houses are mud walled, and solid compared to the lighter, more airy Chinese and Japanese structures. Still, like most Oriental dwellings, the Korean houses

are ill suited to provide adequate protection against severe winters (Fig. 25.8). There is no dominant religion in Korea. The people adhere to many faiths and beliefs, including Christianity. Indeed, it has been said facetiously that the country has more gods and devils than inhabitants.

Resources and Industries. Korean mineral resources are neither great in amount nor of special significance. Since World War II **tungsten** deposits in the center of the country have been developed to become important contributors to the world supply of this metal. Beds of good anthracite occur in the northwest corner of the peninsula, and bituminous deposits in the southeast.

Forest resources consist mainly of the good timber still standing in the northeastern highlands. Although about three-quarters of Korea is "forested," most of the area so designated is of second-growth trees whose wood is generally utilized only as fuel.

The Japanese, in addition to developing the mineral resources listed above during their period of rule, also undertook numerous **hydroelectric** projects in the northern mountains. Some of these involved the construction of very large dams. Substantial hydropower resources still remain undeveloped, however.

The Japanese also managed to establish some industries on the meager natural resource base. In order of value of output before World War II these were: chemicals (especially nitrogen fertilizers), food processing, textiles (cotton and silk), and iron and steel. Heavy industry is confined to small plants, most of which are concentrated in the north of the peninsula. The textile industry is located in the southern end.

Agriculture. Despite the scant measure of arable land, Korea is an agricultural country. Although Korean practices are typically Oriental, and cultivation is handicapped as in China by the vicious, age-old, tenant farming system of the Far East, it differs from that of neighboring lands in such features as the substitution of compost and green manure for night soil as fertilizer.

Rice is the outstanding crop and staple food of the Koreans. Grown on the western lowlands and as far up the slopes as terraces can be flooded, rice paddies occupy one-third of all the tilled land (Fig. 25.9). **Barley** supplements rice in the national diet. In the south it is planted as a winter crop in the drained rice fields. The southern rice-barley combination is associated with the growing of **sweet potatoes** and of **cotton** as a cash crop. In the north of Korea wheat, millet, kaoliang, and soybeans supplement the rice crop.

CITIES OF KOREA

Name	Type	Population
Seoul	Governmental, commercial, industrial	1,400,000 (1949)
Pusan	Seaport-industrial	474,000 (1949)
Taegu	Commercial	314,000 (1949)
P'yongyang	(Governmental)-industrial	286,000 (1945)
Inchon	Seaport	266,000 (1949)
Chongjin	Seaport-industrial	184,000 (1944)

Cities. **Seoul** (Fig. 25.10) is the capital (formerly of all Korea, now of South Korea),

Fig. 25.9—Korean Rice Paddies After Harvest. The sheaves of cut grain are piled along the paddy border. The boys are catching fish in the reflooded paddy. (Courtesy, U.N.K.R.A.)

commercial, industrial, and cultural center of Korea. It is located a few miles inland from the west coast in the center of the peninsula.

P'yongyang, also inland from the west coast, midway between Seoul and the Manchurian border, is the North Korean capital and an industrial center based on the nearby mineral deposits.

Pusan and **Inchon** are the two chief South Korean ports. The former, at the southeast corner of the peninsula, is the port for trade with Japan, and a textile center. The latter is the port city serving Seoul.

Taegu is the largest inland city of southeast Korea, at an intersection of local trade routes. **Chongjin** was formerly the largest port of northeast Korea, but it is possible that Soviet concentration on the development of other nearby port towns rather than on the rehabilitation of Chongjin after its destruction during the Korean War may have relegated that city to a lesser status.

Korea as a Whole. In previous chapters the Baltic and Balkan States have been described as politically oppressed countries. Korea has suffered alien overlords for centuries and exists now as a nation half "slave" and half free. It does not follow that had there been no World War II and no Korean War the country would be in happier circumstances. If World War II had not occurred Korea would probably still be a Japanese possession. Even before that war overpopulation—despite continuous heavy emigration to Japan—was pressing down heavily on the Korean standard of living.

The division of the country in the armistice of 1953 at the 38th parallel separated rather exactly two natural geographic regions, but as these were previously complementary in resources and production the problems of Korean existence have been aggravated rather than ameliorated by this political parting of the peninsula.

3. NORTHEAST CHINA

Topography. Humid continental China includes some 400,000 square miles of Manchuria and another 200,000 square miles of the northeast corner of China proper, an area roughly one-fifth that of the continental United States (Fig. 25.11). Most of this area comprises two large plains, the **Manchurian Plain** and the **Yellow Plain**.

The Manchurian Plain is a lowland with

Fig. 25.10—Seoul, Korea. View over the housetops of part of the city showing mixture of Oriental and Western architecture. (Courtesy, U.S. Army.)

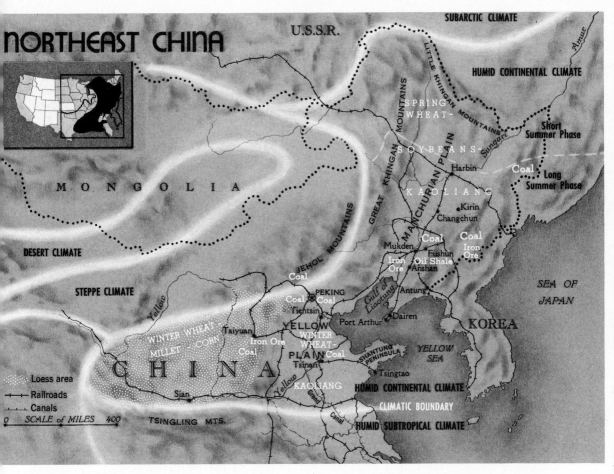

Fig. 25.11—Northeast China. The inset compares the area of the region with an equivalent area of the United States (states in white).

gently rolling relief surrounded by mountains except for water gaps through the ranges in the northeast and south. The **Great Kinghan Mountains** and the **Jehol Mountains** form a north-south barrier separating the plain from the arid Mongolian lands to the west. On the north the **Little Kinghans** come between the plain and the Amur River on the Siberian border. In the east and southeast there are highlands along the Siberian and Korean borders. The gaps in the mountain rim are exits for the two river systems of the plain. In the north the **Sungari** flows northeast to join the Amur; in the south the **Liao** empties into the **Gulf of Liaotung.**

A very narrow strip of plain along the northwest coast of the Liaotung Gulf connects the Manchurian Plain with the Yellow Plain of north China proper. This plain takes its name from the **Hwang Ho** ("Yellow River") that flows northeastward across it and has formed it through the deposition over countless centuries of sediment from wide-spreading floods. This origin accounts for the extreme flatness of the plain and its slight elevation above sea level.

In the west the Yellow Plain borders on higher ground composed of enormous deposits of *loess* (Fig. 25.12). Loess is a soil material consisting uniformly of particles finer than sand grains but coarser than particles of clay. This siltlike material is porous enough to be permeable by water. The loess forms a blanket 100 to 200 feet thick over a large area of hilly country and is derived from an arid district of Inner Mongolia lying to the west. In winter the dry antimonsoon picks up light soil particles in Inner Mongolia and drops them from dust storms which

Fig. 25.12—View in the Loess Country, Chiao-pei, Shensi Province, China. (Courtesy, American Geographical Society, photograph by F. G. Clapp.)

develop as it blows southeast. The humid monsoon winds of summer cannot blow the loess back to its source region because the rains they bring have wetted it down. The loess has a characteristic yellow color; hence come the names of the Yellow River that carries loess particles, the Yellow Plain where it deposits some of them, and the Yellow Sea, into which the river empties. As one approaches the coast of China after sailing over the blue and green seas of the open ocean the roily yellowness of the Yellow Sea is an impressive phenomenon.

Protruding northeastward into the Yellow Sea is the **Shantung** peninsula, with its base at the middle of the Yellow Plain. This is an upland district which rises to an elevation of 5000 feet at its highest point. It was formerly a mountainous island in the Yellow Sea, but the Yellow River, by changing its course so that it emptied first on one, then on the other side of the island, ultimately built its delta so far out as to convert the island to a peninsula.

In the southern portion of the Yellow Plain there is a small but significant eastward-flowing stream, the **Hwai.** The Hwai empties into the Yellow Sea through an in-

tricate complex of lakes and artificial channels resulting from the invasion, in past times, of part of its channel by the Hwang Ho (see Chapter 2, p. 39). West of the Hwai there is encountered the line of the great mountain range of central China, the **Tsingling Mountains.** These are an eastern spur of the vast Tibetan massif. In the far west even the spur has peaks of 20,000 feet; in the center the summits do not rise above 12,000 feet; in the east the mountains peter out in low hills before disappearing altogether. The Tsingling, however, is a sharply defined range which has special significance because it serves as a notable geographic boundary between North and South China. Not only climate and agriculture but customs, language—almost the way of life—differ markedly on the two sides of this wall-like boundary. Beyond the mountains the Hwai continues this division line, although less distinctly, eastward to the sea.

People. The Chinese are the direct descendants of the primitive peoples who first inhabited these parts. It was on the Yellow Plain that the Chinese civilization had its beginnings and later attained its fullest flower. Although the Chinese are a single ethnic group there are nevertheless some physical differences between the North Chinese and their countrymen in the south. In North China the "almond-shaped eye" commonly though to be the distinguishing characteristic of all Orientals is possessed by only 10 to 20 percent of the population compared with twice that frequency in the south. North Chinese also have a larger build and tend to be temperamentally less excitable than those of the south. The dominant speech of North China is a form of Chinese known as *Northern Mandarin,* comparable to Castilian Spanish as the most cultured and beautiful form of that language. There are in addition many local language variations within the provinces.

In common with the rest of the Chinese the people of North China are capable of enduring long hours of grueling toil without complaint or rest. Like all Chinese they are imbued with an extremely strong sense of family loyalty and solidarity. The family has traditionally been the focus of all life interests. Other common traits the North Chinese share with Chinese generally are friendliness and a sense of humor.

The Manchus after whom Manchuria is named are a Tungus people. Manchuria was originally their homeland, but for almost three centuries ending in 1911 they also ruled China. More recently, in the 1920's, large-scale Chinese immigration from the Yellow Plain into Manchuria converted it to Chinese territory as to both population and social customs. The Manchus had previously emigrated widely to other parts of Asia so that the few who were left in Manchuria were absorbed by the hordes of newcomers who occupied what had become a sparsely populated land.

Agriculture. The dominant characteristic of North China agriculture, as in South China (see Chapter 18, p. 364), is grimly intensive use of the land under tremendous population pressure. There is the same concentration of dense population on farms as in South China —a distribution quite unknown in the Western world—the same incredibly tiny farm plots and the same high yields obtained through prodigious, unremitting application of human labor.

The single outstanding difference between types of agriculture in North and South China is due to climate. Whereas the farmer on the Yellow Plain must make the same desperate struggle for maximum yield as the farmer of the Yangtze district, he must in addition face the hazard of insufficient rainfall. Not only is the distribution of precipitation highly seasonal in North China because of its association with the in- and outblowing monsoon winds, but it is also extremely variable in amount from year to year.

It will be recalled (see Chapter 18, p. 365) that in the south the pressure of population on food supply is so great that a crop loss for any reason makes famine a possibility. In the north, however, a really dry year results in total crop failure and means death from starvation for millions of people.

North China includes much more arable plains area than South China. This advantage is partially offset, however, by rather infertile soils in some districts and by serious gully erosion in others. The soil erosion damage has resulted chiefly from the complete denuding, in the course of centuries, of trees from the hills, loess lands, and flood plains because of the relentless utilization of every kind of plant growth for fuel. It is probable that most of North China was originally covered with dense forest. The mountains of eastern Manchuria are still forest covered and yield a good lumber crop, but in the loess land and on the Yellow Plain if forests ever existed they have long since vanished utterly. Only the mulberry trees raised by the farmers at the corners of their plots show that plants larger than shrubs can grow.

The northern farmer must also contend with bitter cold. In a land where fuel, even if it is only straw, to cook the food may cost more than the food itself, such expedients as orientation of the farmhouses to catch the winter sun's rays within the courtyard enclosure are deemed essential to even meager comfort.

On the other hand the evils of tenant farming and moneylending are much less prevalent than in the south, and a greater variety of crops is produced in the north.

Wheat is the dominant and characteristic crop of humid continental China just as rice is that of humid subtropical China. The inadequacies of Chinese transportation are epitomized in the fact that rice, the staple crop of South China, is a luxury in the north. Other than wheat the most important crops are **kaoliang, soybeans,** and **millet.** Each of the three major topographic divisions of North China grows these crops in a different pattern.

In the Shantung peninsula and the surrounding Yellow Plain a summer crop of millet, kaoliang, and **cotton** is sown in the spring before the winter wheat has been harvested. After the harvest soybeans are grown on the wheatland. Many vegetables are raised, almost entirely under irrigation.

In the western loess district **corn** is an added crop. Much of the land there is terraced and cultivated for millet. Despite the smaller percentage of arable land in the loess areas more people per acre must be supported there than on the Yellow Plain.

In Manchuria the pattern is again different. The latitude is enough higher to account in part for a variance. In addition, recency of the Chinese occupation of the land has permitted much larger farms and there is even a trend toward mechanization of agricultural operations. About equal acreages of **soybeans** and kaoliang are grown, supplemented by millet and wheat.

But acreage figures alone do not sufficiently emphasize the significance of soybeans in the crop picture. This is the great soybean district of the world and accounts for more than half the total production of this food substance. The range of uses the soybean serves is impressive. It can be processed into a variety of human foods, including a milk substitute; it serves as animal fodder; it is the source of widely used vegetable oils and their derivatives; and the residues serve as a soil fertilizer.

Mineral Resources and Manufacturing. Whereas southern China is well endowed with nonferrous metals, especially some of the rare kinds, there is a general lack of basic industrial mineral resources. In North China the situation is reversed. Humid continental China contains one of the world's larger **coal** provinces. Deposits range from lignite to anthracite, the majority of good quality except that reserves of coking coal are limited in amount. The largest deposits are found in the loess district of the middle Hwang Ho. Other seams occur in southern Manchuria and in the Shantung peninsula. Since these are closer to existing transportation facilities they have been more fully exploited than those of the remoter areas.

At **Fushun** there is exposed at the surface a bed of bituminous coal with the astounding thickness of 400 feet! (The greatest U.S. seam is only 50 feet thick.) Fushun is also one of the three places in the world where **oil shales** are utilized.

The **iron ore** resources of humid continental China, though they also comprise the bulk of all such deposits in China, do not match those of coal in either amount or quality. The best deposit is one recently discovered at **Anshan,** near the Korean border. Besides this there are scattered small and medium-sized deposits over much of North China.

Communist China has put great effort into the development of an industrial complex based on the Manchurian resources. Such heavy industry as iron and steel, machinery, and basic chemicals, and light industry such as textiles and paper are being developed with Soviet aid.

Cities. **Peking** ("North Capital") is on the Yellow Plain 70 miles northwest of Tientsin. It is the capital of all China and the seat of Chinese culture, a city of palaces, temples, the national library, and several colleges and universities. Its suburbs contain many light industries. Despite its prestige the site of Peking is inferior to that of the centrally located Nanking for use as the national

CITIES OF HUMID CONTINENTAL CHINA

Name	Type	Population
Peking	Governmental, educational	3,000,000 (1955)
Tientsin	Seaport, industrial	2,700,000 (1953)
Mukden	Commercial, industrial	1,550,000 (1950)
Dairen-Port Arthur	Seaport, industrial	1,000,000 (1950)
Tsingtao	Seaport	850,000 (1948)
Harbin	Commercial, industrial	760,000 (1947)
Changchun	Commercial, industrial	630,000 (1947)
Sian	Commercial, industrial	628,000 (1948)
Tsinan	Industrial	575,000 (1947)
Anshan	Industrial	400,000 (1953)
Fushun	Mining	280,000 (1940)
Antung	Seaport	271,000 (1947)
Taiyuan	Commercial, industrial	252,000 (1934)
Kirin	Industrial, commercial	247,000 (1947)

capital (see Chapter 18, p. 368).

Tientsin, the second city of North China, is situated on a small stream of the Yellow Plain 30 miles inland from the coast. Although the river city is referred to as the port of the Yellow Plain district, it has proved so difficult to keep the channel open that actual harbor activities are concentrated at the river's mouth. Tientsin as such is, however, the manufacturing center of the Yellow Plain and has many light industries in addition to an iron and steel works.

Mukden, in the southern part of the Manchurian Plain, is the largest city of Manchuria and the focus of the heavy industrial complex of that region. Thus **Fushun,** one of the satellite cities, mines coal and also processes oil shale and refines aluminum. **Anshan** is the chief iron and steel center of China. Its steel manufacture is completely integrated on the basis of the local coal and iron ore deposits.

The other large interior cities of Manchuria are **Harbin, Changchun,** and **Kirin.** Harbin is the metropolis of the north Manchurian Plain, situated on the Sungari River where the Manchurian cutoff of the Trans-Siberian Railroad crosses that stream. Changchun is the rail center of central Manchuria and the rail junction for the ports of northeastern Korea. It was formerly more important as the capital of Japanese Manchuria. Kirin is a Manchurian provincial capital 60

miles east of Changchun. All of these cities are industrial centers, especially for the processing of agricultural produce.

Tsingtao is a seaport on the southern side of the Shantung peninsula. It is a center for light industry and because of its excellent harbor has an associated naval base. The city had its early growth as a treaty port governed by Germany. Traces of the German occupation are still to be seen in the architecture of some of its buildings.

The largest interior cities of North China proper are **Taiyuan, Sian,** and **Tsinan.** Taiyuan and Sian are cities of the loess district. Tsinan is a city of light industries located at the edge of the Yellow Plain where the Yellow River comes closest to the Shantung highlands.

Dairen and **Antung** are Manchurian ports. The former is the chief port of Manchuria, located at the end of the Liaotung peninsula. Along with its neighboring naval base, **Port Arthur,** Dairen occupies a highly strategic site on the Yellow Sea. Antung is a lesser seaport on the Korean border at the mouth of the Yalu.

China as a Whole. In terms of size, whether in area or number of inhabitants, China is one of the outstanding countries of the world. In extent it is second only to the Soviet Union; in population it has not even a close rival. Its present importance for eastern Asia and the world at large, however, is its conversion to a Communist state in 1949, when the "Chinese People's Republic" attained control over the entire continental extent of the country.

The old China disappeared, in effect, with the downfall of the Manchu dynasty in 1911. There never was a Chinese nation as such during the subsequent decades. While a national government nominally controlled all the territory, it was the provincial warlords who really ruled the country through exercise of local authority by their own might. From 1931 to 1945 there was a steady expansion of the area of China under Japanese control; between 1946 and 1949 the country was rent by civil war.

During this long period little if any progress was made in developing the country's natural resources other than the arable land, except for the Japanese effort to establish heavy industry in Manchuria. Neither was anything done to correct the social evils that reduced the mass of the people to grinding poverty. Under the new Communist state there is for the first time since Manchu days centralized control of the whole country, and direction of an all-out effort to develop the natural resources. The doctrinal Communist program of industrialization is, moreover, being pursued with fanatical zeal.

Despite such concerted effort it does not follow that China can attain the level of industrialization of the leading Western nations. Abundance of coal provides an adequate supply of fuel (except that there remains the problem of transporting it to where it will be utilized). But the iron ore resources of China are probably too meager to support a comprehensive industrialization of the country. China's basic dependence must always be on the land; the major economic activity of the country will always be agricultural.

Nevertheless China's enormous size makes it inevitable that even a modest industrialization as a unified state will enhance the country's position as a world power. As such it is already the outstanding country of southeast Asia. It is significant in this connection that Communist China is unmistakably not a Soviet satellite but a junior partner in the Communist power world. The Soviets appear to be disposed to help China by providing technical assistance, rather than attempting to exploit the economy for Soviet ends.

The drive toward industrialization has only dubious promise of benefits for the people. Peasant resistance to collectivization and state control must be overcome. But the existence of the unified country with a strong sense of nationalism and the beginnings of economic power to support its program cannot be ignored.

QUESTIONS. Explain how the monsoon and the Okhotsk Current affect the climatic characteristics of the east Asian region. Describe the areal extent of the region. What is the general topography of the "Maritime Province"? Name and locate the chief city and chief port of this province. What is unusual about the city of Komsomol'sk?

Locate the country of Korea. Describe its topography. What is the racial background of the Korean people? In what ways do their living habits differ from those of the other Oriental peoples? Their agricultural practices? Name the outstanding crop. Discuss the geographic significance of the 38th parallel in Korea.

Describe the extent and topography of humid continental China. What is loess? What is its relation to the Yellow River, the Yellow Plain, the Yellow Sea? Describe the characteristics of the people of North China. Compare the agriculture of North China with that of South China. Name the four outstanding crops in the region and note where each is most important. Describe the uses of the soybean. Contrast the mineral positions of North China and South China. Locate the largest single coal deposit of North China. Why has Manchuria been developed as a center of heavy industry? Explain the significance of the new Communist China in terms of national power as compared with China under previous regimes. Discuss the advantages and disadvantages relevant to the Communist drive to industrialize China. Name and locate the largest city of North China. Describe Peking. What are the chief industrial centers of Manchuria? What is the unusual geographic significance of Dairen?

CHAPTER 26

The Humid Continental Climate: North American Region

C. CENTRAL AND EAST CENTRAL NORTH AMERICA

Introduction. The humid continental climatic region in North America is large. It embraces all of the United States east of the 100th meridian and north of the Ohio River, and a belt along the southern border of Canada from the Rocky Mountains to the mouth of the St. Lawrence River. Its climatic situation matches that of the east Asian occurrence. Both have a middle-latitude steppe region on the west, a cold climate on the north, and a humid subtropical region on the south.

Accordingly, variations of climate within the region parallel those of the east Asian development. Its western margin is much drier and has more pronounced continental characteristics than the eastern parts. It encroaches on the land of the blizzard and the 100-plus temperatures of summer. Like North China, the southwest corner of the region in the Midwest gets precipitation from the monsoon blowing from the southeast; and like North China it has its loess district. New England and the Middle Atlantic states are under a strong marine influence.

Agriculturally the North American region is the type occurrence of this climate. The western portion of the long-summer phase is the site of the greatest corn district of the world (Fig. 26.1). The winter wheat district in the southwest corner of the region and the spring wheat district in the northwest merge with the wheat districts of the steppe lands on the west, and together they constitute the greatest wheat-producing area in the world. The north central portion is the leading dairy district of North America. The corn district is also the greatest hog country in the world, and the region as a whole produces enormous numbers of fattened beef cattle and poultry.

The region contains the greatest coal and iron resources on earth, measured with regard to both quality and quantity. It is also the world's chief source of nickel and asbestos.

Not only does the region contain the greatest population concentrations of the North American continent; it also includes the outstanding industrial district of the world, whose output is not even remotely approached by any other district of comparable area. It is indeed difficult to characterize the economic resources and development of the region except by use of superlatives.

The two phases of the humid continental climate in North America are separated along a line drawn roughly even with the lower Great Lakes (Figs. 26.2 and 26.3). Although the region is a unit climatically, except for this division into two phases, it contains so many diverse districts that it would be confusing to discuss as a whole. Instead it is treated in relation to the human occupation and utilization of these distinctive districts.

Fig. 26.1—Cultivating Young Corn in Iowa. (Courtesy, Iowa Development Commission.)

There are five such subsections to be considered: (1) New England–Adirondacks, (2) corridors to the West and their terminals, (3) the Lake Ontario–Lake Erie belt, (4) the prairie plains–pine forest belt, and (5) southern Canada. Each of these is discussed in turn.

1. THE NEW ENGLAND–ADIRONDACKS SECTION

Topography. Roughly two-thirds of this area is within the short-summer phase of the climate, one-third in the long-summer phase (Figs. 26.2 and 26.3). The former includes all of northern New England and the Adirondacks; the smaller portion is comprised mainly of Massachusetts, Rhode Island, and Connecticut. The short-summer phase is almost exclusively rugged, forest-covered, mountainous country, nearly everywhere dotted with lakes, ponds, and swamps. In the northeast it begins with the wilderness of northern Maine, continues westward in the somewhat more populated and habitable **White** and **Green Mountains** of New Hampshire and Vermont, and extends into New York to include the **Adirondacks**. Although the highest peak of the White Mountains is above 6000 feet, most of the upland in these mountain areas is between 2000 and 5000 feet in elevation. Because the whole area, including the highest peaks, was overridden by the continental glacier of the ice age,

the summits are all smooth and rounded.

The long-summer phase is mostly a low upland cut across by numerous rivers in deep and commonly wide valleys, of which that of the **Connecticut River** is the best example. The New England coastline is extremely irregular, everywhere marked by a succession of bays, headlands, and offshore islands. It is, in other words, another example of a drowned or submerged coast (see Chapter 1, p. 13). In consequence, secure harbors, large and small, with deep sheltered waters, occur along its whole length.

Natural Resources. New England has little mineral wealth. The principal activity in this field is the quarrying of **granite, slate,** and **marble** in Vermont. On the other hand, there was a marked revival of **iron** mining in the eastern Adirondacks after World War II. Iron deposits in this area are now proving valuable because of their content of **titanium,** the element whose presence defeated earlier attempts at the utilization of the ores for their iron content.

Most of northern New England and the Adirondacks is covered with forests of coniferous trees, chiefly spruce on the higher slopes, hemlock intermixed with deciduous trees on the lower slopes and in the wooded southern parts of New England. Practically all the forest cover, however, is second- and even third-growth timber. In the Adirondacks, preserved by New York State as a wilderness area, some small tracts of prime-

Fig. 26.2—Humid Continental Region of North America—Long-Summer Phase. Because of space limitations some natural features and products mentioned in the text are omitted from the map.

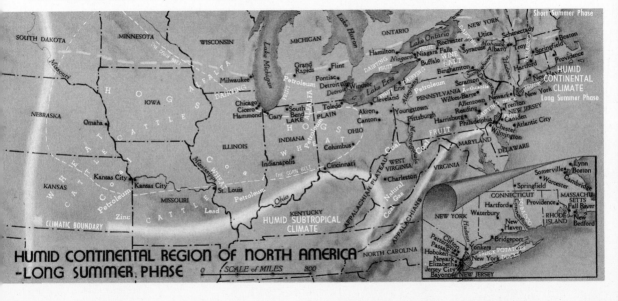

HUMID CONTINENTAL REGION OF NORTH AMERICA
-LONG SUMMER PHASE   SCALE of MILES   800

val forest remain. The White Mountains are also a reservation, a national forest under scientific forestry management. In it trees are harvested as they mature and the cut-over lands are replanted with young trees, a practice also followed by the lumber companies of New England.

Almost all the yield of the New England forests is converted to **wood pulp** for paper-making, chiefly newsprint. Lumbering is done in winter with sledges and tractors over the wood's roads, which are rough and commonly swampy in summer.

The offshore waters of New England are ordinarily shallow, the so-called "banks," over which fish congregate in incredible numbers. The near shore coastal fisheries have been greatly depleted of food fishes, although the lobster industry is still important. Power trawlers now sail regularly from New England ports for the Grand Banks off Newfoundland to catch **cod** and **halibut.** The annual take from these waters continues to be enormous.

Agriculture. The short-summer phase of the New England–Adirondack section of the humid continental region has always remained in the original forested state, so that agriculture is of little consequence in that portion. Lands of the long-summer phase that are better suited to agriculture are typified by the Connecticut Valley. Here high-quality **tobacco** is raised under cloth cover, and **peach** orchards are common. In **Aroostook County**, Maine, the soils and climate are unusually favorable for **potatoes,** which

are the great specialty of that district.

Elsewhere the poor, stony soils (Fig. 26.4) of the New England short-summer phase have in the twentieth century been put to use by French Canadian immigrants who, with the same patience and capacity for hard work possessed by the original New England settlers who first cultivated such lands, laboriously clear the stones from the fields to engage in subsistence farming.

Manufacturing. New England industry is concentrated very generally on specialty manufactures that involve the processing and assembling of small metal articles, such as screws and locks, firearms, jewelry, and builder's hardware. Shoes and lacemaking are representative of nonmetal production of the same nature. In fact, if mention is made of any fabricated article of small bulk ranging from wooden clothespins to fine watches it is almost certain that there will be one or more concerns in New England engaged in its production and marketing. The New England Yankee was probably the first gadgeteer and continues to manifest his talents in this field. As transportation charges are percentagewise only a small item in the costs of specialty manufactures, the relatively remote position of New England from many markets is not a significant factor in the competition for such business.

Almost all the manufacturing enterprises are located in southern New England, in the southern phase of the climate. It is rather remarkable that aside from the difference in the length of the growing season and the

Fig. 26.3—Humid Continental Region of North America—Short Summer Phase. Because of space limitations some natural features and products mentioned in the text are omitted from the map.

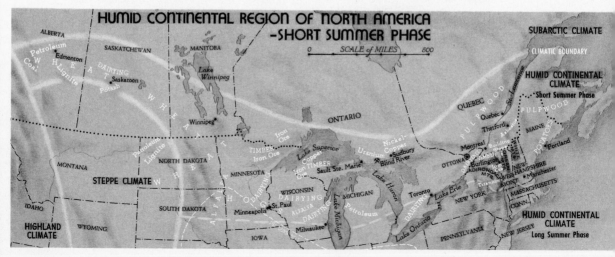

Fig. 26.4—Stony Soils of Glaciated New England Uplands. Montague, Massachusetts. (Courtesy, G. J. Callister.)

CITIES OF NEW ENGLAND

Name	State	Type	Population (1950)
Boston	Mass.	Seaport, governmental, commercial	801,000
Providence	R.I.	Seaport-industrial	249,000
Worcester	Mass.	Industrial	203,000
Hartford	Conn.	Industrial	178,000
New Haven	Conn.	Industrial-educational	164,000
Springfield	Mass.	Industrial	162,000
Bridgeport	Conn.	Industrial	159,000
Cambridge	Mass.	Educational-industrial	120,000
Fall River	Mass.	Seaport-industrial	112,000
New Bedford	Mass.	Seaport-industrial	109,000
Waterbury	Conn.	Industrial	104,000
Somerville	Mass.	Industrial-residential	102,000
Lynn	Mass.	Industrial	100,000
Manchester	N.H.	Industrial	83,000
Portland	Maine	Seaport	78,000
Burlington	Vt.	Commercial	33,000

effect of this on agriculture, so sharp an economic differentiation should exist between the areas of the two phases. To be sure, the difference in their utilization does not depend on climate only; there is, for one thing, far more level land in southern than in northern New England, and there is direct access to the sea in the south. Moreover, the labor force originally derived from the old seafaring and rural populations has through the years been greatly augmented by the influx of tens of thousands of immigrants from the poverty-stricken countries of Europe. Their descendants and French Canadians from the north comprise the bulk of the factory workers of today.

The bulk industry, **paper** making, had an early start and still flourishes within the area. It was originally based on the salvage of rags, good water (of which enormous quantities are necessary), and hydropower, all abundantly available in New England. Rag papers are fine papers used in stationery, books, checks, and currency. In addition, there has been a great expansion in the north in the making of newsprint and other cheap papers from wood pulp.

Cities. The number and distribution of New England cities are indicative of the marked population density and intense economic activity of the region. There are 13 cities with populations of 100,000 or more, all within the southern section of the area. These cities are located in states with a total area of only 14,000 square miles, a high concentration of population.

Boston's prominence is clearly shown by its size. It is a great seaport, educational and financial center, capital of its state, the leading wool market of the United States, and also notable as a fish market. In addition, Boston has most of the manufacturing industries also present so regularly in the other large cities.

Each of the other cities has its specialty. **Providence** may be singled out for silverware and jewelry; **Worcester** for abrasives; **Hartford** for firearms and international fame as an insurance center; **New Haven** for brass products; **Springfield** for firearms; **Bridgeport,** as the chief industrial city of Connecticut, which makes almost everything in the nature of small manufactures. **Cambridge,** though noted as an educational and residential center, also has its share of industry, including a new one, "nucleonics." **Fall River,** with hydropower, is a great cotton textile center; **New Bedford** has textiles and glass; **Waterbury** is a brass center with clocks and lighting fixtures as its specialty. **Somerville,** just outside Boston, is residential but nevertheless has the usual array of manufactures and meat packing in addition. **Lynn** is a center for shoes and shoe supplies.

By way of contrast is the list of largest

cities of each of the states in the short-summer phase. **Manchester** is another industrial center noted for textiles, on the northern fringe of the industrial district. **Portland** is a commercial and shopping center, as well as a seaport. **Burlington** is the commercial center of a region that produces maple sugar and quarries building stone and talc. None of these places, however, approaches the size of the industrial cities in the south of New England.

Fig. 26.5—Hudson River at Bear Mountain Bridge. (Courtesy, NYSPIX-Commerce.)

2. Corridors to the West and Their Terminals

Nature of the Corridors. The rugged New England and Adirondacks areas are terminated abruptly, the former on the west, the latter on the south, by continuous lowlands. The **Hudson River, Lake George,** and **Lake Champlain** define the western boundary of New England. The wide, level, and low **Mohawk Valley** abuts directly on the southern base of the Adirondacks (Fig. 26.2).

From its mouth to where the Mohawk River enters it the Hudson River (Fig. 26.5) is hardly more than a cleft between uplands, gouged out so deeply in the ice age as to make it a tidal inlet all the way to the Mohawk junction. In fact, the explorer Henry Hudson sailed up the river in the lively hope that he had discovered the eastern end of

a northern sea route across North America.

Between the Mohawk Valley floor and the Hudson River (whose surface is practically at sea level) there is a difference in altitude of only 45 feet. This descent was easily overcome in the nineteenth century with the establishment of a canal connection, by a series of locks, between the two valleys. The Erie Canal continued without a break to the plain south of Lake Ontario, where another rise of 60 feet, again easily negotiated, gave access to Lake Erie. Thus through the upper Great Lakes the whole central and northern interior of the continent was opened, by a water route, to the Atlantic Ocean.

Other routes to the West across the **Appalachian Mountain** barrier farther south were through the water gaps of the **Delaware** and **Susquehanna rivers.** These routes, to be sure, had only small significance for the exodus from New England which initiated the settlement of the West, but they did tap the rich mineral resources of the Appalachian districts.

Topography. Immediately south of the Mohawk Valley there is an abrupt rise to plateau levels over the **Helderberg Escarpment.** South of Lake Ontario there is the broad, low basin occupied by the **Finger Lakes** of central New York. At the western end of the Ontario Plain there is another abrupt rise over the **Niagara Escarpment** to the level of the Erie Plain. It is over this escarpment that the **Niagara River,** outlet of Lake Erie, plunges in **Niagara Falls** (Fig. 26.6).

South of the areas thus outlined most of this section of the humid continental region is plateau and mountain country. In the east the Helderberg Escarpment is succeeded southward by the **Catskill Mountains.** At about the point where the Delaware River becomes the boundary between New York and Pennsylvania the eastern front of the true plateau country swings off to the southwest. Directly southward its place is taken by the parallel ridges of the Appalachian Mountains. These mountains trend southwestward into Maryland, Virginia, and Tennessee, still part of the humid continental region because their altitudes are sufficiently high to offset the higher temperatures of the lower latitudes.

Beyond the mountains there is a belt of country between New York City and Philadelphia that has a rolling topography. Still farther south and east is the coastal plain that includes the southern half of New Jersey.

It is apparent that this portion of the humid continental region is comprised of diverse topographic elements. Climatic unity alone would hardly warrant consideration of these topographically unlike areas as a distinctive geographic province. However, the fact that these different areas are connected by corridors of access links them in a transportation and economic pattern that invites collective discussion of their utilization.

Economic Activities. The Susquehanna River in Pennsylvania traverses the part of the Appalachians containing the great **anthracite** mines of North America. This hard coal is a premium product, for it is the cleanest solid fuel there is for domestic heating. Three important railroads owe their existence to the traffic thus generated, following the lines of the Delaware and Susquehanna corridors to reach their seaboard terminals.

The lowlands of the Mohawk corridor are regions of high agricultural yield. Diversified farming and dairying are practiced partly for subsistence, but with bulk production of such cash products as **milk, potatoes,** and **apples** for city markets.

In the Catskills and the **Poconos** (within the Appalachians of northeastern Pennsylvania) entertainment of summer and winter vacationers has become big business from which local agriculture profits in furnishing farm products to hotels and boarding houses.

Fig. 26.6—Niagara Falls. The escarpment is 167 feet high at the falls. (Courtesy, NYSPIX-Commerce.)

Fig. 26.7—Duck Farm on Long Island, New York. (Courtesy, NYSPIX-Commerce.)

The southern part of this section, which includes **Long Island** to the east, has developed into a vast truck farming area. The light soils of the coastal plain in New Jersey are especially adapted to **vegetable** production. The eastern end of Long Island is a favored **tomato** and **potato** region. A specialty of eastern Long Island on the south shore is the raising of **ducks** by the hundreds of thousands (Fig. 26.7). Another specialty crop of these parts is **asparagus.** Nearly all such produce is truck-transported to the nearby metropolitan markets.

Even more popular than the mountain and plateau country are the ocean bathing resorts of the Long Island and New Jersey coasts. These are so immediately accessible to the big city populations that they are utilized by millions on every summer week end and vacation period. The vast reaches of gently shelving sand beaches of the coastal plain have permitted a seashore resort development here that is matched or approached in only a few places elsewhere in the world.

Unlike that of the New England section the manufactures of the corridor-terminal section of the humid continental region include all possible types—heavy goods, light goods, durable goods, consumers' goods. Be it locomotives or safety pins, pills or baseballs, bridges or carpets, ships or rubber hose, there are manufacturing enterprises here to supply them.

These processors and assemblers are mostly situated within the corridors and are concentrated at their southern terminals. But some, especially those producing high-value, small-bulk products, are located at relatively remote interior points. The Mohawk Valley region is famous alike for massive electrical machinery, men's shirts, and women's gloves. One place specializes in all types of copper wire—bare and covered, solid and stranded.

The greatest variety of industries is found at the mouth of the Hudson. As Boston and the other New England ports were, after colonial times, severely handicapped in competition for trade because they lacked easy routes to the interior of the continent, seaborne commerce with all the world has been more and more focused on the great harbor at the Hudson's mouth. As a consequence raw materials of all kinds and in large bulk were there made available from foreign ports by cheap ocean transport for processing and assembling into finished goods.

There they met similar supplies pouring out from the interior of North America. In turn, the finished goods could be shipped expeditiously and economically to the constantly expanding inland market. It is no accident that vast manufacturing enterprises ring about the southern terminal of the Hudson-Mohawk corridor.

The terminal positions of the other corridors to the south have profited similarly as centers of manufacturing. The routes through the mountains provided by the Delaware and Susquehanna were, however, far inferior to the Hudson-Mohawk route that by-passes the mountains. Attempts to canalize the two rivers were not economically successful. Nevertheless, as coal and other basic raw materials came down these valleys the raw materials for heavy industry were conveniently available at their terminals. The seaport locations of the terminals meant that all ocean freight could be delivered to them cheaply. Thus a multitude of light industries could also flourish.

Coal still comes down the valleys from the Pennsylvania mines, but iron ore formerly obtained from local deposits now comes chiefly from overseas, especially Venezuela. While the great output of such ore from the deposits in Labrador will mostly move up the St. Lawrence Seaway to the interior coal fields for smelting, these supplies can as readily be carried over ocean routes to smelters in the eastern seaport districts.

Cities. At· first thought it would seem rather difficult to conceive any readily comprehensible grouping of these many cities of considerable size. It quickly appears, however, that a large proportion of them belong in two distinctive classes: the corridor-terminal conurbations (clusters of closely spaced cities) of New York and Philadelphia as one class, the industrial cities of the Mohawk Valley area as the other.

The **New York** conurbation includes **Newark, Jersey City, Yonkers, Paterson, Passaic, Clifton, Elizabeth, Bayonne,** and **Hoboken.** All these are, in effect, satellites of the world's premier seaport and metropolitan commercial center, New York City. Four of

CITIES OF THE CORRIDOR AND TERMINAL SECTION

Name	State	Type	Population (1950)
New York	N.Y.	Seaport-commercial	7,900,000
Philadelphia	Pa.	Seaport-commercial	2,100,000
Newark	N.J.	Industrial	439,000
Jersey City	N.J.	Seaport-industrial	299,000
Yonkers	N.Y.	Industrial	153,000
Paterson	N.J.	Industrial	139,000
Albany	N.Y.	Governmental	134,000
Trenton	N.J.	Governmental-industrial	128,000
Scranton	Pa.	Mining	126,000
Camden	N.J.	Seaport-industrial	125,000
Elizabeth	N.J.	Seaport-industrial	113,000
Wilmington	Del.	Seaport-industrial	110,000
Reading	Pa.	Industrial	109,000
Allentown	Pa.	Industrial	107,000
Utica	N.Y.	Industrial	101,000
Schenectady	N.Y.	Industrial	92,000
Harrisburg	Pa.	Governmental	90,000
Binghamton	N.Y.	Industrial	81,000
Bayonne	N.J.	Seaport-industrial	77,000
Wilkes-Barre	Pa.	Mining	77,000
Troy	N.Y.	Industrial	72,000
Chester	Pa.	Seaport-industrial	66,000
Clifton	N.J.	Industrial	65,000
Atlantic City	N.J.	Resort	62,000
Passaic	N.J.	Industrial	58,000
Hoboken	N.J.	Seaport-industrial	51,000

these are themselves harbors. The other five are industrial centers nourished by the immediate availability for processing and assembling, at the low coast of ocean transportation, of all the world's raw materials, together with' the advantage of position at the terminal of the great Hudson-Mohawk corridor from which pours out, as through a funnel, the export products of the whole interior of North America.

New York City itself is unique among seaports in the manifold advantages it has in its harbor (Frontispiece) (see Chapter 3, p. 48). The water is deep enough for the largest ships to come directly to the docks, yet shallow enough to permit easy anchorages on good holding bottom. There is complete shelter from storms. Space for ships is, in effect, unlimited, especially if the areas and facilities of the satellite cities are included. The low tidal range of four to five feet makes no difficulties for loading or unloading at piers, or for time of arrival or departure. The harbor is not icebound in winter; fogs are infrequent. In fact, it is difficult to cite an unfavorable natural condition. Strong currents in a few places and the necessity for a moderate amount of dredging are about all that can be mentioned.

New York City itself, where the merchandise of the world in all its variety and enormous bulk arrives, and where the products of the interior of North America are concentrated by water, rail, and road, is a market place such as has never before existed. The city has street after street, block after block of business structures, dozens of skyscrapers (Fig. 26.8), hundreds of buildings 10 or more stories high. Great numbers of these buildings are hives of offices; many are given over to display or sales rooms; some contain wholesale stocks of this, that, or the other commodity. Retail trade is catered to by establishments ranging from imposing, internationally famous department stores to tiny, hole-in-the-wall enterprises.

Here, on a comparatively few square miles of land, live 8 million people who need to be supplied with all the necessities and conveniences of life. They provide a local market for consumers' goods of unprecedented size, and one also of enormous general buying power. A producer anywhere in the United States who thinks his merchandise has good general sales appeal is strongly impelled to seek a New York City outlet.

Ringed about the enormous, throbbing heart of commerce that is the city's center are a multiplicity of subsidiary structures and enterprises. There are apartment houses —cities in themselves—as numerous, massive, and compactly placed as the business establishments. There are innumerable factories making light goods, as in the notable garment district. There are printers, food processors, and vast warehouses.

Impressive also are the transport services that convey goods to and from the warehouses and piers, from place to place within the city; for the essence of commerce is the transfer of commodities from one place to another. And, too, the people who service

Fig. 26.8—New York City at Dusk. Skyscrapers lighted before close of the business day. (Courtesy, New York Convention and Visitors Bureau.)

all the diverse activities of the city must be moved to and from their homes and about the city during the business day.

Although there are plants for the production of heavy goods within the city, such enterprises are for the most part concentrated in the satellite cities. In fact, the chief function of these satellites, especially those on tidewater, is to provide sites for such manufactures and for the conversion of bulky crudes. Thus **Bayonne** makes boilers, refines oil. **Hoboken** makes iron products; **Jersey City** has machinery and electrical manufactures; **Elizabeth** makes mill machinery and does shipbuilding.

Newark is the largest of the nonport cities (though it has itself a harbor satellite in **Port Newark**) of the New York conurbation. Newark's industrial activities are typical. It produces paint and asphalt products, radiators and electrical machinery, as well as a great variety of consumers' goods.

The sea approaches to **Philadelphia**, situated some distance up the Delaware River from its mouth in Delaware Bay, are more devious than those to New York City, which in part accounts for the disparity in size of the two metropolitan centers. Moreover, traffic may be said to filter down the Delaware corridor rather than pour down as it does through the Mohawk-Hudson route. And the pace of commercial and other activities is traditionally held to be more leisurely in Philadelphia than in New York.

On the other hand, the coal and iron of the Appalachian country move directly into Philadelphia, whereas New York has no such direct access to these basic mineral resources. The Philadelphia area is also one of the great oil-refining centers on the east coast. In addition to being a leading seaport Philadelphia was the first American industrial city; it has always been a notable printing, publishing, and educational center.

In keeping with its smaller size the conurbation of the Philadelphia district is less extensive than that of New York but is still impressive. A modern development is the enormous steelworks just upriver from the city, fed with South American and Labrador

ore brought directly to the plant by ship. Nearest of the satellite cities is **Camden,** across the river from Philadelphia, which builds ships, makes phonographs, radios, oilcloth, and canned soups. It is comparable to Jersey City in the New York area. **Trenton,** the largest of the Philadelphia satellites, is at the head of navigation on the Delaware. It specializes in the making of wire and steel cable and is the capital of its state. A third member is **Chester,** just south of Philadelphia, with a good harbor and shipbuilding activities. **Wilmington,** the other side of Chester, has another good harbor and shipbuilding, with a large chemical plant immediately outside the city.

Here mention is appropriately made of **Atlantic City,** almost the type resort city. It is located on a sand bar about a mile wide and ten miles long, eight of which are traversed by a boardwalk. The inland side of this walk is solidly lined with hotels, shops, theaters, and amusement concessions.

Scranton and **Wilkes-Barre** are mining centers in the anthracite district. **Reading** and **Allentown** are industrial cities situated where both coal and iron from their surrounding regions are conveniently accessible. The former is notable for mining machinery, the latter for cement manufacture. Though **Harrisburg** is primarily a governmental city it is also close to supplies of iron and coal, and has an iron and steel industry. **Binghamton** is classified as an industrial city through its manufacture of a variety of consumers' goods but also serves as the commercial center of a wide area of dairy and general farming country.

There remain to be considered the cities of the Mohawk corridor. **Albany,** a representative example of the governmental type, is also the head of navigation on the Hudson. Its significance as a seaport is growing, and it has commercial and industrial interests. The other cities are distinctively industrial, although serving as local trading points for the productive farm lands of the Mohawk Valley. Each of them has a special manufacturing field to which its activities are largely, if not exclusively, confined. **Troy** makes men's shirts; **Utica**, knitted wear; **Schenectady**, electrical products.

QUESTIONS. Compare the humid continental climatic region of North America with that of east Asia in terms of the bordering climatic regions and the climatic variations within it. Why can the region be considered as the type example, agriculturally, of the humid continental regions? In what other respects is it outstanding as a region of human settlement? Describe the topography of the New England–Adirondacks area. What states are within the long-summer phase. The short-summer phase? Name the agricultural product for which the Connecticut Valley is best known; that for which Aroostook County, Maine, is best known. What is characteristic of New England manufacturing? Explain the basis of this characteristic. Name five manufacturing cities of New England and the product associated with each.

Describe the topography of the "corridor" section of the humid continental region, naming the corridors and explaining their significance. What is the large mineral resource of this section in Pennsylvania? What do the Poconos and the New Jersey and Long Island coasts have in common? Name the chief agricultural products of the Mohawk Valley, of Long Island, and of New Jersey. Compare the manufactures of this section with those of New England. Explain the concentration of industries at the terminals at the mouths of the corridors.

Name the major cities of the New York conurbation. What does the word "conurbation" mean? Why is New York the outstanding seaport of the world? Explain the significance of New York as a commercial city. State why Philadelphia has always lagged behind New York in growth. Name two of Philadelphia's satellite cities and the products associated with each.

3. THE LAKE ONTARIO–LAKE ERIE BELT

Topography. The Lake Ontario–Lake Erie belt extends from the eastern end of Lake Ontario to the western end of Lake Erie. Southward it includes central and western New York, western Pennsylvania, eastern Ohio, western Maryland, and practically all of West Virginia (Fig. 26.2). Like the cor-

ridors section it is all within the southern phase of the humid continental region.

Topographically it is made up of two clearly defined units. The first is a rather narrow strip of country on the south side of the two lakes, the **lake plains** region. All the rest is the **Appalachian Plateau.** This second aspect is an extension westward and southward of the Helderberg-Catskill area, although in general the relief of the Appalachian Plateau is here less mountainous.

The plateau region farther west and south, especially its core development in West Virginia, was for many years a region of marked isolation, occupied by a "hillbilly" mountaineer population. Travel in this rough country was exceedingly difficult and was confined to the floors of the watercourses. Not uncommonly a stream bed served as the road. With the advent of the motor age and the associated construction of a network of hard-surfaced roads this isolation has been largely overcome. Now even the remotest sections of the plateau area are relatively accessible by bus and truck.

The **Ohio River** divides the northern and southern sections of the plateau country. In many respects the Ohio is the most important navigable stream in the United States. Its entire course is canalized and its flow regulated. Steel, coal, oil, grain, and other products are loaded in trains of steel barges pushed by Diesel towboats (Fig. 26.9). It is found profitable to put truck trailers on barges for a night's travel down river to avoid a night of driving over hilly, curving highways. The Ohio flows through a region abounding in bulk products that require cheap transport, and its course is in the right direction for this commerce.

Mineral Resources. This belt is excellently endowed with four great mineral resources: **salt, bituminous coal, petroleum,** and **natural gas.** Northern and central New York is one of the chief salt-producing areas of the United States. Western Pennsylvania, eastern Ohio, and West Virginia comprise the major part of the great Appalachian coal, oil, and gas province.

The coal resources are unmatched in the

Fig. 26.9—Ohio River at Steubenville, Ohio. Barge loaded with gasoline moving upriver. (Courtesy, City Service Company.)

world for richness and ease of working. The coal occurs in flat-lying layers six and more feet thick extending under thousands of square miles of country. In places the coal beds crop out on the sides of the steep-walled valleys of the plateau area (Fig. 26.10). Then it is necessary only to tunnel into them and haul out the coal on the horizontal, with no hoisting.

In 1859 the first oil well in the United States was drilled in northwestern Pennsylvania. It constituted the discovery of a district that eventually included all the plateau territory south of the Finger Lakes region and west of the anthracite belt. Though its yield of both oil and gas reached a peak at about the turn of the century and has since fallen off greatly, this section of the Appalachian field is still a significant producer. West Virginia is particularly notable as a natural gas source.

Agriculture. The mixed farming and dairy industry of the Mohawk Valley extends without interruption across the lake plains and over all the Finger Lakes area. The region is part of what is termed the New York City "milkshed" in the sense that from here fluid milk flows by truck and train to New York City as water drains down a river basin.

The lake plains are notable as a fruit-growing area. **Apples, pears, peaches, small fruits,** and **berries** are produced in quantity here for city markets. The success of this orchard culture is primarily due to freedom from unseasonable temperatures. The wide expanses of the lake waters exercise a moderating effect on the temperature of winds blowing over them from the north and west, insuring against both too early warm spells and late killing frosts in spring. In fall the warm lake waters similarly prevent inclement early frost.

The same circumstances apply to belts of land bordering the shores of the Finger Lakes. There relatively steep hill slopes open to the sun and protected from frost hazards by the lake waters are the site of flourishing vineyards and a notable **wine** industry.

The eastern plateau country is an extension of the city **milk**shed, with **hay** and **potatoes** as subsidiary crops. In the rugged western and southwestern areas agriculture is of little consequence. Corn and hogs are grown for subsistence, with some of the corn illicitly converted into whiskey.

Industry. The utilization of the full 167-

Fig. 26.10—Bituminous Coal Seam Seven Feet Thick Along Roadside at Vestaburg, Pennsylvania. (Courtesy, U.S. Bureau of Mines.)

foot drop of Niagara Falls was the foundation for an enormous development of the **electrochemical** industry in the Niagara area. Many chemical processes require the application of extremely high temperatures on small masses of material, which can best be accomplished in an electric furnace. Other large uses of electricity are in **aluminum** reduction and the grinding of logs to make paper **pulp.** Such industries are located at lesser hydroelectric sites within the belt.

Along the plateau border at the northeast flank of the Finger Lakes a combination of available limestone with the underlying salt has fostered the development of a great **chemical** industry involving the production of sodium chemicals of large economic significance.

In general, all the lake plains region south of Lake Ontario is readily supplied with bulk raw materials and fuels by both water

and rail transport and is, therefore, a region of diversified manufactures of both light and heavy types. In the part of the lake plains south of Lake Erie coke from the plateau district to the south and east meets iron ore from the Great Lakes shores to the northwest, constituting the basis of the very large **iron and steel** industry of that area.

The chief concentration of the steel industry is, however, in the heart of the bituminous coal country of the plateau, where Pennsylvania, West Virginia, and Ohio come together at the head of the Ohio River. Although there are now other great steel centers in the United States this is traditionally the focus of the American steel industry. Here is perhaps the most economical site in the country for bringing together ore, fuel, and the other materials necessary for iron and steel making. The industrial concentration surpasses even the intensity of development in the Ruhr and the Soviet "Donbas" and "Kuzbas" described in the preceding chapter.

CITIES OF THE LAKE ONTARIO–LAKE ERIE BELT

Name	State	Type	Population (1950)
Cleveland	Ohio	Lake port-industrial	915,000
Pittsburgh	Pa.	River port-industrial	677,000
Buffalo	N.Y.	Lake port-industrial	580,000
Columbus	Ohio	Governmental-industrial	376,000
Rochester	N.Y.	Commercial-industrial	332,000
Toledo	Ohio	Lake port-commercial	304,000
Akron	Ohio	Industrial	275,000
Syracuse	N.Y.	Commercial-industrial	221,000
Youngstown	Ohio	Industrial	168,000
Erie	Pa.	Lake port-industrial	131,000
Canton	Ohio	Industrial	117,000
Niagara Falls	N.Y.	Industrial-hydro-power	91,000
Charleston	W.Va.	Governmental-industrial	74,000

Cities. **Cleveland,** the largest city in this belt, has benefited from its location and possession of one of the few good harbors on the eastern Great Lakes. With the development of the Lake Superior iron ore deposits

Cleveland became the greatest iron ore market and transshipment point of the world. From its harbor the best and shortest overland route leads to the heart of the bituminous coal fields and their steelmaking centers. A natural corollary was that Cleveland became a notable center for heavy industry —iron and steel, foundry and machine shops. In the postwar period it has also become a center for chemicals and automobile production.

The other three lake ports, **Buffalo, Toledo,** and **Erie,** also owe their growth and significance primarily to their sheltered harbor sites. Buffalo has the largest of the Lake Erie harbors and is the eastern terminal for lake shipping. There transfer of cargoes for further water carriage is made to vessels of the **Barge Canal,** successor to the old Erie Canal that gave Buffalo its start. Accordingly, Buffalo's harbor is a forest of grain and coal elevators. As ore can also be delivered by ship, steelmaking is important, as well as other industry stimulated further by available hydroelectricity from nearby Niagara Falls. Toledo also has a larger harbor, but as it is situated off to the west of the coal fields its commercial activities are of greater significance than its industrial development. Erie is similarly important commercially, but being nearer coal and natural gas is also important in heavy manufactures.

Pittsburgh is the metropolis of the distinctively industrial steelmaking cities. It was for years a notoriously dirty place because of the smoke and grime from its furnaces, but this nuisance is now greatly abated through control measures. Pittsburgh is situated where the **Allegheny** and **Monongahela** rivers join to make the Ohio, from which point the river's traffic begins. The point between the rivers is the heart of the city and is known as the "Golden Triangle" because of the concentration of business there (Fig. 26.11). Although locally mined iron ore originally fed the furnaces, it was the meeting here of the Lake Superior ores with the coke of the district that fostered the growth of the enormous industry developed since. Further, the bulk products of such industry

could be economically shipped down the Ohio to supply steel for the expanding economy of the Mississippi Basin.

Unlike those around New York City, the Pittsburgh satellite steel cities are not clus-

Fig. 26.11—The "Golden Triangle" of Pittsburgh. This was the original defensive site of the city, at the confluence of the Allegheny and Monongahela rivers. (See Fig. 3.13.) This district went through a long period of urban decay until it was rejuvenated in the 1950's by the new buildings, parks, and parkways seen here. The bridge piers on the right attest to further projects not completed at the end of 1955. (Courtesy, Allegheny Conference on Community Development.)

tered about the mother city. **Youngstown** and **Canton** may be said to anticipate Pittsburgh in getting possession of the iron ore as it moves overland from the lakes, and use their local fuels to process it. This practice was called "forestalling" in the days of medieval commerce and was considered an exceedingly reprehensible activity.

Columbus and **Charleston** are appropriately classified as governmental cities, the capitals of their states. Both are also focal points of railroad traffic. This fact and its position at the geographical center of Ohio has brought about the concentration at Columbus of diversified heavy and light industry. Charleston, with abundant coal and gas, supports such industries as glass, fire-bricks, pottery, and forges, all of which are dependent on large supplies of fuel to provide high heat.

Akron is unique among the industrial cities as the rubber center of the world. About one-half of all the world's crude rubber is processed in Akron, mostly into tires. **Niagara Falls** is also unique as the greatest hydropower city of the world. Its dominantly chemical concerns were noted previously.

The two large cities of the Ontario lake plains were both on the old Erie, now Barge, Canal. But their commercial significance derives from overland transport. Both are the trading centers of rich agricultural districts; **Rochester,** the larger, is in the better district. Its industrial fame is for cameras, optical goods, and photographic materials. **Syracuse,** the other city, is especially known for salt chemicals, typewriters, and chinaware.

4. THE PRAIRIE PLAINS–PINE FOREST BELT

General Aspects. The prairie plains–pine forest belt extends westward without interruption from the western end of Lake Erie to the 100th meridian, which passes through the middle of North and South Dakota, Nebraska, and Kansas. The northern limit of the belt is the Canadian border; the southern boundaries of Ohio, Indiana, Illinois, Missouri, and Kansas roughly coincide with that of the belt (Figs. 26.2 and 26.3).

The continental aspects of the climate are progressively more pronounced with distance westward. Localized summer showers are a significant element of the rainfall. The western border of the belt marks the limit of the lands that can be cultivated without resort to irrigation or dry farming.

The major part of the belt is in the longsummer phase. The upper Great Lakes region constitutes the short-summer phase, including Michigan, Wisconsin, Minnesota, and the eastern part of the two Dakotas. The lands of the long-summer phase, plus the Dakota areas, comprise the prairie plains country; the remaining territory is the pine forest section.

The belt as a whole may be considered the agricultural heart of the United States.

The inhabitants tend to be conservative and unresponsive to many of the international political concerns that agitate dwellers on or near the Atlantic and Pacific seaboards. It is a region with metropolitan centers but characterized by many small cities, market towns, distributed rather uniformly at convenient distances over the whole countryside.

Topography. Topographically almost the whole belt is plains country. Northern Ohio, Indiana, and Illinois and the eastern Dakotas are extremely level. These are the true prairie plains—in part bottoms of earlier lakes, in part very smooth deposits of the ice age glaciers. The topography of the other states of the belt is hilly and rolling. In Wisconsin and Minnesota irregularity of the thick glacial deposits has given rise to thousands of lakes.

These are, in general, the districts traversed by the upper **Mississippi** and lower **Missouri** rivers. The Mississippi is navigable up into Minnesota, but the amount of bulk traffic available for such transportation is nowhere comparable to that moved over the Ohio. The Missouri, which could be used to advantage, is unfortunately shallow, heavily burdened with sediment, and subject to alternate high water and drought stages. When fully regulated with dams and storage basins its usefulness may be greatly enhanced and its destructive floods controlled.

All the west end of Lake Superior is surrounded by a region of ancient rocks referred to as the **Superior Uplands.** Actually, the altitudes are only slightly greater than those of the surrounding country, and the relief is due in part to the thick glacial deposits.

Mineral Resources. With the exception of Wisconsin, Minnesota, and the Dakotas, the **bituminous coal** beds of the plateau regions occur also in the prairie plains. This is also true of **petroleum** and **natural gas.** Accordingly, there are plentiful supplies of fuel near at hand over most of the region.

Especially noteworthy, however, are the **iron ore** deposits, referred to as the "ranges," of the Lake Superior Uplands. Until the middle of the twentieth century three-quarters or more of all the iron ore consumed in the United States came from these ranges. The Superior deposits are by no means exhausted, but much of the richest and most easily recovered ore has been removed. A development since World War II has been the utilization of the practically limitless *taconite* resources of the ranges. The iron content of the taconite is much lower and the rock itself is very hard, but great processing plants produce a material from it that has a higher iron content and is better suited for blast furnaces than the best of the previously mined ore. In some ranges underground mining of hard ore is done, but the enormous Mesabi deposits are of soft ore that can be dug from the surface with power shovels. The ore is loaded directly into railroad cars, hauled to Lake Superior, and dumped into large ore vessels. During the summer these ore carriers ply incessantly from Lake Superior to the ore ports of the lower Great Lakes.

Agriculture. The core of this region is known as the *corn belt*, although there is also much diversified farming of increasing importance toward the east. Nowhere else in the world is there so extensive an area uniformly provided with climate, topography, and soils ideally suited to food crop production, especially of the grains **corn** and **wheat**. Although droughts sporadically defeat the farmer the volume of precipitation is normally adequate to his needs and well distributed throughout the growing season. Over much of the corn belt the relief is so slight that natural runoff must be supplemented by tile drainage. Practically the entire area is mantled by deep soils well suited to the growth of **clover, soybeans, alfalfa,** and other nitrogen-accumulating crops. The primeval cover of grass of the prairie plains also contributed to the productivity of the soil by building up large stores of nitrogenous humus. In every respect these northern interior lands of North America are an agricultural paradise.

In view of their settlement by pioneers during the early nineteenth century the original landholdings of the farm family were uniformly adequate—in fact, commonly too large for efficient cultivation by the horse-power available to past generations. This relationship has been reversed by the mechanization of farm operations during the twentieth century. The farm family unit now seeks to increase its holdings. Plowing, harrowing, seeding, cultivating, harvesting, and transporting are all tractor- and truck-powered (Figs. 26.1 and 26.12). The prairie plains are the ideal site for such use by farm family units. The machine needs no rest; when weather and soil conditions are right work proceeds around the clock. The horse has all but disappeared from the scene, and as the farm population has declined the volume of production has gone up.

Fig. 26.12—Harvesting Corn by Machine, Nebraska. (Courtesy, Division of Nebraska Resources.)

Corn spreads over huge fields from Ohio westward across Indiana, Illinois, Iowa, Missouri, eastern Nebraska, and eastern Kansas. Farther west and north, in the Dakotas, wheat supersedes corn because of lower rainfall and shorter growing season, as the Dakotas are in the short-summer phase of the region. This merges with the wheat districts of the steppe lands still farther west (see Chapter 23, p. 481). Minnesota, Michigan, and Wisconsin are also in the short-summer phase, but as these are better watered they have developed as the great **dairy** district of the United States.

The corn belt could as well be called the

"corn, hog, and feeder belt," for associated with it west of Indiana is the raising of **hogs** and the fattening of **beef cattle** shipped in from the western ranges. The corn farmer commonly faces the problem of whether he will do better to sell his crop as grain or convert it to meat, in the form of hogs (Fig. 26.13) or beef, on the farm. The decision depends on the relative market prices of the grain and meat. As it takes time, during which the price ratios may change, to grow the hogs and fatten the cattle, good judgment in forecasting the market is required on the part of the corn belt farmer to insure his getting the best returns from his work.

Fig. 26.13—Feeding Corn to Hogs on the Farm, Missouri. (Courtesy, G. Massie, Missouri Department of Resources and Development.)

Industry. With the three mineral fuels coal, petroleum, and natural gas present or easily available in almost every part of the region, adequate power for manufacturing can be provided at low cost almost anywhere. Moreover, the low relief fostered railroad construction in essentially straightline routes between those points requiring transportation facilities.

As a consequence the industries of the belt are highly diversified. There are certain focal points where exceptional transportation facilities have concentrated commodities both in bulk and in variety. In these industry has had an above-average development, especially the heavy goods type. There is also a gradation east to west in that the far western districts engage primarily in food processing, although even there other light industries are not entirely lacking. Many of these depend on a restricted local market, but others make specialty products that have attained national distribution.

The most striking development of industry is the concentration of **automobile** manufacturing in southern Michigan. Aside from the immediate availability of coal and steel in these parts the presence of a large supply of skilled labor at the beginning of the automobile era may be cited as a factor making for localization. Once established, moreover, the industry found the district an admirable distribution point for its products to the east, south, and west.

The geographic basis of the focal point for industry at the southern end of Lake Michigan is more obvious. Transportation over the Great Lakes has a terminal there. All overland transportation from the east and west must swing past the southern end of Lake Michigan because of the water barrier it constitutes.

Thus the vast production of hogs and beef in the corn belt and of much of the range country farther west naturally gravitates to this lake terminal area and has resulted in the greatest **meat-packing** industry of the world. Meat packing is also important at other points in the belt where transportation facilities favor collecting and fattening the animals and marketing the product.

At a later date, when transportation of the Superior iron ore down the lakes had attained its modern stature, it was appropriate that the Lake Michigan terminal area should take its place with the harbors on Lake Erie as the site of large-scale **steel** manufacture. Coal was readily available from the southern hinterland of the Lake Michigan terminal area as it was from the Ohio-Pennsylvania territory serving the Lake Erie ports. Moreover, the Middle West was a vast, directly accessible market for iron and steel.

CITIES OF THE PRAIRIE PLAINS PINE FOREST BELT

Name	State	Type	Population (1950)
Chicago	Ill.	Lake port-commercial	3,600,000
Detroit	Mich.	Lake port-commercial	1,800,000
St. Louis	Mo.	River port-commercial	857,000
Milwaukee	Wis.	Lake port-commercial	637,000
Minneapolis	Minn.	Industrial	522,000
Cincinnati	Ohio	River port-commercial	504,000
Kansas City	Mo.	Commercial	457,000
Indianapolis	Ind.	Commercial-governmental	427,000
St. Paul	Minn.	Commercial-governmental	311,000
Omaha	Neb.	Commercial	251,000
Grand Rapids	Mich.	Industrial	177,000
Flint	Mich.	Industrial	163,000
Gary	Ind.	Industrial	134,000
Kansas City	Kans.	Industrial	130,000
South Bend	Ind.	Industrial	116,000
Hammond	Ind.	Industrial	88,000
Pontiac	Mich.	Industrial	74,000
Cicero	Ill.	Industrial	68,000

Cities. The prairie plains and pine forest belt of the Midwest contains 54 cities with 50,000 or more inhabitants and 40 others with a population of over 25,000. The distribution and location of the small and medium-sized cities show that the great majority of them are basically crossroads towns (Fig. 3.18). When railroads superseded roads as the basic means of overland transportation the sites of rail intersections became the focal points for shipping and trade and rapidly outdistanced settlements not so favored. In descriptions of the corn belt cities one reads with monotonous regularity "railroad center, railroad shops." Their rather considerable number reflects the high agricultural yield of the whole belt; the volume of produce suffices to maintain this large number of sizable market towns.

The large cities of the belt are also primarily commercial centers, but in addition they are, with few exceptions, also lake or river ports and hence from the first were transshipment and distribution points. Industry is now equally significant, however.

Commonly the industrial enterprises of the corn belt cities are concerned with food processing, based on the local production, and with consumers' goods, clothing, furniture, farm machinery, and the like.

Chicago is to the Midwest what New York City is to the East—the dominant metropolis. The second largest city in the United States, it is the terminal port of shipping from both the upper and lower Great Lakes, the Lake Michigan focal point referred to above. Chicago's business, accordingly, is basically concerned with the collection and distribution of the products of Midwest agriculture, its vast annual yields of corn, wheat, and meat. Here are the greatest grain and livestock markets of the world; here the foremost meat-packing plants. In reverse, Chicago is the source of supply for a large part of the enormous volume of clothing, home furnishings, building materials, and agricultural machinery used by the farm people of all the upper Mississippi Basin. Much of this is merchandise manufactured in Chicago itself, for here, as in all great import centers, the ready accessibility of raw materials fosters their processing and assembly.

In the Chicago conurbation **Hammond** is the ordinary type of diversified manufacturing city. Other industrial satellites are more specialized, such as **Gary**, the steel city, and **Cicero**, the electrical equipment city.

Detroit, the second city of the belt, is situated on the **Detroit River**, part of the waterway connecting Lake Huron and Lake Erie, and rivals Chicago in the tonnage handled by its port. It boasts that more ships pass through the river than through the Suez Canal. But commercial Detroit, the parent, lives on the bounty of its industrial child, the center of the American automobile industry. Here, in perhaps a unique instance, industry has displaced commerce as the factor of first importance at a site geographically indicated as a trade center. It is not an unusual outcome, for Detroit, in common with other automobile centers (e.g., **South Bend**), was early a center of wagon making.

The almost explosive expansion of the industry at Detroit not only engulfed neighboring communities but gave rise to large satellite cities such as **Dearborn, Pontiac,** and **Flint,** which function solely as automobile manufacturing centers. Dearborn, moreover, is what the Soviets would consider ideal in their own industrial centers—a complete vertical integration. There iron ore and coke, sand and coal are brought together to make first steel and glass; then these are shaped to requirements. The blocks of engines are cast and machined; all their moving parts are fabricated and finally assembled as the finished product.

The third large lake port, **Milwaukee,** is a smaller edition of Chicago. It participates in the commerce of the Great Lakes and has acquired national fame as a brewing center. Its growth has been in defiance of the lake barrier to east-west traffic. This handicap is overcome by operating car ferries across the lake.

The four other cities of over 500,000 inhabitants, **St. Louis, Cincinnati, Minneapolis,** and **Kansas City** (Missouri), are river ports. St. Louis is the great distributing center for the Southwest. Cincinnati has lost some of its earlier commercial importance but has become notable for the great diversity of its manufacturing enterprises. Minneapolis has become the world's greatest flour-milling center. Its twin, **St. Paul,** is at the head of navigation on the Mississippi and is the capital of the state. Kansas City, Missouri, also has its twin in **Kansas City, Kansas.** They are on opposite sides of the Missouri River at its junction with the Kansas River, which established the twin cities as the focal commercial center of a wide district. **Indianapolis** is representative of the crossroads cities referred to above, although it is in addition the capital of its state and has rather diversified industries.

QUESTIONS. Describe the extent and topography of the Lake Ontario–Lake Erie belt. Name the four major mineral resources of the belt. Explain the term "milkshed." In what way does it relate portions of the belt to New York City? What is the chief type of agricultural product of the lake plains? What is the climatic basis for this specialization? Distinguish between the chemical industries of the Niagara Falls and Syracuse areas in terms of their resource bases. What is the great industry of the belt and where is it located? Explain its occurrence and location.

Explain the factors responsible for the development of Cleveland as the leading city of the belt. Do the same for Pittsburgh. Why are Pittsburgh's satellites not clustered around it, as are those of most large cities? What is Akron known for?

Locate the prairie plains–pine forest belt and describe its topography. Distinguish between the areas of long- and short-summer phases, and the prairies versus pine forest areas. Name the chief mineral resources. What is "taconite" and what is its significance? Describe the agriculture of the corn belt. Explain the basis of the hog production and cattle feeding carried on in it. Locate the major dairy district of the United States. Locate the two chief centers of industry within the prairie plains–pine forest belt. Name the major types of industry.

Compare the activities of Chicago and New York as commercial and industrial cities. With what product is Gary associated? Cicero? Detroit? Explain why Detroit's industrial importance exceeds its commercial importance despite its superb commercial location.

5. Southern Canada

General Aspects. Humid continental Canada is almost all within the short-summer phase of the climate (Figs. 26.2 and 26.3). The belt extends from the mouth of the St. Lawrence on the east to the Rocky Mountains on the west. The political divisions of the region are: all of the "Maritime Provinces" of **Nova Scotia, Prince Edward Island,** and **New Brunswick** in the northeast; a narrow zone of southern **Quebec** along the St. Lawrence; **Ontario** east of the Great Lakes; and a 100-mile-wide extension that curves northwest, beyond the 100° meridional boundary in the United States, from Lake Superior, through southwestern Ontario and southern **Manitoba,** then west and southwest again through middle **Saskatchewan** and **Alberta.**

This odd arc in the west is, like the long eastward extension of the Eurasian region, a transitional zone between continental aridity and a high-latitude cold. Although the rainfall declines to as low as 12 inches, the lower temperatures so reduce evaporation that the climate can still be called "humid" in an agricultural sense. The altitude, moreover, is low enough so that the latitude's effect on temperature is at a minimum (though still significant). In the southwest the region ends abruptly against the eastern side of the Rockies. Here the chinook winds (see Chapter 22, p. 450) aid in keeping the winters milder and shorter than the latitude and continentality would otherwise have it.

Topography. The Canadian belt of the humid continental region is nearly all plains and hill lands. The only mountains it includes are on the **Gaspé Peninsula** at the mouth of the St. Lawrence, where the highest peak is less than 4500 feet in altitude. The plains bordering the lower St. Lawrence are only slightly above sea level; the hilly lands of interior Nova Scotia and New Brunswick rarely exceed 1200 feet. Around Lake Ontario the plains stand at 300 feet and in the upper Great Lakes region, at 600 feet. From **Lake Winnipeg** in Manitoba, at 500-foot elevation, the land rises to the base of the Rockies by a series of steps, reaching a 4000-foot elevation in Alberta. These western lands are wide reaches of level or gently undulating uplands, a factor of marked importance that has greatly facilitated the settlement and utilization of the western part of humid continental Canada.

People. Although the inhabitants of various sections of the humid continental region in the United States may be considered to have distinctive traits—thus New England Yankees, Pennsylvania Dutch, and Indiana Hoosiers—such differentiation only exaggerrates minor variations in characteristics between these regional populations. In Canada a different situation exists. Historic backgrounds, comparative isolation, religious affiliations, and an involved political development have resulted in distinctive and noteworthy regional associations of people.

The Maritime Provinces are inhabited by remarkably localized communities of Scotch, German, and English descent. The populations of the St. Lawrence Gulf coasts of Nova Scotia and New Brunswick are exclusively Scotch. In south central Nova Scotia there is a block of Germans; and the Bay of Fundy coast is occupied by descendants of the English who displaced and transported the Acadian French from there in 1755.

Beginning with the Gaspé and extending up the St. Lawrence Valley through all of interior Quebec the French were the original settlers of the land and remained in possession when the British took Canada in 1763. Today Quebec is in many respects an image of French life and customs of the eighteenth century. French is the language, Roman Catholicism the religion, and there are strong emotional ties with a France that exists only in the minds of the Quebec inhabitants. The people are not merely Canadians, they are French Canadians. The French Canadians contend fiercely to preserve their group identity, resisting even the mildest attempts to assimilate them into a homogeneous Canadian nation. Some families from non-French Canada who for one reason or another take up residence in Quebec find the environment too alien for comfort, and when opportunity offers are glad to leave the province.

The natural head of ocean navigation on the St. Lawrence is the **Lachine Rapids,** which also fixed the point of farthest inland penetration of the French settlers. Beyond them, upriver, is Ontario, the citadel of British conservatism in America before the Revolution, and anchored in that tradition by the American Tories who fled there when the colonies won their freedom. Many generations later this stock displays the same tendencies. The chief religious affiliation remains with the Episcopal Church.

These British fidelities are most in evidence in peninsular Ontario, which lies between the Great Lakes. Westward the Tory tradition diminishes. In the prairie provinces Canadian nationalism is no less strong than in Ontario but resides in a population which is made up largely of recent European and American immigrants.

Mineral Resources. The mineral resources of humid continental Canada include some of the most important constituents of the country's enormous mineral wealth. The mineral fuels are important in its eastern and western extremities; in the central portion the metals and nonmetals have the greatest significance.

In the east **coal** occurs in four fields in Nova Scotia, and together with neighboring fields in New Brunswick these are the source of two-fifths of the total Canadian output. Much of the Nova Scotian mining follows gently sloping coal seams several miles out under the sea. This is expensive, but the coal is of good coking quality so that it repays the high cost of recovery. The New Brunswick coal is used chiefly as railroad fuel. In Alberta the humid continental region includes portions of the huge fields that lie mostly within the dry climatic region (see Chapter 23, p. 482). The bulk of all this western coal is lignitic, but in restricted areas it is good-quality bituminous. The great handicap of the western coal is remoteness of market and expense of overland haulage. Its chief use has been for railroad fuel.

In Alberta the region also includes some of the great **oil** and **natural gas** fields of that province. The **Leduc** and **Turner Valley** fields are especially important. These very large reserves were tapped in the early 1950's when the construction of pipe lines brought the fuel east to the populous Great Lakes district of Canada. The modest natural gas and petroleum resources of Ontario and New Brunswick previously available were completely inadequate to meet the local demand.

With the ominous decline in the volume of the rich Mesabi reserves of the United States the **iron ore** resources of southern Canada assumed great importance, and their development since World War II has been rapid. Just north of Lake Superior in western Ontario is the large **Steep Rock** deposit, which was developed by emptying a large lake and changing the course of local drainage. East of the lakes in peninsular Ontario several smaller deposits are also being worked.

Several other mineral resources of southern Canada are unusual. In the **Blind River** district on the north shore of Lake Huron **uranium,** discovered in 1952, is mined on a very large scale. At **Sudbury,** to the east, is the **nickel** deposit which provides the great bulk of the world's supply of that metal. Large yields of **copper, platinum, gold,** and **silver** are by-products of the nickel recovery. At **Thetford,** south of the St. Lawrence in Quebec, is the world's most important **asbestos** district. Part of Ontario is also underlain by large **salt** deposits like those of New York State.

In the early 1950's a marked expansion of mining activities in the Maritime Provinces began with the discovery and development of an important copper deposit in the Gaspé and a new **lead-zinc** district at **Bathurst,** New Brunswick.

Other Resources. Only Nova Scotia and New Brunswick have extensive **forest** areas within the Canadian humid continental region. These consist of spruce, pine, birch, and maple, transitional stands between the prevailingly deciduous forests to the south and the coniferous forests of the north. In Nova Scotia such forests still cover most of the upper slopes and summits of the hilly interior. Except along the coast and the valley floors New Brunswick is still forest country.

The timber in both provinces is harvested chiefly for pulp production, under government supervision to insure the observance of conservation practices. The numerous interconnected lake and river routes facilitate lumbering by the time-honored method of winter cutting and downstream log drives in spring.

Southeastern Canada also has very large **hydropower** resources. In Quebec these are concentrated along the north shore of the St. Lawrence. Its northern tributaries, especially the **Saguenay,** tumbling down in great volume over falls and rapids from a plateau to the St. Lawrence Valley, provide eastern Canada with a huge power source that is still only partly developed. Moreover, the large river itself is being utilized for power as part of the St. Lawrence Seaway project. Canadians already enjoy some of the cheapest electricity in the world, and per capita consumption is unusually high.

Agriculture. The agriculture of humid continental Canada is typical of the short-summer phase of the climate, with **wheat, oats,** and **potatoes** as the chief crops. The severity of the short-summer phase is moderated in several districts by neighboring large bodies of water whose presence tends to delay spring and prolong the fall by postponing frost dangers.

Such climatic modifications are especially significant in the Maritime Provinces. There the chief crops are oats and potatoes. A considerable portion of the potato yield is marketed for seed. A particular feature of maritime agriculture is the **apple** growing that extends up the valleys of Nova Scotia, where the orchards are sheltered from the bitter west winds. The apple crop is a profitable item of export to Great Britain. In general, however, the agricultural productivity of the maritime district is so poor as to be a chronic economic problem.

The St. Lawrence lowlands are sites of subsistence farming and dairying. Intensive cultivation is practiced on small farms that extend in narrow strips at right angles to the river up to the sterile higher ground on the north shore.

Peninsular Ontario has its apex in the Niagara peninsula between Lakes Erie and Ontario. There the two lakes serve most efficiently to mitigate climatic extremes. In consequence this has become a notable **orchard** and **berry** district. The fruits, such as apples, pears, and blackberries, are marketed both fresh and canned. A large **dairy** industry for the Ontario urban centers is also important in this area.

In Saskatchewan the great spring **wheat** belt of Canada begins and, as a projection of the United States belt in the south, extends westward without a break to the base of the Rockies. This district and its American counterpart are the site of wheat fields that are measured in terms of square miles rather than acres and are farmed with the ultimate

in mechanized techniques. The wheat yield from this and the adjoining steppe region is Canada's greatest agricultural product and a leading item among the country's exports.

Industries. The industrial heart of Canada is in peninsular Ontario. Lesser industrial districts have developed in Nova Scotia and the western prairies. Much of Canadian industry is concerned with the production of goods for local markets. Small-scale food processing, clothing and building materials, furniture and office fixture manufacture are representative. National distribution of a Canadian product is the exception, a situation in large part due to easy access to the huge output of the United States and active promotion of their goods by American concerns. Tariffs imposed to foster domestic industries have resulted in the establishment, by American manufacturers, of assembly plants or completely independent works in Canada. Such "over-the-border" enterprises are an important element of Ontarian industry. Peninsular Canada in consequence produces automobiles, agricultural machinery, railroad rolling stock, textiles, rubber goods, books, paints, and other diversified products.

Iron and steel plants exist in Nova Scotia, at the base of the Niagara peninsula, and at the **Sault Ste. Marie** connection between Lakes Superior and Huron. The Nova Scotian industry uses local resources entirely; the others rely on United States coal.

The great power resources of Quebec have been utilized in a large **aluminum** reduction industry, and in **paper and pulp** mills. All these items bulk large in Canadian exports.

In the Maritime Provinces manufacturing is subordinate to **fishing**, since the coastal fishery resources are similar to those of New England and the ocean banks are shared with American fishermen. The packing and canning of the fish and lobster catch provide an income for the provincial populations that is more their basic source of livelihood than is agriculture. Nova Scotia's waters yield one-third of the world's lobster supply. Another supplementary source of income is **fur farming,** or the raising of silver fox and mutation mink on "ranches."

In recent decades there has been a constant growth in a new "industry," **tourism,** as the Canadians discovered the monetary rewards to be obtained by providing resort facilities for Americans. The Maritime Provinces afford a cool sea environment; Ontario, east of Lake Huron, offers picturesque small lakes and streams close to the great cities of that province and the northern United States. North of Lake Superior a wilderness land of lakes and forests provides exciting hunting and fishing for the more venturesome.

igational methods have largely overcome this handicap.

The great export commodity shipped from Montreal is wheat. The city's elevators can store ten million bushels of the grain while awaiting loading. Montreal is also the market place and source of supplies for adjacent regions. Almost a third of the city's working population is employed in trade activities. On the other hand, more than a third are in industry. Along the water front this is in heavy goods industry, but light manufactures employ the most workers.

CITIES OF HUMID CONTINENTAL CANADA

Name	Province	Type	Population (1951)
Montreal	Quebec	Seaport	1,395,000 (1953)
Toronto	Ontario	Lake port, industrial, governmental	676,000
Winnipeg	Manitoba	Commercial-governmental	236,000
Hamilton	Ontario	Industrial	208,000
Ottawa	Ontario	Governmental	202,000
Quebec	Quebec	Governmental-seaport	164,000
Edmonton	Alberta	Commercial-governmental	160,000
Windsor	Ontario	Industrial	120,000
Halifax	Nova Scotia	Seaport-governmental	86,000
Saskatoon	Saskatchewan	Commercial	53,000
St. John	New Brunswick	Seaport	51,000

Cities. Although there are relatively few large cities in Canada, over half of all Canadians are urban residents—this despite the fact that so great a part of Canada's economic activities is in the field, forest, "banks," and mines. Most of Canada's large cities are within the humid continental region, just as industry and agriculture are also concentrated there.

Montreal, the largest city of Canada, is the seaport at the head of ocean navigation on the St. Lawrence, a thousand miles upstream from the mouth of the river. Montreal is in line with the shortest or great-circle route across the Atlantic to Europe, so that its location provides an inviting entry for overseas trade to the heart of the American continent. Montreal's disadvantage is that the St. Lawrence is closed by ice from December to April. The shroud of fog that too commonly wraps the lower river was formerly a difficulty that slowed traffic and led to many marine disasters. Modern radar nav-

The city is built on a series of terraces rising to 200 feet surrounding the base of **Mount Royal,** whose summit is some 500 feet higher. The population of Montreal is two-thirds French, one-fifth British in tradition. In the narrow streets the problem of modern traffic is perhaps even more acute than in other large cities.

Toronto is the second in size of the Canadian cities and the most urban. Thus it was the first Canadian city to have a subway. Toronto is the best and greatest lake port of Canada, accessible to all ships plying the Great Lakes and, even before completion of the St. Lawrence Seaway, to small ocean vessels. Besides being the capital and commercial metropolis of Ontario and the financial center of Canada, Toronto is an industrial city of first importance. Light industries predominate. Toronto's shopping district is strung along one street for seven miles. Eighty percent of its population are of British origin, and this background is a

Fig. 26.14—Ottawa, Canada, Showing Government Buildings in the Foreground, Ottawa River in the Distance. (Courtesy, National Film Board of Canada.)

dominating influence in their political and social attitudes.

Winnipeg, the fourth in size of Canadian cities, is in many respects the counterpart of Chicago. Like Lake Michigan, Lake Winnipeg compels east-west overland traffic to swing around its south end, making the city the gateway to the Canadian West. Originally Winnipeg was the focal point of the fur trade of the northwest wilderness. It is now the market center for Canadian wheat as Chicago is for American wheat, and is also the distributing point to the west of all the commodities brought from the East as it is on a transcontinental rail line. Over one-third of its inhabitants are non-Canadian by birth, although 60 percent have British origins.

Hamilton is strictly an industrial city, with over 500 manufacturing plants in which nearly three-fifths of its working population are employed. Hamilton is the third city of Canada in industrial output, though only fifth in size. The major production is of iron and steel, the large output of which has earned it the designation "Pittsburgh of Canada." For steel, iron, and heavy machinery Hamilton has, in effect, the whole Ontario market at its doors. Three-fourths of Hamil-ton's population are still of British ancestry, as it is, like Toronto, in the "Tory" district of Canada.

In contrast with Hamilton, **Ottawa** (Fig. 26.14) is distinctively a governmental center, the capital of all Canada. As is appropriate to a capital city, Ottawa has impressive government buildings and handsome parks. It is in the eastern corner of Ontario on the Ottawa River, which is the boundary here between Ontario and Quebec.

Quebec, as the capital of that province, rivals Ottawa as a governmental center and surpasses it in picturesqueness and historical interest. Quebec's Old World aspects, its French-speaking people, and its commanding site combine to make it a Mecca for American tourists. Near at hand to the United States, it provides the setting and atmosphere of European lands. Almost all the inhabitants of Quebec are Roman Catholics, and its street traffic has a special aspect due to the presence of large numbers of the 2000 or more robed priests, nuns, and brethren of various monastic orders who live in the city.

The physical setting of Quebec is also impressive. The city consists of a rocky fortress and a walled city situated on a plain at the summit of a promontory where the St. Lawrence estuary narrows down to river width. At the foot of the cliff the ancient Lower City is strung along the water front. The harbor facilities of Quebec make it significant in overseas commerce, and it is also an important railroad center. The lower St. Lawrence Valley is its exclusive trade hinterland.

Edmonton and **Saskatoon** are prairie cities, serving as the market centers for their respective areas of the plains country. Edmonton's early importance was derived from the Alberta coal fields in which it is located. Since 1947 the nearby highly productive Leduc oil and gas field has enhanced this advantage and provided the basis for refinery and other petroleum industries. Edmonton is strategically located at the center of Alberta, is the capital of the province, the hub of seven radiating rail lines, and an important station on a transcontinental rail route. Its publicity writers style it the "Gateway to the North" or, in less restrained mood, "The Crossroads of the World."

Saskatoon promoters call it the "Hub City of the West." These slogan designations indicate the rivalry and basic similarity of the prairie centers of population. Although Saskatoon had no railroad connections until the turn of the century it now serves as the market town for some 100,000 square miles of surrounding country and is a center of potash mining.

Windsor is an exception, and perhaps a unique example, of city occurrence and development. It is, in effect, a mirror image of Detroit across the river, which it duplicates in almost everything but size. Windsor is physically connected with Detroit by bridge,

tunnel, and ferry but is separated commercially from its prototype by the international boundary. Thus it is the business of Windsor to make automobiles, machines, and other manufactures chiefly of American design and conception but stamped "Made in Canada." In fact, many Windsor industries are the Canadian branches of American companies.

Halifax (Fig. 26.15) has as its major advantage what was early described as the best harbor on the Atlantic coast of North America, but the city suffers from not having an immediately adjacent productive hinterland to serve commercially and industrially. For the most part Halifax receives from and transships commodities to remote regions. It is, however, the leading commercial center of Nova Scotia and does about two-thirds of the wholesale trade of the province. It is a sedate city rooted in the traditions of its historic past extending over 200 years.

St. John in New Brunswick is the close rival and in many aspects the counterpart of Halifax. It too has a spacious, deep, sheltered, and ice-free harbor and is a transcontinental rail terminus. But St. John shipping has to contend with a tidal range of 28 feet, a condition which produces the extraordinary phenomenon of a reversible falls between the inner and outer harbors. When the tide is out the water from the upper basin pours through a narrow passage as a

Fig. 26.15—Halifax, Nova Scotia. View of the harbor front with the city in the background. (Courtesy, National Film Board of Canada.)

rapids 15 feet high. When the tide returns the rapids run the other way. Ships must wait for the short periods of slack tide to proceed through the gap in quiet waters.

QUESTIONS. Describe the extent and topography of the humid continental climatic region of Canada. Explain the occurrence of the far western extension of the region. Describe the general population make-up of the various sections of the region. Explain the existence of the two dominant groups within the population. Where are the coal fields of the region? The oil and gas fields? The iron ore deposits? The world's outstanding sources of what two mineral products are found within this region? Locate the area of greatest hydropower resources and explain why they are so large.

What is the leading agricultural product? Explain the relation between American and Canadian industry and how this has influenced the present character of Canadian industry. Why are aluminum refining and paper and pulp mills all concentrated in the same general area? Nova Scotia is an important source of what sea food? What new "industry" is of increasing importance in the Maritime Provinces and the districts east and north of Lake Superior?

Compare Montreal and Quebec as to atmosphere, commercial importance, and population. In what respects is Winnipeg the "Chicago of Canada"? Hamilton the "Pittsburgh of Canada"? What is unique about Windsor's relation to Detroit? What is the chief handicap of Halifax? Why is St. John nevertheless inferior to Halifax as a port?

Low-Temperature Humid Climates:
The Subarctic Climate

CHAPTER 27

The Subarctic Climate: Eurasian Region

■ DEFINITION AND CAUSES OF THE SUBARCTIC CLIMATE

As its name implies, the subarctic climate is transitional between the middle-latitude climates and the true arctic, or polar, climates. Low temperatures of the subarctic climate are due to continentality in association with high latitude, rather than to high latitude alone, as is true of the polar climates.

The subarctic climate borders on a polar climate on its high-latitude side. The boundary, which approximates the line of the polar limit of tree growth, is the line along which the warmest month of the year averages 50° Fahrenheit. On the low-latitude side the climate borders either on the short-summer phase of the humid continental climate or on the middle-latitude steppe climate. This in turn is roughly coincident with the average annual temperature line at which the conifers supersede the broad-leafed trees of lower latitudes.

■ CLIMATIC CHARACTERISTICS

PRECIPITATION

On the basis solely of precipitation this climate in the tropics would be arid, and in the middle latitudes semiarid. Only in coastal districts of subarctic regions does precipitation exceed 20 inches a year; in many places it is less than 15 inches. Nevertheless, because of the rule that the lower the temperature the lower the evaporation, much less precipitation is necessary for vegetation in the subarctic climatic regions than in lower-latitude climates.

The subarctic regions are typically high-pressure areas in winter, when continental cold chills the air over the land. Consequently, only a few of the low-pressure cyclones of the westerlies belt pass across the subarctic regions. Such cyclones as do intrude during the winter generate frontal storms that produce snow. This snow is very dry and powdery, not at all like the wet snowflakes of the middle-latitude winters. Despite the relatively infrequent storms, however, the steady cold allows successive snowfalls to build up a permanent snow cover over open ground during the winter. In forested areas daytime melting and evaporation are so low that two to three feet of snow may accumulate. Precipitation is higher in summer because an occasional convectional thunderstorm supplements the cyclonic rainfall.

TEMPERATURE

Temperature is the dominating factor of the subarctic climate. As the most continental of all climates it has the greatest temperature ranges on earth. On the low side the extreme staggers the imagination—the official record is minus 93.6° F., the lowest naturally occurring temperature ever noted on the earth's surface. To be sure, this is the maximal cold of the climate, but temperatures 60 degrees below zero Fahrenheit are common every winter at many places in subarctic regions.

The physical effects produced by and

583

human reaction to such low temperatures are most extraordinary. Materials behave strangely—unless absolutely dry, wood cannot be cut with an ax; iron becomes brittle and may shatter easily. There is a saying that spittle freezes before it reaches the ground when the temperature is under 60 below. Even a minimum exposure of the bare human body to such low temperatures is dangerous. Direct, deep breathing of the cold air can freeze the lungs.

The temperature range, though not so directly productive of dramatic effects as are the extremes of cold, is nevertheless impressive. The place where the record low was experienced also had a summer temperature of 94° F. plus. The highest temperatures recorded within the regions exceed 100° F.

Of more significance is the great range between seasonal averages. Technically, part of the definition of the subarctic climate is the occurrence of at least one month but no more than three months of the year with average temperatures over 50° F. Obviously, therefore, most of the subarctic year is cold. For the six or more warmer months the average daily temperature may be below freezing; during most of the winter months it is below zero. This deep, continual cold is in part the result of the very short days and long nights of winter in the higher latitudes, with consequent high heat loss during the commonly clear nights and low insolation during the day.

On the other hand, the 18 to 20 hours of daylight in summer bring about a marked diurnal temperature build-up, and short nights keep the temperature drop at a minimum (although frost danger is never really absent through the whole summer). Yet many summer days may have temperatures in the 80's. No other climate has such seasonal temperature extremes.

The low average annual temperature gives rise to a unique phenomenon. It is evident that the frost of winter under the extreme cold will penetrate farther into the ground than the warmth of the short summer can offset. The ground at depth thus remains permanently frozen, and is called *perma-*

frost. The districts where permafrost exists are determined by the wide local variations in the below-surface temperatures of summer and winter, dependent in turn on such factors as the nature of soil and topography. Permafrost areas thaw at the surface during summer, and as the melt-water cannot drain down through the frozen ground beneath, the land becomes soft and water-logged.

Between the short, three-month summer and the long, seven-month winter are the two brief transition seasons. Spring in the subarctic is like the action of a movie shown at double speed, for the vegetation struggles to sprout, blossom, and fruit before frost strikes it down. With all plants blooming at once the ground then is carpeted with flowers. The traditional herald of spring in the subarctic is the "breakup" of ice. This takes place with a sudden roar and crash as the ice on the rivers gives way under pressure of melt-waters from upstream.

Fall arrives with equal swiftness. After a first few frosts in rapid succession full winter takes over.

■ REGIONAL ASPECTS

Taiga is a Mongol word for "forest." Geographers have adopted it as a technical term to designate the coniferous forests of the subarctic regions (Fig. 27.1). Low precipitation is matched by low evaporation so that there is sufficient moisture in the ground for tree growth. Cold, on the other hand, eliminates all but a few of the hardier deciduous species. Only the rainforest climate of the tropics is more completely identified by a specific type of vegetative cover. But the taiga is quite unlike the rainforest. Taiga trees in permafrost areas cannot take deep root. They can thus be easily blown over, so that there are no giants protruding their crowns above the general forest level.

Taiga country is alternately forest and swamp, a type of landscape that covers by far the largest part of the subarctic regions. In the north the trees are mostly fir, spruce, tamarack, and larch, with birch, alders, and willows representing the broad-leafed trees.

Fig. 27.1—Taiga, Coniferous Forest in Labrador. Here drilling to explore an ore deposit is in progress. (Courtesy, National Film Board of Canada.)

In the south poplars, pines, maples, and elms come in. The ubiquitous oak of lower latitudes cannot stand the subarctic cold and so is absent from the taiga. Everywhere the coniferous evergreens predominate, except in the swampy areas (called *muskeg* in North America), where clumps of the deciduous trees may occur.

A large portion of the Eurasian and practically all the North American subarctic regions were covered by the ice age glaciers. Ice erosion left only thin soils, if any. Low, rounded hills of barren rock rise above the general surface. Glacial debris irregularly deposited confused the drainage pattern and created thousands of ponds and lakes.

The dominance of coniferous evergreens and lakes in the landscape gives it an aspect uniquely characteristic. In summer the scene is a study in shades of dark green and blue, the tree-covered land surface alternating with the open lake waters. In winter the dark conifers stand out in sharp contrast with the pure white of the snow-covered, frozen water areas and the ground.

The trunk rivers of the subarctic regions are mostly north-flowing. As noted in the earlier discussion of streams (see Chapter 2, p. 38), the northward flow means that the springtime thawing, progressively from south to north, is downstream. In consequence the still ice-choked lower portions of the streams experience great floods. Vast overflowed tracts together with the many swamps and the water-soaked earth in permafrost areas provide ideal conditions during the spring and summer for breeding astronomic swarms of insect pests. Veritable clouds of mosquitoes and stinging black flies make life a torment for four-footed animals and almost unbearable for man. Although the insects do not carry disease, as do those of the tropics, their greater number and fierceness may cause their victims as much anguish as a severe sickness.

Despite the rigorous climatic conditions the animal life of the subarctic is abundant and varied. The common defense against the cold of winter is fur, on such common animals as the fox, mink, wolf, muskrat, beaver, and bear, and the rarer sables and ermines. The larger herbivores are represented by reindeer, caribou, moose, and deer. The birds are chiefly migatory, summering and breeding in the open spaces of the subarctic and flying far south to warmer climes for the winter.

■ UTILIZATION OF SUBARCTIC REGIONS

Agriculture is definitely a subordinate economic activity in the subarctic regions. Despite the warmth of the summer days the frost-free growing season is very short—well under 100 days. Frost may occur in every month of the year. The short growing season is to some extent offset by the long daylight hours, since the cultivated plants will, like their wild relatives, speed up their growing cycle to get it completed within the season. Quick-growing vegetables, fruits, root crops, and field crops are produced. Cauliflower, cabbage, lettuce, and berries are representative items. Rye and oats are the chief cereals, and hay can make a good crop. Barley, the hardiest of all the cereals, is raised in the farthest north. The long daylight hours that tend to offset the short growing season are of no avail, on the other hand, against the large proportion of land that is bare rock, swamps, and poor soils within the subarctic regions. Thus it is that agriculture is of real significance in only a few exceptional localities.

The dominant economic activities of the subarctic environment are lumbering, mining, and fishing, as befits the characteristic resources of such regions. Thus the forest resources of the taiga are the greatest in the world, whether measured by the total quantity of timber or by areal extent. Nevertheless, in availability they fall far short of the almost ideal forest resources of the marine west coast climate (see Chapter 19, p. 383). For one thing, the taiga trees are not large. They do not grow tall, and as they are slow-growing in the cold climate, most of them are only a foot or so in diameter. Moreover, in areas along the high-latitude border of the subarctic regions, in those with thin or poor soils, or where recent growth exists after forest fires (which are easily started because rot does not destroy fallen trees, and the high pitch content of the conifers permits easy kindling), only scrubby trees of no value for lumber are found. Nonetheless, the extent of the taiga lands is so great that on balance their forests must be regarded as of marked significance in evaluating the timber resources of the world.

Mining is important in the subarctic regions partly because agriculture and industrial activities are absent, more because the mineral resources of these lands are varied and extensive. Although fuel deposits exist, the dominant mineral wealth is in metallic ores (Fig. 27.1).

Fisheries in the offshore waters are widespread and highly productive. The minute marine life on which many fish feed flourishes where the waters of cold and warm marine currents mix. This is a regular phenomenon off the coasts of the subarctic regions, in consequence of which some of the world's best fishing grounds are located there.

Although the fur industry does not approach lumbering, mining, and fishing in significance it has a special place because in modern times it is best developed in the subarctic climate. The subarctic "fur resources" constitute the last undepleted such occurrence in the world. The fur-bearing animal life of lower latitudes was as abundant if not more abundant but has long since been all but exterminated.

The final notable resource of the subarctic regions is hydropower. The many lakes and swift streams in rocky beds that are an outstanding feature of the glaciated topography afford immense possibilities for hydroelectric development. For the most part particular descents are not great but the volume of the streams is commonly large and their flow constant because the many lakes act as excellent regulators of volume.

The subarctic regions are still frontier regions of human activity. Although some large cities have arisen there they are the exception. Mining, fishing, lumbering, and trapping are ordinarily solitary or remote human activities. But all this is slowly changing. As the rich natural resources of the lower-latitude population and industrial centers become depleted, man is turning to the less accessible resources of the higher-latitude regions. It becomes economically worth while to overcome the handicaps of remoteness and climate, and improved technology makes this possible. Power lines, for example, can now be operated from subarctic hydroelectric sites to existing industrial centers in neighboring regions, whereas previously these sites were beyond the limit of economic transmission.

The basic climatic handicap remains: The cold of the subarctic climate depresses the human spirit. The long periods of darkness and twilight are very hard on morale. Nevertheless winter is the subarctic work period. Cold can be compensated for, whereas the summer difficulties are not so easily dealt with. In winter there is blessed relief from the stings and bites of the flying insect hordes. Winter brings snow to provide easy overland transport in lands with no roads, because frozen-over swamps and lakes are then no barrier to travel. Here too, however, technology is making for change. With air transport, especially helicopters, to provide access to even the most inaccessible places, construction activities now proceed throughout the year.

■ SUBARCTIC REGIONS AND COUNTRIES

The subarctic climate is confined to latitudes between 50° and 65°. Thus it occurs only in the Northern Hemisphere. In the Southern Hemisphere South America extends into these latitudes, but only where it is too narrow to develop a continental influence on the climate.

Like the humid continental climate the subarctic climate occurs in a belt across part of each of the two great land masses of the Northern Hemisphere (Fig. 27.2). But unlike the humid continental climate, the subarctic region extends without interruption across all of both Europe and Asia. Hence there

Fig. 27.2—World Distribution of Subarctic Climatic Regions.

are two regions: the **Eurasian region** and the **North American region**.

A. EURASIAN REGION

The Eurasian region of subarctic climate extends across all of northern Europe and Asia from the Scandinavian peninsula on the west to the Pacific Ocean on the east. Narrow in the west (present only between 60° and 70° north latitude), it widens considerably in the east as the continental influences become stronger. At its maximum, in eastern Siberia, it extends from below 50° north to 70° north.

The district of extreme continentality in eastern Siberia is the location of the cold pole of the land world. There the lowest known temperature was recorded. The continentality of this area also intensifies aridity. Some places even lack a snow cover throughout the winter.

The glaciated topography of bare rock and irregular glacial deposits so typical of subarctic lands is markedly developed in the western section of the Eurasian region. On the other hand, much of the eastern portion is swampy territory of nonglacial origin.

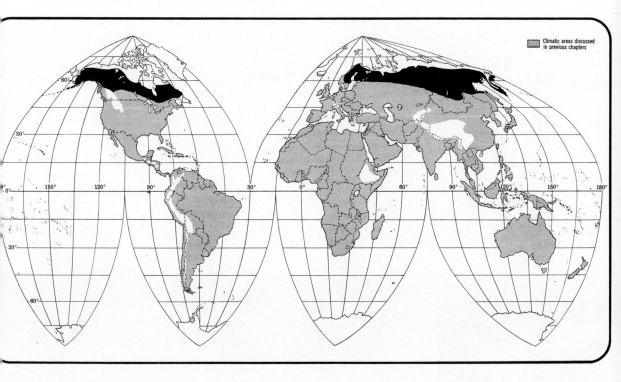

Climatic areas discussed in previous chapters

1. Northern Russia and Siberia

General Aspects. The Eurasian subarctic region includes a huge portion of the Soviet Union, but its boundaries fail to coincide even approximately with either political or physical provinces. It is, accordingly, difficult to describe the Soviet Union portion in terms of major political divisions except to say that it includes in Europe all of what was the **Karelo-Finnish** Soviet Socialist Republic until 1956 and the northern portion of the Russian Soviet Federal Socialist Republic, and in Asia by far the greater extent of the Siberian part of the R.S.F.S.R. (Fig. 27.3). In Siberia alone the region stretches 4600 miles west to east and varies from 600 to 1300 miles in its north-south dimension. All told this probably amounts to 4 million square miles, about one-half of the area of the Soviet Union and about a third again as much as the continental United States.

It is thus not inappropriate to refer to the Eurasian subarctic region in the Soviet Union as "northern Russia and Siberia," for

Fig. 27.3—Subarctic Russia and Siberia. The inset compares the area of the region with that of the United States.

the region includes all of the former and not only the largest but the most typical part of the latter.

Topography. The topography of this enormous region can best be described in subunits, proceeding from west to east, rather than by considering plains, mountains, rivers, and other land features as groups. Even major topographic units are so numerous that it is easiest to grasp their relationships when described in sequence.

In the northwest the subarctic region of the U.S.S.R. begins with the eastern margin of **Fenno-Scandia,** the great peninsula that juts north and then southeast on the north side of Europe. This is a district of low hills, under 500 feet in elevation, a surface of hard rock modified by the ice age glaciers and covered with clay and gravel. Fenno-Scandia is bordered on the west by a lowland belt with depressions occupied by the **Gulf of Finland, Lake Ladoga, Lake Onega,** and the **White Sea,** in order from southwest to northeast. North of the White Sea is a southeast-trending projection of Fenno-Scandia, the **Kola peninsula,** with a mountain backbone of 4000-foot altitudes.

Again to the east is a low plain across

which two rivers, the **Northern Dvina** (to distinguish it from the Dvina to the west in Latvia—see Chapter 25, p. 531) and the **Pechora** flow toward the White Sea. The rivers are separated by a low ridge, the **Timan Hills,** about 1000 feet in elevation. East of this plain is the northern portion of the **Urals,** the highest and most rugged section of the range, with mile-high altitudes.

East of the Urals, in western Siberia, is the vast, swampy plain of the second largest river system of Siberia, the **Ob** and its tributaries. The subarctic region includes the middle reaches of the river, where the excessive flatness and slow spring thaw cause the stream to stagnate and spread out in wide floods. The plain is between 300 and 600 feet above sea level.

East of the west Siberian plain is the upland district of central Siberia. This upland averages 1000 to 1500 feet in elevation, rising to 3000 feet in the **Anabar Hills,** in the north central part of the area. The western portion of the upland is composed of the **Tunguska Hills,** the eastern portion the **Lena Hills.** Various plain and plateau subdivisions occur within these broader divisions. The drainage of this very large area is by means of two river systems, north-flowing as are all the systems of the subarctic Soviet Union. On the west is the **Yenisei,** the largest river of Siberia; on the east the **Lena,** the third river in size. The rivers have cut deep valleys in the plateau, whose surface is only slightly undulating when seen from the plateau level.

The plateaus of central Siberia are ringed on the south and east by a continuous string of mountain ranges. On the southwest the **Sayan Mountains** average 8000 feet, with the highest peak at 11,500 feet. The Sayans form the northern rim of the Tuva Basin (see Chapter 22, p. 465). East of the Sayans are the **Baikal Mountains,** curving northeast on either side of the deep trench in which lies **Lake Baikal.** Within the enclosed area formed by these ranges and the high southern edge of the central uplands is the **Irkutsk Basin,** or amphitheater.

The eastern portion of the mountainous southern rim of eastern Siberia is a complex assemblage of ranges and plateaus known in general as the "**Transbaikal,**" in reference to its location beyond Lake Baikal. This district lies to the north of Mongolia and contains the divide between drainage to the Arctic Ocean and drainage to the Sea of Okhotsk. Along its northern edge runs a mountain chain that continues northeast, north, west, and then north again in a great "S" like that of the Carpathians (see Chapter 24, p. 519), forming the eastern border of the central uplands section. The southern portion of this chain is the **Stanovoi Mountains,** the northern portion the **Verkhoyansk Ranges.** The Lena and its tributaries follow this great curve on its western side.

Northeast Siberia is a country of more mountains and lowlands, trending north-south in alternating belts. The mountains are extremely rugged and the lowlands contain the cold pole of the world, owing to the settling down of cold air from the mountains under the calm of the polar highs. The **Kamchatka peninsula** that dangles south to enclose the Sea of Okhotsk is composed of a string of active volcanoes. Several large but little-known streams emptying into the Arctic Ocean comprise the drainage system of extreme northeastern Siberia.

The foregoing generalized recital of the topography should convey some understanding of the truly great extent of the subarctic region of the U.S.S.R. It is a region of diverse topography, with all features on a grand scale. Three of its rivers are in the same class as the Mississippi-Missouri system; four others are also more than 1000 miles in length. Its plains and plateaus are like the Great Plains and Colorado Plateaus of the United States, and its mountains are the equal of the Sierra Nevada in height and ruggedness, and of the Rockies in extent.

People. Owing to their recent colonization of Siberia, Russians are the predominant people of the subarctic region of the Soviet Union. In the European portion of the region they are concentrated in Karelia. In Siberia they are mostly in the southern part, especially where the climatic region includes sections along the Trans-Siberian Railroad. There is also a Russian concentration in Kamchatka. As is usual in all the Soviet regions there are many diverse minority groups. In Karelia the dominant minority groups are the *Karelians* and *Finns* (about one-quarter of the local population). Most of the Finns who had lived there moved to Finland when a large portion of the territory was annexed in 1940. (The S.S.R. that was first established there was incorporated into the R.S.F.S.R. in 1956.) The Karelians are closely related to the Finns but are more Russified, and Russian is their language.

In northeastern Europe the non-Russian minority is mostly Finno-Ugric (see Chapter 24, p. 520), specifically the 400,000 *Komi* who inhabit the Pechora plain. These people have assimilated Western science and technology better than any of the indigenous peoples of the Soviet subarctic region. They supply many of the professional personnel for work with the less-advanced peoples.

Western Siberia within the subarctic region is the home of the 25,000 *Khanti* and 6000 *Mansi*, more Finno-Ugrians, who still follow their old life of hunting, fishing, and trapping.

Eastern Siberia harbors the most diverse collection of minorities. The Lena watershed is known as "Yakutia" after the 250,000 *Yakuts*, the most numerous of the Siberian native peoples, who inhabit it. The Yakuts have become highly adapted to the climate. They have achieved farming and stock-raising techniques despite their being the occupants of the "cold pole" district. The Yakuts are of Turkic stock. A second group is the 40,000 *Tungus*, or *Evenki* (see Chapter 25, p. 541), whose chief center is in the eastern half of the Yenisei watershed. The three major tributaries of the Yenisei on the east—the Lower, Stony, and Upper Tunguska—all get their names from this local people. Tungus are also found in the northern Transbaikal and along the coast of the Sea of Okhotsk. The Tungus have various occupations in their different environments, but the majority are forest hunters who keep reindeer for food and transport.

In the south are the 50,000 *Khakass* northeast of Tuva. These are the same people, in their original home, as the Kirghiz of the Soviet Socialist Republic of that name (see Chapter 22, p. 460). The Transbaikal is the home of the 240,000 *Buriat-Mongols*, a pastoral Mongol group (Fig. 27.4).

The inhabitants of the northeastern portion of the region are chiefly small tribes of the *Paleo-Asiatic* group, so called because of the languages they speak. Representatives of this group are also found on the south coast of the Sea of Okhotsk.

Fig. 27.4—A Buriat-Mongol With His Flock. (Courtesy, Soviet Embassy.)

Mineral Resources. It would be surprising if a region as large as the Soviet subarctic did not contain some mineral wealth of importance. Although the west Siberian lowland region is notably poor in minerals, the remainder of the region affords a variety of significant mineral deposits.

The outstanding occurrence is of **gold,** found throughout almost the entire extent of eastern Siberia. The **Aldan** district, along the chief tributary of the upper Lena of that name, is the leading producer. Other important districts are on the upper Amur, north of Manchuria; the **Kolyma** district north of the Sea of Okhotsk and northwest of Kamchatka; south central Siberia north of Tuva; a plateau northeast of Lake Baikal; and the Transbaikal.

Although the Soviet government professes to be uninterested in the production of gold, a capitalistic symbol, output is pressed full blast and new districts are developed as soon as they are discovered. Moreover, reports of fugitives from slave labor camps tell grisly tales of hardships endured in connection with the gold mining, for which much of Soviet slave labor seems to be used.

The second outstanding resource of the region is **coal,** of all types and qualities, from many districts. The major district is the Irkutsk Basin, where a belt 45 to 50 miles wide runs for 150 miles along the Trans-Siberian Railroad northwest from Lake Baikal and contains larger reserves than those of the Donbas (see Chapter 22, p. 457). Deposits elsewhere in eastern Siberia are in the Tunguska district, in Yakutia, in the **Minusinsk Basin** north of Tuva, in the **Chita** district east of Transbaikal, and northeast of the Verkhoyansk Ranges. Most of those coal fields are untapped because of their remoteness and lack of transportation, but the Soviet eagerness to develop all natural resources has led to some production along the middle Lena and elsewhere.

In the European portion of the region an unusual assemblage of mineral resources occurs at the base of the Kola peninsula. One of the world's chief **nickel** districts occurs here. The development at **Pechanga** on the coast of the Arctic Ocean was originally Finnish but was taken over by the Soviets in 1940 as war booty.

The Soviets have also developed a **copper-nickel** district extending south from the original area. In this same general vicinity is also the major producer of **phosphate fertilizers** and **aluminum,** from unusual rock sources. There are indications that this area may also yield molybdenum, vanadium, titanium, and zirconium in quantity. A second important aluminum-fertilizer district is in the northern Urals. The fertilizer in this instance is **potash.**

The leading **iron ore** district of the subarctic region of the U.S.S.R. is on the **Angara** (the major tributary of the upper Yenisei) north of the Irkutsk Basin. The ore occurs on both sides of the river at a site where there are large rapids. The significance of the site in terms of hydropower potential and its proximity to the Irkutsk coal resources is evident.

The Chita district possesses in addition to coal very important lead-zinc-silver mines and significant producers of tin, molybdenum, and tungsten.

The only petroleum production of any consequence in the region is from the Pechora plain, for use in the Leningrad district.

Other Resources. The **forest** resources are of outstanding importance. Although the region is solidly forested throughout almost all its extent the timber of certain districts is more valuable and better exploited than that of others. The most important is the White Sea–Karelia district, where good transportation facilities permit the excellent stands to be intensively worked. Mine timber, lumber for construction, box flats, matches, alcohol, and pulpwood are some of the many products. This district supplies two-thirds of the Soviet paper output.

The Irkutsk Basin has better forest resources than the Karelia area, and the Dvina-Pechora plain has the best in all the Soviet Union. These regional resources are not yet fully exploited, but eventually they will become the most important timber areas of the Soviet Union.

The forests are the chief source of **furs.** In early czarist times Siberian furs were the major product of the region. But excesses in hunting and trapping reduced the fur resources. Strict conservation measures are now enforced by the Soviets to assure the maintenance of an important occupation. The less-developed regions of eastern Siberia are, as one might expect, the major sources. Pelts and skins are accumulated during the winter and brought in spring to the railheads or river ports for shipment to fur markets.

Fisheries are also an important element in the economy of the region. The terminal effect of the Gulf Stream is to produce superb fishing grounds in the waters north and east of Fenno-Scandia. The Kola–White Sea district is a leading source of fish for the Soviet Union, especially for herring. Other good fishing grounds are Lake Baikal and the waters around Kamchatka.

Although the coal resources of the Eurasian subarctic region are good the **hydropower** potentials are even better. In Kola-Karelia the combination of lakes and short but swift-flowing streams provides good prospects despite the winter freeze. Owing to its accessibility from and proximity to the centers of population on the south the resources of this district have been well developed and include the northernmost hydroelectric station in the world.

It is in eastern Siberia, however, that the truly great possibilities for hydropower exist. The Soviets have already engaged in hydroelectric projects of a scale that matches the largest of those in the United States. But the possibilities in the east are even greater than any so far developed in all the Soviet Union. The combination there of great streams, high heads, and narrow gorges affords nearly ideal conditions for such exploitation. The middle and upper courses of the Lena, Yeni-

sei, Angara, and Ob, in that order, provide the major opportunities.

Industry and Transportation. The most characteristic and widespread industrial activity of the subarctic region in the Soviet Union is the operation of **sawmills**. In keeping with the Soviet practice of developing all industrial possibilities in every city and town, each urban center has its collection of local processing industries. There are, however, two significant industrial concentrations, both located in eastern Siberia. The Irkutsk district utilizes local coal, lumber, and hydropower supplies. Heavy machinery (such as dredges for some of the gold fields) is produced there. The Chita concentration has an iron and steel mill using local coal and ore, and accompanying machinery and other manufactures.

Transportation facilities differ greatly within the region. In the Kola-Karelia district they are excellent. The lakes and rivers of the lowland belt have been linked by ca-

Fig. 27.5—Major Railroads of the Soviet Union. Note the well-developed network in Russia, centered on Moscow; the long, isolated Trans-Siberian line; and the complete absence of railroads in most of Siberia. The Trans-Siberian line provides a link between the eastern and western extremities of the country, but the extension of railroads into the rest of Siberia in order to stimulate and sustain economic development will be a very difficult and expensive undertaking.

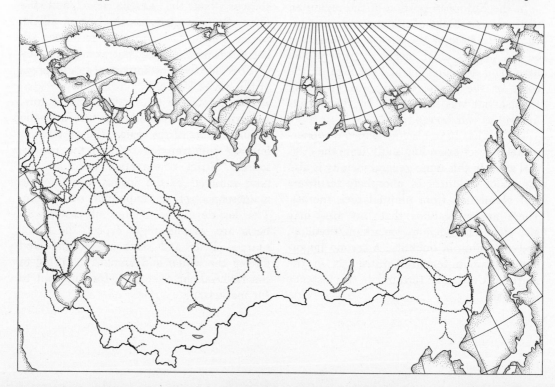

nals which provide a water connection between the White Sea and the Baltic. In addition, the Kola area of mineral resources has been provided with a rail network, so that the entire district has adequate rail service (Fig. 27.5). The Dvina-Pechora district has a rail line running through it from south to north.

The Siberian portion of the region is much less well equipped. Only a few short spurs extend northward from the trunk Trans-Siberian line, which skirts the southern border of eastern Siberia. The north-flowing rivers are without significance for the major east-west movement of traffic but are used whenever and wherever possible to move bulky, low-cost freight north or south. Hard-surface highways are nonexistent.

Agriculture. The agriculture of the subarctic region of the Soviet Union conforms to the climatic pattern in most districts. The hardy grains **rye, oats,** and **barley,** in that order, are the leading crops in the European portion. Barley is the staple in Yakutia. In line with the Soviet drive to extend the range of all crops as far north as possible, some wheat is grown in Yakutia. The agricultural handicap of the climate is overcome (at a high cost of materials, labor, and fuel) near the large cities of the European portion of the region by growing vegetables in greenhouses for urban consumption.

Along the southern border of the region in the east the climate is a little warmer than typical, and some crops of the westerlies climates are grown there. Thus sugar beets are produced in the Minusinsk Basin, flax in the southern part of the west Siberian plain, and wheat in the Irkutsk and Chita districts.

The characteristic domestic animal is the **reindeer,** raised by all the native peoples in the northern part of the region. The Tungus saddle these animals and use them as mounts. Surprisingly, **cattle** raising is also widespread. Special small, hairy breeds have proved to be able to withstand the cold, even the bitter low temperatures of Yakutia. **Dairying** is a significant occupation in the European portion of the region. Some sheep are raised in the Transbaikal.

CITIES OF THE SUBARCTIC REGION OF THE SOVIET UNION

Name	Type	Population (1946–48)
Krasnoyarsk	Commercial	300,000
Irkutsk	Commercial	300,000
Arkhangelsk	Seaport	300,000
Murmansk	Seaport	150,000
Ulan-Ude	Commercial	150,000
Chita	Commercial-mining	150,000
Cheremkhovo	Mining	70,000 (?)
Yakutsk	Commercial	60,000 (?)

Cities. **Krasnoyarsk** is located on the Trans-Siberian Railroad where it crosses the upper Yenisei, in the southeastern corner of the Siberian plain north of the Minusinsk Basin. In addition to its sawmills and paper plants Krasnoyarsk manufactures gold-dredging machinery and has a collection of light industries.

Irkutsk, the metropolis of its basin, is located on the Angara River 40 miles northwest from its Lake Baikal outlet. The Trans-Siberian line parallels the river at this point, so that it is also a railroad city. Its industries are similar to those of Krasnoyarsk.

At the other end of the region in the Kola–White Sea district are two important seaports. **Arkhangelsk** is the largest sawmill center in the Soviet Union and does a large export business in lumber. It is located on the Dvina delta 25 miles up a distributary. Although the White Sea freezes in winter, it is kept open by icebreakers for most of the season. **Murmansk,** a smaller city, is perhaps more important, for it is the Soviet Union's only ice-free port with direct access to the Atlantic. The city is located at the base of the Kola peninsula on a fiord, 20 miles inland from the Arctic Ocean. It owes its freedom from ice to the Gulf Stream and has the further distinction of being, at 69° north latitude, the largest city north of the Arctic Circle. Murmansk is also the western terminus of the Northern Sea Route around Siberia (see Chapter 25, p. 542).

East of Lake Baikal are two centers of local importance on the Trans-Siberian line —**Ulan-Ude** and **Chita.** The former is the Buriat-Mongol capital, and the jump-off point for the route into Mongolia. Chita is at the junction of the Trans-Siberian Railroad with the north-south line across Manchuria. It has some coal mines in its outskirts.

Cheremkhovo and **Yakutsk** are two much smaller cities. Cheremkhovo is the mining center of the Irkutsk coal district along the Trans-Siberian line. Yakutsk, the capital of Yakutia, is the most isolated of all the larger cities of Siberia. It is located on a branch of the Lena where it makes the large bend south of the Verkhoyansk Ranges, at a point 500 miles north of the populated Trans-Siberian belt. It has the appearance and atmosphere of an isolated frontier town although it is over 200 years old.

QUESTIONS. Describe the boundaries of the subarctic climate in terms of vegetative cover. What is the average precipitation over areas in this climate? Why is this climate not considered arid? Why is there more precipitation in the summer? Explain how the snow can accumulate to a depth of several feet during the winter despite the low precipitation. Describe and explain the outstanding temperature characteristics of the subarctic climate. Define the climate in terms of temperature. What is permafrost? Explain its origin. What happens in permafrost districts during the summer? Describe the four seasons in the subarctic climate.

What is the original meaning of the word *taiga?* The geographical meaning? Compare the taiga with the tropical rainforest. Why are the effects produced by ice age glaciers of special significance in subarctic regions? What are the typical landscape characteristics of the regions? What agonizing torture is experienced by human beings during the subarctic summer?

How long is the growing season in subarctic regions? What other factors minimize agricultural utilization of these regions? Name three economic activities and state why they are dominant. Discuss the fur and hydropower resources, relating them to the climate and topography. Why is the frontier characteristic of subarctic regions currently changing? What is the season of greatest human activity? Why? Locate the subarctic regions of the world.

State the extent of the Eurasian region of subarctic climate. Why is it wider in the east? List the general topographic features of the subarctic region of the Soviet Union. Characterize the different peoples of the region. What is the outstanding mineral resource? Locate the major coal districts. Name the chief mineral products of the Kola-Karelia district. Where are the best forest resources of the region? The chief fisheries? Describe the hydropower resources. Name the two industrial centers of the region.

What is the significance of Arkhangelsk and Murmansk to the Soviet Union? In what respects are Ulan-Ude and Chita similar?

The Soviet Union as a Whole

With the discussion of the subarctic region the whole of the Soviet Union has been described except for the arctic region along the north Siberian coast. The regions thus far considered include practically all the population, the natural resources, and the economic activity of the country. It is therefore appropriate at this point to consider modern Russia and Siberia as a whole.

The rest of the world has been made well aware of the Union of Soviet Socialist Republics as a political phenomenon. This phenomenon is the establishment of a Communist state, with absolute control by the leaders over men's activities, thoughts, and personalities.

It needs to be recognized that the Soviet Union is also a geographic phenomenon. In physical size it is in a class by itself; its area of 8.6 million square miles, equal to 15 percent of the entire land surface of the earth, is more than twice that of the second largest country and three times that of the United States. The Soviet Union ranks third in the world in population, with some 200 million inhabitants as of 1955. The country's development from a backward and impotent monarchy at the time of World War I to the world's second-ranking economic and political power after World War II was so unexpected in its scope and rapidity that the rest of the world still finds it difficult to accept its rise to such status as a fact.

In association, these political and geographic circumstances have created a situation of unparalleled import for humanity. The rulers of the largest country in the world, with one of the few very large controlled populations, and second only to the United States in industrial strength, evidently have as their dominant objective the exercise of world-wide political power; or, if not that, at least the aim to mold all the world's peoples into their governmental pattern. It is, therefore, instructive to summarize the geographic advantages and disadvantages that will promote or hinder the attainment of this goal.

Size, location, and shape are all handicapping factors. The vast area includes regions made relatively inaccessible to commerce by mountain barriers. The latitudinal extent from middle to high latitudes, and the fact that the country comprises most of a continent, means that there must be large areas of inclement and extremely inhospitable climates. In combination, difficult topography and unfavorable climate reduce the total land area potentially available for agricultural use to one million square miles. In the far north large areas are virtually of no economic use except for the minerals they may contain. The large size and vast dimensions of both length and breadth necessitate an elaborate network of interior transportation facilities if remoteness and isolation are to be overcome (Fig. 27.5). Coastal transport can be of little use. Thus an unusually high consumption of fuel for transportation purposes is required. River transportation is icebound seven to nine months of the year and is available mostly in the wrong directions. Connecting canals can partly remedy this difficulty, but at best the development of an adequate transportation net by land or water over such vast territories is an enormous undertaking. This is related to the Soviet effort to develop regional self-sufficiency through utilization of local resources in so far as is possible.

The composition of the population also creates problems. If it be assumed that the Communist system is acceptable to the average citizen, the dominance of the Great Russians over the other Slavs and the different peoples of the north, south, and east is undoubtedly distasteful to many of these groups. Hence their whole-hearted coöperation in the grandiose plans and schemes of the Soviets may be doubted. This is not necessarily a matter of open resentment and obstructionism. It refers to the difference between forced compliance and enthusiastic contribution. On this difference the success or failure of a national policy may depend.

Paradoxically, the impeding factors listed above, otherwise viewed, constitute geographic assets. As the occurrence of mineral deposits under any particular spot on the earth's crust is essentially random, the great size of the U.S.S.R. almost insures great mineral wealth within its borders. The benefits already accruing to the Soviets on this basis have been amply demonstrated in the regional discussions. Coal, the most important such resource, is abundant and sufficiently well distributed for the Soviet economic schemes; the supplies of iron ore are also entirely adequate. Although the distribution of many mineral substances may not be ideal, and annoying inadequacies of certain special materials may exist, the overall mineral resources position of the Soviet Union is unusually favorable.

Similarly, the great extent of the country means that no adverse climatic or topographic feature can be dominant. The deserts and mountainous areas, the swamps and arctic wastes, vast as they are, constitute only portions of the whole. Thus despite these inutile tracts there are sufficiently wide areas of agricultural land in the Soviet Union to feed the population reasonably well, subject to the vagaries of weather and the competence of Communist planning. High mountains and great streams with large drainage basins provide the country with enormous hydropower potentials.

In the matter of shape there is an advantage in compactness. Although the transportation system of the European portion of the U.S.S.R. is inadequate to meet the demands on it and that of the Siberian portion is far below the needs it should satisfy, the problem of a sufficient provision would be virtually insurmountable if the country were of the same size but even more elongated. Its compactness, then, is basically a unifying asset.

As with the physical aspects of the country, the large size of the population contributes significantly to Soviet success. Great numbers are necessary for the development of such a vast area. Indeed, the Soviets struggle constantly with labor shortages as measured against the things they would like to accomplish. Moreover, the many previously isolated and backward peoples are rather easily turned toward Soviet ends because of their very ignorance and lack of knowledge of any better existence or governmental system.

Of fundamentally greater importance than all the geographic factors is the unified and absolute political control exercised by the Soviet leaders. Consolidation of so vast an area into a single political unit makes possible ordered recognition of geographic units in national organization without regard for previously existing artificial boundaries resulting from historical circumstances and tribal prejudices. This is the advantage possessed by the 48 divisions of the United States organized as a federal union. Lack of such a union tends to nullify much of western Europe's enterprise. Beyond this, the Soviet totalitarian state is able to force all human activity into channels designed to derive the utmost benefit from each different geographic environment. Thus industries are systematically established where best suited to their resource base rather than allowed to develop where and when private individuals or business firms take the initiative. Further, national emphasis is placed on forcing crop production beyond natural geographic limits in order to speed the development of areas that would otherwise be neglected. Everything is planned, ruthlessly and relentlessly, to take advantage of every geographic factor that can contribute to the enhancement of national strength. Mistakes are made, but on the whole the effort has been successful.

In brief, while the Soviet Union exhibits elements of both geographic strength and weakness, the limitations are not such as will preclude its further growth as a world power.

2. FINLAND

Topography. The Republic of Finland is a small country of 150,000 square miles—midway between California and Montana in size—comprising most of the 700-mile eastern arm of the Fenno-Scandian Peninsula (Fig. 27.6). It borders on the Soviet Union on the east and southeast, the **Gulf of Finland** on the south, the **Gulf of Bothnia** on the west, Sweden on the northwest, and Norway on the north.

The topography of Finland is simple. The northern and eastern sections of the country are part of the same natural region as the Soviet Karelian district which it adjoins. The core region of the southeast is a low plain, 300 to 500 feet above sea level, composed of a thick blanket of gravel, sand, and clay deposited by the ice age continental glaciers. North of this plain ancient underlying rocks emerge to form a district of low, rounded hills rising in places to elevations of 1000 feet.

The small irregularities of the glacial blanket have made southeastern Finland a land of lakes (Fig. 27.7)—40,000 of them—of all shapes and sizes, that convert half the area to water. In some districts the land surface is restricted to long, narrow ridges winding about sinuously between the lake-filled depressions. Farther north the lakes are fewer but larger. The monotony of this landscape of low relief is considerably enlivened by the contrast between the shining waters and the dark taiga forest that extends down to the shorelines of the lakes.

Coastal Finland is a belt 20 to 80 miles wide in the west and southwest, along the Gulfs of Bothnia and Finland. Despite recent slight uplift it is still a drowned coast; the shoreline is fringed with low islands and is made irregular by many small bays and inlets.

People. The 4.2 million Finns have given

their name to the non-European Finno-Ugric languages; their original derivation is Mongoloid. The Finns are old inhabitants of their present homeland, however, and other than a tendency toward short, stocky build there is little apparent of their Asiatic origin. The present population contains a

strong Scandinavian admixture, referred to as Finnish, as opposed to pure Finns. In this group blue eyes and fair hair predominate.

Moreover, a large proportion of the

Fig. 27.6—Finland, Northern and Central Sweden. The inset compares the area of the region with an equivalent area of the United States (states in white).

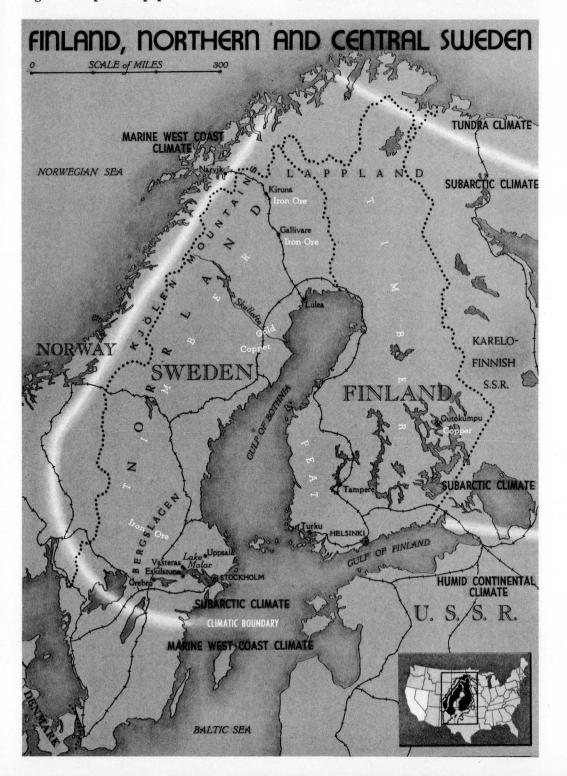

FINLAND, NORTHERN AND CENTRAL SWEDEN

SCALE of MILES

0   300

NORWEGIAN SEA

MARINE WEST COAST CLIMATE

TUNDRA CLIMATE

Narvik

L A P P L A N D

SUBARCTIC CLIMATE

Kiruna
Iron Ore

Gallivare
Iron Ore

Lulea

KARELO-
FINNISH
S.S.R.

NORWAY

SWEDEN

FINLAND

Skellefte
Gold
Copper

KJÖLEN MOUNTAINS

NORRBERLAND

GULF OF BOTHNIA

PEAT

TIMBER

Outokumpu
Copper

SUBARCTIC CLIMATE

Tampere

BERGSLAGEN

Iron Ore

Turku

HELSINKI

GULF OF FINLAND

Lake
Malar

Uppsala

Vasteras

Eskilstuna

Orebro

STOCKHOLM

HUMID CONTINENTAL
CLIMATE

U. S. S. R.

SUBARCTIC CLIMATE

CLIMATIC BOUNDARY

MARINE WEST COAST CLIMATE

DENMARK

BALTIC SEA

Fig. 27.7—Southeast Finland, "A Land of Lakes." View shows Lake Saimaa and taiga. (Courtesy, Finnish Travel and Information Bureau.)

coastal population is made up of Swedes. These total several hundred thousand and comprise the largest minority group. They are the descendants of Swedish colonists who settled on the coastland during the Middle Ages and had control of the country until the nineteenth century. Swedish is still spoken locally by about 10 percent of the population. The Swedish influence is also evident in the dominance of the Lutheran Church. Collectively the Finns are extremely literate and intelligent people. What is possibly the largest bookstore in the world is located in their capital city.

In the north of Finland are some 2500 *Lapps* (Fig. 27.8), remnants of an earlier Mongoloid invasion of that district. Through intermarriage with the Finns the Lapps are gradually disappearing as a distinctive people.

Resources. Finland's great natural resource is its **forests**, which cover 65 percent

Fig. 27.8—Finnish Lappland. General aspect of the country, glacially eroded rock knob in the foreground. (Courtesy, Finnish Travel and Information Bureau.)

of the land area. Wood is used for every conceivable purpose, even to stoke the furnaces of railroad locomotives. Railroad stations are identified by great woodpiles stacked alongside them.

Although useful minerals are present at many places in the ancient rocks of Finland their concentration in deposits of economic value is rare. The outstanding occurrence is the **copper** ore at **Outokumpu**, in the southeast part of the lake district, which is the largest copper producer in Europe (although the amount of metal recovered is insignificant in comparison with that of the large mines in the Western Hemisphere). **Peat** bogs are of widespread occurrence and are especially numerous along the Bothnian coast.

Next after the forests as a resource is **hydropower.** The "head," or drop of the water, is in most instances small, only 20 to 30 feet, but the interconnected lakes act as ideal reservoirs, so that a constant flow is available even in winter. Hydroelectric developments, although modest, are of vital significance in a country lacking coal, oil, and gas.

Economic Activities. Although extraction and utilization of the country's forest resources dominate economic activities in Finland, less than one-quarter of the population is engaged in "wood" industries (Fig 27.9). Winter is the logging season. In spring, after the ice goes out, streams are filled to their banks with logs being floated to the sawmills in the coastal district. The national importance of "wood" industries derives from the export of forest products (80 percent of total exports), by which the country is enabled to buy foreign food and manufactured imports. Besides timber, "wood" industries produce **pulp and paper, plywood, cellulose, naval stores,** and **furniture.** Finland is the world's foremost plywood exporter; a leading item is the especially valuable birch veneer.

Fig. 27.9—Sawmill and Pulp Mill at Kotka, Finland. (Courtesy, Finnish Travel and Information Bureau.)

As a consequence of the Soviet demands for reparations other manufactures have increased in importance since World War II. Even so, there are only two furnaces producing pig iron, so that the bulk of this basic material for heavy industry must be imported. Finland nevertheless has a rolling mill and manufactures heavy machinery such as locomotives and turbines, also farm machinery. Another industry of considerable importance is textiles. This, too, is based on imported raw materials and the output satisfies only a fraction of the domestic demand. Most manufacturing is concentrated in the south of the country, where the bulk of the available power is produced and where the population is chiefly concentrated.

As is typical of the subarctic climatic regions agriculture has only a minor place in the economy despite the fact that more than half the population is engaged in it. Most farms are small. Many of them are newly cleared from the original forest land, the result of a large-scale repatriation project undertaken to accommodate 35,000 families who emigrated from the territories lost to the Soviets in the Russo-Finnish War.

Three-quarters of the farm land is devoted to fodder crops, **hay** alone accounting for over half the total (Fig. 27.10). Oats, barley, wheat and potatoes are secondary field crops. There is a large livestock population (1.9 million **cattle** and 1.3 million **sheep**) based on the fodder crops. **Dairying** is important. Finland is able to supply its citizens with dairy products and meat, but despite strenuous efforts to achieve that end the country cannot quite meet the other food requirements of its population.

CITIES OF FINLAND

Name	Type	Population (1954)
Helsinki	Seaport-governmental	396,000
Turku	Seaport-educational	108,000
Tampere	Industrial	108,000

Cities. Finland is a rural country. The eight cities and towns with over 10,000 in-

Fig. 27.10—Drying Hay on Stakes, Finland. This is a regular practice in moist, cool north European regions. (Courtesy, Finnish Travel and Information Bureau.)

habitants include only one-quarter of the total population.

Helsinki is the capital as well as the commercial and cultural center of the country. It is on a peninsula surrounded by islands, in the center of the southern coast on the Gulf of Finland. The city is very attractive and clean in appearance, with many examples of modern architecture, in which the Finns are leaders. From the windows of an upper-floor room in one of its tall hotels an impressive view is had of the expanse of low-lying, granite-knob, lake, and stream-dotted landscape that is southern Finland.

Turku is an old city on the southwest coast in the center of the Swedish district. It was the former national capital of Finland and was converted to an educational center by the Swedes. It is now the site of both Swedish and Finnish universities.

Tampere is Finland's industrial capital, in the southwest of the country on the border between the lake and coastal districts. Good local hydropower resources have made it the site of most of Finland's industries other than those engaged in wood manufactures. The country's textile and heavy-machinery plants are in Tampere.

Finland as a Whole. Finland is a remarkable nation. Physically and climatically it is a poor country. Its major resource, the forest, can be exploited at no faster rate than the best conservation measures permit. Its agriculture is inadequate to the food needs of the population. Its manufacturing depends on imported raw materials and is further handicapped by limited power resources. Despite the formidable array of difficulties the Finns have, through hard work, unrelenting perseverance, and innate ability, created a sound nation and a distinctive national culture.

Finland achieved its independence following the Russian collapse in World War I. Prior to this time the country had been a Russian grand duchy. In 1940 Finland became a victim of the new Soviet imperialism in a "winter war." But it succumbed only to greatly superior military might. Aligned with Germany against the U.S.S.R. in World War II, Finland was again a loser in 1944. In consequence of this double defeat it was forced to cede to Russia its second largest city, its most important mineral resources (the nickel deposits of the north), 10 to 15 percent of its farmland, forests, forest industries, and other manufacturing, and, worst of all, one-third of its hydroelectric generating capacity. In addition the Soviets demanded large reparation payments in the form of annual deliveries of heavy manufactures. To the surprise of the rest of the world as well as the Russians, Finland made good on all demands.

As the only nation contiguous to Russia that is not a Soviet satellite, Finland politically treads a cautious but firm path. Similarly, it must keep a precarious balance in its economy between manufacturing, agriculture, and forest industries. But the free world could not have a better example of healthy democracy on the Communist doorstep. The Finns in their cold and somber land will never be a wealthy nation, but their firm determination to make the most of what they do have makes them a model for other small countries of modest means to emulate.

3. CENTRAL AND NORTHERN SWEDEN

Topography. Subarctic Sweden includes all of the country east of the Norwegian border, about four-fifths of its total area (Fig. 27.6). Most of this territory is known as **Norrland** and consists of the east slope of the ridge that forms the backbone of the Scandinavian peninsula. In the far northwest the backbone, the **Kjölen Range,** with peaks of nearly 7000 feet, is itself included. Most of the district, however, is an east-sloping plateau, between 700 and 1500 feet in elevation on the west, 300 feet on the east. The plateau is furrowed by the long, narrow valleys of a great number of east-flowing streams. Many of these valleys have lakes in their upper reaches which are the land equivalent of the fiords of Norway (see Chapter 20, p. 422) and were eroded by the ice age glacier that covered the entire country. The eastern margin of subarctic Sweden bordering on the Gulf of Bothnia is a coastal plain 20 to 30 miles wide.

In the south the Norrland plateau declines in level to the lowland of central Sweden that extends east-west across the country. Subarctic Sweden includes the northern and especially the northeastern part of this district, where it is widest.

Resources and Their Exploitation. Appropriate to the climatic classification, subarctic Sweden has great **forest** resources; more than half the land area of the country is forested. Birch predominates in the northern uplands, with pine, spruce, and a sprinkling of hardwoods elsewhere. The lumbering operations and general utilization of the resource are very similar to those of Finland. Logging is done in the winter. The spring thaw and high waters see great drives of logs down the rivers to their mouths on the Bothnian Gulf. Wood is common fuel in locomotives and steamers in the region. It is significant that most of the lumbering operations are now in second-growth forest. Conservative forestry practices, however, assure indefinite maintenance of the forestry industry at its present level.

Owing to the high altitudes of much of the Norrland district Sweden's **hydropower** resources are very large. The lakes in the upper parts of the valleys serve as reservoirs to maintain a rather constant flow in the many streams with steep descents down to the Gulf of Bothnia. Eighty percent of Sweden's hydropower resources are in Norrland, and these supply one-half of the country's electricity, with plenty of undeveloped potential remaining.

In the mineral field Sweden is the most richly endowed country of northern Europe. There are three separate mineral districts. The most important is the **Lappland** district of Sweden in the far north. There two large **iron ore** deposits, one at **Kiruna,** the other at **Gallivare,** are mined on a large scale. The ore is of high quality (60 to 70 percent iron) although it has a high phosphorus content. But as the German steel industry has been adapted to the use of such ore there is a good export market for it. The Kiruna development is especially large. It involves surface mining on two hills that are slowly being carved away in a round-the-clock operation. During the long winter night (the site is above the Arctic Circle) work goes on under lights. Because none of the Swedish ports on the Gulf of Bothnia is ice-free, the bulk of the ore is shipped over the mountains to the open Norwegian port of Narvik, on the Atlantic.

Farther south on the edge of the coastal district is the **Skellefte** mining district. Here underground bodies of complex ores are mined for **copper, arsenic, gold,** and **silver.** And on the southern margin of Norrland is the **Bergslagen** district, in which more than 500 mines are operated on an abundance of small, varied deposits. Iron, copper, lead, zinc, and selenium are all produced. The iron ores, with a lower phosphorus content, are actually superior to those of Lappland.

Other Economic Activities. In subarctic Sweden forest product industries, mining, and manufacturing are so completely dominant that agriculture is of no importance. Each of these activities is significant in certain districts, some of which overlap.

The sawmills and pulp and paper plants

are concentrated along the Bothnian coast at the mouths of the many streams of Norrland, and in the southwest, in the Bergslagen district. Sweden is the leading European pulp producer.

The country also rates as one of the major industrial nations of Europe because of its fully developed manufacturing complex, based almost entirely on hydropower. It differs in industrial activities from the other great manufacturing districts of Europe and North America, however, in that the Swedish pattern is one of small, scattered plants in rural surroundings. In addition, the Swedes have placed their emphasis on quality, not quantity.

The chief industrial district is a belt along the northern margin of the central lowlands, but many cities in southern Sweden have industrial concentrations. The Bergslagen section of the main district specializes in metallurgy. The modern Swedish **iron and steel** industry has been built on ancient beginnings from the time when charcoal was used for smelting. The vast forest resources of the area insured adequate fuel supplies. But when iron smelting using coke developed on a large scale elsewhere Sweden was outdistanced in quantity production and so wisely concentrated on quality, obtainable with the

Fig. 27.11—Stockholm, Sweden. City and part of the water front. Bridges lead to islands which are part of the city site. (Courtesy, American Swedish News Exchange, Inc.)

more painstaking charcoal technique and by using the small output of very pure Bergslagen iron ore. Today superior-quality, charcoal-smelted pig iron constitutes almost half the Swedish iron output, and superior Swedish steels (from electric furnaces) have a world-wide reputation.

In the east the emphasis is on manufacturing, with the production of such famous Swedish products as high-quality steel tools, telephone equipment, precision instruments, and silverware. Other manufacturing plants scattered throughout the central lowlands and even well down into marine west coast Sweden make machine tools, locomotives, electrical equipment, bicycles, armaments, automobiles, ball bearings, textiles, rubber goods, and chemicals.

CITIES OF SUBARCTIC SWEDEN

Name	Type	Population (1954)
Stockholm	Governmental, seaport, industrial	770,000
Örebro	Industrial	70,000
Uppsala	Educational	67,000
Vasteras	Industrial	65,000
Eskilstuna	Industrial	56,000
Lulea	Seaport-industrial	27,000

Cities. **Stockholm** (Fig. 27.11), the capital, largest city, and economic and cultural center of the country, has one of the most unusual sites of any modern city. It is astride the narrow outlet of **Lake Malar** where it drains into the Baltic Sea. As a seaport the city conducts its commerce through a maze of channels behind an offshore island screen. The city was founded on small islands in the middle of the outlet and, as it grew, spread over the neighboring islands and hills. Today the business of a large governmental and commercial city is conducted through medieval streets, across bridges, through tunnels, and up elevators connecting different parts of town—so many are the different levels and waterways that Stockholm is built on and across.

Stockholm is the center of the eastern end of the lowland industrial district and is the site of many industries. It is a clean, well-kept city with an air of prosperous activity and, like Helsinki, contains many striking examples, among which the town hall (Fig. 27.12) is outstanding, of the Scandinavian contributions to modern architecture.

Fig. 27.12—City Hall, Stockholm, Sweden. An example of Scandinavian architecture. (Courtesy, American Swedish News Exchange, Inc.)

Örebro lies in the center of an industrial district, with paper and shoe factories and railroad shops. Nearby is the Bofors armament works, which has contributed weapons to the armies of the world.

Uppsala is a university town and religious capital. It lies 45 miles northwest of Stockholm and has an air of solemnity and quiet dignity.

Lulea is the largest town of Norrland and the Baltic port for the Kiruna and Gallivare iron ore. The recent installation of an electric steel plant based on a local hydroelectric development is a departure from the traditional export of all Lappland ore.

Vasteras and **Eskilstuna** are representative of the industrial satellite towns surrounding Stockholm. Both cities are at the west end of Lake Malar, one to the north, the other to the south. Vasteras specializes in electrical equipment and Eskilstuna makes specialty steels and cutlery, rivaling Sheffield, England, for supremacy in the latter.

Sweden as a Whole

Subarctic and marine west coast (see Chapter 20, p. 425) Sweden together comprise a country of 173,000 square miles, almost equal to the combined area of Idaho and Wyoming. It is the largest country of Fenno-Scandia and is among the larger countries on the European continent. It is also the first-ranking of the northern countries in population and national strength.

The 7 million Swedes who have made their country one of the most prosperous in Europe are descendants of the prehistoric inhabitants of the area. They are Teutonic Nordics, tall, fair, and blue-eyed. The only minority of any significance is the 7000 *Lapps* who follow their own ways in the extreme north, in Swedish Lappland. The Lutheran Church is the state church.

Such homogeneity provides the country with a very different social basis from that of the United States, where diverse stocks, nationalities, and races have contributed largely to the population. There is, in Sweden, a unanimity of public opinion on national questions that would astonish the politicians of the United States. Much of the business in consumers' goods is done by coöperatives, which are strong throughout Fenno-Scandia. The large-scale enterprises are commonly state controlled. Single individuals or families are not allowed to own more agricultural land than can be well handled by the proprietor as a personal operation. In a word, Sweden is a democratic, socialized country.

Every child is afforded advancement in accordance with his talents, through compulsory primary education, vocational schooling, and opportunity to attend higher schools. Again, every person is respected in the pursuit of his occupation no matter how humble this may be. The consequence is that human relations are very pleasant; there is little evidence of strife between groups, and a spirit of mutual helpfulness prevails. It may fairly be said that Sweden is the most civilized country in the world.

The position of Sweden between the Russians and the Germans, or at least their power spheres, has fostered a strong tradition of neutrality in relation to the struggles between those two bitter enemies. This was precariously but satisfactorily maintained through two World Wars. The political problems the Swedes face are matched by others of economic nature. Sweden must import various kinds of food and many of the raw materials used in its manufacturing industries. To maintain prosperity, sales of Swedish products abroad must equal, roughly speaking, what is bought from foreign countries. Accordingly, the Swedes watch world markets closely and are ready to take advantage of all opportunities these offer. In these exchanges Sweden is far better off than many other important nations in that it has ample quantities of timber, pulpwood, and iron ore to trade for the basic products of other countries.

QUESTIONS. Explain why the Soviet Union is a "geographical phenomenon." An "economic phenomenon." Assuming a Soviet po-litical goal of world dominion, discuss the geographic features of the country in their relation to the attainment of such an end. Compare the geographic potentialities of the Soviet Union with those of the United States.

Locate Finland. Describe its topography. Describe the ethnic background of the Finns. What are the largest minority groups and where are they concentrated? Name the one great resource of Finland. Why were manufactures other than those based on local resources developed in Finland? Describe the Finnish character as exemplified by the nation's policies and activities since it achieved its independence.

Describe the general topography of subarctic Sweden. List and characterize the outstanding mineral resources of Sweden. What Swedish resources match those of Finland? Locate the concentration of the forest product industries of Sweden. What are its chief products? Explain Swedish emphasis on quality manufactures. Describe Stockholm.

Describe the social and political aspects of Sweden. Explain the geographic basis of its "neutralist" tradition. Why is Sweden so active in world trade?

CHAPTER 28

The Subarctic Climate:
North American Region

B. NORTH AMERICAN REGION

The North American region of subarctic climate extends, like the Eurasian region, as a belt all the way across the northern part of the continent. On the west it includes Alaska except its western and northern coastal districts and the coastal Panhandle extending to the south. The remainder of the North American subarctic region lies wholly within Canada and constitutes by far the greater part of that country's territory.

The North American region, unlike the European development, is narrower on the east side of the continent than on the west. This difference is due to the very strong polar influence in the east of North America, which brings polar climates down to unusually low latitudes.

The eastern portion of the subarctic region in North America presents a typically glaciated topography like that of Fenno-Scandia. The broad plains and north-flowing rivers of the central portion, in western Canada, much resemble those of western Siberia. The topography of the Alaskan portion, with its high mountains and greater relief in general, is roughly comparable to that of northeastern Siberia.

1. MIDDLE CANADA

Topography. Somewhat more than half of continental Canada (omitting the Arctic islands) is included in the subarctic region (Fig. 28.1). From east to west it includes the larger portion of almost every province: all of the island of **Newfoundland**, middle **Quebec**, northern **Ontario**, and the northern portions of **Manitoba, Saskatchewan, Alberta,** and **British Columbia.** In addition the region takes in the southwest part of the **Mackenzie Territory** and almost all of the **Yukon Territory** save for its Arctic coastland.

The eastern half of the climatic region is wholly within the geologic and topographic region known as the **Canadian shield** (Fig. 28.2). This enormous territory includes a large part of Canada in the form of a huge crescent embracing Hudson Bay in the northeastern quarter of North America between its horns. It is geologically very similar to the lake and Karelian districts of Fenno-Scandia—a region of very old rocks severely eroded by the ice age continental glaciers of North America. It is, broadly considered, a low plateau country, standing between 1000 and 1500 feet above sea level, with low, rounded hills, thin soils and bare rock exposures, many lakes, and short, swift streams on rocky beds. The plateau is highest in the east, and in general slopes gently from all sides down to the depression of Hudson Bay and the lowlands around its shores.

At its western border the shield gives way to the high plains of Alberta, 1000 feet or more in elevation, which in turn rise to the great mountain cordillera of western North America, 400 miles across from east to west. The eastern range of the cordillera is the

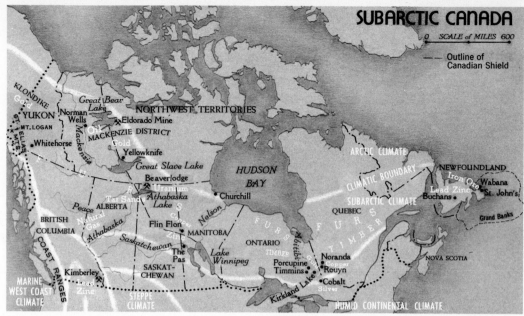

Fig. 28.1—Subarctic Canada.

Rocky Mountains; the **Coast Ranges** border the Pacific, and various local ranges occur in between. In the northeast the **Mackenzie Mountains** (Fig. 28.3), a lower range with a high peak of 8500 feet, straddle the Yukon–Northwest Territories border. The greatest elevations in Canada are reached in the **St. Elias Range**, at the Yukon-Alaska corner, where **Mount Logan** attains 19,850 feet. The island of Newfoundland off the Gulf of St. Lawrence is a plateau with an easterly slope from 2000 feet to 500 feet.

Subarctic Canada is a region of many large streams and lakes. The largest river is the **Mackenzie**, which drains the entire northwest portion of the region east of the Rockies. Within its drainage basin are three of the large lakes of western Canada, **Lake Athabaska, Great Slave Lake,** and **Great Bear Lake,** the first-named in northern Saskatchewan, the other two in the Northwest Territories. The Mackenzie, like the great rivers of Siberia, flows northward into the Arctic Ocean.

Middle Saskatchewan and Alberta are drained by the **Saskatchewan River,** which flows east from the Rockies to **Lake Winnipeg** (the other large lake of western Canada). Lake Winnipeg in turn drains northeast to Hudson Bay through the **Nelson River.**

Fig. 28.2—Canadian Shield. Air view in the Northwest Territories showing the rounded hill and lake aspect characteristic of thousands of square miles of this region. (Courtesy, Royal Canadian Air Force.)

Mineral Resources. The mineral resources of subarctic Canada belong in one or the other of two broad categories: those of the shield area in the east and center and those of the plains and mountains in the west.

The great mineral treasure house contained within the wide area of the shield is only beginning to be exploited; previously most of the exploration and development was along its southern margin. Outstanding are the metalliferous deposits. The shield is one of the world's great sources of **gold.** Enough is mined there to rank Canada second among gold-producing countries. The precious metal is found at many places across

Fig. 28.3—Mackenzie Mountains, Canada, on Yukon-Northwest Territories Border. (Courtesy, Royal Canadian Air Force.)

the entire extent of the region. The leading districts are **Porcupine** and **Kirkland Lake,** near the central Ontario-Quebec border about midway between Hudson Bay and the Great Lakes. Another important district is **Yellowknife** on the north shore of Great Slave Lake. Still farther northwest are the famous **Klondike** placer deposits of the Yukon, scene of the great Gold Rush of 1898. South of the Porcupine–Kirkland Lake dis-

tricts is the **Cobalt** district, known for its **silver.**

The association of both precious metals and base metals in the same deposits is a distinctive characteristic of many Canadian mines. Thus the **Noranda-Rouyn** district, on the Quebec side of the Ontario-Quebec border east of Kirkland Lake, is equally important for **copper** and gold. It ranks third in the country as a producer of the precious metal. The **Flin Flon** district of Manitoba, midway along the Saskatchewan border, is also a copper-**zinc**-silver-gold producer. In the lead-zinc-silver deposit at **Kimberley,** British Columbia, in the Selkirks 50 miles north of the United States border a single mine accounts for the great bulk of the Canadian output of lead, zinc, and silver. Canada is a major world producer of all three metals.

An important copper-lead-zinc deposit is worked at **Buchans,** Newfoundland. Also in that province are the easternmost **iron ore** deposits of economic significance in North America. Mines at **Wabana,** located on a small island off the northeast coast of Newfoundland proper, were the first Canadian iron ore producers. Like so much of the mining of the Maritime Provinces (see Chapter 26, p. 574), the Wabana workings follow the deposit out under the sea. With ocean transport available at the mine mouth Wabana ore can be very economically shipped to market; hence it continues to be a significant contribution to Canadian iron ore output even though recoveries elsewhere in the country are of far larger volume.

Perhaps the most important of all the metal-mining activities is the operation of the government-owned **Eldorado Mine** situated on the east shore of Great Bear Lake. This mine works one of the three truly great deposits of **uranium** and **radium** ores in the world and is the original outstanding uranium source in the Western Hemisphere. A later discovery north of Lake Athabaska, in the corner of Saskatchewan, resulted in the **Beaverlodge** uranium district, another important source of the atomic fuel.

The conventional fuel resources of subarctic Canada are mentioned only because of their future potential. Thus, the farthest north producing **petroleum** field is located at **Norman Wells,** on the middle Mackenzie River west of Great Bear Lake. It is a minor field. On the other hand, the constant expansion northward of the great oil and gas fields of Alberta offers immediate economic possibilities. The **Peace River gas** field is the largest in Canada. Eventually the entire belt from Norman Wells down to the United States border may prove to be oil and gas producing.

The extraordinary possibilities of the fuel resources of subarctic Canada are further indicated by the enormous deposits of "tar sands" along the **Athabaska River** in the region south of the lake of that name. The oil content of the surface rocks that extend over a wide area there constitutes the greatest single accumulation of petroleum in the world, larger than that of any known oil field. Unfortunately the economic extraction of the oil from these sands has so far defied technological ingenuity. But in time research will no doubt solve the problem.

Other Resources and Economic Activities. Since subarctic Canada is the taiga region of North America and since this climatic region extends over a great part of Canada, it follows that **forest** industries have a major place in the regional and national economy. The Quebec and Ontario taiga (and associated mixed forests of the humid continental region) accounts for almost two-thirds of the currently accessible Canadian timber. The chief utilization of these resources is in the production of **pulp and paper.** At one time these industries were the largest in Canada in value of output. They are still the leading export industries, especially through sale of newsprint to the United States. The Newfoundland development of the paper and pulp industry is on a smaller scale but is nevertheless of local importance. The taiga timber of the Northwest is still largely inaccessible to commerce; its present major use is as fuel.

The Canadian subarctic **fur** industry differs from that of the similar Siberian region

in its far more general reliance on fur farming. Fox, mink, and muskrat, the animals whose pelts are most in demand, are raised on so-called "ranches." Although it would appear at first thought more sensible to undertake fur farming in the more accessible and congenial districts to the south (as is indeed done in part), fur farming in the same region as the wild habitat results in better pelts, for thicker fur is induced by the colder climate.

Fishing is a major economic activity in Newfoundland. As with New England and Nova Scotia (see Chapter 26, pp. 556, 575), the limited agricultural possibilities, the many good harbors, the nearness of large markets, and, above all, the rich fishing grounds of the "banks" are factors that contribute to promote fishing enterprise. The **Grand Banks,** one of the largest of all such shallow-bottom ocean areas, lies just to the east of Newfoundland.

What agriculture exists in the subarctic region of Canada is mostly the subsistence type of frontier farming. The climatic handicaps and remoteness hinder both the procurement of supplies and the marketing of the product where anything more is attempted. The hardier grains and a little wheat are grown. Most of the barley and rye is fed to cattle and hogs. The only agriculture of even limited commercial consequence is confined to two districts: the Peace River of northwestern Alberta and the **Abitibi River** south of the **James Bay** extension of Hudson Bay. In the latter district rather good soils occur in what is known as the "great clay belt." There organized pioneer settlement has resulted in the development of dairying and general farming on a far greater scale than is normal in the subarctic region of North America.

The **hydropower** resources of subarctic Canada are large, as could be expected in view of the topographic characteristics of much of the country. Their development has progressed furthest in Quebec on the southeastern margin of the region. In only a matter of time, however, their utilization will be general throughout the region. The largest potentials occur in the Yukon and in northwestern British Columbia east of the Alaskan

Panhandle. In these districts it will be possible to reverse an entire drainage system as was done in the Kitimat project of southwestern British Columbia (see Chapter 21, p. 432), but here on an even larger scale. Utilization of this resource in the near future is probable because of evidence of large base metal deposits in the district. To date industry has been content to remain within the humid continental and marine west coast regions of Canada, based on power supplied from the subarctic region.

CITIES OF SUBARCTIC CANADA

Name	Province	Type	Population (1951)
St. John's	Newfoundland	Seaport-governmental	53,000
Timmins	Ontario	Commercial-mining	28,000
Noranda	Quebec	Mining	10,000
The Pas	Manitoba	Commercial	3,400
Whitehorse	Yukon Terr.	Commercial-governmental	2,600

Cities. Reference to the "cities" of subarctic Canada is somewhat euphemistic. The region in general is one of low population density, and collections of human habitation above the settlement or village level are rare. Nevertheless there are a few concentrations of people that function as city communities.

St. John's, the largest urban center, is quite untypical for the region. It is a seaport, the capital of Newfoundland, the headquarters of the large Newfoundland fishing fleet, and has a large fish-processing industry and several other light industries. As the easternmost seaport in North America it is, interestingly, closer to London than to New York. Because of its maritime location and other attributes it can be considered exceptional as a city development in the North American subarctic.

Timmins, although only half as large as St. John's, is still a good-sized town. It is the commercial center of the Porcupine mining district and has local pulp, paper, and lumber mills. It is on the southern border of the subarctic region very near to the economic heart of Canada and, like St. John's, is not really representative of the subarctic environment.

Noranda is the town after which the local mining district was named. Its small size and complete identification with the mining to which it owes its existence are typical of all the mining towns of the region.

The Pas, on the Saskatchewan River in western Manitoba midway along the Saskatchewan border, is a typical frontier commercial center, where the mining and fur trapping activities to the north are outfitted. It is, however, more important than most such centers, as it is the "civilized" southern terminus of a special railroad to the port of **Churchill** on Hudson Bay. The rail line was built to carry the great wheat crops of the Canadian prairies over a short land route to ocean ships at Churchill. Unfortunately, only a limited volume of traffic developed, and Churchill is hardly more than a dot on the map.

At the lower end of the population numbers scale **Whitehorse,** the capital of Yukon Territory, is representative of the typical isolated settlements of the subarctic wilderness area. As a governmental center its size is indicative of the insignificant degree of development of the territory. The Yukon Territory comprises 207,000 square miles, about twice the size of Colorado, but has a population of only about 5000 compared to Colorado's 1.3 million people.

Canada as a Whole

Canada's 3.8 million square miles make it areally the third largest country in the world, almost one-third as large again as the United States. Its population of 14 million, on the other hand, is less than that of New York State alone.

Comparisons of Canada with the Soviet Union are inevitable because of the similar locations and climates of the two countries. Both occupy the northern part of the two great land masses of the Northern Hemisphere. Both extend east to west all the way across their respective continents. Both border on the Arctic Ocean on the north. Glaciated shield areas, wide plains, and high mountains are chief topographic features common to both.

Except for the greater size of the U.S.S.R. it may be said that Canada is geographically better off than its Eurasian counterpart in the northern climates. Perhaps the most significant geographic difference is that Canada has direct access to the world's oceans from ice-free ports. On the west this advantage is partly offset by the mountain barriers inland from the coast. Canada also derives great benefits from having the United States as its neighbor on the south. Quite aside from cultural and political congeniality, Canada profits immensely from direct contact with the world's greatest center of economic activity. In view of the open border between the two countries it cannot help but share in some of the peripheral activity generated by that center. The U.S.S.R., by contrast, borders on undeveloped desert and steppe along the greater length of its southern border. This results in a drain-off rather than an infusion of economic energy.

Among Canada's geographic disadvantages as compared to the Soviet country are the greater proportion of territory within the polar climatic regions and the far smaller proportion of good agricultural land. Canada has only one large river flowing northward across arctic wastes in contrast with several such in Siberia, but this difference is more than offset by the geographical vacuum of Hudson Bay. Although practically the entire shield area drains into the bay, no advantage derives from this fact. Navigation of the bay is dangerous (see Chapter 1, p. 6) and it is ice-free only from August to October.

Canada, although chronologically as old as the United States, is clearly a young country in terms of its development. Industrialization has come slowly, for although Canada began early to exploit its rich resources, this was in the pattern of underdeveloped countries, that is, natural resources were extracted for processing and use elsewhere. With such an unbalanced economy it could not grow very fast. Even so Canada has long been underpopulated. It has not had enough people to do its pioneering work. Only in recent decades have greater numbers, new economic forces, and new technology combined overcome the climatic and locational handicaps.

The strain of World War II greatly stimulated Canadian development. The pace of industrialization was then much accelerated. Canada at the middle of the twentieth century began to achieve the balance between manufacturing, extractive industries, and agriculture that is essential for enduring national strength. This general upsurge was enormously reinforced by the post–World War II discoveries and utilization of the great oil and gas resources of the Canadian West.

But Canada is in many respects behind the Soviet Union in its development of the northern climatic regions. To be sure, Canada has three transcontinental railroads to Siberia's one, and a rail link with the northern coast. The major reason, however, why the Soviets have forged ahead of Canada in exploitation of the north lands is their earlier appreciation of the geographic potentialities of these regions. Shortly after the initiation of their regime the Soviets directed all the technological skills at their command to the conquest of these areas and the full utilization of all their resources. Soviet success in the extension of agriculture northward and colonization of the subarctic and even arctic regions shows the way for Canada. It has demonstrated—to be sure, through regimentation —that the northern wilderness can be made productive. It remains to be proved that free initiative under a democratic system can achieve the same results. Thus extension of agriculture, colonization, and exploitation of the economic mineral resources discovered since World War II confront the Canadians with tremendous tasks and the prospect of great enhancement of their material welfare.

2. Alaska

Topography and Climate. Alaska, with 571,-000 square miles of land area, is the largest single political division of the United States, equivalent to about one-fifth the extent of the 48 states (Fig. 28.4). Southern Alaska consists of a great mountain arc that curves northwest as a continuation of the Coast Ranges of the Alaska Panhandle (see Chapter 21, p. 427) and the St. Elias Range of British Columbia, then turns southwest into the long, reverse arc of the **Aleutian Islands.** In interior Alaska the St. Elias Mountains are paralleled by the **Alaska Range,** which swings southwest as the **Aleutian Range,** then constitutes the **Alaska Peninsula.** The Aleutian Islands are volcanic peaks resting on the submerged western portion of the system. The 150-mile-wide Alaska Range is

the most imposing mountain chain of North America. Many of its peaks rise over 15,000 feet and one, **Mount McKinley,** is the highest point (20,300 feet) on the continent.

On the northwest a much lower range, the **Kuskokwim Mountains,** parallels the Alaska Range. The Kuskokwim's highest peaks average only 5000 feet.

Across the northern third of Alaska runs the slightly crescentic **Brooks Range,** with peaks of over 9000 feet in the east, under 5000 feet in the west. This range effectively isolates the polar north coast of Alaska from the rest of the territory.

Between the Kuskokwims and the Alaska Range on the south and the Brooks Range on the north is the lowland and plateau country

Fig. 28.4—Alaska. The inset compares the area of Alaska (less the Panhandle) with an equivalent area of the continental United States (states in white).

of central Alaska, the drainage basin of the **Yukon River** and its tributaries. The lower Yukon flows generally westward across the country over wide, open plains.

The climate of much of Alaska is considerably milder than is commonly assumed and is, in fact, milder than the average subarctic region. Owing to Alaska's peninsular shape the maritime influence on the climate is significant throughout most of subarctic Alaska and in the coastal districts is dominant. Moreover, the warm **Japan Current** (see Chapter 18, p. 361), which bathes the southern coasts, further moderates the temperature extremes and increases precipitation. This is not to say that Alaska basks the year round in warm sunshine. Actually, the coastal lands are under cloudy, chilly skies much of the time, and the Yukon Basin lands are bitterly cold in winter. The south central and southwestern districts of Alaska, however, are warmer in winter than the north central states of the humid continental United States proper.

People. Alaska has the lowest population density of any political subdivision of the United States, in all not quite 130,000 people. Moreover, the distribution of the population is far from uniform. The bulk of the inhabitants are concentrated in the Panhandle and the south central district. Large areas of the west and north coasts are virtually uninhabited.

Most Alaskans are Americans—first, second, and third generation settlers from the continental United States. There are in addition several native groups. The Alaska Peninsula, the Aleutians, and the associated islands in the southwest are the home of some 6000 *Aleuts,* a fishing and hunting people closely related to the Eskimos of the true arctic environment. In central Alaska and the southeast are about 12,000 *Indians.* The major coastal tribe is the *Tlingits* of totem pole fame, a fishing and forest-dwelling people. Interior tribes are of the same stock as the British Columbia Indians to the southeast.

Since Alaska is still mostly wilderness country Alaskans in general manifest the so-cial attitudes characteristic of frontier places in the United States in former times. Many conventions are not rigidly observed. Informality is the keynote. Social standing and public respect depend more on personal reputation than on family background and material wealth.

Transportation. Alaskan transportation is also in the frontier stage. The total railroad mileage is 560 miles, almost all of which is in a single line running from the south central coast, across the Alaska Range, to the central interior. The line was built and is owned and operated by the federal government. There is, however, a highway net—in all, 3000 miles of roads, most of which are all-weather construction. But this system extends over only the south central and east central districts. The most significant Alaskan road is the **Alaska Highway,** constructed during the years of World War II to provide a land link across Canada between Alaska and the United States proper.

With such meager facilities for overland transport, rivers are used wherever possible. The Yukon and its chief tributaries provide the major water routes. For western Alaska and most of the Yukon Basin river travel is the only means of surface transportation in the summer. In winter the time-honored, picturesque dog sled powered by a team of huskies is still in use (Fig. 28.5).

Fig. 28.5—Dog Sled and Team of Huskies, Winter, Subarctic Alaska.

Fig. 28.6—Gold Dredge in Fairbanks District, Alaska. (Courtesy, S. C. Mosser, Jr.)

The outstanding characteristic of Alaskan transportation is air travel. The absence of other facilities offsets the expense, so that commercial air service developed earlier and faster in Alaska than in the United States proper. Alaska is still ahead of the continental United States in the extent to which airplanes are utilized. Some villages and settlements depend entirely on air service for transport of freight, express, and mail, and for passenger travel.

Mineral Resources. After fishing (see Chapter 21, p. 431) mining is the ranking industry of Alaska. The industry was closed down completely during World War II and has never fully recovered its former status. The great resource and product is **gold.** The recovery of the precious metal since the Gold Rush of 1898 has been literally hundreds of times the purchase price of Alaska. Gold is found in many places. In the south central district lode, or hard rock, deposits are the rule. Placer mining (by dredging) (Fig. 28.6) is important in the Yukon district

found at the north end of the Alaska railroad.

Platinum is another important mineral product, from deposits at **Goodnews Bay** on the southwest coast.

Good, commercial **coal** deposits are worked in the **Matanuska Valley,** in the south central coastal district, and on the north side of the Alaska Range on the rail route across the range.

Agriculture. Research indicates the possibility that Alaska may some day be able to satisfy 80 percent or more of the food requirements of a population not much greater than that of 1950. At present, however, agriculture is significant only in a few districts. The greatest deterrent to agriculture in Alaska is the fact that most of the country north of the Alaska Range is underlain by permafrost except in a few scattered local districts. The two chief agricultural centers are the Matanuska Valley and the valley of the **Tanana River,** the Yukon's largest tributary, northeast of the Alaska Range. Cash crops of potatoes and vegetables are the major products, and dairying is important in the Matanuska district.

Other Resources and Economic Activities. The taiga covers about three-fifths of the area of Alaska, with spruce, Alaska birch, aspen, larch, and cottonwood the predominant tree types. The spruce constitutes the most valuable **timber** resource and is worked with portable sawmills. The Alaska birch provides a quality hardwood for finishing and furniture. Lack of adequate access is, however, a severe handicap to full exploitation of these forest resources.

Alaska's **hydropower** potentials are not finally known. As of 1952 the indicated annual generating capacity of sites that had been investigated to date totaled more than one-tenth of total United States power production from all sources in that year. In 1955 there were, however, only four small hydroelectric developments in operation.

The possibilities of **tourism** as an Alaskan industry are only just beginning to be appreciated. But lack of accessibility is the stumbling block to their rapid realization. As better transportation facilities are slowly provided, lodging accommodations and other facilities needed for catering to tourists are making their appearance. Alaska's attractions are many and varied: In the Alaska Range, the most spectacular mountain scenery in North America; the largest valley glaciers in the world along the southeast coast; volcanoes on the Alaska Peninsula; fishing and hunting the abundant wild life; and thousands of square miles of wilderness for those who want to rough it.

CITIES OF SUBARCTIC ALASKA

Name	Type	Population (1950)
Anchorage	Commercial	11,000
Fairbanks	Mining-commercial	6,000
Seward	Seaport	2,000

Cities. **Anchorage** is the largest city in Alaska, the commercial capital of the south central district. It is at the head of a long inlet on the south coast, with such extreme range of tides that the port facilities of the city are virtually unused. Anchorage is on the Alaska Railroad but, what is now of much greater importance, is an international airport by virtue of its position on the northern air route between the United States and the Orient.

Fairbanks is the largest and, indeed, only interior city of any consequence in Alaska. It is 270 miles north of Anchorage, near the geographical center of Alaska, on the Tanana River. It is the northern terminus of both the Alaska Railroad and the Alaska Highway and is the center of the Yukon gold-dredging district.

Seward, 75 miles south of Anchorage, is the southern terminus of the Alaska Railroad, on the Gulf of Alaska. It is a year-round port known as the "Gateway to Alaska."

Alaska as a Whole. The word "Alaska" is from an Indian term meaning "The Great Land." In terms of area Alaska is unquestionably great; in terms of its resources and their development the territory's greatness is a perennial subject of debate. Some Alaskan resources have provided the basis for enduring industries; the fishing and wood-pulp industries of the Panhandle are large and important. Overall, it is equally clear that Alaska is still an undeveloped country. The argument is in regard to the pace and extent of the development possible.

In the past Alaska, in common with all nonagricultural regions, those too dry or too cold, has been practically uninhabited wasteland. As in the other subarctic areas, however, new techniques, such as air transport, and slowly developing overland accessibility are leading to expanded utilization of the kinds of resources that are available.

Aside from the coastal fisheries these are minerals, hydropower, timber, furs, and attractiveness to tourists. The continuance of gold as the leading mineral product reflects the significance of high transportation costs, which can be afforded only for precious metals. But with extension of the rail and road connections these costs will be lowered, movement of goods both inward and outward will be facilitated, and more intensive exploitation of mineral deposits will result.

The food and manufactures of the agricultural lands will be brought in to make life comfortable despite the rigors of the climate. Abundance of hydropower may serve not only to provide the amenities of urban communities but also to furnish the energy for activities such as pulp and paper making, smelting, and refining. For lesser enterprise and even for agriculture under glass tourism may provide the basis, with the products of the greenhouses used to feed the customers. In brief, increased utilization of subarctic Alaska will come from the utilization of opportunities as these slowly but progressively open up. Each accomplishment will thus afford the base for a further advance.

QUESTIONS. Describe the extent of the subarctic region of North America, and compare its broad topographic features with those of the Eurasian region. Outline the general topography of the region. What is the most notable characteristic of the region's mineral resources? Locate the major gold fields, the copper districts. Why is the ore deposit at Kimberley, British Columbia, one of the most important in North America? Locate the major source of uranium in North America. Why are the petroleum resources of subarctic Canada of more potential than actual significance? What is the significance of the Athabaska "tar sands"? What is the chief use of the forest resources of subarctic Canada? Compare the fur industry of subarctic Canada with that of the Soviet Union. Locate the chief areas of hydropower resources.

Why is St. John's untypical as a city? What type of urban development does Noranda represent? The Pas? Compare the geographical positions of Canada and the Soviet Union as these contribute to the strength and weaknesses of each country. Compare the Soviet and Canadian approaches to the utilization of their respective subarctic regions.

Describe the major topographic features of Alaska. In what respects does the subarctic climate of Alaska show untypical characteristics? Why? Describe the Alaskan population. Compare the development and relative importance of the various methods of transportation—railroad, road, waterway, and air —in Alaska.

What is the outstanding mineral product of Alaska? What is the chief handicap to agriculture? Briefly discuss Alaska as a resort area and explain the significance of tourism in its further development. What districts do Anchorage and Fairbanks serve? What is your opinion of the future of Alaska? Why?

The Polar Climates

CHAPTER 29

The Tundra and Icecap Climates

■ DEFINITION AND CAUSES OF THE POLAR CLIMATES

The polar climates begin where the taiga ends, that is, on the line where the warmest month of the year averages only 50° Fahrenheit. They are the direct effect of progressively higher latitudes in lowering average annual temperatures.

The word *tundra* is from the Finnish. Originally the term referred only to bare mountaintops, but it subsequently came to be applied to any barren area in the polar lands—and barrenness is the characteristic aspect of the tundra regions. The icecap climate exists where continuous ice sheets cover the ground—not local glaciers due to high altitude but great regional glaciers due to high latitude.

Just as deserts and steppes are differentiated on the basis of precipitation differences, so polar climates are differentiated by reason of temperature differences. The boundary between the two polar climates, tundra and icecap, is the "line" along which the warmest month of the year averages 32° F. In other words, the icecaps accumulate beyond that line because the ice, once formed, never gets a chance to melt.

■ CLIMATIC CHARACTERISTICS

GENERAL

In the polar climates both the average summer temperatures and the average for the entire year are lowest of any of the climates, and, since the cold of winter is extreme, there is a range of 75° to 80° F. or more between seasonal averages, despite the low average summer temperature. In general it is the duration of severe cold rather than the maximal lows that earmarks the polar climates. The sensible temperatures (see Chapter 6, p. 90) of the polar climates are the lowest of all because of bitter cold winds that rage on and around the icecaps, especially those of the Southern Hemisphere. Each mile per hour of wind velocity affects sensible temperatures roughly equivalent to lowering the temperature one degree Fahrenheit. Thus a temperature of minus 50° F. with a 50-mile-per-hour wind has the same effect on a human being as a temperature of minus 100° F. in still air.

Precipitation throughout the polar regions is low for the same reasons that apply in regard to the subarctic climate—namely, low absolute humidity and high air pressure. As elsewhere, however, marine influence affects precipitation in the polar regions. It tends to be higher along coastlines and decreases with distance from the sea.

TUNDRA CHARACTERISTICS

By definition, the warmest months in the tundra climate have average daytime temperatures between 32° F. and 50° F. Summer daytime temperatures will ordinarily rise into the 50's and occasionally into the 80's, but the sojourner in the tundra summer finds that it is cool. At any time during the summer frost is even more probable than in the subarctic region. Polar climate summers are cool despite the long or even 24 hours of continuous daylight because of the low angle of the sun (see Chapter 6, p. 89). Much of this diminished insolation, moreover, is reflected from the cover of ice and snow, and more is expended in partial evaporation and melting of this cover.

The tundra winter can best be described as one of constant, extreme cold. The January and February *averages* are as low as minus 40° F. For six months of the year the average monthly temperature is below zero. This is especially true where continental air from the subarctic regions moves into the tundra regions. Where the marine influence is felt the averages are higher, only minus 10° F. for the coldest months. Only three months of the winter average below zero.

Annual precipitation averages about 10 inches throughout the tundra regions, and, as in the subarctic, the warmer months have more than the cold months. The source of the precipitation is middle-latitude cyclones, and their relatively infrequent invasion of the tundra regions accounts in large part for the low figure.

Despite the low winter temperatures and no melting during that season large areas of the tundra regions have no snow cover. This is in part because of a lack of vegetation to catch and hold the snow. The strong winds drift the snow into sheltered places where it accumulates because it cannot be picked up. Some is lost by evaporation into the dry air. Thus in contrast to the subarctic, there is no continuous snow cover for overland transport by dog sled.

In brief, the tundra seasons are a long, constantly cold winter, a short, cool summer, and the virtual absence of any transition conditions that could be called spring and fall.

ICECAP CHARACTERISTICS

The icecap climate really has no summer, only a season of lesser cold. Where the continental influence is strong even the warmest month averages almost minus 10° F., and "summertime" lows in the minus 60's have been recorded. Where the marine influence is strongest the warmest months attain the upper defined limit of the climate: 32° F. or slightly lower.

The icecap winter is unbelievably severe. Month after month averages between minus 20° F. and minus 30° F., and the continental extremes are even colder. In the Antarctic fierce storms—the most violent blizzards on earth—rage for days with winds at temperatures as low as those that occur elsewhere in high-latitude regions only when calm and clear air allows maximum nighttime radiation. It may well be that the subarctic record of maximum cold is actually exceeded annually in the remote interior icecap regions, but records are understandably few.

Precipitation data are even more meager than temperature data for the icecap climate. Precipitation is, however, apparently at about the same levels as in the tundra regions. It is rather uniform throughout the year, although slightly greater during the warmest months. At first thought evaporation and loss through outflow glaciers at the edge of the icecaps would seem to be too great to be balanced by the relatively low precipitation. Apparently, however, a very slight excess of precipitation over annual loss, maintained for many thousands of years, is sufficient to bring about the build-up of icecaps.

■ REGIONAL ASPECTS

In surface appearance the tundra and icecap regions are wholly unlike. They have in common chiefly the seasonal variation of light and dark. At the poles the year is evenly divided between six months with the sun above the horizon and six months below it. On the Arctic and Antarctic circles the summer continuous sun period is at the minimal length of three months. Between these two extremes the duration of the 24-hour daylight period varies, of course, with latitude. Because of twilight, however, the polar regions everywhere have a much longer light period than dark period. In fact, during even the winter months there are many days with dawn and twilight hours sufficiently light for a newspaper to be read outdoors.

During the dark hours of the long "night" periods some light is provided by the moon and stars. In addition the *aurora* (popularly termed the "northern lights" in the Northern Hemisphere) often lights up the sky. This phenomenon of the upper atmosphere is most intensely developed near the poles. The silent auroral displays are beautiful beyond description. In the most spectacular occurrences gigantic multi-hued curtains appear to be hung across the heavens, swaying and rippling as though moved by a breeze.

The term "tundra" refers not only to the climate but also to the typical topography and vegetation of the regions of such climate (Figs. 29.1 and 29.2). Most of the tundra regions are low and flat, as is the vegetative cover. The absence of tall trees is not due solely to the low temperatures but more perhaps to the excessive evaporation under the cold air and dry winds.

Fig. 29.1—Tundra, Arctic Ocean Shores, North America in Summer. Caribou herd. (Courtesy, National Film Board of Canada.)

The tundra vegetation where the tundra adjoins the taiga is chiefly composed of stunted, scrub trees less than three feet high. Birch and ash are predominant, constituting "forests" in sheltered places. Poleward the vegetation grades into a mixture of sedges (grasslike plants), lichens, mosses, and creeping bushes. Grasses are present on the lower-latitude marine margins. At the polar edge of the tundra regions, beyond where the warmest month averages 41° F., the vegetative cover becomes discontinuous and wide patches of bare rock occur—"cold desert" conditions are there reached.

Newcomers to the tundra experience a great surprise in the abundance and brilliant colors of flowering plants present there. With virtually no spring the speed-up of the summer life cycle must be even greater than in the subarctic regions (see Chapter 27, p. 584).

The regional aspect of the icecap regions can best be described as that of a frozen world. In their central areas the surface of the icecaps is like that of a vast snow field. Near their borders the snow cover develops

undulations, and where the ice shows itself it is likely to be quite rough, with hummocks, valleys, and great cracks, or *crevasses*. These are caused by the movement of the glacier as it flows slowly outward in all directions from the center of the icecap, a spreading due to its own weight. Where the ice reaches the coast and pushes out into the sea, icebergs of

blocks to make pressure ridges house high.

The average thickness of the ice pack is only 15 feet, and in places is much less. A United States Navy expedition reported in 1952, on the other hand, that the ice at the North Pole measured thousands of feet thick. An unusual feature of the ice pack is the presence of true "floating islands" of ice.

Fig. 29.2—Tundra, North America, Winter. Reindeer with calves. (Courtesy, National Film Board of Canada.)

all sizes, from small "growlers" to gigantic blocks the size of the largest man-made structures break off and float away. The central highest areas of the icecaps are known to have ice thicknesses up to 10,000 feet.

Where extreme development of icecaps occurs the line between land and sea may become almost indistinguishable. The continent of Antarctica, for example, is partly rimmed with a floating shelf of ice that has moved off the land onto the surrounding sea. Much of the Antarctic coastline is shelf and sea ice, so that it is impossible by inspection to tell where the land ends and the sea begins. The greater part of the Arctic Ocean is also the site of an "icecap," in this instance formed almost entirely by the freezing of the ocean surface. In winter this "pack ice," as it is called, is a solid mass, but in "summer" winds and ocean currents break it up into patches of all sizes. These move about in part at random, in part as slow general drift, meanwhile colliding in grinding crashes that upend and splinter into great

These were first discovered through radar indications during United States Air Force flights over the Arctic Ocean in 1946. By 1953 two dozen or more of these ice islands had been identified. Their thickness ranges from 100 to 200 feet, and the size of the largest ones is between 200 and 300 square miles. Apparently these ice islands are relics of the ice age, broken off from the shelf ice of the arctic islands during great storms in the present century. The significance of the islands is that they provide enduring sites for the camps of scientific teams. It has been determined, for instance, that the ice pack moves at random under the influence of the wind rather than sea currents and can attain velocities of one to two miles a day.

The wild life of the polar climates is surprisingly abundant and varied. During the summer the underlying permafrost (see

Chapter 27, p. 584), which is always present in the tundra regions where there is a soil cover, gives rise to swampy conditions identical with those typical of the subarctic region (see Chapter 27, p. 585). These swamps are the breeding grounds for insect hordes, if anything even larger and more ferocious than those of the subarctic. Because of these pests winter is the season when most of the larger animal life is found in the regions, although, contrariwise, insect-devouring bird life is abundant in summer.

The typical and unique animals of the polar lands and ice are the *musk ox, reindeer* (Fig. 29.2), *caribou* (Fig. 29.1), and *polar bear* in the Northern Hemisphere, the *penguin* in the Southern Hemisphere. The musk ox is a bovine version of a shaggy dog. An outer coating of long brown hair festoons its undercoat of thick wool, a combination that enables it to withstand even the extremely low temperatures of arctic winters. The favorite diet of the musk ox is the sedge and grass of the tundra, but when necessary it can exist on tundra shrubs. The musk ox is found only on the arctic islands of Canada and in northern Greenland; it formerly ranged over all the extensive tundra region on the North American mainland but was exterminated on the continent through overhunting by the Indians and Eskimos. In this instance, remarkably, the white man was not responsible for the slaughter. Indeed, an attempt has been undertaken in northern Vermont to build up a herd of domesticated musk oxen based on five young wild animals captured in the arctic in 1954.

The reindeer is a native of Eurasia but was introduced into North America and thrives equally well in the Western Hemisphere. It is actually no longer wild, having been domesticated so long that, like the dog, it does not exist in the wild state. The reindeer is a moss- and lichen-eating animal of great value in the arctic as a source of food and clothing, and as a draft animal.

The caribou is protected against the cold of its environment by a combination of fur and thick cellular skin that acts like cork insulation. It is the only animal left in North America that exists in the great herds so common among the indigenous grazing animals of the continent before human depredations eliminated them. It ranges throughout the tundra and bordering subarctic regions in North America. Like the reindeer, which it resembles, it feeds on mosses and lichens, which it obtains in winter by shoveling away the covering snow with its broad hoofs. The occurrence of chinook winds in winter is catastrophic to caribou herds of the vicinity, for they melt the snow cover, which then freezes hard, making it impossible for the animal to dig down to the pasture plants.

The polar bear is really an animal of the icecap climate, for it spends most of its time on the arctic ice pack and in the open water between ice floes pursuing seals, the chief item of its diet. Other sea animals include whales and walruses, as well as sea birds.

On land such carnivores as the wolf and fox prey on the larger grazing animals and such smaller types as the lemming and arctic hare.

The penguins of the Southern Hemisphere have the Antarctic Continent to themselves. Although they live on land they are restricted to the coast, for their food is entirely fish. Their presence in Antarctica indicates the absence of any other large land animals. If any such existed they would almost certainly include carnivores, to which the penguins would have been such easy victims that they could not have survived.

■ UTILIZATION OF THE POLAR REGIONS

Agriculture is, as would be expected, of even less significance in the tundra than in the subarctic regions. The growing season may be as long as 70 days but is commonly under 50 days. Annual and locational variations in its length are considerable. At a few isolated outposts specialized techniques have been successful on a small scale with such crops as radishes and other hardy vegetables. As part of their intensive campaign to develop their own arctic regions the Soviets have even raised some hardy grains in the polar regions.

Nevertheless it is likely that successful agriculture in the arctic will always be on a petty scale at restricted localities.

The important polar resources are thus animal and mineral. The former is the basis of native life; the latter is the chief reason for the incursion of men from the warmer climatic regions to take up life in the polar regions.

Furs have been traditionally the most important resource of the arctic, which ranks with the subarctic regions as a source of "wild" furs and skins. The Soviet Union has gone so far as to establish fur farms on some of its remote arctic islands. **Fisheries** are likewise important, with cod, herring, and halibut the leading catches. Other marine animals such as **seals** and **whales** are significant also. The seals yield valuable furs and skins. The whales are the source of oil that has many industrial uses. They are hunted today in the antarctic seas from great "floating factory" ships that are a far cry from the old whalers of the last century.

Reindeer are a potential meat source for the populations of the middle-latitude regions. They require no extra feeding or shelter during winter, and if the tundra pastures were fully utilized they could be raised in large numbers rather cheaply. In the Soviet Union reindeer "ranching" has been developed to the point where the reindeer carcasses are utilized as completely as those of the cattle and hogs in American meat-packing plants. Some **sheep** are raised in southwest Greenland and in Iceland.

The mineral resources of the polar regions are only now becoming known. Indications are that they are large and varied. At a few places deposits of extraordinary richness or significance have been developed in advance, so to speak, of the general push into the area by modern civilization that is being brought about by the ever growing demand for mineral raw materials. As yet, however, the polar regions are not notable as sources of mineral products in comparison with those of other climatic regions.

Commerce in the arctic is currently undergoing a revolution. The airplane has made possible year-round transportation and communication. The U.S.S.R., moreover, has developed a shipping route from Europe to the Pacific coast of Asia via the Arctic Ocean. This *Northern Sea Route*, as it is called (see Chapters 25 and 27, pp. 542 and 593), carries a traffic of only a few ships a year, but its operation is indicative of the increasing economic activity in the polar regions.

■ PEOPLE OF THE POLAR REGIONS

The population of the polar regions is very small, probably only a few hundred thousand all told. Men from the middle-latitude regions have shunned the polar regions except for those few individuals who seek a hermit existence, scientists and military personnel on exploratory expeditions and manning defense posts, and those citizens of the Soviet Union who are forced to live there.

The native population is low because of the relatively small food resources, with only primitive means of obtaining them, and the constant danger to life, especially in winter, when a single mistake or moment of carelessness may prove fatal.

The three noteworthy native peoples of the polar regions are the *Eskimos* (Fig. 29.3), *Lapps* (Fig. 29.4), and *Samoyedes*—all of Mongoloid origin. The Eskimos are found in northern North America and northeastern Siberia. Of all the peoples of the earth they are the most perfectly adjusted to their environment. Their continued existence in the harshest of all climates is possible only by constant struggle and desperate ingenuity (in the absence of the products of industrial civilization). The Eskimo subsists entirely on animal food—chiefly the sea animals such as the seal, walrus, and polar bear, and in addition fish and, to a lesser extent, the caribou. Moreover, the other necessities of life are also obtained from animal sources. The Eskimo lives in skin tents (stretched over driftwood) or in driftwood huts in summer, in sod huts both in summer and winter, and occasionally and in places in snow *igloos* in the winter (Fig. 29.5). His garments are en-

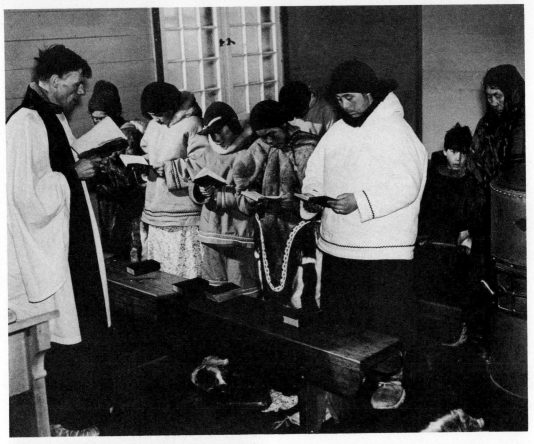

Fig. 29.3—Eskimos Attending Church Services. Baker Lake, Keewatin, Canada. (Courtesy, National Film Board of Canada.)

Fig. 29.4—Lapplander With Reindeer, Norway. (Norway Official Photo.)

tirely from animal sources, using skins for cloth and tendons for thread. Animal oils furnish fuel for lamps to light the dark winter night. Animal bones are carved into personal and household equipment.

The Eskimos are traditionally nomadic hunters and fishermen whose natural habitat is the seacoast and whose hunting and fishing grounds are the coastal sea and ice pack. In a few places the Eskimos have settled down in tiny coastal villages. In Alaska and Canada the United States and Canadian governments have imported reindeer and have rather successfully started the Eskimo on a pastoral life.

The Lapps are found in northern Russia and Fenno-Scandia (see Chapter 27, p. 588). In Norway they are a coastal people who look to the sea for their food. Farther east, in plateau and highland environments, the Lapps are entirely dependent on reindeer. As a pastoral people these Lapps are completely identified with their reindeer herds, which are pastured on the higher tundra in-

Fig. 29.5—Eskimos Building a Snow Igloo. (Courtesy, Department of Mines, Canada.)

land during the winter and along the coasts during the summer. Aside from this seasonal migration, the Lapps are constantly on the move, since the moss on which the reindeer feed grows so slowly that it cannot be grazed annually. The sparseness of the pasture, moreover, is such that each reindeer requires some five square miles of ground to sustain it. Nevertheless the Lapps have the advantage of an assured food supply whereas the Eskimos not uncommonly suffer death by starvation because of poor luck in hunting and fishing.

The Samoyedes inhabit eastern Siberia and, like the Lapps, are a reindeer-herding people. They supplement their monotonous diet from the yield of their herds with that of their hunting and fishing. They spend their winters in the taiga, where their reindeer herds are in some degree sheltered by the forest from the winter storms and where they themselves live underground in dwellings that are merely covered pits dug in the earth. In the summer the Samoyedes move north to the tundra and live in skin tents while they are following the reindeer.

■ POLAR REGIONS AND COUNTRIES

The polar climates, including the Arctic Ocean, cover more than 10 million square miles of the 197 million square miles comprising the earth's surface (Fig. 29.6). Because of their remoteness and lack of immediate significance for the inhabitants of the civilized world, the very considerable fraction of the entire area of the globe this represents is not generally realized.

The disposition of land and sea at and around the two poles is exactly opposite in the two hemispheres. In the Northern Hemisphere the pole is situated in the middle of the Arctic Ocean, which in turn is surrounded by the northern rim of the Northern Hemisphere continents and their bordering archipelagos. In the Southern Hemisphere the pole is situated in the center of the Antarctic Continent, which in turn is surrounded by an ocean zone of considerable latitudinal extent before the southern tips of the inhabited continents are reached.

As a result of this the tundra climate is well developed in the Northern Hemisphere and the icecap climate is best developed in the Southern Hemisphere. The major tundra regions are the **northern coasts of North**

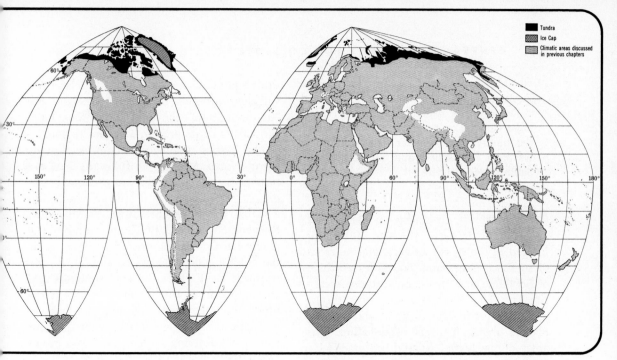

Fig. 29.6—World Distribution of Polar Climatic Regions.

America and Asia. Two-fifths of the Northern Hemisphere region is within the U.S.S.R., slightly over one-fourth is within Canada, and another fourth is in the island of Greenland.

Europe is practically all outside the tundra regions because of the North Atlantic Drift (see Chapter 19, p. 384). In Labrador on the eastern coast of North America the tundra climate extends farthest equatorward (almost to 50° latitude) because of the cold **Labrador Current** that parallels the coast of that peninsula. There is no tundra region in the Southern Hemisphere because of the absence of land in the latitudes where the temperature averages that define the tundra climate are present. Although places with the warmest month averaging 50° F. are found in the southern extremity of South America, the coldest month there is above 32° F. This region really has an extremely inclement development of the marine west coast climate.

The icecap climate is found over almost all of **Antarctica;** all of **Greenland** except the southern, eastern, and western coasts and, curiously, the far north of the island; many of the other **arctic islands;** and the higher-latitude portion of the **Arctic Ocean** (where the pack ice is impenetrable to ships even in the "summer" season).

QUESTIONS. Define and explain the terms "tundra" and "icecap." Describe the general characteristics of the two kinds of polar climates. Describe the tundra winter and summer seasons in terms of temperature. Compare with the seasons of the subarctic climate. What is the average amount of annual precipitation in the tundra climate? What is the source of most of this precipitation? Explain why large areas of the tundra regions lack a snow cover throughout the year. Compare the icecap summer and winter seasons. Explain the paradox of low precipitation and accumulation of ice.

Describe the variation of daylight and darkness with the seasons in the polar regions. Why is it rarely pitch dark in the polar region even in the middle of the winter night? Describe the vegetation of the tundra. What is an "ice shelf"? "Pack ice"? Compare the icecaps of the North and South polar regions. What is the significance of the "ice islands" of the Arctic Ocean? Describe the wild life of the polar regions. Give examples of the adaptation of the arctic animals to the extreme cold.

How is agriculture carried on in the polar regions? What are the most important polar resources? The leading products? Explain the potential importance of the reindeer to middle-latitude populations. What is the "Northern Sea Route" and what is its significance?

Why is even the native population of the polar regions small in numbers? Name the three major native peoples of the polar region and describe the general mode of life of each. Which of these peoples is most thoroughly adapted to life in the polar environment? Explain.

Describe the general distribution of the polar climates on the earth's surface. Why is the tundra climate better developed in the Northern Hemisphere and the icecap in the Southern Hemisphere?

A. ICELAND

General Aspects. Iceland is an island 40,000 square miles in area (the size of Virginia) located in the North Atlantic 200 miles east of southern Greenland, 500 miles northwest of Scotland, and the same distance west of Norway. The Arctic Circle passes through its northern tip. The island is chiefly a lava plateau about 2000 feet in elevation. Large areas of the higher ground are glacier covered (Fig. 29.7). Active volcanoes are present, and eruptions and earthquakes are not infrequent. Geysers and hot springs are numerous.

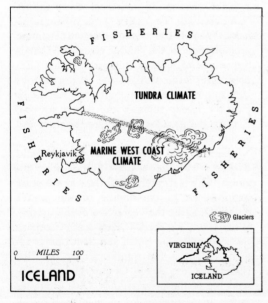

Fig. 29.7—Iceland. The inset compares the area of Iceland with that of Virginia, which is approximately equivalent.

The climate of Iceland is quite untypical of the tundra regions. The southern half of the island has a cold variety of the marine west coast climate, and the northern half has a warm variety of the tundra climate. Nevertheless, the glaciers and the presence of tun-

dra vegetation over most of the island are sufficient grounds for terming Iceland *the* "tundra nation," the only one with a large proportion of its area in a tundra region.

The marine influence and especially the warm North Atlantic Drift to the east are responsible for Iceland's warm climate. Underground heat from volcanic activity is also a factor. Its winters are 50° F. warmer than the average for the latitudes just south of the Arctic Circle. On the south and west coasts the coldest month averages only 30° F., the warmest 50° F. It is the cool summers and strong winds of the higher altitudes, combined with the fresh volcanic rock not yet decomposed into good soil, that prevent trees from thriving in Iceland. Grass grows along the coast and in the lower valleys. Elsewhere the vegetation is the typical tundra assemblage of moss, sedges, lichen, and low shrubs.

With a population of only 141,000 Iceland is sparsely inhabited. Virginia, with the same area, has 23 times as many people. The Icelanders are a highly resourceful, hardy people, descendants of Vikings from Norway who settled the island in the ninth century and who speak Icelandic, their own Scandinavian language. The culture and traditions are thus basically Scandinavian; the religion is Lutheran. Iceland is, however, no decadent outpost of civilization. Its Parliament and democratic constitution, which date from the tenth century, are the oldest existing developments of their kind. For most of its history Iceland was associated with either Norway or Denmark, but in 1944 it declared its complete independence as a republic. Despite their isolated location the Icelanders have maintained a position in the forefront of European material and intellectual progress in culture and civilization. Education is at an extraordinarily high level, as is also public health.

Resources and Economic Activities. The most important resource of Iceland is its **fisheries.** Although less than one-fifth of the population is engaged in fishing almost the entire foreign revenue of the country is derived from it. Like so many other North Atlantic coastal regions on both sides of the ocean the inhospitable hinterland and the presence of many small but good harbors led the inhabitants to concentrate on the exploitation of nearby good fishing grounds. Herring and cod are the chief catches and are exported in all forms—fresh, frozen, salted, and pickled.

Agriculture is developed only to a limited extent. Less than one percent of the land is cultivated, though a third of the population is engaged in farming. The major crop is hay; potatoes and turnips are secondary crops. Fruits and vegetables are raised for the urban markets in hothouses heated with hot-spring water.

The principal farming activity is the raising of livestock, especially **sheep, cattle,** and **horses.** The number of sheep relative to the human population is on a par with that in such great sheep countries as Uruguay and New Zealand. The livestock are fed during the winter on the harvested hay and during the summer graze in the pastures that account for some 10 percent of the total area of the country.

Iceland's only mineral resource is some low-grade peat. The country has excellent hydropower resources, more than ample for any foreseeable need. Only a small part of the potential capacity has been developed, but this has helped greatly in the establishment of small processing industries. The hot springs are another significant resource. In addition to the greenhouse use mentioned above they are used to supply heat to the homes, thus reducing the need for imported fuels for space heating.

Industrial beginnings have been in evidence since World War II. Industries ancillary to the fisheries include the production of fish oil for medicinal and other purposes and of fish meal as fertilizer. A cement plant and nitrate fertilizer plant are further indications of the manufacturing possibilities that can develop as more power becomes available. Transportation has been facilitated by construction of a network of interior roads during the American occupation of World War II.

CITY OF ICELAND

Name	Type	Population (1953)
Reykjavik	Seaport-governmental	60,000

City. **Reykjavik,** the capital, is the only city of any consequence in Iceland. On a wide bay on the southwestern corner of the island, it is the major foreign-trade center of the country and by virtue of an airport 30 miles distant (built during World War II) is of some significance in commercial air traffic over the North Atlantic. The city is handicapped both as a seaport and as an airport, however, because of the frequency of fogs and mists. Water from hot springs 11 miles distant piped to the city serves to heat most of its houses.

Iceland as a Whole. Iceland is fundamentally a poor country and is subject, moreover, to distressing natural vicissitudes. Thus an unusually stormy year not only means too much fog and drizzle to cure the summer hay crop but also a low fish catch because it prevents the fisherman from putting out to sea. In addition to such recurring misfortunes due to weather Iceland has also suffered from occasional disasters due to volcanic eruptions. That the Icelanders have not only withstood such calamities but made an intellectual mark on Western civilization indicates their competence and endurance. If Iceland were any less remote and the climate less adverse it would with Icelandic inhabitants unquestionably have had a large population and figured more prominently in European history. The major prospect for the future is the further development of the hydropower resources, which would put the Icelanders in a position to emulate the industrial accomplishments of the Swiss. The handicap of remoteness has been largely offset by airplane travel and transport. With the increasing importance of the arctic in the air age, Iceland occupies a highly strategic position.

B. THE NORTHERN COAST OF FENNO-SCANDIA

The polar region in Fenno-Scandia includes the northern coast of Norway and portions of the extreme north of Sweden and Finland. The coast is mainly a continuation of the bold fiord coast of Norway farther south. The eastern part of the area is somewhat lower and less rugged. This portion of Fenno-Scandia is **Lappland,** the home of the Lapps.

The most significant resource of the region is the desposits of **iron ore** at **Kirkenes,** in extreme northeastern Norway on the Russian border. The deposits are of good size, and although the iron content of the ore is low the objectionable impurities are also low. Hence the ore finds a ready market in Europe. The favorable location adjacent to an ice-free port (thanks to a deeply penetrating fiord and the warm waters of the North Atlantic Drift) has been of great significance in the development of this resource.

C. THE ARCTIC COAST OF THE U.S.S.R.

The tundra climate occupies the entire Arctic coast of the U.S.S.R. from the Finnish border on the west to Bering Strait on the east. The tundra strip is extremely narrow on the west, along the **Kola peninsula** (see Chapter 27, p. 588), is at its widest (200 miles or more) in western Siberia, and reaches farthest south (below 60° latitude) in the Kamchatka peninsula.

East of the Kola peninsula and the White Sea is the northeastern portion of the Russian plain, the basin of the **Pechora River.** East of the Pechora Basin are the northernmost **Urals,** which, beyond a narrow strait, reappear as two long, narrow, banana-shaped islands called **Novaya Zemlya** ("New Land"). The water gap separating them from the mainland is a highly important link in the Northern Sea Route.

East of the Urals the West Siberian Plain is encountered. It is here deeply penetrated by the **Gulf of Ob,** into whose southern end the Ob River empties. Still farther east the mainland bulges north in the wide **Taimyr peninsula.** The small archipelago that projects north from the peninsula reaches above 80° latitude and is the northernmost extension of Asia. The peninsula and archipelago have a somewhat higher elevation than the lowlands of western Siberia.

Still farther east is the delta of the **Lena River;** then comes the coastal plain of northeast Siberia. The extreme eastern tip of Asia, the **Shukotski peninsula,** is mountainous, forbidding, and virtually uninhabited. The coastal plain here is very narrow.

The resources and activities of the arctic region of the Soviet Union are in the main those described as typical of the region. Human enterprise is, in general, at a low ebb, localized and relatively unimportant. There are some exceptions, however.

The most important one is the development of the **coal** deposits of the upper Pechora Basin, reported to be equal to those of the Donbas (see Chapter 22, p. 457). The coal includes beds of good heating quality as well as excellent coking coal. This fuel source is one of growing importance to northern Russia, since it serves the heating and industrial needs of the Leningrad district and the northern Ural industries.

A second mining district in the tundra country is at **Noril'sk,** east of the mouth of the Yenisei. Here **nickel, copper, platinum,** and **coal** are all mined. A 60-mile narrow-gauge railroad connects the mines with a small river port on the Yenisei; the ores are processed at the mines.

No other outstanding mineral resources occur in the arctic region of the Soviet Union. Local coals are, however, found along the coast in eastern and northeastern Siberia, and there is minor oil production in both the Pechora and Noril'sk districts.

CITY OF THE ARCTIC REGION IN THE U.S.S.R.

Name	Type	Population (1950)
Vorkuta	Mining	30,000

Vorkuta is the largest and indeed only city of any size in the entire region. It is the center of the Pechora coal district and the terminus of a spur built from the Leningrad rail net.

Other communities which, though small, have geographic significance are the way stations along the Northern Sea Route: **Dickson,** on the northwest corner of the Taimyr peninsula; **Nordvik,** on the coast east of the Taimyr peninsula; and **Anadyr,** on the east coast of Siberia south of the Shukotski peninsula.

D. ARCTIC NORTH AMERICA

In Alaska the tundra region extends south along the western coast to include the **Seward Peninsula** and the delta of the **Yukon River** (Fig. 28.4). Its development along the Arctic Ocean coast consists of the northern slope of the **Brooks Range** and the coastal plain between the mountain base and the sea. The total tundra area of Alaska is on the order of 200,000 square miles, or about one-third of the total area of the territory.

In Canada the tundra region is restricted to a narrow coastal strip in the west but broadens southward over inland country almost to the mouth of the St. Lawrence in the east. The arctic archipelago of Canada consists of low-lying islands; the northeastern corner of mainland North America is part of the Canadian shield (see Chapter 28, p. 605). Most of this is within the political division of Canada known as Labrador. It is a country of low mountains and typically glaciated topography. Small glaciers are still present in the highest mountains along the east coast.

The mineral resources of the North American arctic region are varied. Known occurrences give indications of discoveries to come, and at least one mineral area acquired prime importance in the decade of the 1950's.

In the far west the Seward Peninsula of Alaska is the site of important **gold** mining based on placer deposits. In certain localities even the beaches of the seacoast are profitably exploited. The Arctic coast of Alaska is of potential value as a petroleum source.

Coal occurs along the coast both east and west of the Mackenzie delta, and especially throughout the northern islands of the arctic archipelago. Because of its remoteness this coal has no present commercial value, but many explorers have found the deposits most convenient as a source of abundant fuel in a frigid land.

The total value and significance of all these resources is dwarfed, however, by the **iron ore** deposits of southwestern Labrador and northeastern Quebec. Here a new Mesabi (see Chapter 26, p. 568) was discovered after World War II. A great belt of iron ore deposits was found to run from **Ungava Bay** in the far northeast corner of Quebec down through the southwest projection of Labrador. The southwest region was developed first. In that district alone hundreds of millions of tons of ore higher in grade than that now obtainable from the Mesabi district were brought into production. A 365-mile railroad was built from the mines to a port on the St. Lawrence River (Fig. 29.8). In 1954 the first cargo of the ore was shipped to the great steelworks located in Philadelphia. It is probable that the commercial and strategic significance of this great iron deposit was the largest single factor in bringing about United States participation in the development of the St. Lawrence Seaway.

Development of the northern portion of the district around Ungava Bay was begun later. Its significance lies mainly in its nearness to Europe and the relatively easy ocean route for its transport. All in all, this iron ore province is without question the greatest known mineral resource of the arctic regions.

E. GREENLAND AND SVALBARD

Greenland, the world's largest island (see Chapter 1, p. 11), is occupied by an icecap which extends over 85 percent of its area. The interior topography consists of two ice domes, separated by a lower saddle, the whole rimmed by mountains on both east and west. The highest altitudes of the domes are around 11,000 feet; the level of the un-

Fig. 29.8—Opening Railway Route to Iron Ore Deposits of Labrador. Here the roadbed has been opened to the northern edge of the taiga country. (Courtesy, National Film Board of Canada.)

derlying land is unknown, but by sonic soundings the ice thickness is known to be as great as 8000 feet. Great outlet glaciers spill through gaps in the mountains into coastal fiords, calving icebergs at their sea ends by the thousands. Along the border of the ice-cap peaks of the mountains stick up through the ice as "land islands" known as *nunataks* (Fig. 29.9).

Greenland's known mineral resources are small, but access to bedrock is, of course, restricted to the ice-free coastal tundra rim. The island has long been known as the world's only source of *cryolite*, a mineral used in the smelting of aluminum. Depletion of the deposit and development of synthetic cryolite has greatly reduced the importance of this resource. A lead deposit was developed in the early 1950's at **Mesters Vig** on

Fig. 29.9—Nunataks Projecting Through the Inland Icecap of Axel Heiberg Island (West of Ellesmere Island), Canadian Arctic. (Courtesy, Department of Mines, Canada.)

the east central coast and is now the site of the major mineral exploitation on the island.

About 300 miles east of Greenland and 350 miles north of the north tip of Fenno-Scandia is the Norwegian possession **Svalbard,** better known to the English-speaking world as **Spitzbergen** ("Pointed Mountains"). Here, at a latitude of almost 80°, is the northernmost mining camp of the world, for Spitzbergen has sizable **coal** deposits that are of great importance to coal-poor Norway. Year-round operations are carried on

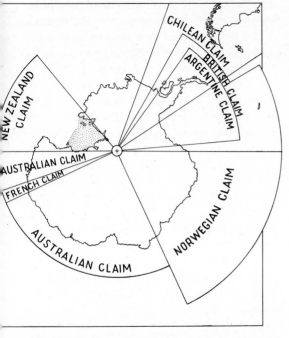

Fig. 29.10—National Claims in Antarctica. Note the claim by three countries on the sector immediately south of South America. The United States has no claims on the continent and recognizes none of other nations.

with the climatic blessing of the North Atlantic Drift, but so barren and isolated is the site that it is almost like working on another planet. Only radio, and electric light and power make living through the long arctic night in the desolate environment of tundra and icecap tolerable. Even so there is a great turnover in the mine personnel.

F. ANTARCTICA

Antarctica, the world's only uninhabited continent, is 5.4 million square miles in area,

or almost twice the size of the continental United States. It is the site of the largest icecap, which covers the entire continent save for a few comparatively small areas along the coast. Little is known of the overall topography, but the basic features are a plateau with many interior and bordering mountain ranges.

Antarctica also enjoys the distinction of being the only area of the earth's surface that is not a nation, part of a nation, or a national possession. Many nations have laid claim to portions of the continent, so that on a map it looks like a pie cut into unequal and overlapping pieces (Fig. 29.10). For many years this claim-staking was not much more than an idle diplomatic game, but in the years since World War II Antarctica has taken on a new strategic significance.

There may be coal deposits of considerable size in Antarctica and there are indications of many metallic ores in the parts of the mountains not buried under ice.

■ THE POLAR REGIONS AS A WHOLE

Certain generalizations have traditionally been made concerning the polar regions: They are of little significance because of their forbidding climates. They have barely sustained their small indigenous populations and completely lack the resources necessary to support any population at the standard of living of modern industrial civilization. They are thus of little value for the future except as isolated occurrences of mineral or animal wealth of sufficient size to warrant local extension of civilized activities into these regions may be discovered.

It must be recognized, however, that the polar regions are acquiring increasing significance for world affairs. Owing to the depletion of immediately accessible natural resources, especially of minerals, and the consequent increased value of remote, high-quality supplies, there have been notable thrusts of modern activities into the high-latitude regions during and since World War II. At the same time there has been an accelerated development of techniques for comfortable high-latitude existence and for efficient conduct of modern industrial enterprises. Discoveries already made and results already achieved are the incentive that prompts further search. Perhaps the current Soviet efforts to develop an economically sound high-latitude agriculture may demonstrate the error of traditional beliefs that economical crop production in the polar regions is impossible.

With the establishment of the air age the Northern Hemisphere polar regions acquired a new significance for the world. The disposition of the land masses around the Arctic Ocean is such that the shortest air distance between many of the important cities of North America and Eurasia is over the polar seas. In the 1930's an air flight into the polar region was an adventurous undertaking. In 1955 a commercial route between Scandinavia and Los Angeles was being operated via Greenland.

The travel and transport significance of polar overseas flight is, however, far outweighed by the strategic significance. The shortest direct route for an air attack on the New or Old World, as the track of intercontinental guided or ballistic missiles, is across the Arctic Ocean. By 1955 daily military flights within the arctic region and even across the pole had become routine. Permanent military bases equipped to provide the comforts of civilization now exist where 20 years earlier exploratory land and sea expeditions found it difficult merely to reach the polar sites, let alone establish residence there.

Although Antarctica does not have the air age significance of the Arctic Ocean, the focal strategic position of the continent on a global basis has led the great nations to reappraise its import. As a consequence territorial claims are repeated in shriller tones than heretofore, and an uneasy *status quo* is maintained through the unvoiced but nevertheless mutually understood determination that no one shall take any positive steps to enforce such a claim.

What, then, will be the future of the polar regions? Aside from a continual acceleration in the tempo of their exploitation, based on existing patterns, there are two fanciful but nonetheless plausible potentialities. The first involves the possibility of utilizing atomic energy in these regions. Atomic energy may permit the application of power on a large scale at remote sites far more cheaply than is possible by any other means. Thus the establishment and maintenance of mining operations under the most forbidding climatic conditions would be made feasible, and the mineral development of the polar regions would be enormously accelerated.

The second possibility derives from a climatic change that is apparently occurring in the arctic. An impressive body of evidence has been accumulating to the effect that the entire arctic is becoming warmer at a slow but perceptible rate. Thus the timber line is observed to be creeping northward; fish and seals are migrating farther north; growing seasons are becoming longer in high-latitude localities. Climatologists are not in agreement as to the extent or future course of this phenomenon, but it is clear that if the present trend continues there should be important geographic changes within the arctic during the coming decades. Over the long term the rise in temperature could lead to the restriction of polar climates to relic areas.

QUESTIONS. Locate Iceland and describe its general topography. In what respects is its climate untypical of the tundra regions? Why? Describe the Icelanders' political and cultural background. Why is their cultural status described as having been achieved "despite" their economic position? What is the most important resource and economic activity in Iceland? What unusual natural resource is highly important? Why is the weather extraordinarily important in the lives of the Icelanders?

Name the major resource and product of the tundra region of Fenno-Scandia. What are the major topographic features of the tundra region of the Soviet Union? Name the major resources of the region and locate their occurrence.

Describe the chief topographic aspects of

the tundra regions of Alaska and Canada. What is the outstanding mineral resource of the Alaskan region? What interest does the United States Navy have in the Arctic coastal district of Alaska? What is the only known significant mineral resource of the arctic archipelago to date? Name the outstanding mineral resource of the entire polar regions and locate its occurrence. Explain why it is unquestionably the most important resource so far discovered within the regions.

Describe the general topography of Greenland. What is a "nunatak"? What is the name and character of the farthest north permanent establishment on earth? Locate Spitzbergen and explain its significance. What is the basic topography of Antarctica? To what country does it belong?

Describe the traditional characterization of the polar regions and explain why and in what ways it currently requires modification. Discuss the future of the polar regions.

CHAPTER 30

Highland Countries

■ INTRODUCTION

The discussion of climatic types is concluded with consideration of the polar climates. There remain, however, regions in all parts of the world that, because of a single factor —*altitude*—do not fall within any of the categories (see Fig. 29.6). In previous chapters it was noted that mountain slopes were divided into different agricultural "zones" in accordance with elevation above sea level. The main reason for this zonal distribution is decrease in temperature with altitude: 3.3° F. per 1000-foot rise. A contributing factor is the thinner, clearer air found at the higher elevations. In mountain regions the sun's rays are brighter and include more ultraviolet radiation; at night these tracts experience a greater heat loss than low-level lands in the same latitude (see Chapter 6, p. 93). Another factor in this distribution of orographic rainfall. In general the higher the altitude the more the moisture of passing winds will be precipitated as they rise over the mountain barrier. (There is, however, usually a belt of maximal precipitation somewhere below the summit levels.) Thus precipitation as well as temperature has a vertical zoning.

These "zones" are actually climatic regions, areally so compressed on the mountain slopes that a small territory on a map may have several distinctive climates. Moreover, in the middle and high latitudes the distinction between north- and south-facing slopes is very marked. This "exposure" factor, involving the unequal distribution of light and heat during the day, season, and year, is often so strong as to obscure the altitude effect.

Technically, therefore, all the world's major mountain systems are regions of unclassifiable climate because of the multiplicity of small climatic regions they present. In the foregoing regional survey of the world the highland areas were usually included within neighboring or surrounding climatic regions. This was done in the interests of simplicity of treatment and on the ground that the mountain climatic zoning ordinarily was of no great significance in the general geography of the region or country.

In a few instances, however, countries lie wholly within major mountain areas or are so generally identified with their mountainous portions as to be termed highland countries. Their mountains, in other words, are the dominant geographic circumstance. Such countries are found on every inhabited continent save North America. They are: **Tibet, Bolivia, Switzerland,** and **Ethiopia.**[1]

A. TIBET

Topography. The country of Tibet lies north of the Indian subcontinent, with the state of Kashmir on the west, China on the east, and Sinkiang on the north (Fig. 30.1). It is territorially a large country, 460,000 square miles in area, about equal to the Pacific coast states plus Montana. Along its southern

[1] The significance of mountains as an environment for human occupance was discussed in Chapter 2. The reader will find it helpful in this chapter to refer to that discussion.

TIBET

SCALE of MILES 300

Road ·····Railroad

SINKIANG

KUNLUN MOUNTAINS

TSINGHAI

CHANG TANG

TIBET

STEPPE CLIMATE

HIGHLAND CLIMATE

GREAT

Lhasa

Shigatse

Tsangpo   Gyangtse   (Brahmaputra)

NEPAL   HIMALAYAS

INDIA   BHUTAN

EAST PAKISTAN

Fig. 30.1—Tibet. The inset compares the area of Tibet with an equivalent area of the United States (states in white).

is a large area of jumbled mountains and plateau basins that covers three-quarters of the country. Basin floors in **Chang Tang,** as the region is called, average 16,000 feet in elevation, and the mountains there also have 20,000-foot peaks. The plateau basins are dotted with hundreds of lakes of all sizes, both fresh water and salt. The largest of these lakes covers 1000 square miles; among them are the world's highest bodies of water.

South of the Chang Tang, between it and the Himalayas, is a great valley extending for 1300 miles east-west across southern Tibet. This is the valley of the **Tsangpo** ("Large River"). Actually it is the upper course of the Brahmaputra before it rounds the Himalayas and crosses India and East Pakistan to the Bay of Burma. The river begins at 17,000 feet in the west and leaves

Fig. 30.2—Mount Everest, Tibet-Nepal. North face of the peak from seven miles distant. (Wide World Photos.)

border there are two small buffer states, the tribal kingdoms of **Nepal** and **Bhutan,** the size of Wisconsin, and New Hampshire plus Vermont, respectively.

Tibet is the acme of highland countries. Although it is often termed "the roof of the world" this phrase does not sufficiently convey an impression of the awesome altitudes that are characteristic of Tibet and its borderlands. Along its southern border is the 20,000-foot crest line of the snow-mantled **Great Himalayas,** which contain most of the world's highest peaks. **Mount Everest** (Fig. 30.2), at 29,002 feet altitude, the highest point on earth, is on the Tibet-Nepal border. All told, 15 of the world's 20 highest peaks are in the Himalayas.

In the west the **Karakoram** range extends westward from Tibet. These mountains are almost as high as the Himalayas and contain the second highest peak in the world. They are even more completely snow covered than the Himalayas. On the north is the 1500-mile **Kunlun** range, another collection of 20,000-foot peaks with several among the first twenty.

Extending south from the Kunlun range

Tibet at 6000 feet in the east, just about the lowest altitude in the country.

The eastern border region of Tibet is the headwater region of a number of Asia's great rivers—the **Irrawaddy, Salween, Mekong,** and **Yangtze** in that order east and north from the Brahmaputra. These rivers flow from the highlands through such narrow valleys or great gorges as to make overland communication impossible through the district they traverse.

In the west the **Sutlej** and **Indus** rivers rise in Tibet and leave the country by cutting across the mountain rim in even more stupendous chasms. These mountain courses are the greatest canyons on earth, three times as deep as that of the Grand Canyon of the Colorado, and with sheer sides for most of the depth!

Climate. Most of Tibet is characterized by extremes of cold and aridity. The Chang Tang is a barren cold desert, with an annual precipitation of only a few inches—a place where almost nothing grows and few humans live. In winter frigid winds make the subzero cold even more intense. The Tsangpo valley in the south is much more habitable. It has a rainfall of over 15 inches (mostly in the summer) and a humid continental climate. Temperatures range from over 100° F. in the summer to below zero in winter.

People. The estimated population of 1.5 million is concentrated in the south, along the Tsangpo valley. The Tibetans' ethnic background has not been fully worked out, but they are apparently related to the Burmese and southern Chinese.

The outstanding social characteristic of Tibet is its political organization as a theocratic state. The country is the stronghold of lama Buddhism. The political head of the state as well as the religious chief is the *Dalai Lama,* considered to be the reincarnation of a Buddhist deity. Religion affects every aspect of Tibetan life. A third or more of the male population are monks or "lamas" housed in huge monasteries, one of which may harbor as many as 10,000 lamas. The citizen's daily activities are strictly regulated by religion; exposed surfaces of every kind are commonly covered with religious inscriptions; prayers are offered in countless numbers by the turning of inscribed wheels and the fluttering of lettered flags. Yet along with this "mechanization" of religion is a cultivation of the mystical and an exploration of the mind and will that have produced results incomprehensible and even frightening to Occidentals.

In addition to the lama group there is a noble class. The nobles and the monasteries control most if not all the land of the country. The aristocracy operate feudal estates with completely subservient peasant workers. The Chang Tang is occupied by scattered nomad herdsmen.

Mores in Tibet are exotic in other respects as well. Thus women occupy a place in the conduct of affairs unusually prominent for an Asian country. Monogamy, polygamy, and polyandry (multiple husbands) are all common practices—polyandry surprisingly in view of the shortage of marriageable males because of high proportion of celibate lamas.

Nevertheless Tibetans are a happy, friendly people, with a strong concern for ceremony and etiquette. They are also numbered among the world's dirtiest people. It has been reasoned that only the antiseptic effect of the severe climate sufficiently inhibits bacterial and germicidal infections to save the Tibetans from the decimating mortality that should follow from their living habits.

The national drink of Tibet is tea, prepared and served in a manner again characteristically bizarre. Cheap Chinese "brick tea" containing twigs and stems is chiefly used. After an initial brewing in the ordinary manner the liquid tea is churned with rancid yak butter, salt, and natural soda scraped from ground accumulations that occur throughout the country. Yak dung may be added for flavor. Tibetans daily consume dozens of cups of this foul-smelling, oily concoction.

Economic Activities. Aside from the time and energy spent on religious ceremonies and administration the chief Tibetan activities are in agriculture and stock raising. There is plenty of arable land, but most of the country is too arid and cold for crop raising. Even so, agriculture could be expanded if manpower could be diverted from the monasteries.

Barley is the chief crop, cultivated on lands with altitudes up to 15,000 feet. Vegetables are mainly limited to cabbages and turnips. Potatoes are well suited to the agricultural conditions but are unpopular. At the lowest levels there is some irrigation, and wheat and fruits are raised.

The plateaus, sparsely covered with coarse grass, are devoted to stock raising. **Sheep** and **yaks** are the chief animals. The yak is a native bovine-like animal with long, thick hair, well adapted to the climatic rigors. It is used both for meat and as a dairy animal; it and the mule are the common beasts of burden.

Home or handicraft industries are the principal "industrial" activities in Tibet. Carpets and metal articles are produced. The monasteries operate paper mills using hand processes. All in all, the standard of living in Tibet is surprisingly high considering the paucity of resources. The extent of the mineral resources, if any, remains unknown.

CITIES OF TIBET

Name	Type	Population (1947)
Lhasa	Religious, governmental, commercial	20,000
Shigatse	Commercial	20,000
Gyangtse	Commercial	11,000

Cities. **Lhasa** resembles Rome and Mecca in that it is the great shrine city and site of the administrative center of a religion. And, like Mecca, it has been world famous as a "forbidden city" to foreigners and nonbelievers. Its setting, however, is strictly Tibetan—at an altitude of 11,800 feet on the banks of a tributary of the Tsangpo. It is also typically Tibetan in its extraordinary filthiness. The street pavements are centuries-old, packed-down accumulations of garbage

and other house refuse, built up as the result of the common practice of throwing everything out the window.

Of far greater importance than the city itself is the Buddhist equivalent of the Vatican in Rome—the *Potala,* one of the world's most remarkable buildings. It is located on a 700-foot hill a mile distant from Lhasa. In the Potala the palace of the Dalai Lama, the offices of the Tibetan government, scores of temples, shrines, and monasteries are all housed in one great building, 400 feet high and 1200 feet long, that rises clifflike on the hilltop.

The only other cities in Tibet are **Shigatse,** 130 miles west of Lhasa, and **Gyangtse,** 60 miles south of Shigatse. Shigatse is the seat of "government" of another important lama, subordinate both spiritually and temporally to the Dalai Lama. Its altitude is 12,800 feet. Gyangtse is in the center of a productive agricultural district and is the official commercial center for trade with India. Few foreigners have been allowed in Tibet beyond Gyangtse.

Tibet as a Whole. Tibet has probably been the subject of more romantic speculation than any other country in the modern world. The unique society, curious customs, and esoteric religion would themselves suffice to excite the curiosity and wonder of other peoples. Tibet's remoteness and isolation serve to preserve the aura of mystery which envelopes the country. No other country is physically so inaccessible, and the Tibetan policy of turning back almost all who reach its borders heightens the effect.

Although Tibet, by Western standards, is a backward, undeveloped country, the Tibetans have evolved what is to them a remarkably satisfactory way of life, one fitted for existence in their harsh environment. The lama government early recognized the political advantage of their buffer-state position between British India on the south and the Russian Empire on the north. Although conventionally listed as the westernmost extension of China, Tibet had in fact long been so independent that its rulers could maintain a policy of isolation from all the powers in that part of Asia, including China.

Developments since World War II have brought about a radical change in Tibet's position and status. India became independent, Soviet activity and expansion on the north increased, and China became a Communist state. Although the exact course of subsequent events is confused, Tibet by degrees has been brought again into the sphere of Chinese influence, that of a Communist-dominated China. It will probably never reacquire its former status, for the Chinese have built new motor roads into the country. These roads, connecting Lhasa with western China, were pushed through to completion despite fearsome topographic obstacles and at the cost of tens of thousands of construction workers' lives. For the rest of Asia the new relationship may have profound significance. It permits Communist militarism to look down on the Indian plains from behind the Himalayan ramparts.

B. BOLIVIA

Topography. Like Tibet, Bolivia is landlocked and isolated. It lies in the heart of South America, hemmed in by Chile and Peru on the west, Brazil on the north and east, Paraguay and Argentina on the south (Fig. 30.3). Although irregular in shape it is a compact country of over 400,000 square miles (about equal to the combined areas of Colorado, Utah, Arizona, and New México). Bolivia differs from Tibet as a highland country in that it is not wholly identified with high-altitude regions. More than three-fifths of its extent is lowland; indeed, Bolivia is remarkable for its topographic diversity. Its climatic diversity is equally great. In this respect altitude is the dominating factor, for the range of climates in Bolivia is almost entirely governed by altitude.

The Andean highland regions are in the western part of the country. The **Andes** themselves in these latitudes consist of two parallel ranges. The western range is known as the **Cordillera Occidental;** along its summits runs the Chilean border. The eastern chain, the **Cordillera Real,** extends north from Argentina into the center of the coun-

try, then turns northwest into Peru. Although the highest of the Andes peaks are not in Bolivia several in the country rise above 21,000 feet, and the ranges average about 16,000 feet along their crest lines.

Between the two ranges is a high plateau, the **Altiplano** (Fig. 30.4) (see Chapter 23, p. 499). The Altiplano is also present in Andean countries north of Bolivia but attains its fullest development here with a width of 80 to 100 miles. The Bolivian Altiplano averages 13,000 feet in altitude and is the center of population despite its height and its almost complete unsuitability for agriculture.

Many accounts of the injurious effects of altitude on human physiology incurred by living on the Altiplano exaggerate the danger. It is true that newcomers, especially those who descend from the pressurized cabins of commercial air liners, have an uncomfortable and unpleasant time before they get acclimated to the thin air. Only the native inhabitants of the Altiplano, moreover, are capable of prolonged physical effort without suffering from exhaustion.

Climatically the Altiplano is distinctly inhospitable. It has a warm season from November to March, when the days are comfortable but temperatures do not reach the degree of heat experienced during Tibetan summers. The rest of the year and every night in all seasons, however, are unpleasantly cold. It seems impossible to keep really warm during the nights because cold, piercing winds then blow regularly. The middle months of the warm season are rainy, but as the water rapidly drains down through the loose soil (the Altiplano is a filled-in intermontane valley) nothing grows except shrubs and some coarse grass. Newcomers to the region find the absence of green vegetation a particularly depressing feature of the landscape.

What passes for agriculture consists of growing scant crops of potatoes and barley, together with a local millet. Most of the grassy land is used for the pasture of **llamas** and **alpacas,** two indigenous high-altitude animals, and some **sheep.** The llama is used as a beast of burden and also supplies wool

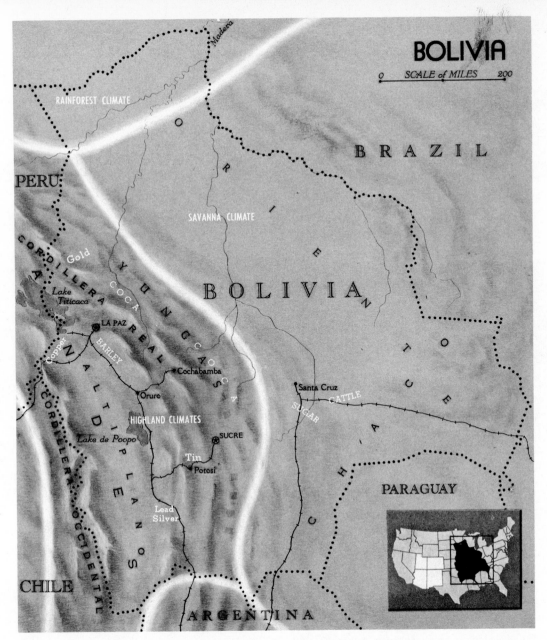

BOLIVIA

0   SCALE of MILES   200

RAINFOREST CLIMATE

PERU

BRAZIL

SAVANNA CLIMATE

O R I E N T E

B O L I V I A

Gold

Lake Titicaca

COPPER

CORDILLERA

LA PAZ

BARLEY

YUNGAS

COCA

REAL

OCCIDENTAL

Cochabamba

Oruro

HIGHLAND CLIMATES

Santa Cruz

CATTLE

SUGAR

C H A C O

Lake de Poopo

A L T I P L A N O S

SUCRE

Tin

Potosi

Lead Silver

CORDILLERA

PARAGUAY

CHILE

A R G E N T I N A

Fig. 30.3—Bolivia. The inset compares the area of Bolivia with an equivalent area of the United States (states in white).

and leather, the alpaca is raised mostly for its wool, to a lesser extent for its meat.

Two large lakes occur on the Altiplano. In the west center of the region on the Peruvian border is **Lake Titicaca,** 3500 square miles in area, at an altitude of 12,500 feet. It is drained by a small stream along the Altiplano southeast to **Lake Poopo,** a salt lake some 1000 square miles in extent. The moderating influence of Lake Titicaca greatly enhances agricultural yields along its shores, and the largest population concentra-

tion of the country resides in these districts. The southern part of the Altiplano is desert.

The eastern flank of the Andes is the second of the distinctive environments of Bolivia. Here the situation is somewhat like that in eastern Tibet—large streams dropping down from great heights through large valleys and steep-sided gorges. This valley country, or **Yungas** district, as it is called, has a semitropical climate at altitudes between 6000 and 10,000 feet. The average annual temperature is 60° F. or higher and in general this belt is the most healthful and agriculturally productive part of Bolivia.

Rainfall is directly related to the altitude.

Fig. 30.4—Indians on the Altiplano, Bolivia. (Courtesy, Bolivian Embassy.)

At the heads of the valleys at 10,000 to 15,000 feet precipitation is not only great but almost constant. It occurs in the form of persistent mists occasioned by the orographic rise of east winds hitting the Andes mountain barrier. Here isolated farming communities remained unknown, even to the Bolivian government, until their discovery when commerical air-line flights passed over them!

At lower levels agriculture becomes subtropical—in fact, the natural vegetation is really a highland jungle. Citrus fruits and others such as bananas and avocados grow well, but little commercial advantage can be

taken of the fertility owing to the almost total absence of transportation facilities.

An exception, however, is the concentration of effort on the production of **coca.** Chewing coca leaves is the Bolivian national vice. It is a more sinister practice than coffee drinking or use of tobacco, for coca leaves contain the drug cocaine. Cocaine makes the coca chewer unmindful of the cares of life. Backbreaking work can be carried on with no sensible discomfort from abused muscles or hunger pains. But along with relief from misery the coca chewer suffers loss of energy and ambition.

The coca plant thrives in the warm, humid climate that prevails at altitudes between 3000 and 5000 feet. But it requires constant cultivation and care. Despite the laborious production and transportation difficulties the avid market on the Altiplano makes coca raising highly profitable.

The eastern lowlands, or **Oriente**, constitute over two-thirds of all Bolivia. The northern portion of the Oriente consists of the rainforests of the Amazon Basin. These are sluggishly drained by the headwaters of a major Amazon tributary, the **Madera**, and its sub-tributaries. In these lands an overabundance of water is the chief problem of utilization, for the land is so flat and the streams are so sluggish that great areas are flooded for several months each year. The somewhat higher land farther south, on the other hand, has good agricultural potentials; there some sugar cane, rice, and coffee are grown, and cotton has been introduced.

In the southeast part of the Oriente is the **Chaco** district, previously discussed under the savanna climatic regions (see Chapter 10, p. 172).

People. Bolivia's population is 3 million people, of whom one-third are *cholos* (the Bolivian equivalent of *mestizos*—see Chapter 7, p. 116), and about 15 percent white. The Indian regional preponderance is even greater than is indicated statistically, for the white descendants of the conquistadors and the later European immigrants are heavily concentrated in the cities. Most of the Altiplano and the Oriente are inhabited by pure Indian stock. The population as a whole is similarly unevenly distributed. About one-half of the total lives on the Altiplano; another heavy concentration is in the valley district. The Oriente is very sparsely populated.

The Indians of highland Bolivia are descendants of the Aymaras of Inca times. Their most unusual characteristic is to surpass all other peoples in ability to perform hard labor under rigorous conditions, and in enduring extreme discomfort from cold and hunger with complete equanimity, even without coca. They are basically intelligent and possess an average degree of aptitude for handling machinery. Such talents, however, have remained obscure because of their extreme stubbornness in clinging to their traditional ways of life, regardless of the poverty to which these condemn them. By refusing to adjust himself to new and better living conditions the Indian has remained available for exploitation in mines and fields.

The significance of the coca habit in the plight of the Indian is a subject of much dispute. Every Indian from early childhood on chews coca daily. There is no question but that the Indians accomplish prodigies of labor and endurance under its influence, but whether lowered vitality and general stupefaction are inevitable results of the habitual use of coca is not yet settled.

At the other extreme of the social scale is the absentee landlord class so common in Latin America. The cholos, intermediate between the Indians and whites in social status, are distinguished as a class on an economic rather than ethnic basis. This permits considerable social mobility, for a cholo can become "white" if he has the means to dress and learns to act accordingly.

Transportation. Bolivia's extremes of relief are the great impediment to the development of a comprehensive transportation system. There are 1500 miles of railroad in the west, which link two important high valleys with the Altiplano and the Altiplano with Chilean seaports. A line across the Chaco from the Brazilian border to the Andean foothills was completed in 1954, after 35 years of negotiation and 15 of construction. It provides Bolivia with a much-needed outlet to the Atlantic Ocean and contact with the countries to the southeast.

Truck transport is the major transportation dependence of the country. Trucks struggle over murderously dangerous roads in the mountains, and in the Oriente on tracks literally beaten out of the bush by the trucks themselves. The "mortality rate" of both vehicles and drivers (the latter by going over precipices) is high. An important advance was recorded in 1954 with the opening of a modern highway linking the Yungas and Chaco districts.

Both railroads and highways are still inadequate, however, to serve even the limited commerce of the country. In brief, the cost of developing overland transport facilities is prohibitively high, especially relative to the local capital available for construction.

Air transport, although far more expensive under ordinary conditions than is overland conveyance, has provided Bolivia with an eminently satisfactory solution of part of the problem. Since its establishment, even on a small scale, rapid internal travel is possible for the first time. Moreover, such items as newspapers can now be delivered quickly to all parts of the country, aiding immensely in internal communication and the development of national unity.

Mineral Resources and Products. Bolivia's mineral resources have been at the same time the nation's economic foundation and its undoing. From the time of the Spanish conquest Bolivia has been a mining country. The complete identification of Bolivia over a period of three centuries with mines was a situation unduplicated elsewhere in the world until the very modern association of Venezuela and the Middle Eastern countries with petroleum recovery was established.

The climax of such association is reached in the Altiplano. All of the mining industry is located either on the Altiplano or in the ranges which surround it; without such activity the Altiplano would be practically uninhabited.

The leading metal of the Bolivian mining industry is **tin**, found in a belt that extends throughout the Cordillera Real. Bolivia ranks second in world production of tin, a position it maintains only by overcoming serious handicaps. The Bolivian tin ores are highly complex, and complicated refining techniques must be used to extract the metal content. Since there is no fuel on the Altiplano the ore cannot be smelted within the country. The cost of the long overland haul to the sea for export is somewhat reduced by

"concentration" of the ore, that is, by getting rid of barren rock and so raising the proportionate metal content of the material to be smelted. Still another disadvantage is the high altitude of the mines—between 14,000 and 17,000 feet. Only the Indians can do the required hard manual labor at such debilitating altitudes, and even so mine operation is notably inefficient. Finally, all supplies and equipment for mining must be imported from overseas and hauled up to Altiplano elevations.

Bolivia is also a significant producer of **tungsten, antimony, lead, zinc, copper, gold,** and **silver,** for the Andes of Bolivia are rich both in kinds and in volume of mineral deposits. Production of all of these metals is subject to the same handicaps that affect the recovery of tin. For many years it was possible to offset the difficulties of tin and other metal recovery by exploitation of only the richest deposits. This was done so successfully, in fact, that great fortunes were made by absentee owners. The richer tin deposits have now been exhausted, and further, the world demand for tin has failed to keep pace with world producing capacity. Accordingly, Bolivia is confronted with increasing mining costs while demand and prices rise little if at all.

CITIES OF BOLIVIA

Name	Type	Population (1950)
La Paz	Commercial	321,000
Cochabamba	Commercial	81,000
Oruro	Mining	63,000
Potosi	Mining	46,000
Santa Cruz	Commercial	43,000
Sucre	Governmental	40,000

Cities. The major cities of Bolivia are noteworthy in that the purposes they served at the time of their founding are not uncommonly subordinate to their present functions. Thus **La Paz** (Fig. 30.5), originally a commercial city, has become the "acting capital" of the country, as it has been the seat of government since 1900. It is 45 miles east of the south tip of Lake Titicaca at 12,000 feet elevation, on the slopes of a ravine in the shadow of the highest Bolivian peaks. La Paz is the metropolis of the country and has grown fivefold during the present century. It owes its growth to its communications facilities. With three rail lines to the Pacific coast, it handles the mineral exports and the food and material imports of Bolivia.

Cochabamba, an exception to the rule of shifting functions, was originally and is now a thriving commercial town in one of the type valleys of the Yungas district 130 miles southeast of La Paz. At an altitude of 8000 feet, its location and climate are both salubrious. It is, in a word, the garden spot of Bolivia. It is also the highland terminus of the highway from the Chaco.

Oruro and Potosi are two cities, which earlier were much larger, associated with the great silver-mining era of previous centuries. Oruro is situated 120 miles southeast of La Paz, at an altitude of 12,000 feet. Its site on the rail line along the Altiplano has enabled it to retain its size and importance in part by functioning as a commercial center for tin mining in the surrounding district. Potosi is 280 miles southeast of La Paz at an altitude of over 13,000 feet, the highest urban devel-

opment in the world. The exhaustion of the local mines has led to its decline, so that it is now a shabby and rundown place.

Santa Cruz is located at an altitude of 1500 feet in the south central part of the Oriente. It is the major trade center of eastern Bolivia and is probably the country's "coming city." It is connected by the new highway with Cochabamba, is the western terminus of the railroad, and is scheduled to have a rail connection with Argentina on the south.

Sucre, at an altitude of 10,000 feet 300 miles southeast of La Paz, is a capital that is not a capital. Founded as such over 400 years ago, it is still the legal capital of Bolivia, but only the Supreme Court remains in the city. The former government buildings are now used for other purposes. Sucre is located in another of the Yungas type valleys, so that it has not fallen into decay as a result of losing its governmental function.

Bolivia as a Whole. Bolivia was characterized at the beginning of this discussion as a land of physical contrasts, but perhaps the

Fig. 30.5—La Paz, Bolivia. In the distance snow-capped Mount Illimani, 22,579 feet in elevation. (Courtesy, Bolivian Embassy.)

greatest contrast of all is that between the present national poverty and the rich potentials of the country's resources. A French explorer of the last century expressed this most aptly when he described Bolivia as "a beggar sitting on a chair of gold." Bolivia has since actually retrogressed. When it attained its independence in 1825 its territory was over twice as large as at present and included a strip of Pacific coast. Chronic internal weakness and foolish wars caused the loss of territory to Chile, Brazil, Argentina, and Paraguay.

In a way, Bolivia is representative of the underdeveloped country that cannot break out of the circle of illiteracy, ignorance, low productivity, and lack of capital which limits every effort. But Bolivia's present difficulties may also be in part ascribed to the mining impasse and to the ethnological peculiarities of the Bolivian Indian. Several studies have demonstrated that it is futile for Bolivia to remain bound up solely in its mining industry, which keeps the national interest centered on the Altiplano. The energies devoted to mining are now an economic drain rather than a source of strength. But if other parts of the country and other resources are to be developed the Bolivian people must enlarge the scope of their activities. Unfortunately, however, the Indians who compose the bulk of the population refuse to be diverted from their traditional pursuits and manner of living. Besides, their productivity is at best rather low.

Still, the picture is not all gloom. The constantly growing cholo class is intelligent and energetic and shows a desire to improve its lot. As yet, however, the cholos are too few to provide the manpower which is essential for new departures. On the resource side there are ample means of broadening the base of the economy. Exploitation of the forests of the lower eastern slopes of the Yungas should afford great returns; hydropower potentialities there are also obviously large. The agriculture of the Yungas district could be substantially improved; likewise that of the Santa Cruz area of the southeast. The lowlands of the northeast are, more-

over, a potentially important cattle country.

New hope has in the meantime come as the result of an anti-peonage law. The necessity of paying workers has made coca so expensive that estate owners have abandoned their lands to the Indians, who have turned to vegetable crops on their newly gained property. Their potential as coffee lands is of great value in the rehabilitation of Bolivia.

In the east the producing oil fields of the Chaco may well extend north into the Oriente. The potential here is a Brazilian market, via pipe line, for the oil and gas.

Just when Bolivia's day will come cannot be foretold. In the meantime most Bolivians struggle only for continued existence.

QUESTIONS. Discuss the factors that cause highland regions to have so many small climatic regions within them that they cannot be classified as having a predominant climate. Locate the country of Tibet and describe its topography. Briefly describe its climate. Who is the Dalai Lama and what is his special significance? Describe the salient features of lama Buddhism. What is its relation to the social organization and problems of Tibet? What are the chief domestic animals of Tibet? In what way is Lhasa similar to Rome and Mecca? What is the Potala? Explain the factors that led to the development of Tibet's unique religion and way of life and to its nominal independence from China. How do the current political position and strategic significance of Tibet differ from its traditional status?

Locate Bolivia. In what respects is it different from Tibet? Describe its topography. Compare the climate of the Altiplano with that of the Tibetan plateau. What is coca and why is it economically and politically significant in Bolivia? Describe the make-up of the Bolivian population. Discuss the problems of transportation in Bolivia and the present status of transportation facilities. Name the outstanding resource of Bolivia in terms of past and present significance in the economy. In what respect is reliance on this resource a national weakness? Why is La Paz the *de facto* capital of the country? Cochabamba and Santa Cruz are typical of which geographic regions of the country? What do Oruro and Potosi have in common? Explain the characterization of Bolivia as "a beggar sitting in a chair of gold." What is geographically favorable to Bolivia's ultimate future development and progress?

C. SWITZERLAND

Topography. Like Tibet and Bolivia, Switzerland is a landlocked country identified with the greatest mountain mass of Europe, the **Alps.** Unlike the other two highland countries it is small, with moderate altitudes. Switzerland is 16,000 square miles in area (about twice the size of Massachusetts) and is located in the center of western Europe between France on the west, Italy on the south, Austria on the east, and Germany on the north (Fig. 30.6).

Switzerland consists of three topographic belts which trend roughly parallel in a northeast-southwest direction. In the southeast is the belt of the Alps. Although the Alps are the greatest and highest mountain system of Europe, their peaks of 12,000- to 15,000-foot elevations are con-

Fig. 30.6—Switzerland. The inset compares the area of Switzerland with that of Massachusetts, Connecticut, and Rhode Island, which is approximately equal.

siderably lower and less massive than those of the Himalayas and Andes. Their relief is nevertheless rugged, since the valley floors are under 2000 feet in altitude. A characteristic feature of the Alps is the gentle, open, grassy shelves that occur at the top edge of the vertical sides of deep valleys. Such perched meadows are called *albs* (Fig. 30.7), a term from which the name of the mountains is derived. The Alps have snow-capped peaks and glaciers despite their relatively low altitudes because the higher latitude means a much lower snow line than in Tibet and Bolivia.

The Alps are themselves divided into two sets of ranges by a major glacier-deepened valley that runs longitudinally between them for almost the entire east-west extent of Switzerland. The southern Alps are known as the "High Alps"; those to the north are sometimes referred to as the "Pre-Alps." The cover of snow and ice that mantles the higher parts of both ranges, together with the limited amount of level land available on their lower slopes, severely restricts human occupance of the mountain regions. Thus,

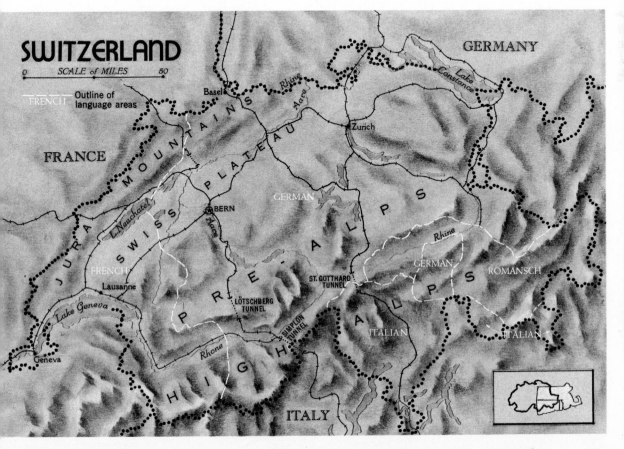

while the Alps occupy three-fifths of the country, only one-sixth of the Swiss population is resident within their confines.

Northwest of the Alps is a parallel belt 180 miles long and 25 to 45 miles wide known as the **Swiss Plateau.** Plateau elevations range from 1200 to 3500 feet; it is a land of wide valleys and rolling hills, with many glacial features such as lakes and minor surface irregularities. The plateau accounts for one-third of the area of Switzerland and is the center of population, agriculture, and industry.

The third belt, on the west and northwest border of the country, is the **Jura Mountains,** comprising about one-tenth of Switzerland's area. These are low mountains composed of parallel ridges like the Appalachians of the United States, with the highest points about a mile in elevation.

Switzerland is the source region for a number of the major streams of Europe. Two large rivers rise in the central valley of the Alps, the **Rhine,** which flows northeast, and the **Rhone,** southwest. Each curves through the mountains at the border of the country to a large lake, the Rhine to **Lake Constance** and the Rhone to **Lake Geneva.**

Fig. 30.7—*Alb,* meadow high up on the side of a deep valley in the Alps. Near Wengen, Switzerland. (Courtesy, Swiss National Travel Office.)

The Rhine then continues west as the northern boundary of the country. On the plateau the **Aare River** flows northeast as a Rhine tributary, draining **Lake Neuchatel** in the southwest and a series of other long, narrow lakes on the north flank of the Alps. In the east, lesser streams drain into the Danube, in the southeast to the Po.

Climate. Despite the higher latitudes the climate of Switzerland is much less rigorous than that of highland Tibet and Bolivia. The country is situated between marine west coast and humid continental climatic regions. In consequence of this position it has moderate precipitation—30 to 50 inches a year—and a pronounced seasonal temperature range. Winters are frequently unpleasant because of long periods of rain, and on the plateau, which is open to continental influences from the northeast, a mist or drizzly fog may persist for days. At the same time the higher slopes of the Alps may be bathed in sunshine. The Jura district has an even more unpleasant climate because the altitude is not sufficiently high to mitigate the

summer heat, and there is very heavy snowfall in winter that leaves the inhabitants
snowbound.

A unique feature of Switzerland is the
foehn, a wind like the chinook of the western
United States. When low-pressure areas over
Switzerland pull in air from the Mediterranean it is first dried by its ascent over the
southern flank of the Alps, then warmed by
its descent on their north side. The warm,
dry wind can raise temperatures 20° to
30° F. in minutes, which is a pleasant change
in winter, but it can also cause avalanches
and in summer scorch crops.

People. The Alpine highlands are the cradle of the Alpine ethnic group, one of the
basic human stocks of Europe (Fig. 30.8).
The 4.7 million inhabitants of Switzerland,
however, are more noteworthy because of
their diverse national backgrounds and the
resulting heterogeneity in language, religion,
and culture than for their ethnic composition.

This complex derives from the remarkable
history of the country, which is in turn directly related to the highland environment.
The mountain topography and the isolation
it engendered early fostered a passionate
love of liberty. As early as 1291 three *cantons,* or local rural districts, located around
Lake Lucerne joined forces to gain independence from Austria. Remoteness favored
their cause, and the cantons when free became the nucleus around which other neighboring cantons of the highland districts were
assembled and gained independence. The
accretion process continued until 1815, when
a total of 22 cantons had seceded from
neighboring countries and joined the confed-
eration.

As a result of this manner of origin Switzerland has today four official languages.
About 75 percent of the population, in the
north, northeast, and center, speak German;
20 percent, in the west, are French-speaking;
in the south Italian is the language of a total
of 5 percent of the people; and in the east 1
percent of the total population speaks *Ro-
mansch,* a relic survival of a Latin-based language. This survival testifies to the potency
of the highland environment in preserving
language, and further testimony is afforded
by the fact that each of the four major languages is spoken in various dialects—more
than 60 according to one survey!

The pattern of religious beliefs is even
more complex. Generalization is difficult, but
roughly stated the west, north, and east are
Protestant, the center and south Catholic (75
percent or more of the local population in
each instance). Otherwise stated, Protestantism is dominant on the plateau and in the
cities. In the overall view Switzerland is
Protestant; about three-fifths of the people
adhere to Protestant denominations.

It will be noted that the geographic patterns of language and religion relate to
neighboring nationalities rather than to the
topographic divisions of the country. The
love of liberty, nurtured in the inner fast-
nesses of the Alpine highland, pulled people
away from surrounding states up to the
point where this attractive force was counterbalanced by the core nationalism of the
several neighboring countries.

Despite this diversity of background Switzerland is the most vital and best-developed

Fig. 30.8—Swiss Peasant Couple in the Bernese Oberland, near Mürren, Switzerland. (Courtesy, Swiss National Travel Office.)

democracy in the world. Cultural differences are rigorously subordinated to an unbreakable determination to preserve political freedom and independence by maintaining a strong Swiss nation. On the other hand, the Swiss have managed to retain individual cultural, religious, and local canton ties by bringing to the art of compromise and political balance a rare degree of skill. The emphasis is on confederacy and a maximum of local government. The Swiss presidency rotates among the seven members of a "Federal Council," and all laws of any consequence are submitted to the people for referendum vote. The democratic approach is further demonstrated by the broad tolerance of individual beliefs. The country is a traditional haven for political exiles. In part such fundamental democracy is made feasible because of the small size of the country, but it is also fostered by the very high educational standards of Switzerland.

Lastly, the Swiss have retained their independence by remaining aloof from the major European conflicts of the past centuries. This has been possible in part because of the topographic barriers to invasion, but such defenses alone would not have been sufficient

to preserve Swiss liberty in the absence of a repeatedly demonstrated readiness to fight in the preservation of the independent status of the country.

Agriculture. Although only about 10 percent of the land of Switzerland is arable, two-fifths of the population are engaged in agriculture. On the plateau cereal crops include wheat, corn, oats, and rye, but, as might be expected, production is not sufficient for local needs. In the Alpine valleys up to 4200 feet elevation, on the average, such hardy crops as barley, rye, oats, and potatoes are grown. Vineyards are cultivated in sheltered areas and on south-facing slopes on the plateau, and temperate fruits are grown in the northern valleys for jams and canning. On the south flank of the High Alps the agriculture has a distinctly Mediterranean cast, with vineyards, olive groves, and cornfields.

In general, however, crop cultivation is subordinate to **dairying**, the major farm activity. Two-fifths of the land is in meadows (Fig. 30.9) and pastures, and the Swiss dairy industry is, in terms of yield, the most highly developed in the world. The leading district for dairying is the Jura, where the

Fig. 30.9—Swiss Peasant Mowing Hay on a High Mountain Meadow, Kandersteg, Bernese, Oberland. Note the angle of the slope. (Courtesy, Swiss National Travel Office.)

harsher climate and poor soils make crop cultivation impracticable. The Jura is the home of the world-famous **Swiss cheese.** Dairying is also associated with the Alpine meadows. Transhumance is practiced between the high mountain *albs* and the villages in the valleys. In the summer the herders accompany the young cattle up on the mountains (Fig. 30.10) while the dairy herds stay down below. In winter all animals feed on the hay harvested from the lower fields. The cattle graze up to 1500 feet above the timber line, and the **sheep** and **goats** that are also brought up the mountains range almost to the snow line.

Resources. One-quarter of Switzerland is forested, and the **forest** resources are an important element in the economy. Over half the forests are on the mountain slopes above the farm land and below the pastures, reaching up to between 5000 and 7000 feet. The forest land is deliberately limited on both the high and low margins so as to obtain the maximum possible farm and grazing land. On the other hand, strict conservation laws prohibit a reduction in the forest area. Conifers account for two-thirds of the total resource, chiefly on the higher slopes. Broadleaved hardwoods grow on the plateau and lower slopes.

The most important natural resource of Switzerland is **hydropower.** As the country is devoid of fuel resources industry is wholly dependent on hydroelectricity. Although per capita consumption of electricity is very high, development has proceeded sufficiently to allow sizable power exports. And yet less than one-third of the total hydropower resources have been exploited, so richly is Switzerland endowed on this score. However, in winter the power output declines sharply because of the freeze-up of the streams, and hydropower must be supplemented with imported coal.

Transportation. Switzerland is unique among highland countries in that it is superbly equipped with transportation facilities. Although the Alps are lofty, their ranges are transected by relatively low passes to which comparatively easy access is had up

Fig. 30.10—*Alpaufzug,* Which Means "Procession to the High Alps," When the Cows Are Ceremonially Headed to the Summertime Pastures. (Courtesy, Swiss National Travel Office.)

large valleys (Fig. 30.11). These passes early acquired great commercial significance as the corridors through which the trade between the Mediterranean ports of northern Italy and central Europe was funneled. With remarkable foresight the Swiss in the nineteenth century recognized that the passes could have only limited value as railroad routes because of their height and burial under deep snow in winter. Accordingly, they

Fig. 30.11—Large Valley at Wassen, Switzerland, Approach to the St. Gotthard Tunnel. (Courtesy, Swiss National Travel Office.)

constructed with their own capital a railroad system featuring great tunnels. Tunnels like the **St. Gotthard** (almost 10 miles long) and the **Simplon** (12 miles long) pierce the mountains far below the level of the passes. Even greater engineering feats are the spiral tunnels, some with double tracks, that overcome the steep ascents and descents to and from the mouths of the tunnels.

The tunnel routes in turn were implemented by a close-spaced network of interior lines and tied in at strategic points with the trunk systems of neighboring countries. Swiss railroads in consequence have become an indispensable link in all the railroad systems of western Europe. The Swiss also pioneered in the utilization of hydroelectricity in railroad operation; almost three-quarters of the mileage is electrified.

Industries. Although only a little over 10 percent of the Swiss population is dependent on manufacturing for a livelihood, Switzerland is basically an industrial country. Industry is concentrated in the northern end of the plateau, where every urban center is the focal point for manufacturing plants. The Jura is a second industrial area; small-scale factory operation is in evidence throughout the country.

As is true of so many other aspects of their land and life the manufacturing enterprise of the Swiss is a unique development. Its origins were the production of handicraft articles in the home during the winter, when outdoor activities are severely curtailed. Large-scale Swiss industry thus inherited traditions of craftsmanship and pride in its products. No small portion of the modern industrial development has resulted simply from the application of electric power to earlier "home industries." These factors have made possible Swiss mass production of quality products and, incidentally, because of the hydropower, without the dirt and smoke associated with manufacturing where fuels are the power source.

Skill and quality were also the watchwords of the Swiss undertakings in heavy industry. In view of the complete absence of domestic raw materials, it was essential

for success that the quantity of imported basic substances should be low and represent only a small proportion of the value of the finished article. This policy has enabled the Swiss to sell the products of their heavy industry in the world market in competition with manufacturers in other countries who have direct access to the basic raw materials.

The oldest and most famous of Swiss industries is **watchmaking** (Fig. 30.12), centered in the Jura. Swiss watches and clocks are synonymous with quality throughout the world. Less well known but fully as important is the manufacture of **electrical machinery** (turbines, generators, etc.), **Diesel engines, locomotives,** textile and agricultural machinery—all products of the plateau.

Textiles are also important, especially silk. The industry is centered in the northern Jura and northeast part of the plateau. The emphasis on quality is signified by the intricate embroidery, lace, and similar goods that require superior skill. Some of this textile manufacture is still home industry.

In the 1930's the development of a **chemical** industry was begun, based on the use of electricity. It now constitutes a large fraction of all manufacturing in the large cities of the Jura and the plateau. Special products are dyes, plastics, pharmaceuticals, and insecticides.

Other industries are less important, but nevertheless typical of the Swiss tradition. In a unique use of the milk supplied by the dairy industry, the Swiss achieved world fame with their superior **chocolate.** Shoes and leather, toys and woodworking are further indicative of the handicraft background. The toys and wood articles come especially from the Jura.

The Swiss have neglected nothing in the utilization of their geographic heritage. Thus **tourism** is a highly organized industry, both in summer for the scenery (Fig. 30.13) and in winter for sports. The cities and mountains are so well equipped with accommodations for travelers that some people think of the Swiss merely as a nation of hotelkeepers. Easy access by bus and scenic railways to vantage points for all important vistas is a

Fig. 30.12—Watchmakers at Work in Newest Type of Factory, Switzerland. (Courtesy, Watchmakers of Switzerland.)

Fig. 30.13—Hotel at Terminus of Rhone Glacier (Source of Rhone River). (Wehrli-Verlag, Zurich.)

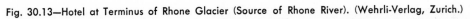

feature of the tourist promotion. Swiss health resorts were famous European institutions long before winter sports became a fad.

The stability of the Swiss monetary system because of its solid foundations and sound legislation has enabled the Swiss to create and maintain some of the world's leading **banking** and **insurance** businesses. Money from all over the world is entrusted to Swiss banks, and Swiss credit standing and recognized ability as financiers are unsurpassed.

CITIES OF SWITZERLAND

Name	Type	Population (1950)
Zurich	Industrial-commercial	390,000
Basel	River port-industrial	184,000
Bern	Governmental	146,000
Geneva	Commercial	145,000
Lausanne	Commercial-resort	107,000

Cities. Switzerland's large cities have several features in common. All but one are located on the plateau; most are situated on large lakes, especially at their outlets; and all are known for their universities though none of them is primarily an educational center.

Zurich (Fig. 30.14) is a class by itself among Swiss cities. In addition to being more than twice as large as any other city it is the center of the insurance and banking business and of the silk industry, and has large cotton mills and machinery plants. It is in the northeastern part of the plateau in very scenic surroundings at the outlet of Lake Zurich, and is at the same time a manufacturing, educational, and tourist center. Its population growth threatens to upset the carefully fostered regional balance within Switzerland.

Basel, the only major city not on the plateau, is in the northeast corner of Switzer-

Fig. 30.14—Zurich, Switzerland, on the Jura Plateau at the Outlet of Lake Zurich. (Courtesy, Swiss National Travel Office.)

Fig. 30.15—Geneva, Switzerland, at the Outlet of Lake Geneva. (Courtesy, Swiss National Travel Office.)

land where the Rhine turns north between Germany and France. It is the northern gateway to Switzerland and, as the head of navigation of the Rhine, is one of the leading ports on that river. It is the chief import center for the raw materials needed by Swiss industry. It is also the chemical center of the country, especially for dye manufacturing.

Bern, the Swiss capital, is referred to in Switzerland as the "Federal City." Situated on the east side of the plateau about midway along its length, Bern is a quiet residential city, much less animated and politically significant than most national capitals because central government is deëmphasized in Switzerland.

Geneva (Fig. 30.15), at the southeastern corner of the country, is the counterpart of Basel in the northeast corner. Geneva is at the outlet of Lake Geneva into the Rhone.

It is the southern gateway to Switzerland but unlike Basel has no river traffic on its outlet stream. Geneva is unique among the cities of the world because of its inherent identification with international diplomacy. Thus after World War I Geneva almost automatically was chosen as the headquarters of the League of Nations. The great buildings built by the League are still used by United Nations institutions and by international conferences of all kinds. Geneva, more prosaically, is also important as the center of the Swiss watch industry.

Lausanne is picturesquely situated on the north shore of Lake Geneva 30 miles northeast of Geneva. Its commercial significance stems largely from its location on the main rail line between Italy and northern France.

Switzerland as a Whole. Switzerland, geographically considered, may be regarded as an economic marvel, for logically it should be hardly more than a nation of impoverished farmers and herdsmen struggling to gain a livelihood in a harsh environment meagerly endowed with natural resources. Its agricultural output is insufficient to feed its population, and it lacks raw materials to support industry. Yet Switzerland not only is able to make ends meet; it is also a thriving, prosperous industrial nation with one of the world's highest standards of living. The Swiss achievement is due to the intelligent use of its highland environment. Switzerland may be regarded as a triumph of applied geography.

Nevertheless there are weaknesses in Switzerland's economic status. Its industry is almost wholly based on the import of raw materials. It pays for these by export of finished manufactures and by the banking and insurance services in which it specializes. Thus Switzerland, even more than Sweden, must be ever on guard against adverse developments in world affairs. No small part of its present superior economic position is due to its having escaped the destruction of the World Wars. Like Sweden (Chapter 27, p. 604), it has adopted and maintained the role of the neutral. Whether it can continue to stand aside when the nations of all the world are divided between two opposed political camps is a large question.

The Swiss position is also imperiled by the possibility of a European Union. Switzerland is opposed to such organization. The Swiss would then no longer be able to "play the field," by taking advantage of the commercial rivalries and jealousies of the neighboring nations which have prevented those nations from making full use of their own resources and economic possibilities.

D. ETHIOPIA[2]

General Aspects. Ethiopia consists of some

[2] The word "Ethiopia" is of Greek origin and means "Burnt Face." Ethiopia is the inhabitants' own name for their country; as such it is the only correct geographic term. "Abyssinia," often erroneously used to refer to Ethiopia, is the Portuguese version of the Arabic name for the country.

365,000 square miles of territory (including Eritrea)[3] in East Africa south of the Red Sea. It is thus equal in size to Texas, Arkansas, and Louisiana combined. It is bounded by French and British Somaliland on the east, Somalia on the southeast, Kenya on the south, and the Sudan on the west (Fig. 30.16).

Highland Ethiopia consists of two plateaus and associated mountain ranges. The larger, or **Ethiopian Plateau,** occupies the western portion of the country. The average altitude of this plateau is 7000 to 9000 feet; numerous peaks with 13,000- to 15,000-foot elevations are distributed over its surface. Streams have cut gorges as much as 2000 feet deep into the plateau, so that the range of relief within the area is extreme.

The general surface of the Ethiopian Plateau slopes gently westward to where it merges into the Sudan. On the east it drops off precipitously in a 7000- to 8000-foot escarpment 600 miles long. On the southeast the escarpment continues at 5000- to 6000-foot elevations where it constitutes the western edge of the **Great Rift Valley** (see Chapter 9, p. 147), which runs from the southern end of the Red Sea to the large rift lakes of East Africa.

East of the Rift Valley there is a rise over a 6000-foot escarpment to the **Somali Plateau.** This escarpment continues in an easterly direction as the **Chilalo Mountains** of 10,000-foot elevations. The Somali Plateau slopes east and south to Somalia and Kenya. Its southeastern portion is known as the **Ogaden.** In the northeast, below the escarpment of the Ethiopian Plateau, is the **Danakil** district, a lowland connecting the Red Sea and Rift Valley depressions.

The streams of Ethiopia are important only as the source of water for neighboring countries. In the northwest **Lake Tana,** 1100 square miles in area, is generally accepted as the source of the **Blue Nile,** the major tributary of the trunk Nile River. The Great Rift Valley contains a chain of seven lakes

[3] Eritrea was federally linked with Ethiopia in 1952 as a partially autonomous district (see Chapter 12, p. 218).

ranging from 60 to 500 square miles in area.

Both plateau regions have a humid climate, with an annual precipitation of 20 to 30 inches in the southeast and as much as 80 inches in the southwest. The precipitation is orographic, from humid winds off the Indian Ocean and also from the Red Sea. Thus the higher the altitude the higher the rainfall. The Indian Ocean winds, of monsoonal type, bring the Somali Plateau two rainy seasons, one from June to September, the other in March and April. The Ogaden district is actually within a savanna region, and the Danakil district and Eritrea along the Red Sea coast are extensions of the Sahara arid region (see Chapter 12, p. 218).

The altitude on the plateaus nicely balances the tropical heat, so that the climate is very pleasant. Temperatures rarely attain the 90's on the Ethiopian Plateau, and the low extremes are sometimes near freezing. Temperatures during the rains are some 5° to 10° F. lower than in the dry season. Danakil temperatures are typical of the warm desert environment.

People. The total population of Ethiopia is estimated to be 9 million (there has never been a census). Of these, some 2 million are *Amharas,* or Ethiopians proper, the dominant people of the country. The Amharas inhabit the center of the Ethiopian Plateau. An indigenous people, they have been Coptic Christians since the fourth century. In the northeast portion of the plateau there is a district of "rock churches," buildings hewn laboriously out of solid rock, probably the most unusual churches in the world.

Fig. 30.16—Ethiopia. The inset compares the area of Ethiopia with an equivalent area of the United States (states in white).

The most numerous people, comprising about two-thirds of the total population, are the *Gallas,* who occupy the southern part of the plateau and who are divided in religion between Christianity and Islam. They are representative of the *Hamitic* peoples of the world, so named because they are traditionally supposed to be descendants of Ham, one of the sons of Noah.

Other peoples of the country include the *Danakil,* Mohammedans of the district to which they give their name, and the *Somali* tribes of the southeastern part of the country. In addition there are Negro peoples in the Sudan border districts. The Empire of Ethiopia is therefore rightly named. It is not a single independent people but a collection of tribal kingdoms ruled by a "King of Kings." The number of languages spoken is large, but Amharic is the official language of the country.

Transportation. For hundreds of years Ethiopia maintained only a minimum of transportation and communications facilities, in accordance with a policy of isolation designed to preserve the area's independence. At the turn of the century the French constructed a 500-mile railroad from their port of Djibouti in French Somaliland to the Ethiopian capital in the center of the country. Although this railroad provided direct modern transportation to and from the outside world, it did not stimulate the development of the country and has never carried sufficient traffic to pay for its maintenance.

During the Italian occupation of Ethiopia in the last half of the 1930's much road building was done. The 3000-mile system then constructed has since been well used by motor traffic. Outside this network, however, camel and mule trails are the rule. The precipitous boundary escarpments of Ethiopia's plateaus and the gorges across them make road construction and repair highly expensive. In Ethiopia, as in Bolivia, progress has been telescoped with the development of air transport. A state air line now provides adequate access from the capital to the outside world.

Agriculture. Over one-half the land of Ethiopia is arable, so that the agricultural potential of the country is much greater than that needed to sustain the inhabitants. The chief crop is **durra,** a sorghum. Corn, potatoes, wheat, and barley are also grown by the agricultural peoples of the plateaus. Large exportable surpluses of wheat and oil seeds could be raised on highly fertile land, but the lack of adequate transportation facilities from the more remote farm lands is a great deterrent to increased and improved production. Agricultural equipment and techniques are still primitive.

At the lower altitudes in the more tropical climates mocha coffee (a premium variety), cotton, bananas, and sugar cane are grown. In the dry southeast and northeast of the country the inhabitants are pastoral peoples who are responsible for the large output of hides and skins that are leading Ethiopian exports. It is estimated that the Ethiopian cattle population is 18 million, in addition to unknown numbers of sheep and goats.

The other resources of Ethiopia are still practically unknown. There are, however, abundant indications of both fuel and metallic mineral deposits throughout the country.

CITIES OF ETHIOPIA

Name	Type	Population (1950)
Addis Ababa	Governmental	300,000
Harar	Commercial	40,000

Cities. **Addis Ababa** ("New Flower") is the capital of Ethiopia, situated in the center of the country on the Ethiopian Plateau at an altitude of 7700 feet. Addis Ababa is unlike the other cities and towns of the country, for it is a purely governmental city founded in the 1880's. There are no imposing buildings in the city; on the other hand it possesses paved streets, electricity and water systems, transportation facilities, traffic lights, and other urban amenities unknown elsewhere in the country.

Harar, located at the northeast edge of the Somali Plateau at an altitude of a little over a mile, is a market city in the center of the coffee district. It is very Arabian in appearance, with jumbled buildings and narrow, crowded streets inside an encircling wall.

Ethiopia as a Whole. The historical parallels of Ethiopia and Tibet are rather striking. Both countries deliberately exploited their highland isolation in order to be able to pursue their traditional ways without interference or modification by outside influences. Both became strongholds of special variants of leading religions. Both evolved their own exotic cultures and ways of life.

The great difference between them, on the other hand, is the retention of the isolationist policy by Tibet and its abandonment in Ethiopia. Ethiopia owes its status as the only surviving native independent nation in Africa (from the pre-colonial period) to its highland environment. The establishment of unified political control of the whole area in the last half of the nineteenth century enabled the leader who brought this about to begin the modernization of the country. This policy was being carried forward by his successor at the time of the Italian invasion and occupation of the 1930's. With the restoration of independent sovereignty during World War II the country was free to resume its modernization.

With great foresight the pace of modernization is being kept down to the ability of the country to finance the necessary projects and to adjust itself to the effects of their operations. Ethiopia is not an impoverished country, as is Bolivia, and its more hospitable climate insures much more comfortable living conditions than those of Tibet. With its continued independence assured, the country's resources can be explored and developed without undue haste. Ethiopia may not be the scene of spectacular progress in the next few decades, but its inhabitants will probably profit steadily by soundly based and well-executed undertakings.

QUESTIONS. Locate Switzerland and describe its general topography. Compare its climate with that of Tibet and Bolivia. Explain similarities or differences. Describe the paradox of Swiss unity in the face of national, religious, and lingual diversity. Describe the unusual features of Swiss government. Name the major agricultural products and the districts from which they come. What are the chief nonagricultural resources of Switzerland? Name three unusual aspects of the Swiss transportation system.

Describe the basis of Swiss manufacturing. What are the major products, and from what districts do they come? In what ways have the Swiss developed tourism as an important source of national income? What other economic activities are based on the well-recognized stability of the Swiss monetary system? In what respects is Zurich like and unlike the other large cities of Switzerland? In what way are Basel and Geneva alike? What is the special tradition of Geneva? Explain the statement "Switzerland is a triumph of applied geography."

Locate Ethiopia and describe its topographic features. What climates are found within Ethiopia? Describe the composition of the Ethiopian population. What is the status of agriculture and the development of natural resources in Ethiopia? Compare Ethiopia and Tibet as to the influence of their highland environment on their history.

Suggested Readings

CHAPTER I

Cooper, Gordon, *Isles of Romance and Mystery*, Lutterworth Press, London, 1949.

CHAPTER II

Addison, H., *Land, Water and Food*, Chapman and Hall, London, 1955.

Lane, F. C., *The World's Great Lakes*, Doubleday, New York, 1948.

Lane, F. C., *Earth's Grandest Rivers*, Doubleday, New York, 1949.

Lane, F. C., *The Story of Mountains*, Doubleday, New York, 1950.

World Population and Resources, Political and Economic Planning, London, 1955.

CHAPTER III

Churchill, H. S. *The City Is the People*, Reynal and Hitchcock, New York, 1945.

Robson, W. A. (ed.), *Great Cities of the World*, Macmillan, New York, 1955.

Saarinen, Eliel, *The City: Its Growth, Its Decay, Its Future*, Reinhold, New York, 1943.

Van Cleef, Eugene, *Trade Centers and Trade Routes*, Appleton-Century, New York, 1937.

CHAPTER IV

Bygott, John, *An Introduction to Mapwork and Practical Geography*, 4th ed., University Tutorial Press, London, 1952, Part II.

CHAPTER V

Chamberlin, Wellman, *The Round Earth on Flat Paper*, National Geographic Society, Washington, 1947.

Deetz, C. H. and Adams, O. S., *Elements of Map Projection*, U.S. Government Printing Office, Washington, 1945.

Raisz, Erwin, *General Cartography*, McGraw-Hill, New York, 1948.

CHAPTER VI

Beckinsale, R. P., *Land, Air and Ocean*, 2nd ed., Duckworth, London, 1956.

Blair, T. A., *Weather Elements*, Prentice-Hall, New York, 1948.

Kendrew, W. G., *The Climates of the Continents*, 4th ed., Clarendon Press, Oxford, 1953.

Tannehill, I. R., *Weather Around the World*, 2nd ed., Princeton University Press, Princeton, 1952.

U.S. Department of Agriculture, *Climate and Man*, U.S. Government Printing Office, Washington, 1941.

CHAPTER VII

Anderson, R. E., *Liberia, America's African Friend*, University of North Carolina Press, Chapel Hill, 1952.

Bellotti, F., *Fabulous Congo*, Dakers, London, 1954.

Buchanan, K. M., and Pugh, J. C., *Land and People in Nigeria*, University of London Press, London, 1955.

Carlson, F. A., *Geography of Latin America*, 3rd ed., Prentice-Hall, New York, 1952, Chapters VI, XIX, XX–XXVI.

Carr, A. F., *High Jungles and Low*, University of Florida Press, Gainesville, 1953.

International Bank for Reconstruction and Development, *The Economic Development of British Guiana*, Johns Hopkins Press, Baltimore, 1953.

Marvel, Tom, *The New Congo*, Duell, Sloan and Pearce, New York, 1948.

Pedler, F. J., *Economic Geography of West Africa*, Longmans, Green, New York, 1955.

Poll, W. N., *Surinam: The Country and Its People*, Van Hoeve, The Hague, 1951.

CHAPTER VIII

Andrus, J. R., *Burmese Economic Life*, Stanford University Press, Stanford, 1947.

Bro, M. H., *Indonesia, Land of Challenge*, Harper, New York, 1954.

Christian, J. L., *Burma*, Collins, London, 1945.

Cook, E. K., *Ceylon, Its Geography, Its Resources and Its People*, 2nd ed., Macmillan, London, 1951.

Forbes, W. C., *The Philippine Islands*, rev. ed., Harvard University Press, Cambridge, 1945.

International Bank for Reconstruction and Development, *The Economic Development of Malaya*, Johns Hopkins Press, Baltimore, 1955.

Rau, Santha Rama, *This Is India*, Harper, New York, 1954.

Robequain, C., *Malaya, Indonesia, Borneo and the Philippines*, Longmans, Green, New York, 1954.

Spencer, J. E., *Land and People in the Philippines*, University of California Press, Berkeley, 1954.

Woodman, D., *The Republic of Indonesia*, Philosophical Library, New York, 1955.

CHAPTER IX

Bellotti, F., *Fabulous Congo*, Dakers, London, 1954.

Buchanan, K. M., and Pugh, J. C., *Land and People in Nigeria,* University of London Press, London, 1955.

Hill, J. F. R., and Moffett, J. P., *Tanganyika: A Review of Its Resources and Their Development,* Government of Tanganyika, 1955.

International Bank for Reconstruction and Development, *The Economic Development of Nigeria,* Johns Hopkins Press, Baltimore, 1955.

Marvel, Tom, *The New Congo,* Duell, Sloan and Pearce, New York, 1948.

Pedler, F. J., *Economic Geography of West Africa,* Longmans, Green, New York, 1955.

Spence, C. F., *The Portuguese Colony of Moçambique,* Balkema, Capetown, 1951.

Thompson, C. H., and Woodruff, H. W., *Economic Development in Rhodesia and Nyasaland,* Dobson, London, 1955.

Wellington, J. H., *Southern Africa, A Geographical Study,* 2 vols., Cambridge University Press, Cambridge, 1955.

Young, F. B., *In South Africa,* Heinemann, London, 1952, Chapters 6 and 7.

CHAPTER X

Blomberg, Rolf, *Ecuador,* Forlag, Stockholm, 1952.

Camacho, J. A., *Brazil,* 2nd ed., Royal Institute of International Affairs, London, 1954.

Ferguson, Erna, *Cuba,* Knopf, New York, 1946.

Galbraith, W. O., *Colombia, A General Survey,* Royal Institute of International Affairs, London, 1953.

Linke, Lilo, *Ecuador, Country of Contrasts,* Royal Institute of International Affairs, London, 1954.

Smith, T. L., *Brazil: People and Institutions,* Louisiana State University Press, Baton Rouge, 1954.

CHAPTER XI

Addison, H., *Land, Water and Food,* Chapman and Hall, London, 1955.

Anstey, V. P., *The Economic Development of India,* 4th ed., Longmans, Green, London, 1952.

East, W. G., and Spate, O. H. K., *The Changing Map of Asia,* 2nd ed., Methuen, London, 1953, Chapters II and III.

East Pakistan: Fourth Year of Independence, Public Relations Department, Government of of East Bengal, Dacca, 1951.

Newman, Bernard, *Report on Indo-China,* Hale, London, 1953.

Rau, Santha Rama, *This Is India,* Harper, New York, 1954.

CHAPTER XII

Etherton, P. T., Across the Great Deserts, Whittlesey House, London, 1948, Parts I and II.

Gautier, E. F., *Sahara: The Great Desert,* Columbia University Press, New York, 1935.

Hodgkin, R. A., *Sudan Geography,* Longmans, Green, New York, 1951.

International Bank for Reconstruction and Development, *The Economic Development of Iraq,* Johns Hopkins Press, Baltimore, 1952.

Issawi, C. P., *Egypt at Mid-Century,* Oxford University Press, London, 1954.

The Middle East, 2nd ed., Royal Institute of International Affairs, London, 1954, Parts II, IV, V, VII, IX

Tweedy, Maureen, *Bahrain and the Persian Gulf,* East Anglian Magazine, Ipswich.

Twitchell, K. S., *Saudi Arabia,* Princeton University Press, Princeton, 1953.

Villard, H. S., *Libya: The New Arab Kingdom of North Africa,* Cornell University Press, Ithaca, 1956.

Wellington, J. H., *Southern Africa, A Geographical Study,* Cambridge University Press, Cambridge, 1955, 2 vols.

CHAPTER XIII

Addison, H., *Land, Water and Food,* Chapman and Hall, London, 1955.

Carlson, F. A., *Geography of Latin America,* 3d ed., Prentice-Hall, New York, 1952, Chapters XV, XXVII, XXVIII.

Ferguson, Erna, *Mexico Revisited,* Knopf, New York, 1955.

International Bank for Reconstruction and Development, *The Economic Development of Mexico,* Johns Hopkins Press, Baltimore, 1953.

Khan, F. U., and Arshad, A., *West Pakistan in Maps and Statistics,* Ferozons, Karachi, 1948.

Khan, R. M., and Stark, H. W., *Young Pakistan,* Oxford University Press, London, 1951.

Rawson, Geoffrey, *Australia,* Chatto and Windus, London, 1948.

Taylor, Griffith, *Australia,* Methuen, London, 1940.

Ybarra, T. R., *Lands of the Andes,* Coward-McCann, New York, 1947, Part I.

CHAPTER XIV

Blakeston, Oswell, *Portuguese Panorama*, Burke, London, 1955.

Firth, Alfred, *Southern France (French Life & Landscape*, Vol. II), Elek, London, 1953.

Guercio, F. M., *Sicily*, Faber and Faber, London, 1954.

Huddleston, Sisley, *Mediterranean Blue*, Evans Bros., London, 1949.

Italy Today, Centro di documentazione, Rome, 1955.

Martin, Rupert, *Spain*, A. & C. Black, London, 1955.

Reynolds, James, *Fabulous Spain*, Putnam's Sons, New York, 1953.

CHAPTER XV

Bisbee, Eleanor, *The New Turks*, University of Pennsylvania Press, Philadelphia, 1951.

de Gaury, Gerald, *The New State of Israel*, Verschoyle, London, 1952.

International Bank for Reconstruction and Development, *The Economic Development of Syria*, Johns Hopkins Press, Baltimore, 1955.

Isnard, Hildebert, *Algeria*, Kaye, London, 1955.

Laitman, L., *Tunisia Today*, Citadel Press, New York, 1954.

Lebanon, Land of Friendliness, Letters Orientales, Beirut, 1948.

The Middle East, 2nd ed., Royal Institute of International Affairs, London, 1954, Parts VI, X, XI.

Newman, Bernard, *Morocco Today*, Hale, London, 1953.

Stuart, G. H., *The International City of Tangier*, 2nd ed., Stanford University Press, Stanford, 1955.

Sweet-Escott, B., *Greece, A Political and Economic Survey*, Royal Institute of International Affairs, London, 1954.

Thornburg, M. W., Spry, G., and Soule, G., *Turkey: An Economic Appraisal*, The Twentieth Century Fund, New York, 1949.

CHAPTER XVI

Butland, G. J., *Chile*, Royal Institute of International Affairs, London, 1951.

Rawson, Geoffrey, *Australia*, Chatto and Windus, London, 1948.

Taylor, Griffith, *Australia*, Methuen, London, 1940.

Wellington, J. H., *Southern Africa, A Geographical Study*, 2 vols., Cambridge University Press, Cambridge, 1955.

Young, F. B., *In South Africa*, Heinemann, London, 1952, Chapter 3.

CHAPTER XVII

de Sherbinin, Betty, *The River Plate Republics*, Coward-McCann, New York, 1947.

Fitzgibbon, R. Y., *Uruguay: Portrait of a Democracy*, Rutgers University Press, New Brunswick, 1954.

Hoover, C. B., and Ratchford, B. U., *Economic Resources and Policies of the South*, Macmillan, New York, 1951.

Pendle, George, *Paraguay, A Riverside Nation*, Royal Institute of International Affairs, London, 1954.

Pendle, George, *Uruguay, South America's First Welfare State*, Royal Institute of International Affairs, London, 1952.

Wright, A. J., *U.S. and Canada, A Regional Geography*, 2nd ed., Appleton-Century-Crofts, New York, 1956. Chapters 10–12.

CHAPTER XVIII

Ackerman, Edward, *Japan's Natural Resources and Their Relation to Japan's Economic Future*, University of Chicago Press, Chicago, 1953.

Cressey, G. B., *Land of the 500 Million*, McGraw-Hill, New York, 1955, Chapters 8 and 9.

Rawson, Geoffrey, *Australia*, Chatto and Windus, London, 1948.

Taylor, Griffith, *Australia*, Methuen, London, 1940.

Webb, H., *An Introduction to Japan*, Columbia University Press, New York, 1955.

Wellington, J. H., *Southern Africa, A Geographical Study*, 2 vols., Cambridge University Press, Cambridge, 1955.

Young, F. B., *In South Africa*, Heinemann, London, 1952.

CHAPTER XIX

Dickinson, R. E., *Germany: A General and Regional Geography*, Dutton, New York, 1953.

Evans, E. E., *France, A Geographical Introduction*, Christophers, London, 1951.

Firth, Alfred, *Paris and the North (French Life & Landscape*, Vol. I), Elek, London, 1950.

Hamilton, Cicely, *Holland Today*, Dent, London, 1950.

Reynolds, James, *Fabulous Spain*, Putnam, New York, 1953, Chapter 17.

CHAPTER XX

Demangeon, Albert, *The British Isles,* 2nd ed., Heinemann, London, 1949.

The Scandinavian States and Finland, Royal Institute of International Affairs, London, 1951.

Stamp, L. D., and Beaver, M. A., *The British Isles,* 4th ed., Longmans, Green, London, 1954.

CHAPTER XXI

Freeman, O. W., and Martin, H. H. (eds.), *The Pacific Northwest,* 2nd ed., Wiley, New York, 1954.

Grattan, C. H. (ed.), *Australia,* University of California Press, Berkeley, 1947.

Hall, D., *Portrait of New Zealand,* Reed and Reed, Wellington, 1955.

Putnam, D. F. (ed.), *Canadian Regions,* Dent, Toronto, 1952, Chapters 19–21.

Rawson, Geoffrey, *Australia,* Chatto and Windus, London, 1948.

CHAPTER XXII

Ali, Mohammed, *Guide to Afghanistan,* Kabul, 1938.

Berg, L. S., *Natural Regions of the U.S.S.R.,* Macmillan, New York, 1950, Chapters V–VIII, XI.

Caroe, O. K., *Soviet Empire,* Macmillan, London, 1954.

Cressey, G. B., *Land of the 500 Million,* Mc-Graw-Hill, New York, 1955, Chapter 13.

East, W. G., and Spate, O. H. K., *The Changing Map of Asia,* 2nd ed., Methuen, London, 1953, Chapter VI.

Friters, G. H., *Outer Mongolia and Its International Position,* Johns Hopkins Press, Baltimore, 1949, Chapters I and VI.

Groseclose, E. E., *Introduction to Iran,* Oxford University Press, New York, 1947.

Haas, W. S., *Iran,* Columbia University Press, New York, 1946.

CHAPTER XXIII

Addison, H., *Land, Water and Food,* Chapman and Hall, London, 1955.

Currie, A. W., *Economic Geography of Canada,* Macmillan, Toronto, 1945, Chapter IV.

de Sherbinin, Betty, *The River Plate Republics,* Coward-McCann, New York, 1947, Chapters V–VII.

McCarty, H. H., *The Geographic Basis of American Economic Life,* Harper, New York, 1940, Chapters VI–IX.

Putnam, D. F. (ed.), *Canadian Regions,* Dent, Toronto, 1952, Chapters 16–18.

Wright, A. J., *U.S. and Canada, A Regional Geography,* 2nd ed., Appleton-Century-Crofts, New York, 1956, Chapters 15–17.

CHAPTER XXIV

Brown, Alec, *Yugoslav Life and Landscape,* Elek, London, 1954.

Gedye, G. E. R., *Introducing Austria,* Methuen, London, 1955.

Gibbon, Monk, *Austria,* Batsford, London, 1953.

Hubbard, G. D., *The Geography of Europe,* 2nd ed., Appleton-Century-Crofts, New York, 1952, Chapters 33–38.

Wanklyn, Harriet, *Czechoslovakia,* Praeger, New York, 1954.

CHAPTER XXV

Andersons, Edgars (ed.), *Cross Road Country: Latvia,* Latvju Gramata, Waverly, Iowa, 1953.

Berg, L. S., *Natural Regions of the U.S.S.R.,* Macmillan, New York, 1950, Chapters IV, XII–XV, XVII, XVIII.

Chung, K. C., *Korea Tomorrow,* Macmillan, New York, 1956.

Cressey, G. B., *Land of the 500 Million,* Mc-Graw-Hill, New York, 1955.

Kolarz, Walter, *The Peoples of the Soviet Far East,* Praeger, New York, 1954.

McCune, G. M., and Grey, A. L., *Korea Today,* Harvard University Press, Cambridge, 1950.

Mirov, N. T., *Geography of Russia,* Wiley, New York, 1951.

Raud, Villibald, *Estonia,* Nordic Press, New York, 1953.

Shabad, Theodore, *Geography of the U.S.S.R.,* Columbia University Press, New York, 1951.

CHAPTER XXVI

Currie, A. W., *Economic Geography of Canada,* Macmillan, Toronto, 1945, Chapters II and III.

Garland, J. H. (ed.), *The North American Midwest,* Wiley, New York, 1955.

National Planning Association, Committee of New England, *The Economic State of New England,* Yale University Press, New Haven, 1954, Chapters 1–6.

Putnam, D. F. (ed.), *Canadian Regions,* Dent, Toronto, 1952, Chapters 3–12.

Ross, F. A., *The Land and People of Canada,* Lippincott, Philadelphia, 1954.

Wright, A. J., *U.S. and Canada, A Regional Geography*, 2nd ed., Appleton-Century-Crofts, New York, 1956. Chapters 6–9, 13, 14.

CHAPTER XXVII

Berg, L. S., *Natural Regions of the U.S.S.R.*, Macmillan, New York, 1950, Chapters II, XVI, XIX.

Kimble, H. T., and Good, Dorothy (eds.), *Geography of the Northlands*, Wiley, New York, 1955, Chapters 22–26.

Platt, R. R. (ed.), *Finland and Its Geography*, Duell, Sloan and Pearce, New York, 1955.

The Scandinavian States and Finland, Royal Institute of International Affairs, London, 1951, Chapters 3 and 6.

Shabad, Theodore, *Geography of the U.S.S.R.*, Columbia University Press, New York, 1951.

CHAPTER XXVIII

Kimble, H. T., and Good, Dorothy (eds.), *Geography of the Northlands*, Wiley, New York, 1955, Chapters 14–16.

Pearson, L. B., *et al., Canada: Nation on the March*, Clarke Irwin, Toronto, 1953.

Putnam, D. F. (ed.), *Canadian Regions*, Dent, Toronto, 1952, Chapters 2, 13–21.

Roberts, L., *Canada: The Golden Hinge*, Rinehart, New York, 1952.

Ross, F. A., *The Land and People of Canada*, Lippincott, Philadelphia, 1954.

U.S. Department of the Interior, *Mid-Century Alaska*, Government Printing Office, Washington, 1952.

Watkins, E., *Prospect of Canada*, Secker and Warburg, London, 1954.

CHAPTER XXIX

Berg, L. S., *Natural Regions of the U.S.S.R.*, Macmillan, New York, 1950, Chapters I, XVI, XX.

Brown, R. N. R., *The Polar Regions*, Methuen, London, 1927.

Currie, A. W., *Economic Geography of Canada*, Macmillan, Toronto, 1945, Chapters VII, and VIII.

Heintz, Anatol, *Svalbard, A Norwegian Outpost*, Eides Forlag, Bergen, 1950.

Kimble, H. T., and Good, Dorothy (eds.), *Geography of the Northlands*, Wiley, New York, 1955.

Leaf, Horace, *Iceland Yesterday and Today*, Allen and Unwin, London, 1949.

Putnam, D. F. (ed), *Canadian Regions*, Dent, Toronto, 1952, Chapter 22.

The Scandinavian States and Finland, Royal Institute of International Affairs, London, 1951, Chapter 4.

Shabad, Theodore, *Geography of the U.S.S.R.*, Columbia University Press, New York, 1951.

CHAPTER XXX

Buxton, D. R., *Travels in Ethiopia*, McBride, New York, 1950.

Egli, Emil, *Swiss Life and Landscape*, Elek, London, 1949.

Leonard, O. E., *Bolivia: Land, People and Institutions*, Scarecrow Press, Washington, 1952.

Maraini, F., *Secret Tibet*, Hutchinson, London, 1952.

Osborne, H., *Bolivia: A Land Divided*, 2nd ed., Royal Institute of International Affairs, London, 1955.

Peattie, Roderick, *Mountain Geography*, Harvard University Press, Cambridge, 1936.

Shen, T. L., and Liu, S. C., *Tibet and the Tibetans*, Stanford University Press, Stanford, 1953.

Siegfried, Andre, *Switzerland, A Democratic Way of Life*, Duell, Sloan and Pearce, New York, 1950.

Talbot, D. A., *Contemporary Ethiopia*, Philosophical Library, New York, 1952.

Ybarra, T. R., *Lands of the Andes*, Coward-McCann, New York, 1947, Part II.

Index

Set in Linotype Caledonia
Format by John Rynerson
Printing by The Murray Printing Company
Binding by The Haddon Craftsmen, Inc.
Published by HARPER & BROTHERS, *New York*